MIRRORS

MIRRORS

JAMES LIPTON

St. Martin's Press
New York

Copyright © 1981 by James Lipton
For information, write: St. Martin's Press,
175 Fifth Avenue, New York, N.Y. 10010
Manufactured in the United States of America

Library of Congress Cataloging in Publication Data

Lipton, James.
Mirrors.

I. Title.
PS3562.I66M5   813'.54   80-29076
ISBN 0-312-53438-8

Design by Manuela Paul

10 9 8 7 6 5 4 3 2

For my wife, Kedakai Turner Lipton,
who did me the small service of
redefining the universe . . .

and for every dancer I have ever known . . .

especially Joan McCracken and Carol Haney,
for reasons that will be apparent
to the reader of this book.

. . . O le plus violent Paradise de la grimace enragée! Pas de comparaison avec vos Fakirs at les autres bouffonneries scéniques. Dans des costumes improvisés, avec le goût du mauvais rêve, ils jouent des complaintes, des tragédies de malandrins at de demidieux spirituels comme l'histoire ou les religions ne l'ont jamais été. Chinois, Hottentots, bohèmiens, niais, hyènes, Molochs, vieilles démences, démons sinistres, ils mêlent les tours populaires, maternels, avec les poses et les tendresses bestiales. Ils interpréteraient des pièces noubelles et des chansons "bonnes filles." Maîtres jongleurs, ils transforment le lieu et les personnes et usent de la comédie magnétique. Les yeux flambent, le sang chante, les os s'élargissent, les larmes et des filets rouges ruissellent. Leur raillerie ou leur terreur dure une minute, ou des mois entiers.

J'ai seul la clef de cette parade sauvage.

RIMBAUD *Parade*

. . . O the most violent Paradise of the mad grimace! No comparison with your Fakirs and other theatrical buffooneries. In improvised costumes smacking of a bad dream they perform ballads, tragedies about highwaymen and demigods more inspiring than history or religions have ever been. Chinese, Hottentots, gypsies, fools, hyenas, Molochs, old lunacies, sinister demons, they mix popular material numbers with bestial poses and caresses. They would interpret new plays and "romantic" songs. Master jugglers, they transform place and person with their magnetic comedy. Eyes flame, blood sings, bones swell, tears and red trickles stream. Their mockery or their terror lasts a minute, or whole months.

Only I hold the key to this wild sideshow.

Pas de Deux: A dance or section of a dance for two performers, usually a man and woman. The classical form consists of an *entrée*, *adagio*, two *variations* and a *coda*.

ENTREE

ONE, two, three, four

First Position

Vibrant. A foot. Pulsing in space. Cruelly arched, against nature, against sense. Under the quivering skin the clenched muscles sent a desperate plea to the distant, unheeding cortex: stop! Enough!

The teacher, narrow and urgent, glided past the rows of students, one hand afloat, ready to point, to prod, to accuse. He paused next to a dancer, standing like all the others on one leg, the other leg extended, foot pointed toward the ceiling, taut knee nearly brushing ear. The dancer, feeling the teacher's close, reproachful presence, dug deeper into the floor with the supporting foot, toes clutching at the unyielding wood.

"Too heavy. Lighten it. Reach *up!*" the teacher rasped and moved on through a thicket of wool: tights, sweaters, leg warmers, stained and tattered as overloved teddy bears, but essential to the never-ending battle against the lurking enemy, cold air on warm muscle. Once again the teacher stopped to scold. "Turn out."

Under the agonized muscles, the senseless bone. No pain there, no signal. But change, anomaly, the big knob at the top of the thighbone twisted backward as if by a powerful hand. Female bone stops growing at fourteen, male at sixteen, so if the bone is to be bent, the twisting must begin early, at six or seven, the first *pliés* beginning the cruel process, rotating the leg outward until the knob at the top of the thighbone grates against the front rim of the hip socket: a not too subtle suggestion that the knob yield. Like braces on teeth, the hundreds of classes, thousands of hours, tens of thousands of clashes between femur and hip socket threaten the knob with dislocation if it doesn't yield. So it does, an agonized angstrom at a time, until after a dozen years, a million clashes, in naked defiance of nature, the two legs face not forward but sideways, the knees pointed in opposite directions. Then, when the leg rises, "turning out," the stretched capsular ligaments and twisted bone permit a pacific fit of knob and socket and the leg floats upward, knee reaching for ear.

The pain returns later, when the brutalized joint begins to exact its revenge, but this morning the first arthritic twinges are very far away, buried somewhere in the dancer's old age, at thirty-six or -seven. Now there is only the dancer's command, the bone's complaisant response, and the weightless, rising leg.

And the demanding teacher, asking for more. "Don't just turn out the *lower* leg, turn out from the hip!" A note of despair raised the teacher's voice half an octave. "If you don't work here, when *will* you work? Onstage you can work just under your capacity, so you'll be smooth; here you have to work be*yond* your capacity, so you'll grow. You're here to push, to shake, to fall on your popo—so you won't when it counts. Understand?"

The dancer nodded, leg trembling, chin dripping sweat like a leaky faucet. The teacher moved on; the music continued. "And *relevé* and hold!"

The heavy knitted leg warmer obscured the leg from ankle to knee, but there it ended in a ragged droop, and above it the line of the leg was clean, the long adductor, sartorius, rectus and tensor muscles visible in discrete layers under the stretched fabric of the tights. At the acute angle where leg and hip met, the dark leotard framed flat abdominal muscles wedged into narrow loins. North of the sculpted abdomen the leotard swelled with the first hint of sexual definition: the sudden, surprising female softness of breasts, confirmed by an anomalous and striking sweep of neck, attenuated by twelve years of stretching up toward an unattainable victory over gravity. At the tip of the waving stalk, the head looked small, the face unnaturally pale.

Sunshine or classroom: choose! Classroom.

But the face's pallor had a cosmetic effect, accenting the pink of the lips, the blue-white clarity of the eyes. Innocent and vulnerable as childhood, the eyes were fixed on an eighteen-year-old girl in dark leotard, jungle-camouflaged with stains of sweat; damp tights; tattered leg warmers from knee to ankle; and frayed Capezio Tekniks, who stared grimly back from the mirrored wall of the steamy room, dissatisfied with her turnout, extension, balance, line, look, progress and life.

As the nagging voice of the teacher drew closer, Carin tightened, and the watching mirror image faltered, slipping out of sync with the other figures in the glass.

The teacher's voice was harsh, grating: *"Épaulement!* Right shoulder forward. Now left! Head left, arms second!" The mirror caught a quick scramble for synchrony, the reflex of countless un-questioning obediences to teacher, choreographer, ballet master snapping the right shoulder forward in the specified direction. Har-mony reappeared in the mirror, acceptance softened the teacher's gaze, relief regulated Carin's heartbeat. The teacher moved on, then paused, eyes narrow, before a second girl.

Not woman: *girl.* People are men and women; dancers are boys and girls, in class and company, on bulletin boards and dressing-room doors, officially, eternally.

There was something different about this girl, something which set her apart from the other bodies moving rhythmically to the piano music issuing from a corner of the room. "Yes," the teacher said, "that's it," then turned to sweep the other students with a stern glance. "Take a look at Diane when you get a chance and you'll see what I'm talking about. Some of you just move—as if you'd been programmed by a computer—but Diane's movement starts in her small intestine. From the inside out. You know what that is? Mile-age. Experience."

The teacher moved on. "Third *port de bras. Attitude* right, *prom-enade* left. Five, six, seven and . . ."

The difference in Diane: mileage. Experience. Her body was indistinguishable from the others in the mirror, honed to a low-calorie, fat-free minimum, but her face—divergence began there. There was something in it that testified to time served, scars ac-quired—one literally, a pale cicatrix that followed the line of her cheekbone into her temple. Makeup usually covered it, but in class makeup would only run. Hence, the faces in the mirror were scrubbed and, apart from Diane's, manifestly young. Diane's eyes set her further apart. There was a hint of wariness in them. Or weari-ness. Perhaps a little too much experience.

Diane's eyes met a mocking gaze in the mirror. The dark-haired boy next to her, dutifully following the teacher's instructions to watch Diane, was trying to catch her eye. When he succeeded, he pantomimed an admiring sigh, and his hand, moving in the *port de bras,* thrust a thumb up in exaggerated approval. Diane's hand, arc-ing with the music, responded with an extended middle finger.

The attention to Gino had cost Diane a beat in the music. As she skipped a step to catch up, her lips formed a flat aperture, suit-able for the emission of one of the most important words in her vocabulary: *shit!*

The rest of her dance vocabulary was in the Esperanto she shared with every other dancer on earth, French. But for maledic-tion she and her international colleagues resorted to English; in sweaty *salles* around the world, Russian, German, Japanese and Cuban dancers could be counted on to respond to a botched *saut de Basque* with the same explosive syllable: *shit!*

Gino grinned at Diane's discomfiture, then resumed his contented contemplation of the young man staring back at him from the mirror: dark hair spilling forward over a feral face—a contemporary Heathcliff, moving silkily, flat and swift as a flanker, every movement of arm or leg raising serried rows of abdominal muscles, framed by a shirt that had been carefully torn up the back, then knotted around the ribcage to leave the abdomen free for affectionate inspection. The face in the mirror beamed again as it occurred to Gino that he ought to do some nude 8-by-10 glossies. Dancing. Tasteful. Nothing important showing.

The music stopped, the dancers reached for the towels draped over the *barre* that bent around the three unmirrored walls of the room and mopped sweat from their faces and necks. The teacher leaned on the piano, conferring with the pianist, then returned to the front of the room, his back to the mirror. Eyes half-closed, he began sketching shadowy steps with little twists and cuts of his narrow body as the pianist and dancers waited. His eyes opened and he said, "All right, let's try this."

Forty-five minutes later, on a floor shiny with sweat, the dancers, riding the waves of music like surfers, rose together in an exultant leap, heads thrown back, muscled necks arched at the same angle, shoulders identically tilted, hands reaching for the same corner of the room, arriving at the apogee of the leap in the same split second, yielding to gravity in the same soft fall, rising from the *plié* in the same smooth blend of a hundred separate flexions and extensions of feet, knees, thighs, hips, chests, shoulders, necks, heads, each muscular unit performing its own series of movements in unquestioning obedience to a separate set of commands, hips facing south, feet east and west, shoulders northeast and southwest, eyes south by southeast, arms at one and seven o'clock high, the whole sequence of movements locked into four counts of music, ending in twenty identical pictures in the mirror as the last note of music died away in flattening waves. There was an instant of silence, punctuated by the dancers' gasping hunger for oxygen. Then the teacher said, *"Entrechat quatre, entrechat quatre, entrechat quatre, royale . . ."*

The pianist struck up a big inflammatory waltz, and the dancers soared skyward in a series of vertical jumps like the ones that customarily concluded their ballet classes, providing it and them with a physical climax, a final, fulfilling ejaculation of movement. Aware that the class was ending, they bounded up and down as if on pogo sticks, emptying themselves of the stream of energy that had sustained them for ninety minutes.

"Okay!" the teacher cried, and a bright bouquet of applause blossomed from the panting dancers. From the first classes of childhood the teacher was mentormotherfathergod, to be obeyed and applauded for applying each day's lash; now the last stroke of the morning had been administered, and the dancers headed for the dressing rooms in two ragged, sweating, nattering lines.

The girls' dressing room throbbed with energy as the process of peeling wet tights and leotards from clammy limbs began. Some of the girls, still high on the movement, decompressed by reiterating the allegro combination that had preceded the jumps. Others collapsed in a slack, dramatic scatter of limbs on the long benches in front of the crowded clothes racks. Moments later the neighboring shower room filled with steam and the chatter of water and high-pitched voices.

Diane, undressing slowly, glanced down the aisle to where Carin was doggedly repeating a combination, each repetition ending in a tangle of feet, a muttered exclamation and a grim resumption of effort.

"I think it was step, *step, chassé,*" Diane said. Carin stopped and looked at her. "You're missing one step when you come out of the turn. That's why you keep winding up on the wrong foot."

"In my case they're both wrong." Carin dropped on a bench, and Diane smiled, one hand unconsciously rubbing the scar on her cheek.

"How long have you been studying?"

"Twelve years."

"You're doing fine."

"Not fine enough."

"Relax. At your age you've got plenty of time. Wait till you reach *my* advanced age."

"What's that?"

"Well—that depends."

"On what?"

"Who you ask." Naked to her socks, Diane moved to Carin and sat next to her, lowering her voice conspiratorially. "My dates get twenty-three—if they're rude enough to ask. My resumé says twenty-four." A shrug. "Advertising. My agent'll tell you twenty-five, but everybody knows agents lie. I told my gynecologist twenty-six, but who knows, maybe they can count the rings." A quick look around, then, "But strictly between you and me and this locker room, I'm twenty-nine, going on . . ." She braced herself, then uttered the word as if it were the ultimate obscenity, "Thirty!" She lofted a foot to yank off a sock. "Fast!"

The waiting room was a zoo. Dancers, some in street clothes, some in leotards and tights, sat, leaned, squatted or stood about, chatting, reading, napping, nibbling at cottage cheese, carrots, candy bars, warming up, cooling off, hanging out. Sneaky jazz quarter-tones, the *pong* of conga drums and the exultant chords of the first *divertissement* from the *Sleeping Beauty* wedding scene resolutely chopped from an out-of-tune upright filtered through the doors of various studios around the waiting room as Carin and Diane came out of the dressing room, their heavy dance bags fifty percent saltwater now.

As they picked their way through the maze, Carin paused at the drinking fountain for a mouthful of water. Straightening, she tipped her head back to let the cool stream trickle past her soft palate in a direct assault on the plexus of nerves in charge of her thirst.

Trained from childhood to care for, coddle and drive her body, Carin had become an innocent voluptuary, focused forever on the world of her senses. Without ever framing a conscious thought on the subject, she had come to know in the marrow of her bones that her past, present and future were wrapped up in one earthly object: her body. Its exploration, care and feeding and gratification had been the principal concerns of her every waking moment from the age of six. Years of this physical fixation had forged a pliant neural chain across which demand and response flowed freely. Since her partner in this continuing dialogue was her own nervous system, she avoided loneliness and boredom by learning to take pleasure in each reciprocal exchange with her dendrites. The result was a peculiar solipsism without vanity, which showed itself at this moment in a slow, voluptuous slaking of thirst. Carin was simply doing what she did best and most often, surrendering instantly and utterly to her body's demands. It was only fair: that body must surrender to hers.

As she bent over the fountain again for one last soothing sip of water, a pale blond dancer, his dance bag dangling from his shoulder, passed Diane, who was waiting next to Carin. "You in the finals today?" the dancer asked.

"Yes. You?"

"Yeah."

Diane raised a knee to kick him gently in the buttock. *"Merde."*

"I'll need it," the young man moaned. "I've got such shin splints!" He limped out.

"Want to come to Fruit and Nuts?" Diane asked Carin.

"What's that?"

"A health-food place."

"Oh. Fruit and nuts. I see."

"No, you don't. It refers to the customers. But they've got honey and wheat germ, and I'm gonna need fuel today!"

TWO, two, three, four
Second Position

The blender churned like a disco dancer, lashing a bile-green mixture to foam and threatening, at moments when its torque seemed to take on a life of its own, to hurl the whole jar of vegetable juice at two massively muscled men seated at a long counter, their glutei maximi so thoroughly consuming the seats of their stools that they looked like sculptures growing out of the floor on metal stems. "I've been bomb-blitzing with bioflavonoids," one of them said, sipping a dusty pink concoction. "Mr. Universe *swears* by them."

Behind the counter a waitress whose pasty skin and lifeless ringlets of bleached hair suggested she ought to try health food assembled an order and headed for the small table where Carin and Diane bent damp heads toward each other.

"The soya butter, honey and wheat germ on unbleached white?" the waitress intoned, her eyes focused through the window on a bent old man lugging a cello case along Fifty-seventh Street.

"Me," Diane said.

"And the rosehip and dandelion tea?" Carin stared warily at the gray brew in the waitress's hand. "Which one of you ordered this?"

"Uh . . . me."

The waitress put the tea on the table and went back to the counter. Carin picked up the cup, suspicion still slowing her, took a tiny sip and shuddered. "It tastes like someone dropped cigar ashes in this."

"That's the tea," Diane replied philosophically and bit into her sandwich. "Jesus, I forgot what a fight this stuff gives you." It was nearly a minute before the mass was malleable enough to swallow. Then Diane caught her breath and asked, "How can you go without lunch? I'm so hungry after class I could eat sweat socks."

"So could I. Usually. But today . . ."

"Sick?" Diane pried a second mouthful out of her sandwich.

"No."

"You will be if you don't eat right. A doctor told me that. He said dancers burn up more calories in a day than real people do in a week. You better have something." She turned to the waitress, who was on her way to another table. "Ann . . ."

"No," Carin interjected, "I don't want anything. I'm not hungry."

The waitress, who had paused, eyes glazed, mind distant, resumed her journey, and Diane grinned at Carin. "Am I coming on too strong?"

"No."

"You sure? The gypsies don't call me Motor Mouth for nix."

Carin stared out the window into Fifty-seventh Street. "I had my fortune told once at a carnival . . ."

"Not that kind of gypsy."

"What kind?"

"*My* kind." Carin stared at her. "Dancers." There was no response from Carin. "In musicals."

"Oh," Carin replied blankly.

"How long you been here?"

"Nearly six months."

"And you never heard anybody say gypsy?"

"No."

"Take any jazz classes?"

"Not yet. I've been thinking about it."

"That explains it."

"Do gypsies take jazz?"

"Sure."

"Then what were you doing in ballet class?"

"Gypsies take everything, man! Jazz, ballet, singing, acting . . ."

"For Broadway?"

"Broadway, movies, TV—wherever we can pitch our tents. Get it? Gypsies." She brought the glutinous sandwich to her mouth and sawed off another bite. When she had forced it down, she winced and put a hand on her flat, hard stomach. "Wouldn't you think after ten years in this rat race, I'd be able to face an audition without qualifying for Blue Cross?" She glared at the uneaten half of sandwich on the plate in front of her, then pushed it across the table to Carin. "Want to finish that?"

"Don't you?"

Diane groaned. "With the stone that's layin' in my stomach?" The palm on her abdomen began to massage it. "Come on, you bastard, move! Get the honey in the bloodstream where it belongs!" Carin studied the sandwich for a moment, then picked it up and took a bite. As she swallowed the first mouthful and quickly bit off another, Diane stared in disbelief. "You *like* that shit?" Carin, busy trying to swallow, could only manage a nod. "You must be starving to death. Wait a minute! You just said you weren't hungry."

Carin swallowed as quickly as she could, then replied, "I'm not. I just wondered what it tasted like." She put the remains of the sandwich on the plate. "Now I know."

"So do I," Diane rasped, her eyes trying to trap Carin's averted gaze. "You're tapped out. That's why you didn't order anything."

"No."

"Bullshit. Nobody cons Motor Mouth."

Carin stared at the table, too disheartened to argue, then finally, yielding to the pressure of Diane's unswerving gaze, reached into her pocket, took out a few crumpled bills and dropped them on the table. "That's it."

"All you got?"

"All that's left."

Carin and Diane, their bodies precariously inclined to balance the weight of the soggy dance bags slung back over their shoulders, trudged south on Seventh Avenue. At Fifty-second Street Diane asked, "All that's left of what?" .

"I had some money when I came to New York."

"Savings?"

"Not exactly."

Diane was patient for two blocks, then she asked, "What do you mean, not exactly?"

"I stole it."

Tilted forward under her burden like a pack animal, Diane risked a misstep by twisting her head to direct an intrigued glance at Carin. "From who?"

Carin's reply was drowned by a screech of rubber as two taxis nearly collided in the street next to the girls and the drivers dueled with outraged horns and shouted imprecations that failed to turn a head on either side of the avenue. When the joust had roared away, Diane repeated, "From who?"

"Me."

"Oh? How do you do that?"

"It was in a bank."

"You robbed a bank?" The admiration in the question was undisguised.

"I took it out."

"You mean with a withdrawal slip?"

"Yes."

Diane emitted a deflated "Oh," reflected in silence for a block, then said, "You could work part-time."

"I did for a while." A glance from Diane brought, "In a restaurant."

"Where?"

"On Columbus Avenue."

"I worked there."

"There are lots of restaurants on Columbus."

"I've worked 'em all," Diane said evenly. "What were your hours?"

"Six to midnight. Two on the weekends."

Diane nodded. "Some fun, huh?"

"It was being on your feet after two or three classes. Sometimes I could hardly get up the next morning—and if I *did* get to class, I could barely move."

"Now let's talk about the creeps," Diane muttered.

"Yeah, sometimes it got hairy. I was followed home a couple of times. And one night . . ." Carin fell silent.

"One night . . . ?" Carin remained silent. "Listen, you stiffed me on the bank robbery. If you're gonna keep on dropping juicy hints . . ."

"I got sick," Carin said. "In the middle of the night. I—I thought I was going to faint. I went out in the hall . . ."

"In the *hall?* How long you been in New York?"

"Six months."

"Man, you're a slow learner."

"I guess so. A man was coming home. I asked him to help me . . ."

"Oh boy!"

"Yeah. I guess he thought I was drunk or something."

"Kick 'em in the balls. They hate that."

"He stopped when I threw up."

"Hey! Good move! I've never thought of that. That'd cool anybody down."

Carin plodded mutely ahead, her head down, her dark gaze fixed on the sidewalk. At Forty-eighth Street Diane asked, "What about your folks?" Carin looked up. "For some more bread." Carin shook her head vigorously. "Come on! That's what folks are for."

"Not mine."

"Poor folks?"

"They don't have much."

"But if you've got a problem . . ."

"They'll say come home."

"They didn't want you to come to New York?"

"No."

"Typical," Diane muttered, then at Forty-seventh Street she added a testy, "Everybody's got a right to do their own thing."

Suddenly Carin was standing still, feet planted, fists clenched.

"What thing!" Diane stopped and turned back. "I couldn't even get an audition with Ballet Theatre, and the only thing they said at New York City Ballet was, 'Why don't you try to get into the School of American Ballet?' I tried Joffrey. Somebody took my name for an audition—next spring. Maybe." She yielded to the snarling Times Square traffic. After a moment Diane nodded southward and the gloomy march resumed. At Forty-third Street Carin growled, "Shit!"

"Yeah, it's all over the fuckin' sidewalk," Diane sighed. "Just walk through a puddle; it'll wash off."

"No—it's just so *dumb.*" Carin gestured at a sign on a trash basket exhorting passersby to PITCH IN! "I might as well have taken my money and thrown it in there."

"Maybe your luck'll change."

"When?" Carin snorted and yanked her dance bag around to her chest. Without slowing her pace she pulled out an envelope. "I wrote home last night. I need enough to pay some bills and buy a bus ticket to Detroit. . . . I've tried to mail it five times since this morning."

She turned with a start as Diane plucked the envelope from her hand with a peremptory, "Don't. Come to the audition with me."

"But that's impossible!"

"We'll tell 'em you were out of town for the preliminary calls."

"But I'd look like an idiot! You said gypsies have to do everything. I've never even taken a jazz class."

"I'm the one who's the idiot," Diane said grimly. "This choreographer's apeshit for classical training. You'll probably get picked and I'll get thrown out on my ass."

THREE, two, three, four
Third Position

Carin's childhood was conventional, with the exception of one element: her dance training. That set her apart, not only from her friends and schoolmates but from her family.

Her father was one of the minutely differentiated human appendages to the roaring machinery of Ford's Wayne plant, twenty-five miles west of Detroit. Her mother, the former Mai Dahlstrom, was the ninth daughter of a Lutheran minister who, apart from his wary relationship with a chill northern God, had two passions in life: male children and baseball. It was his fate to produce nothing but females, and nine of them at that. In moments of doubt and despair (which he considered a sacred part of his Swedish birthright), the Reverend Gunnar Dahlstrom reflected bitterly on the fact that, with just the slightest chromosomal shift, he could have had his own baseball team.

At the age of fifteen he had immigrated to America with his parents, and when he returned to Sweden five years later to attend divinity school, he took with him a nearly flawless command of English, an unquenchable passion for the American sport of baseball and a fielder's glove which he kept in mint condition with frequent applications of neat's-foot oil despite the fact that he could never find anyone in Uppsala to play catch with him.

His ordination was a step toward his twin goals: heaven and proximity to a major-league team. As fan, not player. He was realistic about his vocation: he had always been slow going to his left, and he couldn't hit the curve ball.

An opportunity to serve God in Detroit outshone any other. Perusal of the American newspapers that occasionally showed up in Sweden had convinced him that, if the bullpen held up in the stretch, the Detroit Tigers would be genuine contenders for the American League pennant.

Newly married, his wife pregnant with what would be the first of his nine daughters, Gunnar Dahlstrom arrived in Detroit at the age of twenty-two, ready for battle against Satan and the New York Yankees. To Dahlstrom's dismay the Tigers faded in the last month of the season—"That bullpen!" Gunnar roared in the stentorian voice he had developed at Uppsala for holier purposes.

By the time Carin's mother was born, the middle-aged Swedish religious was a fixture in the Navin Field upper deck, appropriately poised between man and God, humbly accepting God's will when Charlie Gehringer blew one and clinging tenaciously to his teleological faith in God, Mickey Cochrane and Kenesaw Mountain Landis. His faith upheld him, telling him, even on days when Detroit lost both ends of a double-header, that Hume was wrong and the hapless Tigers were part of some divine design.

Baseball metaphors found their way into his sermons: try as we may to conceal our sins from God, the Supreme Umpire keeps a scorecard on every one of us, meticulously marking down each error. Life pitches us curve balls, but faith fattens our batting averages. This often weary, stale, flat and unprofitable earthly existence is the minor leagues; heaven is the bigs.

Mai Dahlstrom never understood her father's sermons, but she loved the cool, beige peace of his church on Sunday mornings, the lustrous sound of the choir, the hushed shuffling of worshipers taking their places in the pews and the majesty of the organ's thundering chords in the Recessional, thick club sandwiches of sound.

At the age of twenty she married Doug Bradley, who sang two rows behind her in the church choir, and a year later Carin was born. Postpartum complications precluded another child, so Carin became the focus of her mother's existence. Carin's maternal grandfather, blessed by now with several male grandchildren whom he could range beside him on the upper deck and with whom he could play protracted games of catch, agile and proud behind a frayed but still serviceable Rawlings, evinced only a passing interest in Carin.

One Sunday night in her sixth year, Carin lay on her stomach in front of the television set, waiting for some acrobats or animals to enliven the Ed Sullivan show, when Ed announced that the audience was in for a rrreally special treat because Rudolf Nureyev and Margot Fonteyn were going to dance what Ed referred to as a "poddy doo."

"Change it," Carin's father muttered from his armchair. "I think there's wrestling on seven."

Carin rose and reached for the dial, and stopped. A fairy tale had sprung on the screen beneath her fingertips.

"I said change it," her father grunted as glistening arpeggios struggled out of the Zenith's little speaker. But Carin stood riveted in front of the screen, struck dumb by the quicksilver princess whose tiara discharged explosions of light that made the watching camera blink.

"You all right, baby?" her mother asked, and Carin could only nod.

"I thought you *liked* wrestling," her father sulked, but Mai said, "Shhh!" and Doug picked up the *News,* snapped it open and glared at it with ostentatious displeasure.

Her eyes on the screen, Carin raised her arms, rose to the ball of one foot and extended a leg in what she would one day call *arabesque.* Bending forward in what she would come to know as *penché,* she fell forward in a heap that would one day evoke a fervent, muttered, "Shit!"

Mai sprang to her daughter's side, clucking and lifting her to examine her reddened nose, but Carin pushed her mother aside and advanced on the set.

"You'll hurt your eyes standing that close," her father pouted over his paper.

The next day the campaign began. Carin wanted shoes like that, a dress like that. She pranced and jumped and twirled in the bedroom, the living room, the kitchen, the bathroom. She fell, she rose, she fell, she rose. Doug told Mai that Carin was going to hurt herself, and Mai replied, "Not if she has lessons."

"What lessons?"

"Dancing lessons."

"Very funny."

"It's not a joke."

Doug resumed shaving, pulling his skin taut with one hand, applying the Blue Blade with the other.

"I'm serious," Mai said.

"No, you're not," Doug said equably, smiling at her in the mirror.

"They have classes at the Detroit Conservatory of Art. I called them."

"That's twenty-five miles away."

"I can drive in."

The illness had progressed far enough to warrant his full attention. He turned from the mirror to face his wife. "Fifty miles?"

"That's both ways."

"I know it's both ways. Who pays for the gas?"

"We've got enough money for that."

"The gas—plus the class! How much does *that* cost?"

"Two fifty."

Doug's eyes were wide above the beard of lather. "Two dollars and fifty cents so she can skin her knees once a week. . . ?"

"Twice a week." The water dripping in the sink behind Doug accented the silence. He searched his wife's face for evidence of a smile that would unmask the joke. She stared resolutely back.

"Five dollars?"

"Plus gas—and maybe lunch because I'll have to wait for her," Mai said quietly. She had inherited none of her father's fervor but all of her mother's strength.

"Do you know what five dollars could buy us?" Doug asked.

"Yes. Two dance lessons a week for Carin."

The only cloud on Carin's brilliant new horizon was the absence of tiara and tutu. She stood in front of the teacher, gesturing at her head and pudgy little bottom. "Like the princess," she said, and Mai explained that she was talking about the crown and costume worn by Margot Fonteyn on the Ed Sullivan show.

The teacher smiled. "Oh, of course. Well, that's later. For now you'll wear a leotard just like the other children. That's so we can see your body and help you."

Carin frowned. Her next disappointment was the discovery that she wouldn't be dancing on her toes.

"That's three or four years away," the teacher explained to Mai. "I have to tell all the mothers: the worst thing we can do is put them on *pointe* too early. Their bones are still soft; we could ruin their legs—forever." Mai said she understood, and the teacher sighed. "I'm glad you do. You'd be surprised how many mothers don't. They pull their children out of class and take them to a school that's unscrupulous enough to put them right on *pointe*. I feel sorry for the children; it's the mother's obsession. That's why we don't let our mothers watch class every day." There was a note of apology in her voice.

"That's all right," Mai said quickly. "I've got lots of things to do while Carin's here."

Doug adjusted, Mai chauffeured and hovered at a discreet distance, determined not to be a stage mother. Carin bent, stooped, squatted, hopped, skipped, ran, tottered, stretched, waved her arms, giggled, cried, exulted and, preeminently, fell. The dumpy, funny six-year-old, clenching her fists and screwing herself into the floor in fifth position, her knees bent and bottom waving, grew taller, thinner, steadier.

At nine she could raise a leg beyond ninety degrees, and after three years of turning out, the all-important malformation of the trochanter at the top of her femur was well and successfully under way.

What she did at class, and endlessly at home, could still only charitably be called dancing, but at least it was something other than stooping, squatting and hopping. The fairy godmother who presided over the Wonderland to which Carin was admitted twice a week had transformed stoop to *penché,* squat to *plié* and hop to *jeté.*

The conservatory secretary was waiting in the lobby when Mai arrived to pick Carin up. "I'm sure there's nothing to worry about . . ." the secretary began.

"What do you mean, nothing to worry about? What happened?"

"She's not feeling well."

"Where is she?"

"In the office . . ."

The office door gave too easily and swung back with a crash that threatened to dislodge the thick panes of glass beveled into its heavy oak hide. The sound brought Mrs. Rome, the school's director, to her feet behind her desk, but Carin, stretched on a leather couch in her leotard and scuffed dance shoes, remained motionless, her head on her dance bag, her eyes fixed vacantly on the ceiling. The director circled her desk as Mai dashed across the room and knelt next to the couch, reaching for Carin's hand. "What is it, sweetheart? What's wrong?" Carin's eyes shifted. She blinked at Mai. "It's me!" Mai exclaimed.

"There's been a lot of it," the director clucked, stout and tweedy behind Mai.

"A lot of *what?*"

"Flu."

"She had flu last week," Mai said. "She got over it."

"Apparently not."

"What happened?" Mai demanded, rising, Carin's hand still in hers. Carin's arm waved like a limp rope.

"She got sick to her stomach."

"In class?"

"No. Not exactly. Well . . ."

"Please," Mai said. *"Tell* me!"

"Miss Nicholas says Carin kept leaving the class . . ."

"And she didn't do anything about it?"

"She asked her what was wrong, and Carin said she was thirsty. That's all; she just wanted a drink of water."

Mai looked down at Carin. Carin stared blankly back. "She's been like that ever since she was sick."

"Did she have a fever?"

"Yes."

"It must have dehydrated her. And they perspire so much in class."

"But when did she get sick to her stomach?"

"Apparently she left the class several times, and when she came back she was very vague—confused. She wasn't getting the combination, and usually Carin's the first one to learn it."

"When did she get sick to her stomach?"

"Finally she just didn't come back. So the teacher went to the rest room, and Carin was throwing up. When she was a little better, the teacher brought her in here."

"Have you called a doctor?"

"No. She's only been here a couple of minutes, and we knew you were on your way."

Mai sat suddenly on the edge of the couch next to Carin. "Why didn't you tell me you were sick?" Carin stared uncomprehendingly at her. "Answer me!"

It was the director who answered. "They *never* admit they're sick." Mai looked up. The director smiled. "They'd have to miss class." Mrs. Rome winked.

Carin mumbled something and Mai bent close. "Water . . ." Carin murmured. "Thirsty . . ."

Mrs. Rome turned toward the secretary, who was hovering in the doorway. "Yes," the secretary said, "I'll get some."

When she returned with two paper cups, Mai took one and asked Carin, "Can you sit up?"

Carin's only response was to lick her dry lips and reach for the cup, her fingers opening and closing feebly. Fighting a growing panic, Mai slid a hand under Carin's shoulder blades and lifted: Carin's head fell grotesquely back. "Oh my God!" Mai exclaimed. Carin raised her head and grasped at the cup. Mai held it to her lips. The water was gone in two long, feverish gulps; then Carin's bleary gaze turned toward the second cup. When it was empty, she muttered, ". . . room."

"What?" Mai demanded.

". . . room."

"I think she wants to go to the bathroom," the secretary said.

"Do you feel sick to your stomach again?" Mai asked.

". . . room!"

"I'll help," Mrs. Rome said quickly, extending heavy arms nubbly with coarse wool. The secretary pressed forward and the three women brought Carin to her feet, where she swayed precariously. Then Mai saw the stain spreading quickly down the inside of Carin's legs, turning her pink tights puce. Urine bubbled out of her shoes and at the same moment her skinny body convulsed, her mouth gaped and the water she had just swallowed jetted at the administrator's tweed. Mrs. Rome darted back, dripping, shocked, and as Carin spouted water from both ends, Mai bent and lugged her daughter aloft. Once again Carin's head fell back, and her arms flopped leadenly as Mai tottered toward the door, leaving a trail of urine in her wake.

"Help me!" Mai barked at the frozen secretary.

"What . . . ?" the secretary stammered.

"My car . . ." Mai grunted, straining at the dead weight. "It's outside. Open the front door!"

As Mai plunged across the lobby, children stared. Loping ahead, the secretary pushed the door open and glanced anxiously at Carin's ashen face as Mai pushed past her.

The intensive-care unit terrified Mai. The sign above its door screamed danger at her, and the sight of Carin impaled in a web of tubes and wires nearly made Mai a candidate for similar treatment. Doug, summoned hastily from Wayne, slid an arm around his wife and fought down his own fear.

Dr. Rothberg led Doug and Mai to a small bare office near the intensive-care unit. When he said, "Sit down," Mai remained rooted in the center of the room. "Please," Dr. Rothberg said. The vinyl couch was cold and it felt sticky even through Mai's clothes. Doug sat next to her, his arm still tightly encircling her. "She's getting salt and fluids," Rothberg said, "and insulin."

Mai's gray face whitened and her question was nearly inaudible. "Why insulin?"

"She has diabetes," Dr. Rothberg said.

Mai sagged against Doug. "No!"

Rothberg smiled. "If you knew anything about diabetes, you wouldn't be taking it like this. Of all the chronic diseases it's by far the most manageable. Carin can live a normal life . . ."

"And die before she's forty!" Mai gasped.

"Where would you get an idea like that?"

"I *know*," Mai said emphatically. She leaned forward, eyes wide and preternaturally bright. "I had a cousin and an aunt—and Grandma—Oh, Jesus!" She sprang up, pulling Doug with her. "I did this to her!"

Doug pawed numbly at her. "What're you talking about!"

She turned accusingly on the doctor. "It's true, isn't it? She got this from me."

"Diabetes isn't contagious . . ."

"You know what I mean!" Her voice caught. She spun against Doug, covering her face, and burst into tears. Doug put his arms around her. Dr. Rothberg remained seated in the vinyl armchair, a placid hand on its pale green arm. After several minutes Doug was able to persuade Mai to sit on the couch again. It was another long moment before she blew her nose into a soggy handkerchief and looked at Dr. Rothberg, managing a choked, "I'm sorry."

He waved a hand. "Believe me, it's not the first time. Parents always want to blame themselves."

Mai glanced guiltily at Doug. "I should've told you—about the diabetes in my family . . ."

"And then what?" Dr. Rothberg asked quietly. Mai turned her red gaze on him. "You wouldn't have had a child? You'd rather not have had Carin?"

"Of course not!"

"Could we have prevented the diabetes?" Doug asked. "Somehow?"

"No. So, now let's talk about what we're going to do."

"You're sure it's diabetes," Mai said.

"No question. When a nine-year-old comes in dehydrated, with her urine full of sugar and ketones . . ."

"She had flu last week. Maybe . . ."

"That's how it usually happens. Another illness reveals the diabetes." Mai's eyes began filling again and Dr. Rothberg said, "She's not going to die before she's forty."

"My grandmother did. My aunt did. My cousin did."

"I don't know anything about their cases . . ."

"I do. There was no cure. They took insulin, but they died."

"*Is* there a cure?" Doug asked.

"A cure? No." Mai's breathing became audible. "But it's a *manageable* condition."

"Will she have to have needles?" Doug asked.

"Yes."

"Can she live without them?"

"No."

"What about pills? I thought they had pills now."

"For adults, sometimes. And some children. Not for Carin."

"She'll have to have injections all her life," Mai said slowly. "Every day."

"Maybe not." Rothberg spread his hands. "The way things are going, who knows what they'll come up with next."

"A cure?" Mai murmured.

"Someday, certainly."

"My aunt went blind before she died," Mai muttered tonelessly, "and they had to amputate Grandma's foot. Then her leg."

"Carin will have to take care of herself. Diabetes can lead to a vascular deficiency of the feet . . ."

"No more dance," Mai muttered.

"I don't want to hear one word about God's will, Papa." Dahlstrom's wounded expression softened Mai and she amended her caveat to a barely audible, "I'm scared, Papa. Look what happened to Grandma, and Marge and Aunt Lena."

"That was a few years ago—and Grandma was in Sweden. Here in America . . ."

"It's the same. Nothing's changed. They still can't cure it." Mai looked around her father's study. "Why do you always keep it so dark in here?"

His big hands, which usually hung lifelessly at his sides, came up in a defensive gesture, fingers widespread, palms luminously pale in the gloom. "This isn't a fancy Grosse Pointe church . . ."

"It's got nothing to do with money. You *like* it dark." Embarrassed by her anger, Mai nevertheless rose and stalked to the window as if to illustrate her need for light.

Her father watched her, long hand on long chin, then he said, "Understanding God's will doesn't mean blaming Him." Mai's only response was an exasperated sigh. Dahlstrom's chair creaked as he rose. He crossed the room and stood behind his daughter, sensing that there was something he should say, or perhaps something he should have said on some previous occasion. He brushed a hand across his forehead, poking at a pale lock. "What do you want, Mai?" He started as she turned to him, eyes brilliant with tears.

"Not to be afraid!" Her fists were clenched, but she reached for him. He took her in his arms stiffly, as he might a bereaved parishioner. The unaccustomed embrace, one of only two or three in Mai's memory, resurrected a train of thought that the first such embrace had evoked when Mai was sixteen: to Dalhstrom's joy, Mai's eldest sister had given birth to a son three months before Mai was born, so that, the sixteen-year-old Mai reasoned, *her* birth must have been a doleful and unnecessary anticlimax. A ninth daughter was God's will, a first grandson was God's blessing.

As delicately as she could, Mai extricated herself from the minister's mummified grasp, returned to the hard chair facing his desk and stood behind it, a hand on its ungiving back.

Rebuffed, uneasy, as he so often was with Mai, Dahlstrom remained at the window. Finally he said, "I know you're afraid."

"Are you?" she asked.

"What?"

"Afraid."

"For Carin?"

"Yes. I want someone else to feel what I feel. I want to share this, Papa. Do you understand what I'm saying?"

He started toward her. "I know how you feel . . ."

"That's not what I said! I need somebody to *feel* what I feel!"

He stopped. "And then?"

She leaned heavily on the chair. "I won't be so alone."

"But you have Doug."

"He thinks I'm being overprotective. Before Carin got sick, he used to kid me about being a stage mother." She directed an imploring glance at her father. "I don't want to be like that."

"You're not, Mai. Any mother would be upset."

She shook her head. "Doug doesn't seem to think so. I don't think Dr. Rothberg does, either. He keeps saying she's normal, normal, normal—but she has to test herself four or five times a day, and everything she eats has to be measured . . ."

"There are worse things that could happen."

"Of course. But she's *nine years old,* Papa." She reflected a moment, then added, "You should see her give herself injections. You know how I am about needles."

"You don't like them?"

"Don't you remember the way I used to be?"

"Oh—yes, of course."

Once again Dahlstrom was nagged by an impression that something was missing. It was, he reflected, like working for days to complete a jigsaw puzzle, then finding that some important pieces had disappeared. The box was empty but jagged holes still gaped. One turned the box upside down and searched the floor under the table, but the puzzle was doomed to incompletion. It was a disquieting sensation.

Dahlstrom drew a hand across his face, feeling old and tired. He often felt that way these days, as if every request made of him were unbearably weighty. At the very least, his faith had always made him feel capable. He no longer felt capable, and not even his daughter's need could reawaken his waning strength. A parishioner in Mai's position would have evoked a stirring scriptural passage, but he knew that when Mai was in this mood, the first holy word would draw a sharp "Don't preach to me, Papa, *talk* to me!" from her.

Besides, he could no longer trust his memory to deliver up the apposite verse. A bulging arsenal of Scripture had always been Dahlstrom's long suit, but in the last few years one after another of his favorite passages had vanished into an infuriating void. In moments of weakness he quailed before this evidence of God's relentless retreat.

Now he felt a tremor of fear, and quickly, as an exercise, he reviewed his daughters' names. When he could only come up with eight, a chill sweat moistened his forehead. Then he noticed that Mai was on her way to the door.

"Where are you going?"

"To the hospital."

"I'll come and see Carin as soon as she gets home. How about Saturday afternoon?"

"Okay."

He went to the door and kissed Mai's cheek. "She's going to be fine, Mai."

"You won't understand this, Papa, but I'm looking for someone who won't say that to me."

Mai went out. Dahlstrom remained at the door for several moments; then he started back toward his desk. On the way he paused next to a lamp, turned it on and peered around the room. A marble bust stared down at him from the top of a bookcase. It was Victorian in manufacture, Roman in style and he couldn't remembering having seen it in years. Someone could have removed it and he wouldn't have known. His head swiveled slowly. Corners came into view, objects, pictures. He crossed the room and took a standing frame from a table. It contained a picture of himself, his wife and a fan of girls. Quickly he scanned the photo in search of the missing daughter.

"Of course," he murmured, "Helena."

He put the picture down, surveyed the room once more and returned to his desk.

Doug tried to pick Carin up at the foot of the stairs, but she drew back, insisting, "I'm okay."

"You bet you are!" Doug replied with a grin, and winked at Mai as Carin marched purposefully up the stairs to her bedroom. Carin had been out of danger forty-eight hours after her arrival in the intensive-care unit. The additional twelve days in the hospital were a period of adjustment and education for Carin and her parents. Carin was a trained diabetic now. "You're the manager," Dr. Rothberg had said. "All I do is give you the best advice I can. You have to take it from there. Testing and treating. Do you understand?" Carin had nodded; three years of dance training had taught her to follow orders. *Développé à la second* . . .

Carin flung open her bedroom door, saw her stuffed animals lined up on the bed waiting for her, raced into the room with a happy howl and flung herself into the toys' furry midst. In the doorway behind her Doug grinned and squeezed Mai's hand. As Carin bounced up and down on the bed, Mai said, "Easy, honey," but she too was grinning uncontrollably.

Doug opened a box of hypodermic syringes and laid three on the dresser. "Here they are, honey. These are for today. I'll just leave three so you can keep track."

Carin glanced at the dresser, nodded casually and returned to her methodical reunion with the stuffed animals, picking each up in turn for a maternal hug, kiss and "Did you miss me?"

Doug laid out two insulin vials, one clear, the other a silvery suspension. Carin's regimen called for three injections a day: a mixture of the two drugs before breakfast, a syringe of the clear medication before lunch, the mixture again before dinner. Her diabetes had proven unmanageable with one injection a day, or even two, and although Dr. Rothberg assured Mai that the severity of a diabetic condition was measured not by the amount of insulin taken daily but by the presence or lack of complications, Mai knew that her daughter would live her life on a diabetic tightwire, balanced precariously between a lethal buildup of unchecked sugar on the one side and the convulsive violence of hypoglycemia, the shock caused by an excess of insulin, on the other. The delicate balance could be affected by any of a hundred factors: the food Carin ate, fatigue, an injury, a common cold, even her mood could change her metabolism enough to topple her off either side of the narrow wire. Although Mai knew that the early symptoms of hypoglycemia could be counteracted by eating enough sugar to restore the balance between glucose and insulin, she remained morbidly fearful of the shock that threatened each time Carin pushed a hypodermic into her flesh, and the homework she had done in the past two weeks—not only in the literature Dr. Rothberg had given her but in every other scrap of diabetic intelligence she could get her hands on—had confirmed and deepened her fears. She had memorized the early-warning symptoms of shock and the more ominous sequelae: behavioral changes, even schizophrenic hallucination, caused by sugar starvation of the brain cells. She knew that once this stage of hypoglycemia was reached—and it could be reached quickly—the progress of the shock was rapid and violent, to convulsions, coma and, if the victim were alone, undiscovered and untreated, death. Once, when she was ten, Mai had seen her cousin Marge in shock, and now that writhing image haunted Mai, asleep and awake. The thought of her gentle, graceful daughter twisted in convulsion . . . It mustn't happen to Carin. It *couldn't* happen . . .

"It's okay," Carin cooed to the last of her stuffed animals, "Mommy's home." She propped the toy against her pillow and turned to Mai. "When can I go to school?"

Mai beamed. "Monday. Your teacher called. She's coming to see you tomorrow."

"Miss Nicholas is coming *here?*"

"No, Mrs. Baker." Carin's glow faded. "You *like* Mrs. Baker."

"Sure; but I meant my other school. When can I go back to the conservatory?"

Doug leaned against the dresser and waited. Mai sat on the edge of the bed, avoiding Doug's scrutiny.

"Not for a while," Mai said.

Carin blanched. "Why?"

"You have to rest."

"Then why am I going back to school Monday?"

"I think—I just think it's better if you don't dance for a while."

"Why?"

"One thing at a time . . ."

"Noooo!" Giant tears welled.

"There's nothing to cry about," Mai insisted. "We'll talk about the conservatory next week."

On Saturday afternoon the Reverend Mr. Dahlstrom visited his granddaughter. He brought several books. Mai noted gratefully that they weren't religious works, but her gratitude was diminished by a

glance at the legend on their bindings: *For Ages Five to Seven.*
Dahlstrom had confused Carin's age with that of a parishioner's
daughter who was suffering from leukemia.

After his visit with Carin, Dahlstrom found Mai and Doug in
the living room. "How's she doing?" he asked.

"Why ask us? You just saw her." Doug said.

"I know, but . . ."

"What?"

"I guess I expected to find her a little—perkier." Dahlstrom
smiled. "I know I'm not the world's most stimulating conversational-
ist, but I can usually get a youngster's attention."

"I hope she wasn't rude," Doug said.

"No, just a little vague and . . . distant. Not herself yet, I guess.
Or maybe I was boring her. She kept leaving the room . . ."

Mai was on her feet. "For where!" Dahlstrom looked at her.
"Where was she going!"

"The bathroom. Every five minutes."

Mai was on her way up the stairs, Doug at her heels.

Carin was seated on the bed, her head swiveling slowly toward
the door as it swung open. She stared blankly at the agitated figures
hurrying across the room.

"What's wrong?" Mai demanded.

"Nothing," Carin said.

"Jesus!" Doug muttered. Mai turned to him; he was staring at
three hypodermic syringes arrayed neatly with their praetorian
guard of insulin flacons. Doug spun toward Carin. "Why didn't you
take your insulin!"

"I did."

He strode to the dresser. "Then what're these doing here?" He
picked up a syringe. "You should've used two of them: one this
morning and one before lunch . . ."

"I'm okay," Carin replied thickly.

"Like hell!" Doug exclaimed and aimed the syringe he was
holding at the vial of clear liquid.

"No!" Carin shouted. She was standing on the bed. Mai
reached for her, and she hopped off the other side. In the doorway
Dahlstrom, winded by his run up the stairs, shifted his gaze from
one tense figure to another.

As Doug poked at the vial, missed and stabbed again, Carin
raced around the foot of the bed, darted at the dresser, knocked the
vial out of his hand and swept the second vial from the top of the
dresser. One of the vials broke; the other didn't. Carin stamped on
the unbroken vial with her bare heel, breaking it, spilling insulin and
blood on the floor. Mai raced down the stairs for the telephone.

"Dr. Rothberg . . . ?"

Three pale faces peered out of the living room. Rothberg came slowly down the stairs, one hand on the banister, his eyes distant. In the living room he sat heavily in the couch, and said, "I gave her some insulin."

"She let you?" Doug asked.

"No."

"But . . ."

"She says she doesn't like me anymore." Rothberg smiled wearily. Mai glanced at the stairs and rose. "She's all right," Rothberg said. "You can leave her alone for a few minutes."

"What about her next injection?" Mai asked.

"That's what we've got to talk about."

Mai sat down.

"Thank God we learned how to do it," Doug said.

"You're going to *wrestle* with her three times a day?" Dahlstrom asked.

"Till she stops this—whatever she thinks she's doing," Doug said.

"What is it?" The three men looked at Mai. She was facing Rothberg. "Why is she doing this?"

Rothberg poked at the small cushion next to him on the couch. Then he looked up. "To punish you."

Mai gasped. Then she murmured, "Her ballet classes."

Rothberg nodded. "She says she won't give herself any injections till you let her go back to ballet class. She's sort of—on strike, I guess you'd have to say."

Dahlstrom raised his hands in a feeble gesture of protest, and Doug looked away from Mai's stricken face.

"She's a tough little kid," Rothberg said.

"We'll give her the shots," Mai said grimly.

"She says she won't let you."

"There are two of us."

"Mai . . ." Doug began.

"If she won't take her insulin, I'll have to put her back in the hospital," Rothberg said.

"Till when?" Doug asked. Rothberg shrugged and looked at Mai. "I guess there's only one solution," Doug sighed.

"No, there isn't!" Mai backed away from three questioning faces. "You don't understand!"

Dahlstrom stood up. "What don't we understand?"

"Those classes—they—they mean so much to her . . ."

"You think we haven't got that message?" Doug asked.

"That's the closest I've ever come to seeing a nine-year-old commit suicide," Rothberg said.

Mai looked desperately from one face to another. Her father took a step toward her, pleading. "Tell us what we don't understand."

She faced Rothberg. "Do you have children?"

"Yes."

"Have any of them ever studied dance?"

"No."

"Well, go to the conservatory and look at the children coming out of a dance class. They're soaking wet and their hearts are beating a mile a minute. Sometimes Carin's so tired she's shaking, and she's always famished . . ."

"What're you trying to say, Mai?" Dahlstrom asked.

"She's describing the symptoms of insulin shock," Rothberg said evenly.

"And how will I know?" Mai rasped. "How will I ever know whether my daughter's just another tired dancer or thirty seconds away from convulsions?" As so often in the recent past, there was accusation in the glance she directed at Dr. Rothberg. "I read all the books and pamphlets you gave me. Every word."

Rothberg nodded. "And memorized them."

"Wouldn't you?"

"Of course. Once I gave myself an injection of insulin so I'd have something besides a theoretical knowledge of insulin shock."

"Then you *do* understand."

"No."

"You think I should take chances with Carin?"

"You can't wrap her in cotton batting. One of the most important elements in the control of diabetes is exercise. I told you that."

"Have you ever looked at her feet?"

"I just bandaged one."

"Did you look at it?"

"Of course. I'll have to check the wound tomorrow."

"Why?"

"Mai . . ." Doug said, but she waved him aside.

"Why?" Mai demanded of Rothberg.

"Because a diabetic's foot may be slow to heal—and vulnerable," Rothberg said wearily, aware of the bait he was being forced to take.

Mai charged. "Then look at her feet again! They're not the pretty little feet you see on a child. They're *working* feet. Callused and misshapen. And pretty soon she'll be ready for *pointe* class. You know what that does to the feet?"

"I can imagine."

"And you want me to take that chance? Every book you gave me said even an ingrown toenail is dangerous."

"It may be."

"Then she'll do all the exercise you want. She'll ride a bicycle, she'll play games—like a normal nine-year-old—she'll take gym class . . ."

"And insulin?" It was Doug. Mai glared at him.

"Your husband has a point," Rothberg said carefully.

"Then what did you bother to give me these for?" Mai exclaimed, yanking a drawer out of the table next to her. Pamphlets and books spilled to the floor around her. She knelt, found a pamphlet and rose, leafing through it. Rothberg noted the cover of the pamphlet and sighed as she read, " 'Diabetics who require insulin should not be positioned where an inadvertent insulin reaction will endanger either themselves or their fellow employees.' " She looked up in bitter triumph. "That's *official*. From the American Diabetes Association." Rothberg nodded gravely. She knelt again, shuffled through the scrambled pile, rose with a book and trumpeted, " 'Kidney failure is the cause of death in twenty to forty percent of diabetics in whom the diabetes is diagnosed before the fifth decade.' "

"That literature isn't designed to make you phobic," Rothberg said, but Mai was shuffling to a new page.

" 'Among those who have had diabetes for twenty years, seventy-five percent have significant retinopathy;' " she read, "after twenty-five years, this figure rises to ninety percent.' " She looked at Doug and Dahlstrom. "You know what retinopathy is? Blindness! 'Blood vessel disease,' " she read, " 'one hundred percent after twenty years!' "

"None of those complications has to happen," Rothberg protested.

"Wait," Mai said, shuffling paper on the floor again. "I can show you statistics that prove they'll happen no matter *how* good the treatment is."

"I don't subscribe to that view."

Mai brandished a book. "This doctor does."

"I told you in the beginning: we still can't maintain a perfect blood sugar twenty-four hours a day, three hundred sixty-five days a year, but if you're going to confuse yourself by reading every word ever written on the subject of diabetes . . ."

Mai rose, and announced grimly, "I don't have to read *one* word. I saw it—with my own eyes. Grandma and my aunt and my cousin—they died. Their hearts gave out."

There was a profound note of weariness in Rothberg's voice now. "The kind of complication you're talking about doesn't show up till the disease is at least twenty years old."

"When the disease is twenty years old," Mai said flatly, "Carin will be twenty-nine. You think it'll be easy for her to change her whole life *then?*"

"Of course not."

"Then now's the time to change it, no matter how much she objects."

"She's not just objecting," Rothberg said quietly.

"She doesn't realize what she's doing."

"Yes, she does."

"A nine-year-old child doesn't know what death is!"

"This one does. One of the children in the intensive-care unit died. I know she saw it because she mentioned it." He nodded toward the stairs. "Ten minutes ago."

Mai inhaled sharply. Then she began shifting slowly from foot to foot, as if seeking her balance.

"Honey, if Dr. Rothberg isn't worried . . ." Doug began cautiously.

"I didn't say I wasn't worried," Rothberg said. He looked at Mai. "Some of your arguments are valid. But it's terribly important not to turn diabetics into—cripples."

Mai peered around the room as if she might bolt.

"Mai . . ." It was her father, looking out of place and embarrassed on the other side of the room. "I—I've been thinking lately. About some mistakes I made—with all the girls. But maybe especially with you. I think—I think I gave you too little. Maybe that's why you want to give Carin too much."

Mai closed her eyes. When she opened them, she turned and went quickly up the stairs.

The director was wearing the tweed suit Carin had vomited on. Or an identical suit. *Maybe,* Mai thought, *it's a kind of school uniform.* Through the heavy office door she could hear the piano that was accompanying Carin and the other children at the *barre.*

Mrs. Rome smiled, invited Mai to sit down and settled behind her desk, still smiling. "Well, this is an important day for Carin."

"Yes."

"You, too."

"Yes."

"We'll look after her, I promise."

"She—she'll be all right."

"The doctor said she could resume her training?"

It was a moment before Mai answered. "She wouldn't be here if he hadn't."

"Well, you can be sure Miss Nicholas will keep a sharp eye on her."

"I—I'd appreciate that. As long as she takes her injections, we don't have to worry about diabetic coma, but there's always a danger of insulin shock—especially when she's exercising, burning up sugar."

"I know."

"You do?"

"We've had two or three diabetic students."

Mai leaned forward. "You have?"

"Yes. They carried sugar."

"Carin has some in her dance bag."

The smile returned. "Then we don't have anything to worry about."

"No."

"One of the girls who was diabetic . . ."

"Yes?"

"She danced in several of our programs. Her mother sewed little pockets inside her costumes. There were bits of candy in them, so if anything happened while she was dancing onstage . . ."

"Oh, I see."

"She was very clever about it. She could tell when something was going to happen, and she'd reach into a pocket for a piece of candy. I don't think anybody in the audience ever saw it." Mai brushed a hand across her eyes. "Are you all right, Mrs. Bradley?"

"Yes. Do—do you know of any—professional dancers with this problem?"

"I've only heard of two," the director said.

"Oh?"

"Both very good, too."

"Would I have seen them?"

"You may have. I think they were both on television."

"Who were they?"

"One was Joan McCracken . . ."

"I think I remember her . . ."

"A lovely dancer. The other was Carol Haney."

"I remember *her!*" Mai exclaimed, enjoying a warm flush of relief. "Are they still dancing?"

"Oh, no."

An errant draft brushed Mai's feverish face. " 'Oh, no?' "

"They're dead. Both of them. Poor things. *Such* good dancers."

"Uh—do you know how old they were when they died?"

"Young. I don't think either one was forty." She leaned toward Mai and added quickly, "But I'm sure that's very unusual."

"Yes," Mai said, "very."

In the classroom Miss Nicholas was saying, "All right, children, relax for a moment."

As she turned to tell the pianist what she wanted next, the children shook kinks out of their legs or bent low, stretching their backs. Carin, her face aglow with sweat and inexpressible joy, raised her arms, fists clenched, and stretched her little body toward a distant, beckoning day.

FOUR, two, three, four
Fourth Position

"Will you shut the door? The goddamn air's blowing right on our legs!"

Frozen in the doorway, Carin stared at the buzzing mass of dancers compacted in front of her until Diane pulled her in, permitting the stage door to close. The brief struggle backed Diane into a young man who reacted with a friendly "Hel-*lo!*" then smiled appreciatively as he turned and saw Diane. "I *thought* I recognized the touch."

As Diane frowned at the young man who had danced next to her in class, Carin reached for the door, but Diane's iron grip on her arm brought her up short. "Please, Diane. Some other time . . ."

"You're here. That's half the battle. You can't quit now."

"Hey, I'm all for dancers making a buck any way they can—but kidnapping?" Gino said.

"Butt out," Diane snapped.

"What're you, her mother?" He took a closer look at Carin. "Wait a minute! I know you. You were in class today, right?"

Diane tried to intervene with a two-note song of protest. "Gino!"

"Di Vito," Gino said, his eyes on Carin. "That's the whole name. I didn't catch yours."

A faint "Carin Bradley" emerged from Carin.

Diane's eyes rolled heavenward. "Let it be recorded forever that I did not make this introduction."

A voice echoed down the corridor from the direction of the stage. "Okay, let's go! Get your numbers from the stage manager."

With a finality that surprised even herself, Carin said to Diane, "You can keep the letter. I'll write another." Raising an elbow for leverage, she pulled free of Diane's grasp and turned back to the door, but several dancers had entered behind her, and now, in response to the disembodied summons, the whole group surged into the narrow passage to the stage, sweeping Carin along. For an instant she tried to fight against the warm, woolly tide, but it picked her up like a cork and carried her backward through the passage, beaching her in the wings as it burst out of the corridor and spread out along one side of the stage in a broad delta of dancers.

Gasping for air, Carin turned toward the stage, and the trickle of oxygen that had reached her lungs evaporated as she confronted a limbo the size of an Alp.

"Wait here," Diane said, and headed for a corner of the stage where a group of men in shirtsleeves were clustered around a small table. Carin's head swiveled toward the black hole beyond the dead footlights and gaping orchestra pit. Somewhere out there, she assumed, there were invisible people, waiting to denounce her invisible talent.

". . . the hell's the matter with you? Are you deaf?"

She turned back toward the stage. Diane had returned and mysterious syllables were floating from her. "I talked to the choreographer. I told him I know your work. He says okay, you can audition. You're number thirty-one. Got it? Thirty-one."

"Okay, let's see the next four—twenty-eight, twenty-nine, thirty, and thirty-one," the stage manager said. Upstage left, Diane and Gino, already among the elect who had danced the requisite combination and been asked to stay, watched as Carin moved numbly out of the right wing with three other girls. The stage manager strolled to a downstage corner and leaned against a chipped proscenium pillar as a pianist began to thump an up-tempo show tune out of the battered upright that jutted from a wing.

The choreographer, a narrow assemblage of acute angles in skin-tight stretch pants and opalescent shirt, watched with pursed lips and crossed arms from an aisle in the middle of the darkened house. One of the dark shapes scattered through the rows around him leaned toward him from an aisle seat. "Sonny, how's twenty-eight for you?"

The choreographer narrowed his eyes to isolate twenty-eight from the three other dancers. Her face was beaded with sweat, her lower lip had disappeared between her teeth and her elbows pumped with each pulse of the music. "She's a little stiff," Sonny said to the director, "and she sells too hard."

"Yeah, I guess so," the director said, sitting back, his eyes on the stage.

A third shadow, seated several rows ahead of the director, turned toward the aisle. "Who you talking about?" the producer asked.

"Twenty-eight," the director said.

"No!" exploded from the producer in a stertorous whisper, and Sonny's head snapped toward the dark round shape in the aisle seat.

"Goddamn it, she's ugly. That's all there is to it," the producer insisted. The director studied twenty-eight. She wasn't ugly, but no one could make a case for her as a beauty. "She's an ugly broad and I don't want her in the show!" the producer concluded.

Sonny pursed his lips, then muttered, "They have to be able to dance, too, you know," at the lifeless terrain of the producer's toupee below him.

Instantly the producer was on his feet in the aisle, thrusting his face at Sonny's. Silhouetted against the pallid light that illuminated the striving dancers, the bumpy tuber of the producer's head pressing close to the sharp angles of the choreographer's profile struck the director as a potato menacing a knife. "If you think the tired businessman cares which one of these broads can jump higher . . ."

"Then what do you need *me* for?" Sonny broke in. "Pick them yourself!"

"Hold it down, they'll hear you. Let's watch the dancers!" the director hissed down the aisle.

Onstage, Carin was sprinting toward the end of an airless tunnel. Nothing was right, nothing the way it should be. A simple step that she'd done in the first class she ever took seemed unfathomably complicated. Her arms and legs were attached to her body in strange, impractical ways that she'd never noticed before. Under these circumstances *walking* would be a problem, and some maniacal impulse was compelling her to *dance*—on a stage—in New York—in front of professionals. Experts! Worst of all, normally involuntary functions like breathing and blinking were breaking down and had to be consciously controlled and performed.

Breathe. Breathe. Breathe. Blink. Breathe. Blink. Breathe. Swallow. And dance!

It was as if all the operations of a computer had to be performed by hand, separately and simultaneously. Every circuit of Carin's mind and body was screaming *overload,* and there were still twenty-four bars of music, two big jumps and several tricky turns ahead—with no oxygen, no hope . . . . The other dancers looked strange, too: twisted and smeared against the glaring lights. Carin had felt the assault of stagefright before, but never like this. This felt like . . .

Shock.

Shock?

In the midst of a jump, Carin cursed silently through her fixed smile, expending a precious puff of air. She had broken a cardinal rule: ordinarily—*always*—before an audition or performance in Detroit, she had undercontrolled her condition. *Undercontrol* was a term and technique she had learned from Dr. Rothberg. When she had confessed her fear of going into shock in the heat of competition or performance, Rothberg had advised skipping the insulin shot before the unsettling event. While the change in regimen would upset her body's carefully calculated chemistry, the first symptoms of a sugar overload were preferable to sudden, violent insulin shock on a stage or in a studio, in front of witnesses, judges. Carin would have skipped her midday shot today, before this audition, but her decision—or rather, Diane's—had been made on the street, *after* the shot she had administered behind the carefully locked door of the ladies' room at Fruit and Nuts, while Diane waited for their table. She had nibbled the end off the ever-present Milky Way while she changed for the audition, but there were no secret pockets, no face-saving, life-saving bits of candy or sugar sewn into the soggy clothes she was wearing at the moment.

She tottered in a turn because she shifted her spot to the murky upstage corner where rescue lay, buried in her dance bag which was itself buried deep in a pile of other dance bags. She was bathed in sweat, her head throbbed, her fingers trembled, her heart felt as if it were going to burst through her leotard and plop pulsing on the stage, pinwheels spun before her eyes and the other dancers assumed weird shapes. Maybe . . . maybe it was only stagefright and the lights. But the candy—the Milky Way—one bite would turn back this vicious tide if this was insulin shock . . .

The combination was over; the music had stopped. Carin put her hands on her hips, mimicking the other shapes on the stage, and tried to suck more of the black unhelpful air of this awful place into her lungs. She blinked to stop the pinwheels. She thought she heard a screeching sound and she wondered how far she was from the appalling embarrassment of convulsion.

"I'm sorry. Something came up out here and we missed it. You'll have to do it again."

Carin's head swiveled toward the void from which the voice had come. Again? Without air? Without strength? Without talent? Without *sugar?* And do what? Somewhere in some distant place and time, someone had shown Carin some steps. But she didn't know their names or order or what they looked like. Her stomach muscles cramped and she suppressed a shudder. The *first* shudder? The small shudder before the gross repulsive ones?

The tension, the inordinate physical demands being made on her body had burned every available milligram of fuel and her body was frantically pumping adrenaline to compensate for the vanishing blood sugar. Deprived of food, jolted by adrenaline, her starving brain cells were taking on a new life, making a new person, physiologically and psychologically unlike the person they normally monitored. Psychosis was being ingeniously engendered.

Carin turned upstage, away from the invisible audience, toward the mound of leather and canvas in which salvation was buried. But Diane misunderstood: her protegée was panicking, stagefright was taking over, Carin was preparing to bolt. Diane had seen it happen at a dozen auditions. She stepped out of the pack into Carin's path, her jaw set, her steely gaze fixed. Carin hesitated, then turned away from the human barrier.

"Five, six, se-ven, eight," the choreographer called from the black house. The pianist struck up the meretricious music and the dancers began to move. Carin's decapitated body took over, exactly as it had in the first performance of the combination, moving in perfect synchronization with the other dancers, twelve years of obedience training providing enough nourishment to reanimate the faltering machine. While Carin's severed mind plunged back into the abyss, her body remembered, responded, performed. The headless chicken danced.

In the house the director rose and stood next to the choreographer in the aisle. As both men watched the stage, Sonny growled under his breath, "I can't pick dancers to satisfy his sexual appetite."

"Come on, Sonny," the director said, "Wally's an experienced producer. He's thinking of the show."

"He's thinking of getting laid in Philadelphia!" Sonny muttered.

The producer half-rose and slid further into row M to sit next to the lyricist, a gaunt shadow leaning forward, chin on forearms on the back of a seat in row L.

"What does he care how a broad looks," Wally rumbled. "They could be stark naked and they wouldn't get a rise out of *him!*"

The lyricist's eyes never left the stage. "Speaking of women, how do you like the boobs on twenty-nine? We gotta have *them* in the show!"

Wally surveyed the stage. "That's nothing. Have you caught the ass on number thirty?"

A sensation more rapacious than any Carin had ever experienced was washing over her in choking waves: she was hungry. Not hungry, ravenous. It was a pathological need, overwhelming every other already heightened sensation. Food floated about her: a tender hand, a juicy flank. She realized she was no longer dancing: but neither were the other hands and flanks. The music had stopped. She had finished the combination. Breathe. Blink. Swallow. Swallow. Don't bite. Don't scream.

The producer glanced at the dark shapes of the director and choreographer in the aisle, half-rose and sidled out of the row in a squat that was meant to protect his legs from any seats in the down position. The lyricist got up and followed the producer to the aisle, where the director was asking Sonny, "You want to keep any of this group?"

"Does anyone care about my opinion?" Sonny sulked.

"Listen . . ." Wally snarled, but the director grabbed his arm and said, "Please! We're going to be here all night! We all want the same thing: the best possible people for the show."

"Who aren't monsters," Wally muttered.

"Agreed," the director said quickly, then turned to Sonny before anyone could reignite the dispute. "Who do you want to keep?"

Sonny consulted a yellow pad in his hand, tilting it to catch a beam of light from the stage, then he said, "Number thirty."

The group waited. When Sonny remained silent, the lyricist erupted. "That's all? What about twenty-nine?"

"What about her?" Sonny asked coldly.

"Well—I thought she was at least as good as a lot of the dancers you've already picked."

"She can't turn."

"So let her dance straight ahead!"

Sonny sagged wearily.

"Look, we can't get into an argument about every one of these broads . . ." Sweet reason from Wally. The lyricist spun on him.

"If she had a big ass, you'd be fighting to get her in!"

The director's silhouette raised its hands. "Gentlemen, please!" He turned to Sonny. "You want number thirty, right?"

"If nobody minds," Sonny mumped.

"Nobody does," the director said before anyone else could respond, then added quickly, "I'd like to keep thirty-one."

Thirty-one was standing with her feet planted eighteen inches apart, her head bent, staring at the floor, praying for rejection because it would mean deliverance. She didn't dare look up at her fellow dancers or Diane, whose unremitting gaze burned into her back. She put out her tongue to lick furtively at her lips, but she couldn't feel them.

"You mean Miss Personality?" the lyricist scoffed.

Feeling a shudder flop about in her belly, Carin tightened her powerful abdominal muscles to wall the incipient convulsion in and thought, *My God, why don't they say something!*

"She's probably just nervous, that's all," the director said. "How's her dancing?" he asked Sonny.

"Maybe a little balletic for what I'm planning, but dynamite technique," Sonny said, evoking a querulous plaint from the lyricist.

"You don't feel she's a little—skinny?"

"That's the whole idea," the director said. "She can double as a little boy in act one."

"And how do we make the audience believe she's a woman in act two?" the lyricist retorted.

Wally intervened, the voice of sweet reason again. "Let's keep her for now. We're not married to her. She's still gotta sing."

"Okay," Sonny said.

The lyricist's voice quivered with disbelief. "What about number twenty-nine! You can't let that kind of talent just walk out of the theater!"

But Sonny was gone, marching down the aisle to whisper to the stage manager, who bent toward him over the orchestra pit, then straightened and turned to the dancers. "Thirty and thirty-one stay, please. Thank you, ladies."

Thirty-one's head came up very slowly. She stared at the stage manager. *"I'm* thirty-one."

"I know. Go over there, please." He pointed at the group that included Diane, Gino and thirty. Carin turned slowly; at least she hoped it was a slow turn. It might have been a triple pirouette; she wasn't sure.

"What's wrong?" It was Diane padding at her side toward the shadows upstage.

Carin didn't look at her. "Nothing." She moved forward, her eyes on the mound of dancers' gear.

"You don't have to be scared anymore. You did great. I told you Sonny would appreciate you."

Carin knelt and dug into the mound, trying to keep her actions moderate, normal.

"What're you looking for?"

"My bag."

"Isn't that it?"

Despite her resolve Carin snatched the bag open and groped agitatedly in it until her fingertips touched the firm oblong in the glossy paper. She ripped the paper and bit off half the bar.

"Nobody to blame but yourself," Diana sniffed. "I told you to order something. Nobody gets away without fuel, not in *our* racket."

Carin nodded, chewed, bit again, chewed, wolfing the sweet relief down. Behind her, four girls were dancing. She sat on the floor and took another bite of candy. She still didn't trust herself to look up at Diane. She took a deep breath. The demented stranger seemed to be letting go.

"Scared the shit out of you, didn't it?"

Settle for that. She nodded and bit again.

"I remember *my* first New York audition. I thought I was gonna faint. Right there on the stage." Diane chuckled. "You did better than I did. I got typed out the first time. Never even danced."

"All *right!*" Now Carin looked up. Gino had drifted to them; he was standing above her, smiling down, his heavy legs nearly straddling her. "Nice going."

"Thanks." She put the last bite of Milky Way into her mouth, swallowed it and said, "Thank God it's over."

"Uh—almost over," Diane said delicately.

"Almost . . . ?"

"You just have to sing," Diane said, her offhand tone placing singing on a scale of difficulty just below skipping rope.

"*Just* have to sing!"

"Loud," Gino volunteered. "That's all you have to remember. They just want to know they can hear you. Don't think *sing,* think *yell.*"

"Where's your music?" the pianist asked.

"I haven't got any."

"Oh?"

Carin was herself again. Petrified but herself. The "other person" who had laid such violent claim to her had retreated before the carbohydrate assault she had mustered.

"Well, Diane thought . . ."

"Diane?"

Carin pointed at the upstage group. "Diane thought I could sing something like 'America the Beautiful' . . ."

The pianist nodded and struck a chord. Carin stared. He played the melody with one finger. She was silent. "Try singing along."

"Oh!" Carin sang, "Oh, beautiful . . ." The first two syllables were a faint bleat, the last two a guttural growl. The miniaccompaniment stopped.

"A little low," the pianist said. A forefinger hovered over the keyboard, then picked a note. The pianist shook his head, moved three notes north, struck another note, then dropped his fingers to surround the note with a chord. He looked at Carin, waited, then began picking out the melody in the new key.

". . . tiful for spacious skies," Carin sang.

"To them," the pianist said, nodding toward the house. Carin looked at the void and stopped singing.

"Uh, thirty-one . . ." said a voice from the house.

"We're just finding our key," the pianist said. It wasn't compassion; a glance at Carin had convinced him that without support she would either faint or vomit, and either eventuality threatened his serenity. "Look at 'em and sing!" he muttered to Carin, and began picking out the melody with a rigid forefinger again. On the fifth note Carin emitted a wafer-thin sound.

". . . for spacious skies . . ."

"*Loud!*"

Gino's sizzling whisper ran downstage like a lighted fuse, exploding behind Carin with such force that she reacted visibly—and audibly. In the house it sounded as if an invisible hand had turned a volume knob up to full. Carin's voice soared out over the orchestra pit. The quaver was gone, but so was the vibrato: the tone was as hard, flat and assertive as a surfboard.

The dramatic change had spun the pianist from the keyboard, startled out of the torpor to which he had gratefully returned once thirty-one seemed safely past the Scylla and Charybdis of losing consciousness or her cookies. The turn from the piano had pulled his hands down the keyboard, shifting the music to a new key, and the surfboard swerved and followed in blind, but not deaf obedience.

In the house, the lyricist grunted. "Beverly Sills she's not."

"She's just as loud," Wally said, igniting a kitchen match with his thumbnail.

"Did you hear the way she followed the pianist when he changed keys?" the composer exclaimed.

The group looked across the aisle at the silhouette of a small man jackknifed in a seat, his knees jammed against the back of the seat in front of him.

"Come on, George!" the lyricist moaned.

"Goddamn it, pitch is important," the composer said, and stood up, gaining hardly any height in the move. "I've been sitting like a fucking mute while you guys debated the relative merits of tits and turns, but now they're singing, and that's *my* department. I let you talk me into sixteen dancers and only four singers . . ."

"Because the show *needs* dancers," the director said, but the composer bulled ahead.

"It's a musical, so it needs singing, too. If that sounds parochial . . ."

"Jesus Christ, I thought we settled this," Wally groaned.

"Because everybody did a number on me about how great the dancers sing," the composer persisted.

"Well, give 'em a chance," Wally said, "you've only heard three."

George's hand flicked toward the stage. "Those kids are going to have to sing *parts,* which means they're going to have to sing on pitch, and I heard this kid change keys when the pianist made a mistake. She went right with him."

The lyricist moved to the composer, lowering his voice. "What're you getting excited about, George? We've still gotta hear about forty of them."

"It's the general attitude," George grumbled. "I can see it coming. All Sonny cares about is whether they can dance." He glowered at the director. "Al wants actors . . ." He turned back to confront the lyricist. "And I guess I've been working with you long enough to know what *you* want."

"You think I don't want the audience to hear my words?"

"Will you guys work out your personal problems someplace

else?" Wally protested, then addressed the blackness above him. "Please, just once, send me a composer and lyricist who can talk to each other without coming to blows."

"All I'm saying . . ." George began.

"We *know* what you're saying," Wally declared, "and we respect it. Give us a chance. Give *them* a chance." He gestured toward the stage, where the pianist, after stopping with an apology to Carin, had begun again in the proper key, and Carin had bellowed her way through "America the Beautiful." Now she was standing in the center of the stage, staring into the blackness from which the muffled sound of voices drifted.

"Uh—just a moment, thirty-one." It was the stage manager's voice from somewhere in the void.

"What're we going to do about thirty-one?" the stage manager asked the skulk of shadows around him.

"Let 'er stay," Wally said. "If George thinks it's a good voice . . ."

"I didn't say it was good," George broke in. "I just said it sounds like she's got pitch, and that's important."

"Of course it is, of course it is," Wally purred. In moments of self-appraisal, Wally liked to think of himself as The Great Mediator. Turning to the stage manager with a spacious wave of his cigar, he said, "Tell thirty-one to stay."

"Stay, please," the stage manager called to the forlorn figure in the center of the stage.

"There you are, gentlemen," the stage manager said to the indistinct shapes slumped in the seats around him. "The two middle groups are your dancing chorus, the side groups are the last rejects. Is that your final decision?"

"Let's not rush it now," Wally said. "We're going to have to live with this for a long time."

"He means that literally," Sonny murmured to his assistant.

Onstage, the four groups waited, Gino and Diane safely ensconced in the winners' circles of eight boys and eight girls centerstage, Carin numbly awaiting dismissal in the knot of girls stage left.

The producer rose from a seat in the middle of one of the rows and sidled into the aisle, calling quietly to another seated figure, "Al." The director rose and moved to the aisle, where the producer had stopped next to Sonny. "Now I don't want any tantrums," Wally began, and Al saw Sonny's shoulders stiffen, "but I'd like to point out that practically every girl we picked has dark hair. There isn't one blonde in the entire chorus. That's a slightly—unnatural look, don't you think?"

Sonny stared at Wally, his mouth a thin line, then said quietly, "Some of them can dye their hair."

"They have to agree to; that's the Equity rule. And they usually won't. So why can't we just take a couple out of the A group and replace 'em with two blondes from the B group?"

"One from column A and two from column B," the lyricist giggled.

"We're down to nothing but good dancers, so what difference does it make to you if we juggle a little?" Wally asked.

"Which ones are you suggesting replacing?" Sonny replied with faintly disguised distaste.

"Well, the third from the left," Wally replied. "I've seen better legs on a piano."

"And who do you suggest we take instead?"

"That one, on the end of the B group." Wally pointed. "Okay?"

Sonny glanced at his assistant, rolled his eyes, then turned and nodded at the stage manager, who snapped on the light at the top of his clipboard, then called toward the stage. "Miss Dorielli, will you go to group B, and Miss Booth, will you go to group A, please." As the legs changed places, the stage manager called again. "This is just for purposes of comparison. Relax, ladies. We won't be long."

Relax! The change had sent new ripples of anxiety through the two middle groups and fanned nearly dead embers of hope in the flanking candidates. All across the stage dancers stirred like penned animals.

"Is that all?" Sonny asked, each syllable dusted with a fine coat of disdain.

A lump of rage shot up Wally's windpipe; then he remembered his genius for mediation and swallowed twice to dislodge the obstruction. "That's still only one blonde," he said. "What about changing that one? The second from the left."

Heads swung. The group stared at Diane.

"She's a good dancer!" Sonny protested.

"They all are!" Wally retorted. "What's so terrible if we change her for a blonde—and somebody a little younger, maybe."

Now the only note in Sonny's voice was weary resignation. "Like who?"

"Like the one in the middle of the first row." The heads swung toward the B group, then the stage manager looked at Sonny.

"I don't give a shit," Sonny said tonelessly.

Wally spun. "Is that the way you feel about the show? You're just here for the paycheck?"

"I'm just here to do the best job I can," Sonny replied. "But if we're going to pick dancers because you've got a thing about blondes . . ."

"I've got a thing about *hits!*" Wally snarled, the lump rocketing back up his windpipe and exploding against his soft palate, warm and delicious.

"Wally . . ." Al reached for his arm, but Wally brushed Al's hand aside, his tuberous head once again pressing perilously close to Sonny's falcon profile.

"And don't give me any of that bullshit about your art! Artists gotta eat, and producers are the ones who lay it out for everything on that fuckin' table."

"What's that got to do with how many blondes we've got in the chorus?" Sonny sputtered.

"Everything!" Wally poked himself in the chest with a blunt thumb. "You know who I am, pal? Joseph H. Q. Fuckin' Public. I may not know who's playin' at the Philharmonic tonight, but I know what it takes to put an ass in every seat in this theater! And if I *don't,* guess whose beautiful dances are never gonna be seen by anybody! Didja ever meet Sol Hurok?"

"No."

"Well, he spoke worse English than I do! So let's cut out the crap. You're not the lily-white artist and I'm not the black-hearted Simon Legree. We're both whores if we gotta be to get the show on, and then we're both heroes if it works. Understand?"

The toneless silence that closed in around the group was broken only by Wally's hoarse breathing and Al's gentle, "It's okay, Wally, you've made your point."

"To *him?*" Wally jerked a thumb at Sonny.

"Yes," Al said and glared at Sonny.

The group waited, tense, then Sonny turned to Wally. "I understand. I wasn't being critical of you."

"Bullshit."

"I'm not *now.* Really."

He nodded at the stage manager, who lit his clipboard, glanced at it and called to the stage. "Miss Allen . . ." The girl next to Carin stepped forward.

"Wait a minute," the director said quietly to the stage manager.

"Just a minute, please," the stage manager called.

"Would you mind if we took the other, to double the boy in the first act? She's blonde too."

"Yeah, sure, no problem," the Great Mediator replied. "As long as we got a couple of blondes."

"The one next to Miss Allen," the director said to the stage manager.

The light on the clipboard glowed again. "I'm sorry, I made a mistake. I meant Miss Bradley."

Miss Allen stepped sourly back into the group, and Carin said, "Me?"

"Yes. And will you go in the B group, Miss Cartier?"

Halfway to the A group Carin stopped, and Diane, on her way to the slag heap, muttered, "Keep going!" The reflex of obedience prevailed and Carin filled the gap Diane had left in the front line of the A group, where she glanced guiltily at Diane as a sound like the distant popping of firecrackers erupted from the house.

A new dispute had arisen. The composer was on his feet in the aisle, his stubby arms waving around his head. "Swell! We sit here and listen to every one of them sing, then you eliminate the best singer on the stage!"

"But she's a brunet," Wally said.

"I don't care if she's chartreuse, *I'm* the one who'll get roasted if the score sounds lousy, and if you don't give me the voices I need, it will!"

"You've got a *bunch* of good voices up there," Wally insisted.

"Not one of 'em's as good as the girl you just eliminated."

"What about twenty-nine?" the lyricist protested. "We never even listened to her. With a chest like that she was probably a natural mezzo."

"Listen!" Wally growled. "It's taken us four calls to get down to this group. We got one more decision to make and we're gonna make it. Now! The little blonde's in because Al needs her. No argument about that, right?" A murmur of assent rose around him. "So that means it's between Cartier and the tall one with no ass in Group A. I got an opinion on the subject, but I'm not gonna impose it on anybody. We're gonna settle it the logical, intelligent way." He pulled his jacket aside and groped in his pants pocket. "Heads, No-ass stays; tails, Cartier comes back in group A."

The dancers saw a spark in the house as a quarter arched up, catching a pale ray of light from the stage. The coin landed with a dull splat in Wally's palm, and the surrounding group bent to see its surface in the gloom. "Tails!" Wally announced crisply. "No-ass goes; Cartier stays. Let's get out of here. I need air." The hunched group ruptured; the producer started down the aisle, followed by the lyricist.

"What about the boys' group?" the stage manager called after Wally.

"They're fine," Wally said without looking back, then sighed. "Why does it always have to be such a fight to get some good-looking girls in the show?"

"What do you expect from a grown man named Sonny?" the lyricist responded.

Moving down the aisle, the stage manager called, "Miss Arnold." A tall, thin girl in group A stepped forward as the stage manager moved out of the shadows to the foot of the aisle. "Will you join group B, please? Miss Cartier, will you come back in group A?"

Carin's head snapped up and she watched the exchange of

bodies with undisguised relief. As Diane took a place in the front row, she grinned and prodded Carin with an elbow.

"All right, that's it," the stage manager said. "All of you in the A groups, come into the office tomorrow to sign contracts. You know the rehearsal date, so if you've got any problems or conflicts, tell us now. You in the B groups will be our alternates in case of replacements. Thank you."

A sigh gusted out over the orchestra pit as the A groups released the collective breath they had been holding. Then the two groups, separated by gender until this moment, sagged toward each other, melting together at the centerstage line in a thicket of encircling arms. At the center of the roistering storm, Carin gaped at Diane, speechless.

Clambering over the footlights, the stage manager looked up, surprised, at the hand pulling him to his feet. It belonged to the lyricist, who asked, "Do you have the addresses of all the dancers who auditioned?"

"Yes."

The lyricist slid an arm over the stage manager's shoulder as they moved into the wings. "Where does that number twenty-nine live? Somebody ought to call her and tell her not to be discouraged."

In the narrow corridor between stage and stage door, the stream of dancers, in street clothes again, bumped its way past Diane, jammed against the pay phone.

"Oregano," she said into the phone, "red peppers. . . . Right. Goddamn it, watch it!" she exploded at a passing boy as his dance bag mashed her into the wall. "It's Grand Central Station here," she explained into the phone. "I'll go to that spice store on Ninth. . . . What difference does it make how much it costs? I'm employed!"

Carin appeared, and Diane's hand snaked out and hooked her. "Hold on, I've got to talk to you." She turned back to the phone. "I'll see you in half an hour. Start the sauce; it needs time."

She smacked the phone into its cradle and eased herself and Carin into the flow of departing dancers. "That's my roommate Terry. We make a top-ten spaghetti sauce. You'll taste it tonight. We're having a party at our place. To celebrate. *Every*body's coming!"

FIVE, two, three, four
Fifth Position

"Of course I'm happy for you," Mai said. "But I miss you."

"I miss you, Mom."

"When does it all start?"

"In a couple of weeks."

"I don't suppose you'll be able to come home for a few days before then."

"No, I've got so much to do."

"Yes, I can imagine. Does Chris know?"

"Not yet."

"Shall I call him?"

"No, I'll—I'll let him know."

"All right."

"Give Dad my love."

"I will. He'll be furious that he missed your call."

"Once the show opens I'll be able to afford *lots* of calls."

"I'm so proud of you."

"I'll write you a long letter in a couple of days."

"I want to hear all about everything."

"You will. So long, Mom."

"Carin . . . ?"

"Yes?"

"You're taking care of yourself?"

"What do *you* think?"

"I know you are. But you'll be working very hard . . ."

"And I'll take *extra* good care of myself."

"You're seeing the doctor Dr. Rothberg recommended."

"I don't have to see him. We talk on the phone if I'm not sure about something, like diet or dosage."

"I just wish you weren't—alone."

"I'm fine, Mom. Better than fine."

"I know, I know. I'm so glad. And—Grandpa would be very proud—you know that."

"Yeah," Carin said quietly. "I thought of that. It'll be funny."

"What will?"

"Opening night without Grandpa out there cheerleading. Nobody'll know whether I'm any good or not."

Mai laughed. "*We* will. And *I'll* lead the cheers." They laughed together, high on vindication and relief, then Mai said, "Well, you're not rich yet, so we'd better hang up."

"Yeah. So long, Mom."

"So long, sweetheart."

Carin sat next to the phone for a long moment, then glanced at a plastic clock and, spurred by her mother's gentle admonition, opened a dresser drawer and took out the leatherette case in which she kept her syringes. Seating herself in an armchair, she slung a leg over its padded arm, deftly attached a 26-gauge needle to a syringe, poked the needle through the rubber stopper that sealed the vial, drew insulin into the syringe, pulled her skirt up and popped the half-inch needle into the long ivory muscle of her thigh, her mind distant and busy.

Removing the needle, she paused, caught by her image in the full-length mirror she had attached to a closet door to reflect her morning *barre*. Sprawled in the chair, a leg over one of its arms, her skirt drawn up, a flash of white panty exposed, Carin reminded herself of an ad she'd seen somewhere, for a movie. French or Italian, probably. R, definitely.

She shifted her leg higher on the arm of the chair, exposing more panty. Yes, that was it, exactly. A sign outside a theater on Broadway.

She put the empty syringe on the end table next to the armchair. The table's desiccated joints were hollow, the glue long since evaporated, so that it swayed pitifully under the weight of a newspaper or magazine, and even the touch of Carin's fingers as she put the syringe down made it tremble.

But Carin's attention had returned to the little drama in the mirror. She tipped her head and pursed her lips, trying to look more provocative. She widened the angle of her legs and laid a palm on the taut nylon sheath. Squinting, she was able to narrow her field of vision sufficiently to shut out everything but the slowly moving hand, distancing it, providing it with a mysterious identity separate from her own.

Suddenly the fascinated observer drew a sharp breath and relaxed her head against the back of the chair, careful not to lose sight of the X-rated mirror as the hand moved more quickly. An errant elbow bumped the end table and it tumbled, spilling the syringe that had been entrusted to it. The hypodermic fell point down and stuck. Ignored, it quivered in the linoleum floor like a dirk in another kind of movie.

In the mirror's movie the hand moved rhythmically, rewarding the respondent flesh beneath it for the day's splendid, unexpected triumph. Twelve years of Herculean labor validated, Carin accepted as her due the congratulations of the pumping hand.

Once Carin had been reinstalled at the Detroit Conservatory of Art, life had resumed a relatively uneventful flow. Mercifully, Mai's worst fears proved groundless, but her lesser fears were confirmed. On the journey toward a proper balance between unchecked ketones and Carin's daily doses of insulin, there were occasional derailments. Her first insulin shock revolted the nine-year-old and terrified her mother. Once again Mai remembered her cousin and aunt and grandmother and quailed at this evidence of mortality, anomalous and obscene in a vigorous nine-year-old. Dr. Rothberg answered her resentful questions with the calm assertion that there would be future instances of insulin shock, and while Carin would never accept them, she would learn to deal with them. He hoped, he said significantly, he would be able to say the same of Mai, and he gave her a kit that held two glass vials. One, he said, contained glucagon powder, the other a liquid with which to mix it before use. "Then," he explained, "you draw the prepared solution into a syringe and inject it."

"Who injects it?"

"You do. Into Carin."

"She does her own injections," Mai said faintly.

"The therapist was supposed to instruct you, too."

"She tried . . . *I* tried . . ."

Rothberg frowned. "You're going to have to try harder."

Mai stared at the kit in her hand. "But why can't Carin do this?"

"She won't be conscious." Mai gasped and he added a hasty, "You may never need it. But one of the problems with shock is that, after a certain point, the patient is too confused to do what has to be done. Someone else has to do it. And an unconscious person can't eat or drink sugar . . ."

Mai nodded numbly, her eyes on the kit, and that night she filled three grapefruits full of holes with dartlike flicks of her wrist, then, closing her eyes, snapped an empty syringe into her thigh and fainted.

After Carin's second shock, Dr. Rothberg suggested she wear an identification tag around her neck, "In case it happens in the street," and she looked at him as if he had proposed a public execution. "Have you told anybody?" he asked. She shook her head. "Your friends at school?" She stared at him in disbelief. "You'd be surprised," he said. "They'll admire you. They can't give *them*selves shots."

"No," Carin replied firmly, and the identification tag Dr. Rothberg presented to her after her tenth shock went into a seldom-opened drawer and stayed there.

Mai had one hope left: that her daughter would lose interest in dance, or balk finally at the ways in which it complicated her already complicated life. When it became apparent that diabetes and dance were to be the twin pillars of Carin's existence, Mai made a nervous truce with her fate—and her daughter's.

At the age of ten Carin began taking three classes a week; at twelve, six, one each weekday after school and one on Saturday morning. All Mai's efforts to fight the swelling encroachment had been in vain; when she had argued that she couldn't possibly drive Carin into Detroit six days a week, the budding ballerina had replied coolly, "That's okay, I'll take a bus. I'm twelve."

The climactic battle detonated when Carin was fifteen. The director of the Detroit Conservatory of Art had been enlisted for added weight. "You have to understand . . ." she said.

"No," Mai interjected, "*you* have to understand. Carin and I haven't spoken to each other since she brought it up."

"I'm sorry."

"Frankly, Mrs. Rome, I think you should be. Carin's barely getting through high school as it is."

"I know."

"Then how can you make such a suggestion?"

"We haven't made it. Carin sees other students taking two classes a day."

"What do *their* parents say?"

The director slid a glass paperweight back and forth on her desk. "Some of them feel the way you do."

"I'm not Cinderella's stepmother, you know. I want my daughter to be happy."

"Of course. And Carin has an extra problem."

Mai dismissed the notion with a wave of her hand. "I'm not talking about her diabetes. I still wish she led a quieter life, but she's managing very well."

"Beautifully."

"And I'm not as neurotic about it as I used to be." She plucked at her skirt, smoothing it. "Thank God."

Mrs. Rome tried to help. "But you want Carin to have an education."

"I want her to have something besides dance! Because she may need it someday." She searched Mrs. Rome's face. "Do you know what I'm talking about?"

"Well, I think you are talking about her—condition."

Mai rose and stalked toward a bust of Caruso, a jowly bronze burgher with an incongruous laurel wreath around his businesslike head. "Not just that. *Every*thing! I want her to be well rounded and complete—and happy."

"That's the problem. We both know what makes Carin happy."

"I've tried to change that," Mai said wearily.

"And you think we've worked against you." She rose and moved to Mai and Enrico. "We're just here, Mrs. Bradley. We don't sell art, we offer it. Some of the children love it, and some of them hate it."

"I know."

"And some of the children are—special. Like Carin."

Mai sat in a chair next to Caruso. Outside the office the sound of pianos, violins and sopranos clashed gently. Mai listened to the soft dissonance for a moment, then asked, "How special is she?"

"Very."

"That doesn't tell me anything. When we came here—nine years ago?"—she shook her head in disbelief—"Carin's idol was Margot Fonteyn." She looked up at Mrs. Rome. "Is she that kind of special?"

Mrs. Rome smiled. "There's only one Fonteyn."

Mai fought a wave of irritation. "But is she good enough to be—something? I mean, besides a kid who dances in school pageants and things like that. Will she be able to *do* something with her dance?"

"I think so. But it depends on so many things."

Mai got up and moved restlessly across the room. "If she's not good enough to dance, then what's she been doing for nine years? And what's she doing now? If she takes two classes a day, you know what that means: high school's just a formality; her life is dance and nothing else."

Mrs. Rome brightened. "Are you saying you're going to let her take two classes a day?"

"I'm saying I have one child," Mai said emphatically, "and I love her very much, and I don't want her to have an empty life—especially . . ." She waved an impatient hand. "Well, I just want her to have a full, happy life. If it's dance, it's dance. But if it's not, I want her to be ready for whatever it'll be."

Mrs. Rome strode toward Mai, bristling confidence and tweed. "No one can make any guarantees. All I know is that Miss Nicholas says Carin's the best student she's ever had. If you'd like to talk to *her* . . ."

"No." Mai stood aimlessly, clutching her pocketbook in both hands. "You know we live twenty-five miles from here. My husband works at the Wayne plant."

"Yes."

"I don't know how I'd get her into town."

"We have an early class that lets the children out in time for school . . ."

"I know; Carin told me. But I'm sure those children go to school here in Detroit. Carin would have to travel fifty miles, twice a day." Mai gestured helplessly. "It just sounds impossible."

"Unless . . ." Mrs. Rome hesitated. "Well—if she were going to school in Detroit . . ."

"But I just told you: we don't live in Detroit."

"Why don't you talk to Carin about it?"

Mai stared at Mrs. Rome. "Why? Have *you* talked to her about it?"

"I think Carin said something to Miss Nicholas," Mrs. Rome responded carefully.

"Maybe Miss Nicholas and I *had* better talk."

"She doesn't interfere!"

"That's not the way it sounds to me."

"She's doing her best. It's difficult. The other children are beginning to take two classes a day, and none of them is as good—or as serious—as Carin. Carin knows that; Miss Nicholas doesn't have to say anything."

"How important are two classes a day?" Mai sighed.

"It's like any other kind of education, Mrs. Bradley: you can't dabble. If Carin's going to grow, if she's going to become a real dancer . . ." She paused delicately.

"Can't she do it later? When she's finished her education?"

"But *this* is her education," the director said.

Dahlstrom stared at his daughter across the desk, his glasses magnifying his watery gaze.

"Just during the week," Mai said wanly. "She'll come home to us on the weekends."

"But—what about school?"

"I've gone all through it. There's a high school ten minutes from the conservatory, twenty minutes from here. They'll take her." Dahlstrom rocked back in his chair, his fingertips together. "I know it's asking a lot," Mai said, "but I thought, with Mama gone, it might be nice for you to have someone in the house. You've certainly got plenty of room."

"Of course. That's no problem. It'd be—wonderful to have Carin with me. The house is so empty . . ."

Mai stirred and sat straighter in the uncomfortable chair. "That's what I thought."

"But how does Doug feel? I'm surprised he doesn't have some questions about this."

"He's got lots of questions. But,"—she spread her hands—"we've run out of answers. To Carin. To ourselves. Right or wrong, this is Carin's life now. It has been for a long time; we just wouldn't admit it. But *she* knew."

"Maybe she could wait . . ."

"We've been through that. It's a matter of bone and muscle. I don't understand it, but if she's going to go into ballet, she has to work *now*." Mai fell silent, twining and untwining her fingers. "I don't know, Papa, maybe I'm just letting her turn into a moron . . ."

"But you said she's going to continue school."

"I don't know how much attention she'll pay to it—or how much strength she'll have for it, with a dance class in the morning and another after school. She's strong, and as healthy as most kids, thank God, but she's not superhuman. I'm afraid she'll fall asleep in class."

"Not if I get her to bed early enough."

Mai looked up. "I know I'm asking a lot . . ."

"No," Dahlstrom said softly, "I think you're doing me a favor. I see so little faith."

The bedroom in her grandfather's house was bigger than the one Carin had occupied at home. She was able to practice in it, extending her legs and arms without impediment, even turning and jumping. In the living room Dahlstrom would look up at the sound of thumps from the second floor and persuade himself for the hundredth time that what Carin was doing was homework.

The system worked. Carin took a morning class at the conservatory, boarded a bus a block away and was in her first high-school class fifteen minutes later, carefully husbanding her energies for the resumption of her real life at the conservatory late in the afternoon.

On her sixteenth birthday Carin arrived at the near shore of the Rubicon. The law at last was on her side, and she could if she wished take advantage of a sixteen-year-old's legal right to shrug off the encumbering toils of formal education. In New York Carin would eventually find herself part of a large uneducated class, many of whom had opted for freedom at sixteen, trading high school cap and gown for full-time *tendus* and tights without a backward glance. But in Detroit there was the immovable obstacle of Mai Bradley, who would, Carin knew, have unsheathed her claws at the merest hint of a dropout daughter. So Carin persevered to her high-school graduation, her only recollection of her last year of formal education an irritating daily pause for breath between classes.

Proms, yearbooks, orchids and organdy evening gowns were as foreign to Carin as the *Kalevala*. She had had few friends in the suburban high school near her parents' home; she made none in her new school. Those friends she did have toiled beside her in her dance classes, sharing her aches, pains and dreams, understanding the frustration of a butchered turn, the elation of a long, steady balance.

Carin wiped her face, tossed the towel over the *barre* and turned back toward the mirror, where Miss Nicholas was pondering an allegro combination. A foreign movement in a corner of the mirror interrupted the familiar rhythm of the class: a tall figure in funereal black was closing the door and flattening itself against a side wall in an effort to be unobtrusive.

Carin started. The dark figure, unobtrusive as a camel, was the Reverend Gunnar Dahlstrom. Circling the room swiftly on the balls of her feet, Carin arrived at the anomalous black shape and hissed, "What is it? Mom? Dad . . . ?"

"No, no."

"Well, why . . . ?"

Dahlstrom's smile exposed teeth the shape and color of the keys on the venerable Baldwin in a far corner of the room. "Can't I come and see my granddaughter dance?"

"Sure," Carin said uncertainly.

"I was in the neighborhood. I can drive you home," Dahlstrom added, feeling the need for amplification.

"Oh. Well . . . there are some folding chairs next to the piano."

"I don't mind standing here as long as I'm not in the way."

Carin glanced across the room, where her fellow students were lined up against the wall. "They're going to be coming this way. You'll get run over."

"Oh. The lady outside said I could come in."

A tremor of guilt stirred in Carin. She waved a hand toward the piano. "If you sit over there you'll be fine." She accompanied Dahlstrom across the room, pausing near Miss Nicholas. "This is my grandfather."

"How do you do. Would you like to watch?"

"If it's not inconvenient . . ."

"No. Sit down—right there, next to the piano."

"Yes . . . Thank you."

Dahlstrom unfolded a chair and sat stiffly, wedged close to the piano, as Miss Nicholas concluded her instructions to the students and, to a sudden burst of music from the piano, a pair of dancers vaulted across the room on a long diagonal line between corners.

"Next!" Miss Nicholas chirped, and two more flying objects were launched. The line edged forward, the students frisking and stretching as they waited their turns. Carin stole a glance at her grandfather. Ramrod straight, immobile, his pale hands spread on his black trousers like gloves laid in his lap, he looked like a sculpted extension of the piano keyboard.

A four-for-nothing measure alerted Carin to draw breath and yield to the pulse of the piano. *Chassé* . . . .

She was away, gliding across the floor, enmeshed in the music. Miss Nicholas, however, remained conscious of the dark figure next to the piano, and designed the class combinations to show Carin's strengths: her supple extensions, her flowing line and whiplike turns and jumps.

Dahlstrom's jaw dropped. Nothing else changed. His hands remained motionless, his head moved only enough to keep his granddaughter in view; but what he saw revised his life, reawakened his faith and answered Hume's disquieting skepticism at last. Willie Mays had never leaped higher against a center-field fence, Brooks Robinson never stretched for a grounder with such agility and grace, Sandy Koufax never unleashed a fastball with such ferocious speed and force. Suddenly baseball seemed slow, football ungainly, basketball boring. At the age of seventy-three the Reverend Gunnar Dahlstrom experienced a conversion.

When they got home, he timidly asked to examine Carin's muscles. Carin extended a leg; his finger bent against the stony resistance of her thigh. Carin grinned and challenged him to poke her in the stomach. For the second time that day his jaw dropped, as the steel mesh under the smooth skin repelled his probing finger.

"Muhammad Ali never had a stomach like that!" the Reverend Gunnar Dahlstrom murmured reverently.

Forty-eight hours later he intercepted Mai when she arrived to pick Carin up for the weekend.

"Let's sit down a minute."

"Doug'll be home before we get there, and I've still got to make dinner."

"Just for a minute."

Mai tried to read her father's expression, then went into the living room and sat on the couch, still shrouded in her coat. Dahlstrom sat in a facing chair, his folded hands between his knees.

"Why didn't you tell me?"

Mai leaned forward, trying to see if the resentment she detected in his voice was visible on his face, but Dahlstrom kept his living room as shadowy as his study. "Tell you what?"

"About Carin—what she can do."

"What're you talking about, Papa?"

"I visited her—at the conservatory."

Mai sat back. "Oh."

"Remarkable."

"Yes."

"Why didn't you tell me?" The resentment was there again.

"Papa," Mai sighed, "would you like to know how many times I've invited you . . . ?"

"You should've insisted."

"I did. But you always had to write a sermon, or go and see Roddy run or Andy play basketball . . ."

"Yes, yes," Dahlstrom said, raising a hand, the palm a white flag. "I've been looking in the wrong direction. None of them can hold a candle to her. *None* of them. The best athlete I've ever seen . . . is my granddaughter." He shook his head, mystified, inspired.

The conservatory's ban on stage mothers applied to Dahlstrom; otherwise he would have haunted Carin's classroom as he once haunted the upper deck of the Tigers' stadium.

He did, however, become a regular at her occasional public appearances, self-consciously shouting "Bravo!" and springing to his feet to initiate a standing ovation at the curtain call. Pounding his palms together, he would turn and sweep the more reticent members of the audience with the flinty regard he usually reserved for the perorations of his most menacing sermons. In recent years his fervor had waned, in both pulpit and upper deck, but Dahlstrom's discovery of his granddaughter and this electrifying new sport had re-awakened it. There could be no such thing as a moderate response to a performance by her; he simply glared at any miscreants until they found the gift of tongues, stood up and cheered with everybody else.

The Reverend Mr. Dahlstrom died in this state of grace. A local impresario, bidding for his share of the rich harvest of kids at home for the holidays and inspired by an article about Carin in the Detroit *Free Press,* had organized an abbreviated *Nutcracker.* The budding dancer, now seventeen and only weeks from her high-school graduation, was a daring choice, not for the part of Clara, the child before whom the *Nutcracker*'s miracles unfold, but the Sugar Plum Fairy, a demanding role danced in professional venues by full-fledged ballerinas.

There were six performances, passably well attended and marked as much by Carin's fitfully impressive performance as by the Ichabod Crane silhouette in the fourth row leading cheers during the curtain calls. Dahlstrom attended every performance, as if his zeal now might compensate for his former indifference, not only to Carin but to her mother. Dahlstrom's ardor confused Mai at first, then amused her and finally touched her. Seated next to him in the dark theater one night, she tried to ignore his incessant fidgeting in kinesthetic response to the movement onstage by counting the number of times she could remember seeing him happy. Three fingers unfolded, then, half a variation later, a fourth. Four times. In her life. She stole a sideways glance at her father. He was leaning forward, his shoulders swaying, transfixed, transfigured.

He had found the perfect sport and the perfect athlete. More important, he felt he had found an irrefutable example of the value and power of faith. Carin had persisted in the face of physical disability, parental objection, grandparental indifference; only her belief, Dahlstrom reasoned, had sustained her. God seemed nearer than He had in years. Within earshot. Within *reach.*

Dahlstrom was on his feet before the last note of music had died, thrusting his long arms aloft, clapping his hands ostentatiously, high over his head. "Bravo!" he shouted, and turned to the row behind him, smiling, nodding, clapping. The row behind smiled back and clapped louder. *"Bravo!"* Dahlstrom commanded, and a teenage girl essayed a timid "Bravo." Dahlstrom beamed. Now he turned, bathed in light, as the curtains parted on the stage. The little corps stepped forward, followed by a swirl of Candy Canes, Marzipan Shepherdesses and Polichinelles. Dewdrop bent low, Clara, Fritz and Drosselmeyer bowed hand in hand, and then the Sugar Plum Fairy and her cavalier swept out of the wings.

"Brava!" Dahlstrom bellowed. His balletomania had reached a level of refinement that distinguished between *bravo* for a man and *brava* for a woman, though he hadn't yet mustered the courage to launch *bravi* at several men and *brave* at a group of women. *"Brava!"* he bawled and turned to see who wasn't standing up.

"Papa!" Mai protested, laughing. "Leave them alone."

"It's the least they can do," Dahlstrom growled, and resumed his baleful survey. Dark shapes sprang up behind him like hyperactive weeds. When the whole audience was finally on its feet, Dahlstrom turned back toward his curtsying granddaughter, his glowing smile ignited by the amber and ruby reflection of the stage lights.

"Brava!" Dahlstrom thundered, and tottered against his daughter. Mai grabbed at the seat in front of her as her father's full weight fell against her. He slid slowly, silently into the space between the rows, his legs jackknifing toward his chin. Mai tried to hold him up but his dead weight was too much for her. He ended in a sitting position, his chin on his knees, his smile intact, accented, if anything, by the pressure under his chin.

Mai screamed, but her father had done his work too well: the audience, inspired by the cheerleading scarecrow, was in full-throated cry, and the avalanche of approval buried Mai's terrified screech. She bent and pulled at her father's arm as if summoning his help in stemming the tide he'd launched. His arm fell heavily when she released it, and she tugged at the sleeve of the man on her other side. "Yeah," the man exclaimed, applauding, his eyes on the stage, "wasn't it great!"

Mai leaned close to his ear. "Help! Help!" The man looked at her and she squeezed back in her seat to reveal her father. The man bent past her as a woman in the seat behind Dahlstrom leaned forward, reaching for him.

The continuing ovation impeded the effort of the men around Mai to haul Dahlstrom to the aisle. Once there, they half-carried, half-dragged his lanky form into the foyer, where they laid him on a bench. Mai bent over her father. "Papa! Papa!"

A gust of applause billowed into the foyer as the auditorium's swinging doors burst open and an usher emerged, followed by a portly, panting man. "There he is," the usher exclaimed, pointing at the bench.

The man hurried to the bench, knelt, examined the inert form, then turned to the usher and said, "Call Police Emergency. Tell them to send an ambulance—for a cardiac."

The usher rushed away. The man pinched Dahlstrom's nostrils shut and breathed into his mouth. Moments later the double doors swung open and the happy crowd began to stream out. The men who had carried Dahlstrom out of the theater tried to cordon off the grim drama on the bench, but soon a new audience had assembled from the remnants of the old one, and when the ambulance arrived, the attendants had to push their way through the crowd. Once needles had been driven into the chilling flesh and an oxygen mask had been fastened to Dahlstrom's face, the portly man rose creakily and surveyed the front row of his audience. "Was he alone?"

The answer was barely audible. "No." He turned to Mai as she murmured, "I'm his daughter."

"My name is Foley. I'm a doctor."

Dahlstrom was on a stretcher now, being wheeled through the curious crowd.

"Is he . . . ?" Mai began.

"You can go along in the ambulance," Dr. Foley replied.

On the sidewalk Mai threw her coat over Dahlstrom's naked chest. One of the ambulance attendants glanced at her but said nothing.

Dahlstrom's estate was predictably small. The only surprise was its division—not nine ways but ten. A recently appended codicil named the additional beneficiary: "My beloved granddaughter, in grateful and inadequate repayment of a debt. Brava."

One tenth of an already modest sum, Carin's bequest came to slightly more than two thousand dollars. Mai saw to it that the money went straight into a savings account, "For a rainy day."

The next day dawned cloudy. That was omen enough for Carin; she was waiting at the door when the bank opened, a suitcase on the sidewalk next to her. The day-old deposit withdrawn, she took a bus to Detroit Metropolitan and boarded the first plane for New York.

ADAGIO

SIX, two, three, four
Changement

With difficulty and buoyant good nature, Diane pushed her way across the crowded living room. This was, after all, precisely what her apartment was designed for. Around her the revelers surged and romped and danced, decked out in such vivid motley that looking unblinking at them was hazardous.

Diane lived on the fifth floor of one of the dilapidated brownstones that line the Forties west of Manhattan's Eighth Avenue. Their position, flanking the Broadway theater district, made them geographically ideal for the gypsies. Actors and singers tended to be more finicky, preferring the more respectable precincts of the Sixties and Seventies west of Central Park, but to the dancers, conditioned by a lifetime of climbing rickety stairs to decrepit classrooms and an annual income hovering (in good times) at the poverty level, this environment was no worse, and in some ways a little better, than the surroundings they were used to.

The price, after all, was right, and the neighborhood was, if nothing else, uninhibiting. The dancers looked on these tenements, once fit and proper as their still chic and costly brethren across town in Murray Hill, as blank slates on which the gypsies' ingenuity and muscle, inspired and honed by their chronic lack of funds, could work miracles. The result was the gypsy neighborhood, a redoubt of eccentric respectability doing daily battle with the corruption that nibbled like rats' teeth at its eastern flank. Eighth Avenue, dead forty years ago, was now in a state of advanced decomposition. As pockets of corrupted flesh collapsed up and down the sprawling corpse, massage parlors, porno houses, sex shops, peep shows and topless, bottomless, lifeless bars filled them like zealous maggots.

For the gypsies, accustomed to seeking out and seizing the main chance, this urban decay was unpleasant but useful, because it served as an effective method of rent control: what Forty-eighth Street landlord would dare hike the rent with Attila encamped at the corner.

While gangrene consumed Eighth Avenue, the gypsies hammered and stapled and glued and sanded and painted and sewed, improvising brilliant impromptus out of the oddments they lugged home from thrift shops, street salvage, garage sales and flops.

The pain of a Broadway disaster, closing after six performances, was mitigated for the gypsies by an ancillary benefit: rising like phoenixes—or buzzards—from the carnage, the gypsies circled for a respectful moment, then fell upon the warm corpse, picking it clean, at a significant markdown, of the chairs, tables, draperies and assorted decor so lovingly selected by the scenic designer a few short months before. Every gypsy's home was equally a memorial to the crushed hopes of Broadway angels and a testimonial to the dancers' highly developed survival skills.

The taste with which the booty was assembled varied from apartment to apartment, but the predominant note was as bright, strident and winning as a Merman finish, and the living room through which Diane forced her way was an archetypal example of the genre.

Somewhere in the din the doorbell sounded again, and Diane tried to quicken her step. Shoving the last few bodies out of the way, she pulled the door open, revealing a slender black man in a crushed velvet cape and flowing harem pants, gingerly carrying a heavy object wrapped in towels. A few steps back Carin was discernible, peering around him. Diane threw the door open, kissed the young man's cheek as he edged into the room protecting his cumbersome cargo, and flung her arms around Carin. "You made it!"

"Did you think I wouldn't?" Carin shouted over the uproar.

"I was considering sending out a posse to blast a trail through Hookersville for you. Did they give you a hard time?"

"No."

Diane studied Carin. "Yeah, I guess they wouldn't."

"Do they bother you?"

"They did till they found out I wasn't competition. At least professionally." She turned to the boy in the cape. "Whatcha got?"

The boy slid back the towel, revealing a brightly decorated cast-iron casserole. Diane hefted the lid. "It's black-eyed peas and greens. I don't know how it'll go with your spaghetti," the boy said.

"Perfect. Our spaghetti's more soul than Sicily anyway." She replaced the lid. "Take it in the kitchen and give it to Terry."

"Which way?"

Diane pointed across the milling mass of dancers, and the young man, grimly shielding his casserole, plunged into the maelstrom that swept him toward its vortex, taming his cape and harem pants with its superior flamboyance.

"You didn't tell me everyone was bringing food," Carin scolded.

"I told you it was a gypsy party. Share the poverty . . ."

"Then *I* should have brought something."

"Not till the money starts coming in. You're still an apprentice."

Diane turned to follow Carin's gaze, which had been caught by something beyond her. Gino, more than usually pantherlike in black shirt and pants, had been signaling to Carin from the jumble of dancers, and now that he had caught her eye he was motioning her to join them. Carin shook her head, and he gestured more emphatically. "I guess I don't have to tell you Guinness is on your trail," Diane said.

Carin looked at her. "I thought his name was di Vito."

"Guinness is what the kids call him. It refers to a little habit of his." She paused, the thunderous music underscoring her silence: *"Jungle love is drivin' me mad, it's makin' me crazy!"* "The last show Gino was in," she resumed, "there were eight girls in the chorus. The show was out of town four weeks and Gino nailed seven of 'em, so a couple of the kids wanted to send it to the Guinness Book of World Records. 'Guinness' is supposed to be a kind of warning. Remember that if he starts comin' on." She corrected herself. *"When* he starts comin' on. Want something to drink?"

"No, thanks." Carin indicated Diane's flamingo pink lounging pajamas. "Where'd you get that?"

"You like it?" Diane asked, beaming.

"Yes."

"Carole Lombard. She was wearing it in a flick on the 'Late Show.' I creamed, so Terry ran it up for me the next day."

"Your roommate can sew like that?"

"This is nothing. Wait a minute! You haven't met Terry yet."

She seized Carin's arm and pulled her through the churning mob, wielding her elbows like machetes.

As the two women broke through to the relative calm of the dining room, Carin stopped and looked around.

Like every other room in the apartment, this one testified to the wit and ingenuity that had cobbled something up from nothing. The room's theme was predominantly Art Nouveau, with clearance-sale touches, as if Alphonse Mucha had been crossed with F. W. Woolworth. Wine-red flocked paper (Orchard Street closeout) covered the walls, and the dining table *(The Rothschilds)* glowed under a Tiffany-type shade *(My Fair Lady,* bus and truck).

"Wow!" Carin exclaimed. "You and your roommate did this yourselves?"

"Loving hands at home. Mostly mine. Terry's the delicate supervisory type, very good at pointing out heavy objects that have to be pushed across the room. By me."

The kitchen had been less successfully converted. Flop shows don't dispose of working stoves and refrigerators, so the 1935 gas range and 1948 refrigerator were still *in situ.* But the moldering walls were covered with travel posters—Skiing in Switzerland, Railroading in France, the Edinburgh Festival—all free for the asking at the travel offices dotting Fifth Avenue. Copper pots, warped and dinged but polished to dazzling luster by loving hands, gave a warmth to the room around which three figures bustled, two young women and a man, all aproned, all, from the lean look of them and their quick deft movements, dancers.

Carin stood in the doorway and watched as the three chefs labored among the pots, casseroles, jars and bowls that had come with the guests. "How's it going?" Diane chirped, and one of the girls turned from the stove to extend a wooden spoon. Diane nibbled at its tip. "Mmmm!"

"Too salty." The acrid comment issued from the aproned man working at a counter near the stove, his back to the room. Carin looked at him. His shape and bearing marked him as a dancer, but even from behind Carin sensed a difference in him. The flesh of his back, visible under a skin-tight T-shirt, wasn't just spare, it was sparse; there was something tight and dry about him . . . He was old! That was it. Thirty-five at least, maybe older.

Diane planted her fists on her hips and challenged the man. "What're you talking about? It's great!"

"To each his taste buds," the man huffed without turning.

"Talk about *salty!*" Diane turned to Carin. "What do *you* think?"

The spoon was extended to Carin. She crossed the room and took a sip of the shiny red sauce in its hollow. "Delicious."

"See?" Diane gloated at the man, who simply shrugged his shoulders and continued to work.

Carin smiled at the girl with the spoon. "Your cooking's as good as your sewing." She indicated Diane's lounging pajamas. "I wouldn't know how to *start* something like this."

"Neither would I," the girl said. "I can't sew buttons."

"That's not Terry," Diane said, "this is." She pointed at the pinched, sullen back.

"Oh," Carin said, "I didn't . . . you didn't . . ."

Diane turned to the man. "Terry, this is Carin Bradley, the new girl I told you about. Think you can stop sulking long enough to say hello?"

Terry turned. Carin's impression was confirmed: lean was lank, taut was tight, spare was sparse. He was old. He held up wet hands. "Hi. I can't shake hands. Sorry."

"It's okay," Carin said. "Hi."

The din from the living room was suddenly augmented by a wild, concerted shout.

"Oh, oh," Diane exclaimed. "Feeding time at the zoo. We'd better get this stuff on the table before they start gnawing on the furniture."

The table, groaning under a mantle of food of various colors, textures and national origins, resembled beef under attack by a school of unusually aggressive piranhas. Once their plates were piled high, the dancers repaired to chairs, couches and studiously selected places on the floor to restoke the furnaces that would have to meet their bodies' immoderate caloric demands tomorrow.

When the gustatory pace finally sputtered and slowed, Diane permitted herself to fill a plate, plant her back against a wall and slide down it to wind up on the floor next to Carin. "Think we're a hit?" Carin nodded. "Who was right, Terry or me?" Carin looked at her. "About the spaghetti sauce."

"Oh. I thought it was fine."

"Tell him; he's still sulking."

As Diane dug into the mound of food on her plate, Carin plugged back into the conversation that had begun in the group around her when one of the girls, ruminatively chewing the last morsel of her dinner, had asked a red-haired boy named Gary which he thought more important, sex or food. Gary's girl friend Janie, seated next to him on the floor, had straightened, declaring herself vitally interested in the answer, and Gary's vague response had precipitated the dead-earnest debate which now absorbed Carin.

"Maybe we ought to slow down a minute and define our terms," Craig was saying.

A modern dancer, Carin thought. *Must've gone to college.* The two facts, Carin knew, were correlative.

Like Carin, most of the classically trained dancers in the room had barely squeaked through high school, picking up the rest of their education literally and figuratively on the fly. But Carin knew that modern dancers were different. Duncan, Wigman, St. Denis, Graham had rebeled against ballet's pointed feet and turned-out legs. Without turnout, without the undeviating demands of the classical repertoire of steps, the bones no longer needed to be broken to harness before they hardened, so sixteen was no longer the point of no return. It could in fact be the beginning, and was in colleges where dance was taught. Seventeen-year-old freshmen, exposed to dance for the first time, were offered modern dance because they were too old for classical training, and many modern dancers held advanced degrees because for them education was not inimical but essential to their study of the dance. Unlike the ballet dancer to whom school was an irritating stage wait, for the modern dancer school often *was* the stage. Anybody who said, "Maybe we ought to define our terms," must be a modern dancer. Carin was right: Craig held a master's degree from New York University, where he had begun the study of dance at seventeen.

"When you say sex," he intoned gravely, "what exactly do you mean?"

"Fucking," a girl in outsize tinted glasses replied matter-of-factly.

"What the hell else could we mean?" a ruddy-faced boy demanded.

"Well, there's cunnilingus and fellatio . . ." Craig said.

"Jesus Christ, Craig!" the ruddy-faced boy exclaimed.

"If you ask me which is more important, food or sex," Craig said slowly, mouthing each syllable as if explaining to backward children, "I ask myself *which* food, *which* sex."

"Girls," the tinted glasses said flatly.

"Are you asking me to compare caviar and cunnilingus," Craig persisted, "or fried chicken and fornication?"

"How about balling and bullshit?" the tinted glasses retorted, leaning belligerently toward Craig over her folded legs.

Craig's measured reply was lost in a chorus of rude remarks, out of which Janie's petulant voice emerged. "I still don't know which one you chose."

"I answered the question," Gary said.

"Yeah, like Craig did. Which do you like better, screwing or eating?"

"Eating *what?*" a boy said, mimicking Craig's condescending tone.

"Pussy," the tinted glasses said, extending a manicured talon to hook a sliver of lettuce from a neighbor's plate.

The girl in the tinted glasses, like the other dancers, had been reared in the cult of the body, *her* body. Unlike Carin, and like Diane, she had lived long enough to make a virtue and sensual philosophy of her physical self-absorption.

Realistic, voluptuous (the pill had long since mitigated the tradition of flat-chested dancers), the girl in the tinted glasses had persuaded a friend to assist her in a self-improvement program she devised shortly after her engagement to the spirited young actor she met in an industrial show. Assessing herself with a dancer's gimlet-eyed objectivity, she had decided she was deficient in the art of oral sex, and, reasoning that no one knew more about fellatio than a male homosexual, appealed to an old friend who was both male and homosexual to give her what she referred to in the plain talk of her simple faith as cocksucking lessons, and he, giggling and demurring, called Three Lessons from Madam La Donga. She hastily explained that the only requirement was that he lie back and offer her a moment by moment, blow by blow so to speak, criticism of her technique as she practiced on him. A kind of didactic going-down was what she proposed, for which, she quickly asserted, she was insistent on paying. Any other arrangement would be an unthinkable infidelity to her fiancé, for whose eventual benefit these lessons were designed. Her iron logic prevailed, and for the past month she had reported to her old friend's apartment twice a week, where, under his punctilious tutelage, and with increasing proficiency, she had blown him halfway through his headboard, to the profit of his prostate and pocketbook.

A young woman who approached life with that kind of scientific detachment wasn't about to mince words in a serious discussion like this.

"You still haven't answered me," Janie said menacingly to her boyfriend.

"I'm thinking!" Gary snapped.

"Oh! He's gotta think!" a boy hooted. The group waited.

"In season or out?" Gary asked finally. Gary was in the corps of a ballet company; his life was measured in seasons.

"What difference does it make?" Janie demanded, increasingly nettled by what she considered a public humiliation.

"*All* the difference," Gary replied firmly. "If it's the season and I'm busting my balls in two, three ballets a night, food comes first." The group murmured firm assent. "But if it's layoff, I'd rather screw." He sat back, satisfied. "Doesn't that make sense?"

"Ye-e-es," Janie said, then added a final challenge. "What about rehearsal period?"

After a pensive pause, Gary's flattened hand dipped right and left. "Mezzo-mezzo."

A brief debate ended with general agreement that Gary's formula was fair and accurate, but Craig suggested a vote, and when the group had been polled, the result was clear-cut: in season, or in the case of a musical prior to opening, the order of priority was (1) food, (2) sleep (a dark horse that came up fast when the voting began) and (3) sex. During layoff and post–Broadway opening, sex and food were win and place.

The discussion ended in a brief and uncharacteristic silence as the dancers contemplated their weighty finding. Then one of the boys suggested an ugly-feet contest, but a girl turned the record player on and the suggestion was buried in a rush of bodies as the dancers, who had been stationary for an unimaginable length of time—almost an hour—sprang up all around Carin, grateful for an excuse to move again. The girl who had turned on the music began to dance to it, and a boy fell into step next to her, facing in the same direction, so that the two dancers formed a rudimentary line. There was a gleeful shout from the group, a rush of bodies, and suddenly

two lines faced each other across an open space, swaying and shuffling in place, their feet moving in perfect unison.

"The Ginger Rogers! Hit it!" a boy called, and the two lines
converged, each of the dancers improvising showy tap steps. The two
lines moved through each other, and, when each line had arrived at
the other's starting position, the dancers turned and resumed the
original step, marking time as they waited for the next call.

"The Toulouse-Lautrec!" someone called, and the lines converged again, the dancers on their knees this time, scooting past each
other like energetic dwarves. Arriving at the two beginning positions,
the dancers sprang up, laughing delightedly, and resumed the basic
shuffling step.

Carin, who had remained seated when the others began to
dance, watched, amused. Then, when one of the lines swayed near
her, she rose and made her way along the wall to an improvised bar.
As she sorted through a bewildering variety of bottles (the dancers'
taste in drinks was as eclectic and exotic as their taste in food),
Gino's sinewy shape snaked out of one of the dancing lines and
drifted toward the bar. Gratefully locating a bottle of Coke, Carin
shuffled through the debris on the bar in search of a bottle opener. A
hand appeared on the periphery of her field of vision brandishing
one. As she turned to face Gino's enigmatic smile, he reached for the
Coke bottle, decapitated it with a flourish and returned it to Carin
with a courtly little bow. Carin responded by taking another bottle
from the alcoholic smorgasbord, handing it to him, and moving purposefully away. Gino looked down at the label on the stubby brown
bottle. It said *Guinness.*

"The Muhammad Ali! Hit it!" the caller shouted, and the dancers headed for each other, shadow-boxing and mouthing off. As
they turned to face each other again, Gino slid into line next to
Diane, his feet automatically falling into the pattern of the basic
step.

"Thanks a lot, pal," he muttered, bobbing next to Diane as
members of the two lines shouted suggestions to the caller.

"For what?"

"Recommending me so highly to the new girl." Gino nodded
toward Carin, leaning against the wall near the dining room. "She
thinks I'm the Boston Strangler."

"Don't blame me, pal," Diane said. "Somebody else must've
got to her. I compared you to Jack the Ripper."

The last act of the culinary drama bore an uncanny resemblance to *The Magic Flute*'s ordeal by fire and water, with clouds of
steam billowing through the kitchen as the cleanup detail scoured
away the gypsies' refuse. When Terry entered behind a teetering

stack of dishes, the girl in the tinted glasses asked, "Was that your spaghetti sauce?"

"Sort of. I had a little uninvited help. Why?"

"It was different."

"How?"

"I don't know. Saltier, maybe."

"See?" Terry whirled on the girl Carin had mistaken for him. "I told you you put in too much salt!"

"Do me a favor, Terry," the girl shot back, "get off my ass!"

"That's the *last* place you'd find me!" Terry bellowed, flinging his arms open. The column of china dropped, bringing the busy room to a dead halt, except for the soapy mist that slunk among the frozen figures, fragrant with lemon-fresh Joy. The tableau was broken by Terry as he marched out of the kitchen, nearly capsizing Diane, who was struggling through the door from the dining room, her arms full of table linen. She turned and stared at Terry's diminishing shape, his shoulders clenched so near his ears his head seemed to have been hammered into his torso.

A narrow vertical bar of light sliced the darkness, then widened to frame a black form that looked as if it had been snipped out of it by the blunt kiddie-scissors of a silhouette artist. The black form reached out and pushed at the edge of the yellow bar and it widened, sliding up the bed until it illuminated Diane's face, pale and pulpy with sleep.

"What . . . ? Who . . . ?" Her eyelids fluttered in protest at the light, opened, then closed tight against the glare. "What is it . . . ? Jesus!"

The bar of light that had been swallowing the darkness was itself subsumed as the bed lamp flickered on. Diane sat up, naked above the blanket, staring groggily at the door where Terry stood framed against the light from the hall.

At this hour his age, which Carin had noted in the kitchen, was as insistent as a tattoo. Clad in baggy jockey shorts, his gaunt body looked gnarled, the muscles lying hard and knotty rather than simply firm under the livid skin, which turned gray as cigarette ash where it puckered at the elbows and knees. Day or night, bleach turned his hair a muddy yellow to conceal the encroaching gray, but the coiffure that normally covered his bald spots with meticulous care had been disarranged by his pillow.

"What the fuck's going on?" Diane muttered thickly, shielding her eyes from the glare of the bed lamp.

"I want to apologize," Terry said dolefully.

"What'd you do, *kill* somebody? It's the middle of the night!"

"It's almost morning."

"It was almost morning when I went to *bed!*"

"Sorry." He turned back to the hall.

"Wait a minute! I'm awake now. Don't walk out and leave me here." She punched angrily at her pillow, bunching it against the headboard so she could lean on it, then reached for a pack of cigarettes on the night table. As she slid a cigarette out of the pack, she paused. "I shouldn't smoke this early . . . Aw, fuck it. It's still last night." She picked up a matchbook and lit the cigarette with a defiant swipe, sat back against the pillow, rearranging the blanket where it had slid from her naked loins, then glanced at Terry, peering at her from the hall. "Well, come in out of the draft at least." As he moved tentatively into the room, she sighed, exhaling a long plume of smoke. "Okay, what's up? Besides you and me."

He stopped a few feet from the bed, avoiding Diane's eyes by staring blankly at the nipple nearest the lamp. Diane sucked irritably at her cigarette. When he finally spoke, his voice was barely audible. "I'm sorry—about last night. I wasn't very gracious to your friends."

"*My* friends! You knew every one of 'em!" He shifted his morose gaze to the nipple further from the lamp; the chill night air was sharpening it to a small pink point. "What was bugging you?" Diane demanded.

"Don't you ever have moods?"

"Sure."

He looked at the pale scar on her cheek, avoiding the malevolent eye above it.

"*This* is what you had to wake me up for?"

"I couldn't sleep."

"Well *I* could!" She took two wrathful puffs on her cigarette, then peered more closely at the mournful figure. "*Why* couldn't you sleep?"

"I was thinking."

"About what?"

He shook his head. "You'll just yell at me."

"How the fuck do you know that?" she shrieked.

"You already are."

"Well, *naturally*, if you say something stupid, I'll . . ."

"How do I know if it's going to be stupid or not?"

"I'll tell you!"

"No thanks." He turned toward the door.

"All right," she said quickly, "I promise I won't yell," then added an ominously quiet, "no matter how stupid it is."

He turned back to her, words spilling. "I just want you to level with me. Will you?"

"Of course. That's what a roommate's for."

He stared uncertainly at her for a moment, then came slowly to the bed. "The handwriting's on the wall, isn't it—and everybody's read it but me."

"What does it say?"

"Old dancers go home."

"What kind of talk is that!" she exploded.

"You promised!" he wailed.

"All right, all right." She forced herself to sit back against the pillow. "But you're wrong," she added firmly.

"Uh uh. I looked around that room last night. I could've been their fuckin' father."

Her voice was so firm the words seemed to take on palpable shape as they left her mouth. "You are ten times better at everything than anybody at that party!"

"Then how come they were celebrating and I wasn't?"

Diane sat bolt upright, the blanket sliding to her knees as she clutched her head. "What an idiot I am! This is *my* fault."

"What're you . . ."

"Somebody said party," she moaned, "and I said my place without even thinking!"

"Why should you have to think? It *is* your place."

"It's yours too."

"Does that mean you can't have a party here?"

"It means I should think twice before I invite a howling pack of gypsies over to celebrate a new job! I'm sorry, Terry."

"That's exactly what I'm talking about! Why should you have to worry about my feelings . . . No, listen, you don't have to apologize, because I'm grateful."

"For what?"

"I've been lying in bed thinking, and I—I realized a lot of things—that I've been hiding from myself."

Diane shifted uneasily against the pillow. "Terry . . ."

"Don't try to shut me up. I'm gonna say it. Do you know how long it's been since I've had a job? If you'd've asked me yesterday I'd've said four, five months—and believed it. But I did a little arithmetic in my bedroom. Eleven months, Di," he intoned hollowly.

"You know that can happen in our business. Then all of a sudden . . ."

"Yeah," he nodded, "that's what I've been telling myself, but it's US Grade-A bullshit. And when you start kidding yourself like that, you're in big trouble. *I'm* in big trouble, Di. I haven't even made a final in six months."

"That's breaks."

"It's handwriting."

Diane shivered and looked down at herself. Her nipples had shrunk to such sharp points they were barely larger than the bumps of gooseflesh around them. Pulling the blanket up, she tucked it under her armpits, clamping it to her body with her arms. In the brief respite this afforded her, she ransacked her mind for a telling argument, but the best she was able to come up with was, "Look at you. You're in great shape."

The blanket slid back to her lap as she reached out to slap his stomach. He looked glumly down at it. "I'm holding it in." His abdomen popped out. It was all muscle and skin, without a visible marble of fat, but nonetheless a little pot belly protruded over his skinny loins like the abdomen of a somehow pregnant prepubescent. He stared at the transparent skin. "I've been holding it in for thirty-nine years. I'm *still* holding it in!" he moaned, and the little pot swelled.

"You're pushing it out!" Diane protested, as fixated on the pearly globe as he was.

"I am not! That's the real me! I'm a middle-aged man; it's time to have middle-aged spread, for Christ's sake!"

The room rang with a sharp report and Terry leaped backward, clutching a flank. Diane, the harsh night light glinting off her naked bottom, was kneeling on the bed, a slipper in one hand, glowering at her anguished roommate.

"You promised you wouldn't!" he howled.

"Did I yell?" she demanded, poised to strike again.

"That was worse. It hurt!"

"It was supposed to!"

"You said you'd level with me," he growled reproachfully.

"I just did." With an air of satisfaction she retrieved her cigarette from the floor where it had fallen, stubbed it out in the ashtray next to the bed lamp and slid under the covers. "Now lets's cut out the crap and go to sleep. I've got a singing lesson this afternoon, and Christ knows it's late."

"No, Di."

The glint returned to her eye. "Whattaya mean, no?"

One hand still rubbed his smarting flank, but he took a breath that swelled his chest and tilted him toward her like an offensive lineman before the snap. "I came in here to say something—and I'm going to say it. Tomorrow's the first."

"The first what?"

"The first of the month."

Diane sank beneath the covers. "Marvelous. Now that we've settled that, I can go to sleep."

"And last month you paid both halves of the rent."

Diane's hand darted from under the covers, the slipper flapping in it. Terry jumped back from the bed, but he went on. "I'm out of work *and* unemployment checks, and I'm not even making it as a goddamn dressmaker! It's not enough to be queer! You gotta have talent and training!"

Once burned, he was ready. He caught Diane's hand an instant before the slipper landed.

"I'm not gonna listen to this shit!" Diane screamed, struggling to free herself.

"Yes, you are! I've been trying to say it for weeks. I've got to move out of here and you've got to get a roommate that can hold up their end!"

But he was shouting into a hurricane, or more specifically into "The Star-Spangled Banner," which Diane, who was covering one ear with her free hand, had begun bellowing when she couldn't free the hand he grasped.

"Damn it, Dinah, stop it!" he screeched over her singing, then yelped in pain. His grip on her imprisoned hand had relaxed for a fateful instant and the slipper had whipped into his flank in a short, vicious arc.

"How many times do I have to tell you my name is not Dinah!" Diane roared.

"It was!"

"It's not anymore! If my fuckin' family can accept it, my horse-shit roommate can!"

"What's wrong with Dinah Herman?" he challenged.

Naked on her knees in the middle of the bed, she planted her fists on her hip bones. "Does Dinah Herman sound like a star to you?" Before he could respond, she flung out, "I'm Diane Cartier now, and if you can't get used to it, you fucking well *can* move out!"

They were face to face, Diane kneeling on the bed, Terry standing next to it, the silence around them punctuated by their breathless panting as they glared at each other, unbudging, unblinking. Then, slowly, despite his desperate effort to will them away, tears filled Terry's eyes. Diane sucked in her lower lip and bit down hard on it, determined to continue the implacable confrontation, but as suddenly as she had struck with the slipper, she burst into tears, flung her arms around her roommate and bawled, "Will you stop it! Will you please just stop it!"

Terry opened his mouth to respond, and she brandished the slipper. "I just want to say one thing," Terry insisted.

The slipper remained poised. "It better not be crap."

"If I don't get a job next month . . ."

Diane broke in matter-of-factly, "We'll bring in another roommate and split three ways." Releasing him, she clambered back under the covers. "You see how simple it was? So why all the hysteria? Good night."

Terry was transformed into a silhouette again, framed against the yellow slab of light from the hall as Diane turned off the bed lamp, settled herself beneath the covers and closed her eyes. The silhouette didn't move, and after a moment Diane opened her eyes and looked at it. "What's the matter now?"

"Are you sleepy?" Terry asked.

"How the hell do *I* know! A man keeps waking me up!"

The silhouette was silent, then it said, "Want to play Monopoly?"

The note of pleading in her voice was genuine. "I've got to sleep, Terry. That singing lesson costs me ten bucks."

"Okay, okay." He turned toward the door.

"What're you gonna do?"

"I don't know."

"Make yourself a glass of warm milk, read a dull book, jerk off. Something'll make you sleepy."

"I'll just go to bed."

"And lie there and think?" She threw back the covers. "Come on." He hesitated. "Come *on!* It's late!" Slowly, his bare feet hissing sulkily across the threadbare carpet, he came to the bed and lay down, several pristine inches of sheet separating his body from Diane's. "Okay," she said, tossing the covers up over him, "now will you shut up and go to sleep?"

"Have you still got the slipper?"

The slipper reappeared above the covers, clutched in her hand. He dutifully closed his eyes. The two figures were still, their clinical disconnection accented by the slanting light from the hall that threw the space between them into deep shadow. After a few moments Terry's hand slid up from under the covers to close gently over Diane's, whether to seek comfort or maintain a wary vigil over the slipper neither Diane nor Terry could have asserted with any certainty. Diane opened one eye and murmured drowsily, "Got enough room?"

"Yes."

Diane's eye closed and she plummeted into sleep.

SEVEN, two three, four
Assemblée

"I still can't believe it . . ."

No! That's wrong. Too happy. It sounds selfish. It is selfish.

Carin crumpled the sheet of paper and looped it at the wastebasket, where it bounced off the rim and landed on the floor next to several balls of similarly aborted efforts. She frowned at the fresh piece of paper in front of her as if it were an impertinent questionnaire.

Say something about him, she reproved herself. *But what?*

"I tried to call you," she wrote in her Junior Miss hand, the *i*'s topped with neat little circles, the lower-case *e*'s shaped like small capitals,

but you weren't in. Then I decided it was better to write anyway, because I know you thought it was only a matter of time before I gave up and came home—and it was. But now everything's different.

Oh, please, Chris, be happy for me. Be happy with me. All these years I've been paying people to let me dance. Classes and tights and leotards and shoes—I had to pay for everything—or Mom and Dad did. And now somebody's going to pay me! I know what you're thinking—it's not Ballet Theatre, it's not New York City Ballet—it's not ballet. But it's dancing, Chris. For people! For money! I'll be making three hundred and fifty-five dollars a week! Guess how many ballet classes that'll pay for!

Wrong! Too happy again. It sounds like I'm celebrating. But I am celebrating. I've got every right to. Why should I have to apologize for finally getting somewhere.

She stood up, confused by her anger, angry at her confusion. At whom was she angry? Herself? Chris? What had he done? He just *was,* that's all. Had he put any pressure on her? Had he tried to talk her into coming home. . . ?

During the first weeks of her New York sojourn, she had thought of Chris often at night, reaching for the phone sometimes, then restraining herself on the grounds that hearing his voice at a vulnerable moment might weaken her resistance to the loneliness and frustration of her new life.

Sometimes she went to dinner and a movie with dancers she had met in class, young women, young men. When the men were gay, there was no problem; when they weren't, Carin was careful not to encourage them.

Red, however, had been a problem. He was young and free-wheeling and larky—and straight. Carin had been sure of that when he asked her out after class, but she had been in New York for three months, and loneliness was making her irritable; worse, it was beginning to affect her work. She felt a need for therapy, one injection perhaps to balance the emotional ketones that were building to a danger point. The danger for Carin was clearly defined: surrender to the doubts and fears that flourished in New York's rich soil, and a consequent return to Detroit's safe, stifling haven. Red was the antidote. After dinner he asked matter-of-factly, "Got a roommate?"

"No," Carin said.

"I do," he said. "Let's go to your place."

Down to her underpants, Red naked and swollen beside her on the bed, Carin rolled away and stood up.

"What's wrong?" Red asked.

"You have to go." Carin said.

Red sat up. "You gotta be kidding."

"No." Carin took a robe out of the closet and put it on. When she turned around, Red was next to her, reaching for her. "Don't," she said.

"Will you at least tell me why?"

"I've got a boyfriend."

"Well, why the hell didn't you say so two hours ago!"

"He's not here."

"Where is he?"

"In Detroit. I haven't seen him for quite a while."

Red fell back a step, arms outspread, teeth glistening in a friendly grin. "I get it. You're looking for a stand-in. Well, fine! No ego problems. I'll be around till he comes back, then you're all his again, and nobody's the wiser . . ."

"No! I'm sorry. It just turns out—I don't want to. Nothing personal."

His hand arced over their pale bodies. "You don't call this personal?"

She turned guiltily away from the stiff pointer admonishing her from his loins. "I mean it's too personal."

"That's what it's supposed to be." He reached for her arm, but she clamped it against her side.

"You have to go."

Muttering, the stymied stand-in dressed. As he cautiously zipped his jeans over mortified manhood, Carin said, "I'm sorry, Red. It's not your fault."

"Damn right it's not," he growled and left.

Moments later, Carin was dialing Chris's number. "I think I'm coming home for the weekend."

"All *right!*"

But at the bank the next morning, waiting in line at the teller's window, Carin opened her passbook and blanched at the sight of her balance. Tapping the passbook against an open palm, she calculated the number of classes represented by the withdrawal she was about to make.

"Uh—excuse me."

She turned. The customer behind her was pointing past her at the gap that had opened as the rest of the line moved ahead.

"Oh," Carin said. "Yes, you go ahead."

Snapping her passbook shut, she left the line and the bank, reflecting that she could buy a vibrator for five dollars.

She reached Chris at the *Free Press.* "I can't come."

"Why not?"

"I've got classes."

"You've always got classes."

"These are different."

"How?"

After a moment's silence she blurted, "I just can't afford it, Chris. When I realized how much it would cost for two days . . ."

"I'll pay for it."

"No."

"Then I'll come there. I have to work Saturday morning, but I could leave at noon and stay till Sunday night." He waited for a response, then he asked, "What do you say?"

"Yes," Carin said quietly. "Please."

He had arrived at her apartment Saturday afternoon and remained there until it was time for him to leave for the airport Sunday night. As they stood at the door, their arms around each other, Chris said, "If you were unhappy—if you felt things weren't really working out here—would you be too proud to say something?"

"No."

"A couple of times last night I thought—maybe this weekend was your way of saying you'd had it in New York."

"No. It was my way of saying I miss you, I love you." He kissed her. Then she said, "You're going to miss your plane."

"Maybe I should."

"We've been through that," she said. "My work's here and your work's there. That's the way it is for now."

"How long are we supposed to go on like this?"

"I don't know. I told you you didn't have to wait."

"The question is, what am I waiting *for?*"

She studied the floor. "I don't know. I told you that too. I love you. That hasn't changed. But I have to be here and I don't know what's going to happen. Or when." She looked up. "I wouldn't blame you for giving up."

He smiled. "You're not getting rid of me that easily. Especially after last night. And this morning. And this afternoon. Did I mention yesterday afternoon?"

She laughed and pushed him away. "Go get your plane."

That lubricious weekend had been his only conjugal visit in six months. While it had scratched the itch, the effect soon wore off and Carin found herself lonelier and edgier than ever. Her letters to Chris didn't help. She had long since resigned herself to the fact that the hours she spent in the classroom and, on rare, happy occasions, onstage cut her off from everyone who wasn't a part of that painful, sweaty, perfect time. Making them understand would have been like trying to explain red or yellow to someone blind from birth. In any case, words had never been Carin's long suit; if they had been, she sometimes mused, maybe she wouldn't have felt such a need to dance. Dance was her way of talking to the world.

Here in New York, without her family, without Chris, she had flung herself into a swelling sea of dance, happy to be swallowed at last by the Moloch to whom she had dreamed of being sacrificed. Someday, in some vague, calm future, Carin could see herself re-dressing the balance of her life, but for now there was total immersion, a charismatic baptism of dance that ruled every moment of her day.

The phone rang. She stared at it.

It could be Chris. If it is, she thought, *I'll just tell him. He'll understand—somehow . . .*

She picked up the phone. "Hello?"

"Listen," Diane said, "things are a little fuzzy this morning, but I seem to remember you saying you're not exactly apeshit about the place you're living in."

Diane indicated the musty space with a dramatic sweep of her hand. "Walk-in closet!" She turned back to the room. "And we'll put all this shit back in Terry's room."

Carin looked at the dressmaker's dummy with bright swatches of cloth pinned to it, the venerable sewing machine and the long table covered with bolts of cloth, cutting tools and patterned sheets of tracing paper. Then she turned to Terry, standing silent next to the table. "I can't push you out of here. This is your workroom."

A moue pursed Terry's face. "If I had any work to do, I might put up a fight for it. But I can sit and stare at the walls in my bedroom just as efficiently as I can in here."

"Actually, this is kind of an all-purpose room," Diane interjected, displeased with the tenor of the discussion, "Hobbies, meditation, sometimes we do a *barre* in here or watch the TV . . ."

"What TV?" Carin asked, looking around.

"Oh, that's one of the most interesting features of this apartment," Diane confided, striding to the window, where she launched another sweeping gesture. "Unobstructed view of an Advent. You know? The giant screen job? Like six feet!"

"Where?"

"There." Diane pointed at the window. Carin crossed the room and peered out. On the other side of a narrow air shaft that smelled dankly of 1935, the window of the next building faced her, and through it there was, as advertised, an unobstructed view of a giant television screen.

"It's Renée's," Diane said.

"Renée?"

"Blond girl? Big boobs? She was at the party last night. Good dancer. Her folks are crawling with money." She looked at Terry. "Oil, I think."

"Banking."

"Oil."

"She told me her father was a banker."

"Popeye told me it was oil."

"Who knows more about Renée's father, Renée or Popeye?"

"Who gives a shit?" Diane said equably.

"Yeah."

Diane turned back to Carin. "Her old man bought her the Advent. It takes up her whole living room, but it's great for us: she's pretty good about requests."

"All we have to do is holler, and she opens up the window," Terry said. "You can hear perfect."

"That's what these chairs are for," Diane said, indicating two canvas sling chairs facing the window. "We'll get another chair for you." She turned and surveyed the room. "But first we'll need a bed—unless you've got your own furniture."

"No. I've been renting furnished." Carin sighed. "Too bad."

"What's too bad?" Diane asked.

"I'd like to move in here, but I can't afford to buy any furniture."

"Who said anything about buying?" Diane demanded. She turned to Terry. "Any closings?"

"Not that I know of," Terry said, "and I can't think of any shows that use real beds . . ."

"Okay," Diane said tersely, "it's Thursday."

"It's Wednesday," Carin said.

"Thursday's the solution. See, the sanitation department only picks up big stuff one day of the week. In some neighborhoods it's Friday morning and in others it's Saturday. If somebody wants to get rid of a bed or a dresser, the only nights they can leave it on the street are Thursday or Friday. Otherwise they gotta pay to have it carted away."

"You're saying you can find furniture in the street?"

"Unless the garbage men beat you to it," Terry said.

"With our training?" Diane hooted. "Fat chance!"

"But nobody's going to throw away a bed," Carin said.

"How do you think I got the one *I* sleep in?" Diane caroled. "Where'd we find it?" she asked Terry. "East Eighty-first?"

Terry shook his head. "That was mine. We found yours on Fifth Avenue."

"Oh, yeah."

Carin looked from one face to the other. "It can't be very good furniture."

"Well, it's not always a hundred percent perfect when we find it," Diane admitted, "but by the time we're done you'd swear we bought the sucker new at Bloomie's."

"Knowing where to look is important," Terry interjected.

"Oh, sure, name o' the game," Diane huffed.

"You think we'll find a bed tomorrow night?" Carin asked.

"Of course it's not quite like it was when *we* were furnishing," Diane said. "These days everybody's a little more conservative about what they throw away. And—there's the other problem." She glanced darkly at Terry.

"What problem?" Carin asked.

"Fuckin' amateurs," Diane growled.

"Everybody and his brother knows about Thursday and Friday now," Terry said.

"We've seen 'em cruising around with U-Haul trailers," Diane said, thin-lipped.

"I think that takes all the sport out of it," Terry humphed.

The little band padded north, stealthy as Indians, peering alertly into the side streets off Park Avenue. Though they were bundled for warmth against the chill night air, their clothes were unencumbering: sweaters, jeans and, most important, sneakers for fast starts and sustained high speeds.

Gold-braided doormen, musing under forest-green canopies or leaping forward to welcome the intermittent parade of Guccis,

Blasses and St. Laurents beginning to trickle back from the evening's festivities, eyed the trio of marauders with the Olympian snobbery of the upper class's serving class.

Diane, striding noiselessly between Carin and Terry, was the point of the wedge, her radar quickly sweeping the eastern and western horizons as the pack arrived at each corner. If no blips appeared, the group continued north.

Midway between Sixty-third and Sixty-fourth streets, Diane seized each of her partners by an arm. As they stopped and turned to her, tense and alert, she signaled for silence, drew them into the Art Deco shelter of an apartment house entrance and pointed at a troop of Hare Krishnas moving north in an orange glow on the opposite side of the avenue. The heads of the men were shaven, all the zealots were brightly gowned and painted, but something was missing: there was no accompanying jingle of brass to signal their coming; nautch bells and finger cymbals had been left in the ashram. Diane shot a significant look at Terry.

"But I've seen people like that all over town," Carin whispered. "All they do is sing and dance."

"Yeah," Diane muttered grimly, "in *sandals.*"

Once again she pointed, and Carin followed the direction of her finger. Beneath the hems of the swirling orange robes there were telltale flashes of Adidas and Puma. Sneakers!

Terry's hoarse whisper summed it up. "We've gotta get ahead of 'em!"

Diane nodded, her eyes alight with competitive fire.

"But if they see us . . ." Carin said.

"Maybe they'll think we live around here . . ." Terry began, then broke off as Diane fixed him with a withering stare.

"If they see us, we'll have to depend on superior speed," Diane said. "Those robes must be a bitch to run in. Come on."

Linking arms with her colleagues, she eased the patrol from under the protection of the canopy and started north at a brisk quickstep, only to be stopped again by the pressure of Terry's fingers digging into her arm. "Ouch!" But she looked in the direction he was pointing. A battered Volkswagen was swinging out of Sixty-fifth Street ahead of them, towing an open U-Haul trailer.

"See what we meant?" Terry growled at Carin. "It's turning into a fuckin' rummage sale!"

"It's okay," Diane exclaimed, "they're heading south."

As the U-Haul passed them, they saw a battered couch in it.

" 'Cause they cleaned everything out already," Terry groaned.

"Maybe they were only interested in couches," Diane said, and the little company pushed north again, trying to regain the ground it had lost on the Hare Krishnas.

At Sixty-eighth Street Diane's group suddenly wheeled left.

There, a few yards from the corner, the shadowy bulks of a large armchair and a single bed loomed next to the curb.

"Whaddid I tell you?" Diane yelped as she led the charge into the side street, flopping facedown on the bed while Terry flung himself into the chair. A raucous fit of coughing followed as Diane and Terry disappeared in billowing clouds of dust.

"Jesus Christ!" Diane gasped, pulling her face out of the lacerated mattress and fighting her way off the bed. Terry simply sat where he had landed, staring in appalled disbelief at the filthy tufts of stuffing he was plucking from gaping rents in the chair's arms.

"What's happening to the East Side?" Diane howled at the heavens. In her philosophy beggars could—and *should*—be choosers. Nursing her wounded sensibilities, she turned her back on this betrayal and led her troops toward Park Avenue and the quest for renewed faith in the openhanded largesse of the upper class.

Midway between Park and Madison on Seventy-third Street, a uniformed maid and a male servant in mufti labored down the steps of a beige limestone town house that looked as if it had been imported stone by stone from the avenue Foch. Between them they bore the base and box spring of a double bed, which they set down on the sidewalk next to the broken remnants of a large cardboard box that had, from the printed evidence on its sides, contained the replacement for the bed they were bearing to its resting place. As the little funeral cortege mounted the steps and reentered the house, the gypsy trio came abreast of the street and froze at the electrifying sight in the middle of the block.

Diane's hoarse, awed whisper testified to faith restored. "Jesus! A *double* bed—" She broke off with a gasp as something came into focus beyond the bed. At the corner of Madison Avenue another group of "shoppers" was mesmerized by the sight of the bed—and the competition at the other end of the block.

"Move!" Diane snarled, and the three dancers catapulted forward like sprinters off their blocks. At the same instant the Madison Avenue group exploded into action, and suddenly Seventy-third Street was the scene of a classic Western showdown at high noon, performed at the surreal high speed of a Keystone chase.

As the rivals converged on the prize from opposite sides, one of the runners left the ground in a towering leap. The Madison Avenue scavengers skidded to a startled halt as the *jeté* dropped Diane on the bed, where, at the last instant, she twisted to land on her back, her hands clasped behind her head, one leg bent, the other crossed casually over it, as if she had been lying on the bed for hours. As the two breathless groups faced each other across Diane, she stared idly up at the black night sky, calm and proprietary.

The Madison Avenue group consisted of two young couples, and one of the men, a reasonably rough-hewn specimen in a vinyl-for-leather jacket, assumed the leadership of his faction by planting himself at the edge of the bed to glare threateningly down at Diane, who elected to demonstrate her insouciance by whistling. Unfortunately, whether out of fear or breathlessness, the sound she emitted quavered thinly and unconvincingly.

"*O*-kay, lady," the man in the vinyl jacket chanted in a nasal singsong, signaling the other man in his group and bending to grasp the bottom edge of the bed.

Before Diane could be dumped, Terry *pliéed* and launched himself into a *temps levé,* landing on the bed, which served as a trampoline to bounce him high above his shocked adversaries. At the top of the bedspring-abetted jump, Terry's body spun in a *tour en l'air,* and the girls from Madison Avenue screamed and clutched their men as this maniacal Clark Kent–turned–Superman landed on the sidewalk next to them in a menacing crouch, teeth bared, feet spread, arms coiled like pincers.

"Lemme go, Corinne!" one of the young men cried as he put up an obligatory, not quite wholehearted struggle to free his arms for combat.

"Will ya please forget it, Cy?" Corinne bleated. "A nut like that's probably got a knife!"

Cy stared at Terry, torn between twin fears: the figurative danger to his manhood if he retreated from this challenge, and the literal danger to his manhood if this wiry, obviously streetwise opponent was in fact armed. The two couples took a sudden anxious step back as Terry, still crouched, crabbed forward, one hand moving slowly toward the waistband of his Levi's.

"Cyyyy!" Corinne screeched, and Diane, inspired, sat up and screamed, "No, Spike, not the knife!"

The hollow pop of sneakers on asphalt ricocheted off Seventy-third Street's limestone and glass facades as the two couples streaked toward Madison Avenue. When they had disappeared around the corner, Terry straightened.

"Where'd you learn to fight like that?" Carin asked, then looked at Diane, who was doubled on the bed, hooting into the ticking.

"In a . . . in a . . . in a gang!" Diane finally articulated.

Carin turned back to Terry, round-eyed. "You belonged to a gang?"

Another hoot from Diane. "The Sharks!"

"She's talking about . . ." Terry began.

"I'm talking about *West Side Story*!" Diane whooped. "Terry was in the national company. Everything you saw—it was Jerry Robbins's choreography—*all* of it—the jump, the turn, the arms! Oh God . . . !"

Terry's gaunt features relaxed into a sheepish grin. "You know," he said to Carin, "the fight between the Sharks and the Jets in Act One. I was—well, like she said—you know . . ." The last words were just short of apologetic. "A Shark."

"Hoo!" Diane howled, wiping the tears from her eyes. "Thank God you didn't have to *say* anything to 'em."

Terry tried to look offended, but in a moment he was grinning again, and soon he and Diane were laughing so hard they had to fall on each other for support. This was the scene that greeted the two servants as they emerged from the town house with the mattress for the box spring on which Diane and Terry rolled and tussled in what the shocked servants took for primitive ecstasy. Carin extended a nervous finger to tap Diane's shoulder. Diane looked up, poked Terry and the cackling pair hopped off the bedspring. "It's okay," Diane said to the frozen figures at the top of the steps, "come ahead."

The man and woman struggled down the steps with the mattress, to find Diane and Terry waiting to take it from them.

"Thank you!" Diane said crisply, as she and Terry relieved the bemused couple of their burden.

Carin stepped back and looked at the bed.

"It's—it's the best bed I've ever had!"

"We'll find a better bedspread," Diane said.

"This one's beautiful," Carin said. "I just hope you didn't take it off one of your beds."

"Terry ran it up," Diane said.

"Terry . . . !" Carin protested.

"It took ten minutes," Terry said. "I had the material."

"I can't believe it," Carin said.

Terry's dressmaking paraphernalia was gone, and the requisitioned bed stood staunchly under a boldly patterned bedspread in the middle of a significantly transformed room. Calculatedly guileful imagery smiled from the walls, where theatrical and travel posters had been appliquéd. Two open suitcases had delivered their contents into the walk-in closet and a freshly painted chest of drawers (Eighty-fifth Street and Madison Avenue, Friday night).

Carin sighed and closed one of the suitcases. "Well, I guess that's it."

"Except for the roommates' sacred oath." Carin looked at Diane, who raised her hand and intoned, "I solemnly swear that I will never, under any circumstances, check out, chat up or mess around with my roommates' boyfriends, so help me David Merrick."

"I swear," Carin said, extending her hand.

"I swear," Diane said, putting her hand on Carin's.

"I swear," Terry said, putting his hand on Diane's and Carin's. The clasped hands pumped up and down, once, emphatically.

EIGHT, two three, four
Développé

Diane propped her feet on the windowsill and settled herself more comfortably in the sling chair.

"A little louder, Renée?" she shouted across the air shaft, and in the facing apartment Renée was briefly framed in the window as she adjusted the volume on her Advent. She turned and looked across the air shaft at Diane, who held up a circled thumb and forefinger in approval. Renée disappeared as she resumed her seat, and thick, heavily marbled chords drifted across the air shaft like smoke.

"Have you figured out what it is yet?" Terry asked.

"I'm telling you, it's an Ed Sullivan show."

"How could it be?"

"Where else would you see an over-the-hill ballerina struggling through *Swan Lake* in living black-and-white? It's a rerun. Maybe it's some kind of anniversary. Too cold for you?"

The last was addressed to Carin, who was standing in bikini underpants a few feet behind Diane as Terry, kneeling next to her, studiously applied a tape measure to various stretches of her lean, pale body, pausing to note his findings in a pad beside him on the floor.

"No," Carin said.

"I don't *have* to watch this," Diane said. "I can close the window."

"No, don't. If I get cold I can put on a leotard."

"Not if you want a good fit," Terry groused, circling her waist with the tape.

"I've never had anything made for me before," Carin said.

"Only way to go," Terry murmured, jotting numbers on his pad.

The operation proceeded, Terry measuring, musing, marking, Diane watching the Advent, chuckling and shaking her head.

"When I was a kid," Carin said quietly, "you know what my biggest dream was?"

"To dance on the Ed Sullivan Show," Terry and Diane said simultaneously.

"How'd you know?"

Diane and Terry laughed, and Diane said, "Haven't you ever *talked* to anybody? Half the dancers I know got hooked watching the Ed Sullivan show." She threw back her head to exult, "Jesus! I can still see 'em hoppin' around on a screen about yay big." She made a rectangle with her fingers. "It was a big dance number from some Broadway show, I don't know which one. I was seven, in Texas; what'd I know from Broadway? But I knew what I liked, and that dance number was the end of Captain Video and Buffalo Bob! All of a sudden I knew exactly what I was gonna do with my life. So did Mom and Pop." She chuckled. "The poor things never had a chance. I kept sockin' it to 'em till they let me take dancing lessons. Tap and acrobatic in a studio half the size of this room, but nobody heard any complaints from me!" The chuckle deepened. "Plenty of complaints from the neighbors, though. I practiced my tap in the bathroom. The whole fuckin' building shook, and the more complaints we got, the louder I banged away. Shit, the echo in there—I was getting four taps for one—it must've sounded like the Rockettes got locked in our bathroom!" She howled gleefully. "But I was happy. Oh God, I was happy!" She paused, then added a more sober, reflective, "Still am, in a way," and settled back to watch the Advent across the air shaft.

"It was exactly the same way with me," Carin said, her eyes aglow with remembered joy, "only it was Nureyev and Fonteyn. She was unreal! Every night for a year I prayed to God to let me be like her." She paused for a sigh. "I guess He didn't hear me."

"How old are you?" Terry asked.

"Eighteen."

"Keep praying," he said, drawing the tape across her breasts and around her back, "and taking class. Sometimes God needs a little help."

"As soon as this is over, Ed'll call her out in front of the curtain and grope her right in front of the whole country," Diane said. "Remember? He was all hands when he brought 'em out for bows."

Carin looked down at Terry, who was kneeling at her feet again, occupied with his note pad. "Who turned *you* on the first time?"

"The newsboy. Oh! Oh, you mean dancewise." He grinned up at her, waiting for acknowledgment of the joke. Carin offered him a mildly appreciative smile. "My first time goes back a lit-tle bit further than Ed Sullivan," he said, then went on quietly, his gaze growing distant and unfocused. "Fred Astaire and Ginger Rogers . . . in *Flying Down to Rio* . . ." It was a reverent whisper.

"A *little* bit further than Ed Sullivan!" Diane snorted.

The reflective shadow vanished from his eyes as he shot back, "It was a revival—at the Museum of Modern Art." Diane hooted and he turned to Carin. "Menopause. Ignore her."

"You couldn't pick a better model for yourself than Fred Astaire," Carin said conciliatorily.

"He's talking about Ginger Rogers," Diane rasped.

"At least *she* had *style!*" Terry snapped at Diane, then turned back to Carin. "Ever seen the movie?" Carin shook her head, and Terry's gaze softened and dimmed again. "There's this number, see? Dozens of chorus girls dancing on the wings of planes. It—well, it just changed my life!"

"That number?"

"That number." Swaying, his hands up, palms out, he sang, " 'My Rio, Rio by the sea-o! Flying down to Rio where there's rhythm and rhyme!' " He looked at Carin, face flushed, eyes shining. "That is my all-time, undisputed, number-one favorite song, that's all! Every time I hear it I get the same incredible feeling—like a magnificent new world is opening up in front of me. A perfect world where nothing's gonna go wrong. Ever!"

Terry's aria had been accompanied by Tchaikovsky's music, ascending through mountainous chromatic changes to its final fervent chords. Now a tidal wave of applause burst from the Advent, flooding the court between the two buildings and smashing into Carin's bedroom. Over it Ed Sullivan's shrill tenor exhorted, "Come on! Let's hear it for this gallant little lady who overcame arthritis to become a grrrreat ballerina!" The applause swelled.

"Yep," Diane said, her eyes on the screen, "he's gropin' her."

"You're shaking," Terry reproved Carin. "Hold still."

Diane twisted in her chair. "I *told* you it was too cold with the window open."

As Diane reached out to close the window, Carin said, "It's not the window. I'm just nervous, I guess."

Diane turned back and stared at Carin. "About what?"

Carin shifted uneasily, plucking at the edge of her underpants. "You know . . ."

"If I knew, would I ask?" The implied threat in Diane's quiet tone was by now familiar enough to Carin to have lost some of its punch.

"I heard they can fire you any time in the first five days of rehearsal, and . . ."

"I refuse to listen to this garbage!" Diane shrilled, clapping her hands over her ears. After a moment she cautiously lifted her hands. Satisfied that the only sound in the room was the inoffensive chatter of a commercial from across the air shaft, she rose and closed the window with an emphatic, "You're not going to get fired."

"You certainly aren't," Terry said, sliding an avuncular arm around Carin's shoulders. "And when you get back from Philly, your opening-night dress will be waiting for you." Releasing her, he picked up his note pad and took it to the bed, where he sat, studying the numbers and sketches he had scrawled on it.

"By the time we get back, I'll be able to pay for it," Carin said.

Terry looked up, aghast. "*Pay* for it! You think I'd take money from a roommate?"

"But the material costs money," Carin said.

"Not as long as the Treasure Chest holds out," Diane said, and Carin looked at her, lost again.

Terry grasped a corner of the ornamental throw, and, with the flashy nonchalance of a magician, flicked it into the air, revealing the steamer trunk beneath, its battered surface plastered with theatrical stickers: *SWEET CHARITY*—THEATER: *PIPPIN*—NATIONAL COMPANY . . .

"It may look like your everyday, garden-variety theatrical trunk," Diane said, "but inside"—she flipped up the top of the trunk—"the wonders of the world!"

Stripes, dots, slashes, whorls, tight patterns and bold ones, on bolts and swatches of silk, linen, cotton, wool, shantung, lace, crepe de Chine, chiffon and lamé, in a riotous confusion of colors, from the subtlest pastels to vision-threatening dayglos, greeted Carin's dazzled eyes as she bent over the trunk. Her hand moved involuntarily toward the cornucopia, then stopped.

"It's okay," Diane said with a grin, "you can touch it."

Carin drew a gossamer piece of sari cloth from the trunk and held it up so that the light from a nearby lamp shimmered through it.

"Wild!" Terry exclaimed. "That's exactly the one I was thinking of using for your dress! And you picked it out of the whole box! Right for her?" he asked Diane.

"Perfect!"

Carin turned to her roommates, clutching the lustrous cloth. "Where'd you get all this?"

"A gift," Diane said proudly, "from a very big man in the garment business."

"Why?"

Diane shrugged. "Love."

"He just gave it to you?"

"Not me. Terry."

Carin looked at Terry, and he nodded, lowered his eyes and smiled modestly.

"The guy was so crazy about him, *nothin'* was too good," Diane said. The room filled with flying flashes of color as Diane snatched bolts, swatches and remnants from the trunk and flung them into the air. "Silk, velvet, satin—you name it, Howard had it. And shared it!" She paused for breath and turned her cooling glance on Terry. "Till

Temperamental Terry here decided Howard wasn't good enough for him . . ."

Terry drew himself up. "Man does not live by lamé alone. I don't choose my personal relationships for material gain."

"What was wrong with Howard?" Diane lamented. "Anybody with half a brain would've realized he was everything a normal person could want: sweet, generous, steady, Jewish . . ."

"If he was so appealing, *you* should've married him," Terry sniffed.

"Fat chance!" Diane snorted, then turned to Carin with the explanation. "He had a wife and five kids in Scarsdale." Diane sighed and began picking up the scattered yard goods, the momentary magic dispelled. "Anyway, when the gravy train went off the tracks, everything that was left got packed away in the Treasure Chest. Terry uses it for his originals—and special occasions like our opening night, when we get some for free."

Terry, who had been studying his note pad, looked up from it to squint professionally at Carin. "I know exactly what I'm going to do for you." He pointed at the sari cloth she still held. "That material, in very soft lines." He rose and waved his hands to sketch lines in the air around Carin's nearly naked body. "To accent those bones. The 'grown-up little girl' look." He nodded, pleased with his inspiration, then stepped closer to take the delicate material from Carin and drape it over her shoulder. "See? Something like this. Soft, subtle, elegant—but cut down to here," he zoomed a fingertip from her throat to her navel, "for some pizazz!"

They played with the Treasure Chest for two hours, draping each other in fantastic improvisations that met with their boisterous approval on either of two grounds: total absurdity or ineffable beauty. Terry and Diane undressed for the game, Terry stripping to his jockey shorts, Diane yanking off her shirt and jeans, to nothing, since she eschewed panties as an obstacle to the unbroken line she demanded of her skintight pants. To a dancer, unbroken line was an unshakable article of faith, and the horizontal line of panties across a vertical sweep of leg offended Diane's highly conditioned sensibilities.

Watery silks and shiny synthetics saturated with primary colors floated and fluttered and fell in blazing heaps as the roommates were draped and pinned into one creation after another, each improvisation more lunatic than its predecessor. Terry and Diane used Carin to explore the further reaches of their imaginations as she parodied the mannered poses she'd seen in fashion magazines. Then it was Diane's turn in the middle, while Carin and Terry draped and twisted and pinned. And finally Terry was the mannequin, while Carin and Diane wrapped him in a lavish drag that made him look like the pampered favorite in an especially sybaritic harem.

Each time all three were fully wrapped and howling into the full-length mirror that framed their elaborate poses, they stripped and began again, seeking even more exotic climes of *basse couture*. The mounds of precious stuff strewn about the floor grew as if some seismic disturbance under Forty-eighth Street were throwing up fleecy mountains, and the deranged trio, dipping repeatedly into the seemingly bottomless Treasure Chest, roared with delight at the debut of each wonderful monstrosity.

Their inspiration gave out before the Treasure Chest did. Posing together in the mirror in *arabesques, attitudes* and elaborate lifts that threatened Terry with hernia as he struggled under the weight of both heavily costumed girls, they collapsed finally in a billowing, bellowing heap on the soft rainbow with which they had carpeted the room.

The doorbell rang. They sat up and stared at each other like three mod rag dolls.

"Anybody expecting visitors?" Terry asked. Diane and Carin shook their heads. Terry rose. "I'll go."

He wriggled his hips and the fuschia gown his roommates had fashioned for him slid to the floor, leaving him in his underpants. "You mind?" he asked, plucking Carin's outsize terry cloth robe from the bed.

"No," Carin said, and Terry slipped into the robe as he headed for the living room.

He was knotting the robe's belt around his waist when he opened the door to reveal a clean-cut stranger in a topcoat, with a suitcase on the floor at his feet. "Yes?" Terry asked, but the stranger stared speechless at Terry's bare torso framed in the gaping robe, and his bare legs and feet below it. "Yes?" Terry repeated, annoyed at this hostile examination in his own home.

The stranger found his voice. "Who're you?"

"Isn't that a rather peculiar question, considering it was you who rang my bell?"

"*Your* bell! Oh—I'm sorry." The stranger looked relieved. "I must've got the apartment number wrong. There's a girl named Carin Bradley somewhere in this building . . ."

"Here."

The relief vanished. "Pardon?"

"I didn't realize you were looking for Carin," Terry said, stepping back. The stranger didn't move.

"She lives here? In this apartment?" Terry nodded. "But you said this was *your* apartment."

"Are you gonna come in or are we gonna stand here discussing the terms of my lease? It's cold!" Terry drew the robe tighter around him as the stranger picked up his suitcase and entered without interrupting his suspicious scrutiny, "What're you? Some kind of sneaky census taker?" Terry asked.

"Isn't that Carin's robe?"

"Yes," Terry said with a weary sigh. "Whom shall I say is calling?"

"Chris Stevenson."

"Does Carin know you?"

"Theoretically."

"What does *that* mean?"

"She'll remember. Just tell her I'm here."

"All right. Have a seat." Chris remained standing. Terry shrugged and headed for the bedrooms with a cool, "Suit yourself, but it may take her a couple of minutes to throw something on."

A moment later Carin burst into the room, hastily wrapping herself in the controversial robe. "Chris!" she cried, flinging her arms around him. "I couldn't believe it when Terry said you were out here!"

"I'll bet Terry couldn't either."

His gelid response opened her arms and backed her a step. "What's wrong?"

"What's *wrong!*" he exploded. "I come seven hundred miles to find you living with a guy. . . ?"

"*Terry?*"

"You can spare us both the histrionics; he admitted it."

"Well, of course he did."

" 'Of course'?"

"Look, Chris, I understand now . . ."

"I'm glad one of us does."

"I can see how you'd be confused; but it's so easy to explain. You see, Terry was Diane's roommate . . ."

"Who the hell is Diane?"

"Why don't we sit down?"

"Not till I know whose apartment I'm sitting down *in!*"

"Very logical. Reasonable."

"You're stalling."

"No, I'm not. It's just that. . . . I've got an idea. I'll put something on and we'll go out for dinner. Just the two of us."

"I don't want to deprive Terry and Diane," he muttered, but he was speaking to an empty room; she had turned and dashed back into the corridor from which she had come.

In her brief tenure on Forty-eighth Street, Carin had discovered another of the sad old slum's dividends: for reasons lost in the mists of time, New York's working-class French had settled in the West Forties and Fifties, and a tight little galaxy of worthy French restaurants had sprung up around them, offering authentic French cuisine of an order seldom approached elsewhere in the city, at a fraction of the prices charged in the better *endroits*. Since the gypsy neighborhood coincided with the French neighborhood, when the dancers did eat out they ate well. Carin took Chris to Chez Pierre, a bistro on Fifty-first Street that would have drawn a nod and star from one of the *Guide Michelin*'s stonier representatives.

"Terry and I are like *sisters*," Carin said, as Chris drained his wineglass and refilled it.

"Your sister's lucky. I almost punched him out."

Carin decided a lighter touch was permissible. "He'd've been flattered to death: his first fight over a girl." She was premature: Chris stared glumly back at her.

"Look," he said, "I know I don't have any right to feel this way . . ."

"What're you talking about?"

"You live in New York, I live in Detroit; we both know what that means."

"What does it mean?"

He chose the words carefully. "That I can't dictate the way you live."

"It's an apartment. I have a room, Terry has a room, Diane has a room . . ."

"But you didn't tell me that."

"I was going to."

"When?"

"When I figured out a way to make you understand."

Chris's wineglass came down so hard its contents spilled. "Jesus Christ, Carin, Detroit may not be Paris, but it isn't Nome!"

"See what I mean?" Carin said dully.

"What!"

"You *don't* understand. Even now. If I'd written you about Diane and Terry, what would you have thought?"

Chris sat back with an explosive sigh, and the silence that enveloped the table reminded Carin of the airless space in which she had auditioned . . . three weeks ago?

Carin's thoughts came to a startled halt, then resumed slowly, tentatively. *It can't be three weeks. Three months, maybe. So much has happened—so much has changed.* She shifted uneasily and permitted herself to glance across the table at Chris, sunk back in shadow beyond the table's candlelight. *He hasn't changed.*

He was staring at his wineglass, so she could study him: the sandy hair, so thick it grew in terraced layers that always made him look a little unkempt—it was one of the first things she'd noticed about him when Miss Nicholas brought her out of the dressing room and said, "This is the man who wants to write about you." She'd noticed his hair, and liked it. She still liked it. That hadn't changed.

She lowered her glance to the sharply defined planes of his face. Once they had stood in front of a Modigliani in the Detroit Institute of Arts, and Carin had said, "It looks like you," and Chris had been offended because he thought she was saying she didn't like his face, and she had covered his face with kisses right there in the museum to prove she'd meant it as a compliment. Sometimes it was easy to hurt Chris, even though he was older than she was, and much tougher.

I've hurt him again. But he should've known better than to show up like that. Why? He has a right. He's not exactly a stranger.

He was still intent on his glass, so she could go on studying him. The color of his eyes had always . . . moved her. She nodded imperceptibly. Yes, that was the only word for it. That was the second thing she'd noticed, in the drugstore where he interviewed her. He was old, in his middle-twenties; she was acting fifteen, and dumb— but she'd noticed—to the point that she could hardly concentrate on the questions he was asking. All she could see was those eyes—the strangest color, paler than blue, denser than gray. It was the same feeling she got from listening to music she loved, Debussy or Ravel, or from the end of a romantic movie. Later, when it began to happen, the sight of his eyes sometimes made her catch her breath, and later, when it *really* began to happen, she would catch sight of them when he was close to her, inside her . . .

She stirred in her chair, tiny, strong muscles, inactive for months, tightening as if she held Chris in her at this moment. The little muscles pursed on moisture.

At least those feelings haven't changed, she thought with relief. *What* has *changed?*

She ducked her head and tried to channel her tumbling thoughts with a question. "Why didn't you tell me you were coming to New York?"

The frayed edge of the checkered tablecloth sprayed red and white tendrils at her lap. She pulled at one. It came loose and she twisted it slowly around a finger, waiting. When there was no response from Chris, she looked up: the gray eyes shone out of the dark, and once again she stirred at the memory of him inside her.

"I guess . . ." he said, then stopped.

"What?"

"I guess I thought I was going to find—what I *did* find."

"But if you just listened to Terry say two words . . ."

"Yeah, I understand."

"Do you?" It was a challenge.

"Yes." Then he veered. "In a way. Your letters the last few weeks—there was something . . ."

He'd noticed!

"It wasn't what you said. It still sounded like you—but there was something missing. Like you weren't telling me everything."

Carin leaned forward. "But it wasn't what you thought."

"What was it?"

Carin flattened against the back of her chair, caught. So much to explain, with balky, unwieldy words. He mustn't think she didn't care about him.

I mustn't think I don't care about him. What do I think? Nothing's changed. I'm so glad he's here. I can't wait till we go home. Isn't that important? Isn't it everything? Isn't it enough?

"Why don't we go home?" she said gently.

"Whose home?"

"Mine."

"What about Terry and Diane?"

"What about them?"

"If you come strolling in to breakfast with a stranger . . ."

"They don't care about that."

"How do you know?"

Carin saw the chasm loom and stepped back from its edge with a charged, "What're you saying?"

Chris chose the moment to apply his napkin to the wine he had spilled. "I asked you a question." He looked up.

Even now, even flushed with indignation, Carin could feel the impact of his eyes on her. But she forced herself to persist. "What're you trying to say, Chris?"

At least he has the decency to squirm a little, Carin thought, as Chris replied, "You said Terry and Diane don't mind when somebody stays with you . . ."

"*If!* You said *if* I came strolling in to breakfast with somebody, and I said they don't care."

He shrugged but avoided her eyes as he replied, "How would you find that out?"

"Not by fucking around."

His head snapped up. "When did you start talking like that?"

She gestured impatiently, angry at Chris *and* herself now. "I guess I picked it up from Diane. She talks like that all the time, but she doesn't mean anything by it; it's like somebody else saying darn . . ." She bridled, then leaned forward, taut. "Why do I keep apologizing to you? I haven't done anything to apologize for."

"That's not the way it sounds!"

"Then go back to Detroit!"

Again his head came up. He found her on her feet. His chair scraped loudly as he rose, reaching for her arm, exclaiming, "I didn't mean that."

"Yes, you did."

The waiter glanced across the room at the contentious couple and wondered if it was time to intervene. He looked at the only other couple in the restaurant: they were intent on each other, oblivious of the break in the room's studied serenity. He'd wait, he decided, and if things got worse he'd summon the *patronne* from her post in the kitchen. She could always handle situations like this by screaming louder than the combatants, in French. Her actions tended to add to the restaurant's discord, but the unpleasantness was momentary; her outburst was usually followed by deathly silence—and compliance.

"Yes, I did," Chris said finally. "I'm sorry." Carin was silent. "Can we sit down?"

"Not till you apologize."

"I just did."

Carin shook her head. "You still think I've been—fooling around."

"No, I don't. Honestly. It's just that—I missed you more than I ever said—and lately your letters *have* been strange." He hurried ahead before she could respond. "You admitted you weren't telling me everything."

"And I explained why," Carin sighed, "and all you're doing is proving how right I was."

"Okay, okay, we don't have to go back over it. I started to get worried. That's why I didn't tell you I was coming."

"So you could sneak up on me!"

"That's right." His gaze was unwavering as he went on. "I snuck up on you. To catch you. With somebody else. Pretty, huh? Would you believe I'm going to be twenty-eight in a few months?" She was silent. He sighed. "What do you want me to do? Fly to Detroit, call you from the airport and come back the right way? Or stay there?"

The airless silence again, the gray eyes, too close, too effective, silver as smoke in this light. Carin reached for her slippery anger. It was gone. "No."

"Then—do you think we can sit down?"

"No."

"What's left?"

"Guess."

Chris gestured to the waiter, and, only too happy to comply, he hurried over with the check.

"Whattaya say, Renée!" Diane yelled across the air shaft. "How about changing the channel? I think there's an old Jackie Gleason on eleven!" The flat planes framed in Renée's window remained as motionless as a Cubist still life. Diane looked down at Terry, slumped in one of the camp chairs, his feet propped on the windowsill. "Is she mad at us?" Terry shook his head, and a threat seeped into Diane's voice. "You sure? Last time she did this, it turned out you'd had a fight with her about some dumb cartoon show you wanted to watch."

"She went to the bathroom a couple of minutes ago!"

"Oh." Diane turned restlessly from the window and watched

Carin and Chris as they unpacked Chris's suitcase. "Whadja do?" she asked. "Take a vacation?"

Chris shook his head. "I told my boss I had a personal emergency."

"And he bought it?"

"It was the truth."

"No, it wasn't," Carin said.

Chris looked at her and smiled. "Well, it felt like it." The smile widened. "And it got me here."

"What kind of work do you do?" Diane asked, stretching out on the bed, her hands behind her head.

"I work on a newspaper."

Carin, hanging one of Chris's suits in the closet, turned back with an amendment. "Chris is the best reporter on the *Free Press*. His name's all over the front page."

"You the one who wrote the article about Carin?" Diane asked.

"Yes."

She glanced at Carin. "How old were you?"

"Fifteen. Nearly sixteen."

She aimed an impish grin at Chris. "Cradle snatcher!"

Chris blanched, and Carin jumped in with, "He didn't *want* to. You wouldn't believe what I had to do . . ."

"I don't think Diane's interested in every sordid detail of our lives," Chris protested.

"Yes, I am," Diane said equably, stretching a leg toward the ceiling.

"Me too," Terry said.

"You'll have to buy my memoirs," Chris said.

Terry twisted from the window. "You writing 'em?"

"No."

"Oh." He turned back to the Advent.

"Wanna write mine?" Diane asked, stretching the other leg.

"Would they be interesting?"

She reflected a moment, then chirped, "Nope. A lotta sweat, a lotta worry, a lotta good times. An average life, you might say." She tugged at the crotch of her jeans. "Jesus, these pants are cutting me in half!" Rearranging herself on the bed, she asked, "How long you plan to stay here?"

"A week."

"That's perfect!"

"Why?"

"We go into rehearsal in a week. If you'd showed up a few days later you'd hardly have seen Carin. Now you got her nonstop."

"I was thinking of taking three classes a day," Carin said.

"*Three!*" Terry spat, turning from the window. "You want to start rehearsals tied in knots?"

"Diane said we probably won't be able to take a class every day once we're in rehearsal."

"You won't," Terry said, "but you'll be dancing eight hours a day."

"But without class you can get so sloppy. And I need some jazz classes before we go into rehearsal."

"You've got all the technique you need. *Too* much. Relax with your boyfriend. *Do* it two or three times a day. Do you just as much good as class. More. It'll send you into rehearsals loose as a goose, and that's the way you want to be. Especially with Sonny running the show." He turned back to the window and settled down to resume his contemplation of Renée's Advent.

Carin reflected, then said, "Okay, *two* classes a day." She slid a hand under Chris's arm. "And the rest of the time with you."

"Ever been in New York before?" Diane asked Chris.

"Once, but I didn't see much." Carin suppressed a smile.

"Know what you ought to do? All the dumb tourist things. Honest to God. The Statue of Liberty, the Staten Island ferry, the Empire State Building. . . . You like that kind of stuff?"

Chris smiled. "Sure."

"Then that's what you oughtta do." Diane bestowed her benediction with a papal wave at the door. "Go and be tourists."

"And get mugged and raped," Chris replied with a grin.

"Bullshit!" Diane retorted. "I wander around this town night and day and nobody so much as pinches my ass!"

"Ever wondered why?" Terry asked, his eyes on the television screen.

"Try to ignore him," Diane said coldly. "He gets this way every once in a while. Premenstrual."

"Ha ha," Terry responded hollowly.

Diane lowered her voice. "Terribly neurotic. Still can't forgive his mother for making him a fairy."

"*God* made me a fairy," Terry intoned loftily.

"You may run into a flasher or two on the subway," Diane said to Chris and Carin, "but that's easy to handle: if you stop and watch like you're interested, they get embarrassed. Or you can vomit." She grinned at Carin. "Right on it."

"Carin's already done the whole tourist thing," Chris said.

Carin looked at him. "When? You read my letters . . ."

"You didn't write about everything."

"Well, I didn't leave *that* out. The only thing I've seen since I got here is me, in sweaty old tights in a mirror—and the inside of that closet I was living in till a few days ago."

"See what I mean?" Diane exulted with a *Q.E.D.* smile. "Perfect!"

NINE, two three, four
Ballonné

As Carin had reported to Diane, the first time Chris had seen Carin, she was fifteen years old. A bony torso, the shoulder blades bigger than the breasts (Chris had jotted in his notebook: "Turn her head a hundred and eighty degrees and the problem's solved"), her arms as thin and characterless as a nine-year-old's, but her legs long and (as Chris noted on the small pad) "as shapely as the legendary Dietrich wheels," ending in tight, round buttocks that made her bottom half look as though a woman's legs had been grafted to the upper body of a child (as Chris duly noted). The head, he found, was a different matter. He sat in the corner of the classroom, inhaling the benign teenage sweat of twenty girls and four boys, his reporter's notebook poised on a knee, his ball point hovering above it as he stared at Carin, trying to find words for that head. And face.

And wondering why he had balked when the city editor assigned him to this demonstration of class work at the Detroit Conservatory of Art.

"What the hell do I know about ballet?" he had asked his editor.

"As much as I do," the editor sighed. Jim Traynor sighed often. He was a large man, vertically and horizontally, crippled in one leg, so that his progress across the newsroom floor resembled the passage of a three-masted schooner in a heavy sea. Every day when he arrived at his desk in a corner of the huge room, a quiet, brilliant reign of terror began.

Jim Traynor was Chris's mentor and model. Traynor worked in shirtsleeves rolled to just below the elbow; Chris worked in shirtsleeves rolled to just below the elbow. Traynor lived by a classic newsman's code; Chris lived by a classic newsman's code. "Journalists," Traynor would occasionally sneer, "work for magazines. Television newscasters are converted radio announcers—pitchmen. But," and his voice would soften, "newspapers are written by newspapermen."

Chris had first encountered Jim Traynor in his junior year at the University of Michigan when, on the advice and with the recommendation of a professor, he had made a bid to succeed the graduating senior who had been serving as campus correspondent for the *Free Press.* Fortunately for Chris, he assumed the duties of U of M correspondent at a time when nearly everything that happened on America's nervous campuses was considered news. Chris's lanky figure became a familiar sight in the *Free Press* newsroom, hunched over an ancient typewriter in the usually unoccupied last row of reporters' desks, hammering out an account of the latest flareup in the class warfare of the sixties. Chris could have filed his stories from Ann Arbor, on the phone, but that would have reduced him to little more than a legman; he wanted the experience of pounding out his prose in the hurly-burly of a metropolitan newsroom, then waiting with thumping heart to snatch the early galleys from a copyboy. If his words had seen print without major revision, his return to Ann Arbor was quick and carefree; if a ham-handed copyreader had bowdlerized his deathless prose, the trip back to campus was long and gloomy. Once he had made the mistake of seeking out the copyreader who had, in his view, emasculated his story, to appeal for a restoration of the discarded paragraphs in the next edition. That was the occasion when he discovered the rocklike rigidity of a newspaper's pecking order, and that night the journey back to Ann Arbor was endless.

But in fact, Chris's stories were being read by the one man who mattered, city editor Jim Traynor, and, increasingly, Traynor liked what he saw. With the competition of television's swiftly reactive reportage, each brief TV story virtually all headline and picture, Traynor and his colleagues had come to the conclusion that the best way for print to compete was by emphasizing the classic virtues of newspaper reporting: sharp, incisive writing based on research that dug deeper and hit harder than a television story could. That kind of reporting required a specific kind of reporter with specific, definable skills: he had to have the hair-trigger reflexes of a street fighter, the nose of a bird dog, the tenacity of a bulldog, and finally, the ability to organize a notebookful of disparate facts into a cohesive logical whole and then relate them in an economical, readable style that didn't have to be mauled into acceptable shape by a copy editor. To the gimlet-eyed city editor, the U of M campus correspondent was beginning to look like the kind of vessel that might accommodate that rare concoction of instincts and acquired skills. Traynor took to asking for the early galleys of Chris's stories, a *noli tangere,* or at least Handle With Care, signal to the copyreaders.

But the occurrence that won Chris a staff job at the *Free Press* had less to do with his energy, instincts and skills, formidable as they might be, than with his equally formidable libido. One pleasant May weekend Chris interviewed an attractive young woman who had come to Ann Arbor with a debating team. The interview finished and filed, Chris invited the debater out for a beer and, when his tentative overtures seemed to strike a responsive note, gallantly offered to drive her back to her school in the venerable convertible he had acquired to ferry himself between Ann Arbor and his borrowed desk in the *Free Press* newsroom. His theory was that his passenger could hardly send him back from Ohio unrewarded, but their arrival at her campus was greeted by an assemblage of students confronting a knot of National Guardsmen backing edgily up a rise, rifles at the ready. As Chris sprang from his car, notebook in hand, one passion supplanting another, the first shots rattled down the hill, the first student fell, the former object of Chris's lust dove to the floor of his car, and Chris wrote feverishly, his eyes darting from the hill to the pad.

Half an hour later he was shouting into a pay phone that he was *here,* at Kent State, that there were at least three dead, maybe more, and he had an eyewitness account. Traynor, whom Chris had called, said, "Hang on, I'll switch you to rewrite," and Chris yelled, "No! It's my story, goddamn it! All I need is a clerk to take it down, word for word—*my way.* And it's Stevenson with a *v,* not a *ph.*"

"*What's* Stevenson with a *v?*"

"My name—for the by-line."

Something meshed in Traynor's memory: a rough sketch appeared of a cocky young reporter who had tried to finesse his first by-line by bombarding the Letters to the Editor column with pseudonymous acclaim for his own uncredited stories, and then, years later, agonized for nearly a month before accepting the editorship that would put an end to the feisty joys of a reporter's life.

"Well?" the voice from Kent State demanded.

Traynor glanced at the copyboy trotting across the newsroom with a banner of wire-service copy flapping behind him. When the copy was flung on the national-news editor's desk, and the editor, after a quick glance at the lead, reached for his phone, Traynor called across the room, "Marv! Hold it! We've got a man on the scene."

"No, you don't!" Chris yelled into the phone.

"Yes, we do," Traynor muttered back.

"With a *v!*" Chris exclaimed, as Traynor switched him to a clerk who took the story verbatim, while Traynor went to the national desk to assure Marv Siegel that they could dump Chris's story and use the wires if Chris didn't measure up. "But I've got a feeling about this kid," Traynor said, "and if he's as good as I think he is, we'll have a by-line story and the *News*'ll have to go with the wire services."

"What*ever* he gives us can go to rewrite," Siegel said.

"That might be a problem," Traynor sighed. "He doesn't see himself as a legman."

The two editors were spared the problem. As a copyboy delivered Chris's story page by page from the clerk, Traynor and Siegel looked at each other and nodded. When the day side left, they remained, hovering over the cluster of desks where the front page was being laid out, and later that night when the bulldog edition of the *Free Press* came up to the newsroom, warm as a baby in the copyboy's arms, a more than usually disheveled Traynor was waiting. The story, as arresting as the accompanying wire photos, dominated the front page under a four-column headline and Chris's by-line—with a *v*—then jumped to page four, then jumped again to the second section. Traynor sat heavily on a desk in the nearly empty newsroom and reread the story from first word to last. Chris had called repeatedly during the night, expanding the story with quotes, interviews, information and insights. Traynor and Siegel had leaned over the clerk's typewriter, then taken the phone from the clerk at the end of each dictation to ask questions and suggest angles. An hour later the phone would ring and Chris would dictate again, questions answered, angles explored.

Traynor put the paper down and nodded. The *Free Press* had scored a clean beat. The *News* would have to go with the wires; they couldn't possibly have had a man on the spot. He shook his head in wonder at Chris's prescience, and on Chris's return, asked him how he happened to be at precisely the right place at the right moment.

"You know," Chris shrugged.

"If I did, I wouldn't ask."

"Rumors," Chris said, "a word here, a word there . . ." and let it go at that. The fact that his scoop had more to do with foreplay than foresight slipped smoothly into the cracks of history, and the day after his graduation from U of M, he joined the *Free Press* as a bona fide staff reporter, at Traynor's invitation.

Giant black clouds boiled up over Windsor as he left home for his first day at the paper, so he stopped at J.L. Hudson's to invest in an Edward R. Murrow trench coat. The slicker that had seen him, reasonably dry, through four years at Ann Arbor was still serviceable, but too Joe College, he judged, for his new life and image. The assignment sheet in the newsroom brought him quickly, rudely back to earth. "Weather?" he demanded of Traynor.

"Weather," Traynor replied.

"What about it?"

"That's what you're going to tell our readers. Take a photographer to Washington Boulevard, Woodward Avenue . . . People leaping over puddles, umbrellas blowing inside out, that's what we want."

"But it's pouring out there!"

"Don't waste insights like that on me. Save it for your lead."

The new trench coat kept Chris's body dry, but his ego, invigorated by his triumph at Kent State, remained sodden for months. Relegated to a desk behind several bustling rows of veteran reporters, he fidgeted his days away trying to catch Traynor's eye every time the editor reached for the microphone at his elbow. But the name that crackled from the loudspeakers was seldom Chris's; time after time someone senior to Chris would emerge from the intervening thicket of journalistic talent to answer the summons. And on the rare occasions that the loudspeaker did say, "Mr. Stevenson, please," the assignment turned out to be a story with all the explosive potential of Chris's account of the rainstorm. After a month of this painful Coventry, Chris summoned the courage to lodge a timid complaint, and regretted it instantly.

"And what do I do with *them?*" Traynor demanded, sweeping a hand toward the rows of reporters facing his command post. Chris colored, praying that his colleagues had been too busy to overhear his effrontery, and retreated to his position behind the lines.

But, in fact, Traynor had plans. Slowly, fitfully, his stubby wing, with the shirtsleeves rolled to just below the elbow, opened—and Chris crept under, only too happy to apprentice himself to this didactic, pugnaciously principled city editor. Somehow the hot stories began coming in just after Traynor had cleared all the desks in front of Chris, and he had no choice but to call on the cub. Like a mother bird pushing a fledgling from the nest, Traynor nudged Chris toward the sleazier combat zones where the troubled city's action lay. Hanging out, radar humming, pencil poised, trench coat now suitably weathered, Chris became a familiar and not-always-welcome figure at Detroit's courts, municipal buildings and commission offices. Month by month, story by story, he acquired the fully operating set of street smarts that Traynor knew would lead him to facts a less persistent reporter might have overlooked, facts which, translated to needle-sharp prose, brought increasingly frequent smiles to the city editor's craggy face—when the cub reporter was safely out of sight. By the time two years of this apprenticeship had passed, Chris had learned how to harry a cop, criminal or commissioner until a precious nugget of information slipped and fell with a barely discernible clink. Then, pouncing, Chris had his story and Traynor his secret smile. Slowly but inexorably, Chris's stories—and by-lines—began working their way back through the paper to page one. He was, as he sometimes reflected contentedly, on schedule.

That was why the assignment to the Detroit Conservatory of Art seemed such a comedown to him. Addicted now to the rough-and-tumble of investigative reporting, he envisioned knock-kneed girls in starched dresses and Mary Janes performing a stately gavotte with forlorn boys suffering from terminal acne.

"What about Sy Lewis?" Chris demanded. "He's your dance critic."

"In New York, on assignment." In conversation Traynor's language was as sparse and to the point as the stories delivered to him by his terrorized staff; he seldom began a sentence with an article or a first-person pronoun.

"Doesn't Judy cover for him?"

"Where the hell have you been? She had a baby last week. You want her to walk into the conservatory trailing afterbirth?"

Chris grimaced. "I get the picture."

"Half-right, Mr. Stevenson. You get the assignment. And don't try to con me. Go read a book about ballet before the demonstration."

Chris found a book of ballet terms and principles by Agrippina Vaganova, read it uncomprehendingly and reported to the Detroit Conservatory on the day set, with little enthusiasm and dim hopes of writing anything more than the kind of vague, uninformed story he called custard when he read it under someone else's by-line.

Then he saw the girl in the second row. First, to his admittedly unpracticed eye, she seemed light years ahead of her coevals in talent and skill. Her movements were more precise than theirs, more decisive, the line of her legs and body cleaner and longer than theirs, her jumps higher, her landings softer.

Chris tried to remember the names of the steps he'd read about in the Vaganova book, but whereas Vaganova's line drawings had stood obligingly still, the dancers' movements—especially those of the girl in the second row—flowed together in what looked to the confused reporter like a single unbroken gesture of hands and feet and body.

He put down his pen, discouraged. He would be able to write nothing but gobbledegook. He hadn't always performed at peak capacity for Traynor, but he'd never returned with *no* story. Well, he thought, there's a time for everything, and it isn't as though Traynor wasn't forewarned.

With no story to write, he sat back and relaxed, enjoying the motion as motion, the dance as dance, without the intervention of his journalist's sensibility. And he watched the girl in the second row. How old was she? Fourteen? Fifteen, maybe. He found his right hand describing patterns on his note pad. He looked at the patterns. They were words—about the girl in the second row. He watched, he wrote. He tried to describe what he saw, not in the mysterious French terms of the book he'd read, but in the terms he would use to describe—accurately, simply, straightforwardly (Traynor was never very far away)—any event to which he was a professional witness.

As the class ended, the director came into the room. "I see you've got lots of notes," she chirruped. "I hope you're not going to say anything bad."

"No. I—I was very impressed. Especially . . ." He hesitated. Nearby, Miss Nicholas rose to half-toe.

"Especially . . . ?" Mrs. Rome trilled.

"There was a girl. In the second row. In blue . . ."

"Carin Bradley," burst from Miss Nicholas.

Mrs. Rome's smile widened. "You've got good taste, Mr. Stevenson. She's one of our best. Wouldn't you say so, Miss Nicholas?"

"Absolutely!"

"I don't know much about dance," Chris said.

"You picked Carin out," the director replied silkily.

"I just know I—enjoyed watching her."

"As you should," Mrs. Rome said. "She's a very talented youngster."

"Uh—how . . ." Chris hesitated again.

"How talented? That's hard to say."

"No. Young."

"How young is Carin? I'm not sure."

"Fifteen," came from Miss Nicholas.

"Thank you," Mrs. Rome said.

"Isn't she very—talented for fifteen?" Chris asked.

"She's talented for eighteen," Miss Nicholas replied firmly.

"What will happen to her?"

"It's hard to say," Mrs. Rome responded. "Some of the children go on to professional companies, some of them lose interest." She smiled sadly. "You know—boys."

"Boys?"

Mrs. Rome lowered her voice and swept a hand at the empty classroom. "This is very demanding work. When the children get to be seventeen or eighteen, they may develop other interests—even the most gifted ones. We lose some very talented students to the social whirl. They just don't seem to have time for this *and* their private lives, and, unless they're exceptionally dedicated, *l'art* loses out." She emitted a gusty sigh. "After all these years I suppose we ought to be used to it, but we've had some heartbreaks, believe me." Again she turned to study the empty room. "It's a shame we can't neuter them." She spun abruptly back to Chris with a nervous laugh. "Just joking, of course. A little *plaisanterie du métier*. We want our students to have full, well-rounded lives."

"Of course."

"Well . . . is there anything else you'd like to see? We have modern classes and *pointe* classes—and, of course, in the other disciplines we have some remarkable young singers and musicians . . ."

"No, I think the *Free Press* expects a story about dancers." He hesitated, his cool professional bearing masking a titanic inner struggle over what he now took to be unmistakable evidence of incipient pedophilia. "That girl . . ."

"Carin?" It was the teacher, still hovering nearby.

"Yes. I—I think I may center the article on her . . ."

"That would be wonderful!" Miss Nicholas exclaimed.

"I—suppose I ought to meet her," Chris said, hating himself.

"Of course!" Mrs. Rome caroled. She turned to the teacher. "Will you go into the girls' dressing room . . ."

"I don't want to bother her," Chris protested. "She's probably still soaking wet."

"How much time do you have?" Miss Nicholas asked.

"Plenty."

"Then maybe you could wait till she's dressed."

"Sure."

"This way," Mrs. Rome said with a little bow.

She took Chris into the waiting room and deposited him on a plastic-covered couch. "I'm sure she won't be long," she said, bestowing a final melting smile on Chris, and chugged away. A moment later the door from the classroom opened and Miss Nicholas peeped out, saw Chris alone, and hurried to him.

"Excuse me . . ."

"Yes."

"Did you mean it?"

"Pardon?"

The teacher gestured stiffly toward a dressing-room door. "About Carin. Are you really going to write about her?"

"I think so. Why?"

Miss Nicholas glanced nervously toward the office. "She's really talented. I know the other children are too," she added hastily, "and Mrs. Rome would probably like you to write about the school, but . . ."

Chris smiled. "Carin's your favorite."

"We're not supposed to play favorites."

"But Carin's your favorite."

Miss Nicholas reflected a moment, then said evenly, "She's the best student I've ever had. And—" She broke off again, studying Chris uncertainly.

"What's wrong?"

"Nothing. It's just—well, a newspaper article would help so much."

"Miss . . . ?"

"Nicholas."

"Miss Nicholas, I get the impression you're trying to tell me something."

She shook her head. "It's not my business."

"What isn't?"

"Whatever Carin tells you."

"I guess you know you're sounding very mysterious."

"I don't mean to," Miss Nicholas replied quickly. "I just think some recognition for Carin—right now—might be very encouraging."

"To Carin?"

"No, her parents."

"Do they need encouraging?"

"All parents do," Miss Nicholas said evasively. "They'd rather see their children go into more—conventional lines of work." Chris nodded understanding, and Miss Nicholas took advantage of the respite to decamp. "I'll see if Carin's ready."

When she returned, Chris was relieved to note that in street clothes the dancer looked older. In flannel slacks, her still-damp hair bound in a wool scarf, a heavy leather bag slung over her shoulder, she could be a Bloomfield Hills matron on her way to the super-market, Chris tried to persuade himself.

"This is Mr. Stevenson, the man who wants to write about you," Miss Nicholas said.

"Hello," Carin said in what sounded to the drowning Chris like a six-year-old voice.

"Uh—do you mind if I write about you?" he asked.

"No, she doesn't!" burst from Miss Nicholas, then she recovered with, "It would be very good—for the school," to Carin. Carin nodded, and turned to stare at Chris from atop her twelve-year-old body and twenty-year-old legs.

"Uh—why don't we go somewhere and have a soda while we talk? You must be dehydrated after that class," Chris said, appalled by his fatuity.

"Yes," Carin said.

They went to a drugstore where the Wayne State students hung out. There were nearer drugstores, but Chris was going on the fretful assumption that college students would be unlikely to condemn a lecherous twenty-four-year-old for plying a fifteen-year-old girl with sodas.

As Carin slid the scarf from her hair, Chris studied her. Until this moment dancers had been outside his ken. *Maybe that's all it is,* he reflected: *I saw her dance, up close in the classroom. That's impres-*

sive. I'd feel the same way if I got to watch any first-rate athlete up close . . .

Like Al Kaline? an inner voice derided, and Chris shook his head in dismay.

"What?" Carin asked.

He glanced at her, embarrassed.

"Did you say something?"

"No."

"Oh. I thought I saw you shake your head."

"No. I mean, I didn't say anything. I was just—thinking."

The sodas arrived. Carin stared at Chris over the top of her glass, her mouth puckered on the straw. Chris opened his notebook.

"How long have you been studying?"

"Since I was six." She sucked on the straw.

"Isn't that pretty early to start?"

"No."

The drugstore was crowded and steamy. Carin took off her jacket. Chris could see tiny nipples under her Beethoven T-shirt, and he sagged. Not from disappointment, but because this reminder of her immaturity seemed to have no deterrent effect whatsoever on his escalating libido. "And you're—how old?" Maybe there would be a wonderful surprise: *The school has it wrong and she's actually twenty . . .*

"Fifteen."

"Yeah." He pretended to make a note on the pad. She sipped her soda.

"What do you want to do?" Chris asked.

"When?"

"When—when you grow up," Chris said, dying another little death.

"Dance."

"You're definitely going to be a dancer?"

"Oh, yes. If I can get into a company."

"But—what's her name . . . ?"

"Who?"

"The woman who runs the school."

"Mrs. Rome."

"Mrs. Rome said a lot of girls your age stop dancing."

"Why?"

"Uh—boys."

"Boys?"

"Yes."

Is there such a thing as a fifteen-year-old lesbian? Chris wondered. *Maybe* every *dancer's gay, the boys* and *the girls.*

"I'm going to dance," Carin said.

"Does that mean no boys?"

"Is that what Mrs. Rome said?"

"Well, she said sometimes . . ."

"Not me." The tone was matter-of-fact, emphatic.

"Do—uh—do you have a boyfriend?" Chris began to hope that an omniscient cop would rush into the drugstore and arrest him before it was too late.

"Not really."

"What does that mean?"

Carin's straw had collapsed. She withdrew it from the glass and began spooning up her ice cream. Chris waited, his palms damp. There was no longer any question about it: this was now the only woman—girl—person in the world he wanted to go to bed with, and if there was thin ice to be trod, he was almost ready to tread it. Carin's cool blue glance shimmered at him over a spoonful of vanilla ice cream.

"Why are you asking me these questions?"

Caught!

"I told you—I want to write about you."

"Is this what you're going to write about?"

"What?"

"Whether I have a boyfriend?"

"Well, no. But I'm not a dance critic; I can't—*review* what I saw, so I decided to do a human-interest story, about one dancer: you. That means I've got to ask some questions about your—background, and your personal life. If that bothers you . . ."

"No, it's okay. Shoot."

Christ! An eight-*year-old's word.*

She spooned up her ice cream, her guileless gaze on Chris.

"Uh—what made you start studying dance?"

She told him.

"How about your regular education? You must be in high school."

"Yes."

"How do you manage high school and dance classes?"

She told him.

"So you're going to keep on dancing." She nodded. "Where?"

"Anywhere I can."

"Detroit?"

She shrugged. "Not much chance here."

"New York?"

"I'd love to, but . . ."

"But what?"

She shrugged again, and spread her child's hands. "Money. And I don't think my parents would like it. Dad wants me to go to college."

"Not interested?"

"Not if I can dance."

"So dance is everything."

"Just about."

"What's second?" He waited, inappropriately tense.

After a few moments she said, "Having fun."

"What's fun?" He waited again, reflecting that if she said paper dolls or hopscotch, he might be saved.

"What's fun for you?" she asked, and he started and sat back.

"Who's interviewing whom?" was the best he could muster.

"It's a hard question," Carin said. "What's second? I don't know." She laughed. "I like to eat. Do you?"

"Yeah, but I wouldn't put it second."

"What *would* you put second?"

He colored. "That's not fair."

"Why?"

"Well, we're different."

"I know you're not a dancer . . ."

"That's not what I mean. You're a girl . . ."

"And you're a boy."

"No."

"You're not a boy?"

"I'm a man."

"Oh. Sorry."

"My feelings aren't hurt. It's just a difference."

"Between a man and a girl?"

"Of course. What I might put second . . ." He halted.

"Oh—*that.*"

He stared at her. "What?"

"That," she said. "Of *course* you'd put it second."

"And—you?" he asked, despising himself, aware that he was steering her. He wondered if there was a law against impersonating a journalist for prurient purposes.

She reflected, turning the long spoon in her empty glass. She frowned and screwed up her nose, then she said, "Maybe third."

Jesus! On the other hand she might be—*must* be—speaking theoretically. Maybe a few experimental sallies . . .

"How old did you say you were?" Chris asked, in the desperate hope that miraculously the number would change.

"Fifteen. How old are you?"

"Twenty-four." She nodded amiably. He felt compelled to add, "I'll be twenty-five in three months."

"I'll be sixteen in two."

At least she didn't say sweet *sixteen,* Chris reflected, prepared to grasp at even microscopic straws.

Carin tipped her glass to see if the last traces of ice cream and soda had melted into anything interesting enough to dig out. Decid-

ing it wasn't worth the effort, she set the glass straight and looked at
Chris. He was fidgeting with his notebook.

"Anything else?" she asked.

"No," he said.

"I thought you were going to write about the school," Traynor
rasped.

"So did I."

"What happened?"

"This girl caught my eye."

"Obviously."

"She's very talented," Chris said quickly.

"Obviously."

"Yeah."

The teletypes clicked noisily fifteen feet away, punctuating their
rim-shot tattoos with syncopated bells on the backbeat. During his
first weeks at the paper, Chris had often listened to the percussion of
the teletypes, snapping his fingers or singing softly to their infectious
rhythms. Then they had faded into the general rumble of the cavernous newsroom. Until now. Now the teletypes clacked jazzily again,
and Chris wondered how anyone could ever get any work done here.
Including himself.

Traynor was saying something, but the machines were drowning him out.

"Pardon?"

"I said, 'And you gave me a hard time about the assignment.' "

"Oh. Well, what do I know about ballet?"

"Maybe I ought to confine you to subjects you don't know anything about."

"You mean it's okay?"

"It's a goddamn poem."

"Is that good?"

"Is the girl that good?"

"Yes!"

"You sure became a ballet expert in a hurry."

Chris colored. "Well, you said, 'Read some books.' "

"You must've read the library." Traynor brandished Chris's
pages. "Unless this is bullshit."

"It isn't," Chris said firmly.

"Better not be," Traynor grunted. "Take a photographer over
and get some pictures."

When the picture session ended, Chris strolled casually to
Carin, toweling herself off in front of the classroom mirror. "Want a
lift home?"

"Sure." Carin tossed the towel over her shoulder and sauntered

toward the dressing room. Just short of the door, she turned back
with an abrupt, "I've gotta take a shower; you may not want to
wait."

"I'll wait," Chris said.

In his car, the venerable convertible Chris had bought second-
hand and named Piglet for its faint resemblance to one of his favorite literary characters, Chris turned to the bundled shape next to him
and asked, "Did you have a chance to eat tonight?"

"I wouldn't eat before I dance."

"Then you haven't had any dinner." She shook her head.
"Hungry?"

"Bet y'r life."

"I haven't had anything to eat either. Want to stop somewhere?"

"Grandpa expects me."

Grandpa!

"No! Wrong. He said he wouldn't be home till late. Something
at the church."

The church!

"So I guess it's okay."

"Fine. What would you like?"

"Food."

"Any particular kind?"

Carin shrugged. "It's all the same to me. Nothing heavy,
though."

"You're worried about gaining weight?"

"Of course. What're you laughing at?"

"You must weigh ninety pounds."

"So?"

"You should be eating malteds." In the dark next to Chris,
Carin's head swiveled back and forth. He glanced at her. "If you
were—my kid, I'd fatten you up."

"No, you wouldn't," Carin said firmly.

"What about Italian?"

"Can I get a salad?"

"Of course, but . . ."

"Fine."

Chris glanced ahead, braked and turned west on Grand Boulevard.

In the restaurant Chris nervously suggested, "You—uh—don't
want any wine . . ."

"No."

"Are you sure? *I* could order it, and then . . ."

"No, thanks. But you go ahead and have some."

Carin studied the menu carefully, her lips moving. "Are you counting calories?" Chris asked. She colored and nodded. He shook his head incredulously. "Have you decided?"

"I told you: a salad."

"How can you live on that?"

"I probably won't even finish it."

Chris summoned the waiter and ordered Carin's salad and some veal and a glass of red wine for himself. The waiter's departure left Chris alone with his problems, the first of which was conversation. "So you live with your grandfather."

"For now." Chris waited for amplification. "I told you my folks live in Wayne."

"Oh, yes."

"Is this the interview?"

"No, that's done."

"Can I read it?"

"In the paper."

"Is it good?"

"Not good enough."

"Why?"

"I don't know enough. I tried to describe my feelings when I watched you dance."

"I wasn't dancing."

"Oh? It looked like dancing to me."

She shook her head. "It was class."

"Is it so different on a stage?"

"I don't know." Another questioning glance elicited, "I've just been in school shows and a couple of conservatory recitals. It's not like real dancing."

"Your teacher thinks you're—marvelous." He reconsidered. "Actually she said you're the best student she's ever had."

Carin sat up. "Did she say that?"

"Yes."

"Holy cow!"

Chris winced at the jump-rope aura of the exclamation, and recovered during the time it took the waiter to put his wineglass down. When the waiter left, he asked, "Do you ever drink wine?"

"No."

"Because you're too young?"

"No. Lots of the kids drink wine."

"Diet?"

"Sort of. I don't like it that much."

The candle flickered, and Carin settled back into a shadowy corner of the booth, one leg stretched along the banquette.

"You must be exhausted at the end of a day," Chris said.

"Sometimes."

"What do you do?"

"Homework."

"Of course. But on a weekend, say."

"On Saturday I take a class. It's a good one."

"Why?"

"Long."

"So Saturday night you're tired, too."

"Sometimes."

"What about Sunday?"

"Now I go to church."

"Now?"

"I told you: I'm living . . ."

"With your grandfather, yes."

He took another sip of wine, then he asked, "Do you enjoy church?"

"Not very much. The pews are hard."

"That's a problem?"

She pointed at a buttock. "Not much padding."

"Oh—yes."

"And if I sit too long, my legs stiffen up, so I give myself a *barre* every Sunday after church."

"Then, Sunday night?"

"Homework."

"Not a very exciting life."

"You think so?"

"What do *you* think?"

She reflected, the candlelight picking up her eyes in the dark. "I get excited in class."

"Always?"

"Always."

"What else?"

"Excites me?"

"Yes."

"This *is* an interview."

"I guess so."

"You going to write another article?"

"No."

"Then why . . . ?"

"I'm interested."

"Why?"

Ah. The trembling sword, the staggering bull, the moment of truth.

"*I* like my work too."

"What does that mean?"

"It means I get interested in—whatever I'm writing about."

"Always?"

"Sometimes."

"You think I'm interesting?"

"Yes." She raised her other leg and crossed it over the first, stretching her feet. "You don't?"

"Not very."

"Why?"

She shrugged. "What do I do? I go to class, I go to school, I go to class, I go home."

"You said it was exciting."

"To me." She peered at him out of her corner and repeated her incredulous question. "To you too?"

"Yes."

She shook her head. "Weird."

"I don't think it's weird."

"To each his own," she said.

The platitude du jour, Chris thought, seeking salvation in his carefully cultivated reportorial cynicism. When it didn't help, he gave himelf a lecture on falling in love with fifteen-year-olds that fell to pieces every time he glanced across the table at Carin. His preoccupation put a damper on their already spasmodic conversation, and during dinner communication slowed to a crawl. When Chris had finished his veal, he asked Carin if she'd like anything else.

"No."

"Do you mind if I have some coffee?"

"Of course not."

"It may be late for you."

"No, it's okay. I don't have much homework tonight."

Chris ordered espresso. When he turned back to Carin, he found her staring at him. "What's the matter?"

"I'm still trying to figure out what makes you think my life's exciting."

"I didn't say that."

"You said . . ."

"I said what you *do* is exciting." He took a breath. "And *you're* exciting." He retreated. "When you're dancing."

"You ought to see a real dancer. Have you?"

"A few times. I can't call myself a balletomane. Until now."

"You like ballet?"

"I like *you,* Carin." She examined her salad. "Did you hear me?"

"Yes."

Chris's hands ached. He looked down at them. They were doubled into tight fists. He opened them slowly. "Do you know what a pedophile is?" he asked.

"No."

"That's a freak who—goes after children."

"So?"

"That's what I feel like."

"You're not a freak."

"But you're a child."

"I'm fifteen."

"That's what I mean."

"I'm going to be sixteen."

Chris pushed his coffee cup away. "Doesn't help."

"Too bad."

He looked up. She was parked in her corner of the booth, her legs extended along the banquette, her eyes placid, her hands relaxed in her lap. "This doesn't bother you at all?" he asked.

"No. Does it bother you?"

"You haven't noticed?"

"Then why did you invite me to dinner?"

"Because I couldn't stop myself." He leaned forward, his forearms on the table. "Listen, let me explain something. You're a very beautiful ki . . . girl. Do you understand that?"

"No."

"Well, take my word for it, you are. Also, I've never watched anybody dance close up, like I watched you. Can you understand *that?*"

"No."

"What you do is very impressive. It's—exotic. It's graceful. It's very, well, it's very sexy. Can you understand that?"

"I guess so. Sometimes I look in the mirror—at myself, or someone else—and I think it looks sexy."

Chris sank into his corner of the booth. "How the hell would you know?"

"I'm not five," she said.

"You're also not twenty." He picked up the check. "Come on," he said.

"Where?"

"Wherever you live. It's time for your homework."

When they pulled up in front of Dahlstrom's house, Chris remained behind the wheel. "I'm sorry, Carin," he said.

"For what?"

He gestured vaguely. "My behavior at the restaurant. I can't believe I let myself say all those things. Just nonsense. I didn't have any lunch today, and the wine . . . You know?"

"Sure."

He sat rigidly behind the wheel. She pulled her dance bag out of the backseat and turned to him. "Thanks."

"Yeah, sure."

"I wish you didn't feel that way."

"I just don't understand myself. I'm supposed to be a professional. And an adult."

"I think you're much too hard on yourself." He looked at her.

She was smiling easily, without a trace of strain. "I had a terrific time."

"You did?"

"Yeah. If you ever want to have dinner again, let me know."

"You know something?" Chris said. "I think you're too old for me." Carin started to get out of the car. He reached out and caught her arm. "When did you say you were going to be sixteen?"

"Two months."

"I'll call you in two months."

"Okay."

"Sixteen is still too young," he muttered.

"You just said I was old."

"Yeah. I'm not making sense to either one of us."

"Are you going to call me?"

"Yes. At the school."

She got out, then leaned back through the car window. "See? I like boys."

"You . . . ?"

"Remember? You asked me yesterday."

"Oh—yes."

"Any more questions?"

Chris was silent a moment, then he said, "No."

"Okay," she said brightly. "Talk to you in a couple of months?"

"Yes."

She tapped the car door with a palm by way of salute, turned and made her way up the walk to the wooden porch of her grandfather's house. There she turned and waved at Chris, who was still parked in front of the house. He waved back, then drove away, amazed, adrift.

Miss Nicholas came into the dressing room. "Carin . . ."

Emerging naked and wet from the shower, Carin turned toward the door. "Yes?"

"It's the phone—for you."

Carin smiled. "Tell him . . . tell them to hang on."

She seized a towel, mopped herself, pulled a terry cloth robe from a hanger, flung it around herself, worked her damp feet back into her dance shoes and hurried into the hall, still dripping copiously.

The receiver hung invitingly from the wall phone, swaying slightly as if in time to some inaudible music. Carin snatched at it. "Hello?"

"It's me."

A grin split her face. "I knew it was!"

"Did it happen?"

"My birthday?"

"Yes."

"Right on schedule."

"How was it?"

"Big party. You know: sweet sixteen." After a moment she inquired, "Mr. Stevenson?"

"Yeah, I'm here—and under the circumstances I think it's Chris."

She laughed. "Okay." When he was silent again, she observed, "Well—I'm sixteen."

"How about a movie?"

She laughed. "I thought you'd never ask."

As they left the theater, Carin said, "Thank you."

"It wasn't *that* good. The reviews made it sound like a masterpiece."

"For the article."

"Oh."

"I thought it was terrific. So did my family."

Chris grinned. "That's not exactly surprising."

"So did Mrs. Rome and Miss Nicholas."

"That doesn't surprise me either."

"But I've had a lot of calls."

"Friends?"

"No. Jobs. I'm dancing in a recital next week."

"Oh. I'm glad, Carin."

"Imagine how *I* feel. You did a terrific thing for me."

"No, I didn't. I just wrote what I felt."

"I'm going to make some money. I never have before."

"I'm glad. You deserve it."

"I'm not so sure about that. I'm scared."

"Of what?"

"Next week."

"Do you think I could come?"

"You'll be disappointed."

"I—don't think that's possible."

When Chris dropped Carin off at her grandfather's house, she gave him a quick, comradely kiss on the cheek and said, "Thanks. You're a terrific friend."

She danced a solo in the recital. It had been choreographed for her by Miss Nicholas, so it showed her off, as the combination Miss Nicholas had designed the day of Chris's visit had displayed Carin's strengths in the classroom.

Chris wasn't disappointed. When a tall, ungainly figure in the second row rose at the curtain call and swept the audience with a glance that threatened mayhem if they didn't match his enthusiasm,

Chris sprang to his feet and beat his palms red in appreciation of the radiant girl onstage.

He was relieved to find that in makeup, under lights, Carin seemed ageless, neither childlike nor adult. She was a dancer, a creature apart from the herd, egregious, exempt, *sui generis*—mercifully nubile.

After the performance Carin, flushed and streaming sweat, said, "This is my grandfather." As Dahlstrom extended a hand toward Chris, Carin said to him, "Mr. Stevenson is the man who wrote the article about me. I wouldn't be here tonight if it weren't for him."

Chris's hand disappeared between Dahlstrom's outsize mitts. "What can we say to you!" the old man exclaimed.

Tides that Chris had thought permanently banished flooded over him again, coloring his cheek, stiffening his tongue. "Oh," he stuttered, "all . . . all it was was a newspaper article . . ."

But the gaunt man had turned away. "Mai, do you know who this is? Just the fellow who wrote the story in the *Free Press!*"

"No!" Mai exclaimed, and seized Chris's hand. Chris wondered if the blush he felt was visible, and how Carin's family might interpret it. Could this mother and grandfather somehow sense the fantasies that had been crowding Chris at his typewriter, in his car, in bed. . . ?

"Dad," Carin was calling.

Chris groaned inwardly. He should have anticipated this. Had she told them he had taken her out to dinner twice? Carin might not think it unnatural, but they would. Someone in her family would be clever enough to question his motives.

Another hand was enveloping his. ". . . really super. *We* thought she was good, but of course we're prejudiced."

Chris stared back at the beaming, grateful faces and made himself a determined promise: it still wasn't too late, thank God; he would cease and desist as of this moment. These genial, trusting faces were just what he'd needed. They'd brought sanity and balance to his disordered thoughts. He felt a warm wave of gratitude. He smiled back and pumped Mr. Bradley's hand. Then he looked at Carin, radiant, touching, fine, ready—and he quickly, guiltily dropped her father's hand.

"I don't know," the copyboy said. "Some kid. She's cute."

Chris had a sinking feeling. "Where is she?"

"Outside."

"Well, send her in."

Without makeup, bundled against the cold, Carin looked as if she had come to audition for one of the title roles in *Hansel and Gretel.* She giggled as she approached Chris. "You were a riot last night."

"Oh, really?"

"You acted like my folks were going to bite you."

"Do they know you've gone out with me?"

"No. Should they?"

"No! That's precisely the point."

But Carin was looking around the big noisy room. "So this is where you work."

"Yes."

"You write here?"

"Yes."

"How can you get anything done?"

"You learn how to tune out."

Carin surveyed the ranks of desks, the hunched figures in shirt-sleeves poking at typewriter keys; she listened to the shrilling of phones and clatter of teletypes, then turned back to Chris. "It's my turn."

"For what?"

"Dinner. Grandpa's out of town for two days, so I'm on my own."

"You think I'm going to let you buy me dinner?"

"No, I'm going to make it."

"Where?"

"At home?"

"You want me to come to your house for dinner?"

"Grandpa's house." She waited a moment, then added, "I'm not a bad cook. Lots of nights I make dinner for Grandpa and me." She waited again, then asked, "What's wrong?"

"I don't know," Chris said slowly.

"Don't you want to come?"

"Yes . . ."

"Can you be there at seven?"

"Maybe."

"Maybe you'll come, or maybe you'll be there at seven?"

"You really think this is a good idea?"

"If I didn't I wouldn't have suggested it," she replied airily.

"Okay." She started out, and he stopped her with, "Do me a favor?"

"Yeah?"

"Try to be twenty by tonight."

"What if I *look* twenty?"

"I don't think the law takes that into account," he said wearily.

"Is there some kind of law says we can't have dinner together?"

"No," he said quickly. "I'm just making nervous jokes. Don't ask me why."

"I'm beginning to think you're right," she said. "I *am* too old for you."

As she strode out, Chris had the impression that she was moving in perfect time with the syncopated clatter of the teletypes.

She seated him at the big oak table in the dining room. Chris could envision the dinners that had taken place in this house over the years, and imagine the conversations about sin and salvation. As Carin sat down opposite him and picked up her fork, she said, "If it's no good just tell me. I *know* I can scramble eggs."

Chris ate a forkful of meat. "No, it's very good. When did you do it?"

"After class."

"Which class?"

"Ballet."

"But you don't finish till six."

"It didn't take long. Some of it's frozen, you know."

"Doesn't taste like it."

"I thawed it."

After dinner she said, "Want to watch television?"

"What about your homework?"

"I did it."

"When?"

"After class?"

"You were cooking dinner, remember?"

"After my first class."

"You were in school."

"Not today."

"A holiday?"

"For me."

"You cut school to make this dinner?"

"Sort of."

"Carin . . ."

"Careful!"

"Of what?"

"You'll sound like my folks." Chris's shoulders dropped, and Carin hurried to him, reaching for his hands. "Will you please cut it out, Chris?"

"When you say things like that . . ."

"You're not old enough to be my father."

"I could be your uncle."

"I'm glad you're not." And she slid her arms around him, pressed her cheek against his chest and hugged him.

He looked down at her hair. "Carin . . ." She didn't stir. "I think you're a lot braver than I am." She raised her head and reached for his lips. She kissed him, gently, for a long time, waiting. Then she simply stared at him, close, unblinking.

"I mean it," he murmured.

"So do I," she said.

"You want me to go to jail?"

"No, just bed." When he didn't budge, she said, "I told you, Grandpa's not here."

"That's not the point."

"What is?"

Nearly a minute later he said, "I don't know," and let her take his hand and lead him up the stairs.

He tried not to look around her bedroom, afraid of being confronted with evidence of rampant teenagism. Out of the corner of his eye, he could see several stuffed animals; he turned resolutely away from them. Unfortunately there was a large stuffed elephant on the bed. Carin dumped it on the floor to make room for them, and drew him to the bed. He sat on the edge of it, and she hovered uncertainly in front of him. When he remained immobile, she backed up and pulled her sweater over her head. Her breasts were only a little fuller than Chris had suspected. She unzipped her jeans and let them fall. Her panties were bikinis, a sign of maturity perhaps, but more likely of her vocation: she probably wore them under tights, Chris reasoned. She slid the panties down and Chris was dismayed to see her nearly bare mons. Another nine-year-old part. He stood up. Carin reached out to unbutton his jacket, but he took her hands and held her away.

"What's wrong?" she asked. He shook his head. "You're disappointed," she said quietly. "I told you you exaggerated in your article . . ."

"No," Chris said gently. "You're beautiful . . ."

"Then get undressed."

"Come here," he said. "Sit down." He sat on the edge of the bed, Carin beside him, her hand in his, his eyes on the empty space in front of him. "Have you ever made love to anybody before?"

"I thought you said the interview was over."

"You going to answer me?"

"Yes."

"Is that the answer?"

"Yes."

"You've made love to somebody."

"How many times do I have to say it?"

"Till it's true." She was silent. He said, "When I *was* interviewing you, you said sex came third."

"There!"

"What did you mean?"

"That it's third. First, dance . . ."

"Was it theoretical or were you speaking from experience?"

"I told you."

"And I don't believe you."

"What difference does it make? I'm sixteen."

"You were fifteen a week ago."

"And a year ago I was fourteen! So what?"

"So—we're not hillbillies."

Carin sniffled. "You just don't *want* to make love to me."

"That may be the biggest lie you've ever uttered in your life," he said softly.

"Then come *on,*" she said, tugging his arm and trying to lie back on the bed.

"Just *tell* me," Chris said. "Is this the first time?"

"Why?"

"Because if you've been with two or three other guys, it makes me a little less—creepy."

"You know you're old-fashioned?"

"No, I'm not. You wouldn't believe some of the things I've done. You meet all kinds of people in my line of work . . ."

"Okay," she said. He waited. "Yes."

"This is the first time."

"Yes." He stood up. She came up with him, clinging to his arm. "But I masturbate like it's going out of style. With objects! Doesn't that count?"

"No!"

"Why not? I come two or three times a week. Some women don't come till they're thirty. That's a known fact!"

Just beyond Carin, Chris could see the stuffed elephant she had unceremoniously dumped off the bed. "I'm going to tell you an *un*known fact," he said. She stared up at him, her eyes wide and empty, waiting to be filled with tears or anger. "I think I'm in love with you."

"But—that's terrific!"

"I also don't know how you're supposed to behave when you fall in love with a recent fifteen-year-old."

"You're only ten years older than me. Not even."

"It's not the difference in our ages. I wouldn't care if I were *twenty* years older than you—provided I were forty. Do you understand?"

Now tears began to fill the void. "I don't care," she said.

"I know," he said. "I told you you're braver, and older—and maybe smarter—than I am. The only thing I know for sure is I don't want to be your first lover. I mean, I do, but I *don't,* if you get what I mean."

"No."

"Then you'll just have to believe me."

She spread her hands. "What else can I do?"

"You can stop wasting your time making dinners for me. You

don't need a neurotic idiot like me messing up your life. I just—can't cope. You can, I can't. Okay?"

"Okay."

When she started to follow him to the door, he said, "Don't come downstairs like that. I can find my coat."

"It's right next to the stairs . . ."

"I know."

He closed the door quickly and hurried down the stairs.

"Let's have *changement, changement, entrechat quatre, entrechat quatre,*" Miss Nicholas said. "And use the *changements* as preparation for the *quatres.* Understand?"

Carin looked around, then hurried across the room to take a place in the last row of students pressing their feet together in fifth position to begin the exercise. The piano thundered, and the dancers rose in a fluttering cloud.

Moments later the class ended in a burst of applause, and Carin turned to the tall blond boy next to her in the last row. "Ben . . . ?" He looked at her. "Uh—are you free tonight?"

"For what?"

She shrugged. "I don't know. Dinner."

"What happened?" he asked suspiciously.

"Nothing."

"Last time I asked, you said you weren't interested. I finally gave up."

She managed a laugh. "Bad timing. I live with my grandfather; he's a minister, but he's out of town . . ."

Ben's eyes widened. He was nearly six feet two, with high Slavic cheekbones, wide shoulders and long arms. Most important, he was straight—and twenty years old. There was one twenty-*two*-year-old boy in the class, but Carin knew he was gay.

"Are you suggesting dinner at your place?" Ben asked.

"It's only fifteen minutes away," Carin said.

Ben studied her. "Still waters run deep," he said.

"Are you coming or not?" Carin asked testily.

"I guess so," Ben said. "Sure, why not?"

Carin had him upstairs before he had finished his coffee. When she saw him naked, she regretted that the only available straight in the class was six feet two inches tall, but beggars, she reasoned, couldn't be choosers. "Take it easy," she warned as he loomed over her.

It was less painful and more pleasurable than she had anticipated, though less satisfying than masturbation; but she had anticipated that, too. It lasted somewhat longer than she had expected, but finally Ben rolled over on his back, stretched his legs and closed his eyes.

She rose quickly, dripping his sperm, and crossed to the dresser where the Polaroid camera the Reverend Mr. Dahlstrom plied at wedding receptions waited innocently in a drawer.

"Ben . . . ?"

He opened his eyes and sat up abruptly. "What the hell are you doing!"

"Just a picture."

"*Just* a picture!"

"One of you and one of me," she said matter-of-factly.

"You keep a record?" he asked incredulously.

"Only if it was dynamite," Carin said.

"Oh," he said, "Well . . ." and lay back against a pillow, tightening his pectorals.

"Grab that stuffed elephant," Carin said.

"What for?"

"It looks cute. Hold it in your lap. No," she amended hastily, "tuck it under your arm. That's fine." The flash whitened the room.

"My turn!" Carin chirped and hopped on the bed, handing him the camera. "It's focused. Just stand where I was." She picked up the elephant and nestled it next to her. "Can you see the elephant?"

"Yes."

"Okay." The room went white. Ben raised the camera again. "What're you doing!" Carin shielded herself behind the animal.

"One for me," Ben said, but Carin was on her feet, reaching for the camera. "Hey!" he protested.

"A girl's got to think of her reputation," Carin said. "How do I know you won't show it to everybody at the conservatory?"

"How do I know you won't show *my* picture to everybody at the conservatory?"

"I'm shy," Carin said, and grabbed the camera.

Chris slit the envelope with a penknife and grimaced as he extracted an overdue bill. He picked up the next envelope and hefted it with a puzzled frown. He applied the penknife and stared in disbelief at the photograph that fell out: a tall blond man on a bed with his legs spread, his penis glistening.

"Freaks of the world, unite," Chris muttered, then brought the photograph close, staring at the stuffed elephant under the man's arm. He examined the bedstead behind the blond head, then snatched up the envelope and shook it. A second photograph fell out: Carin and the stuffed elephant. He didn't move for more than a minute, then as someone passed close behind him, he quickly turned the photographs over on his desk. Then he leaned forward. There was a message on the back of each photo. He had never seen Carin's handwriting before: it was innocent, childish, with *e*'s like little capitals and the kind of circles over the *i*'s that his kid sister had once affected. The message on the back of the first photo said, "This man is <u>twenty years old.</u>" The picture of Carin simply said, "Okay now?"

When Chris called Carin at the conservatory, they agreed to meet at the Italian restaurant to which he had taken her on their first night together. After Chris's wine had been served, he stared grimly at her.

"I can see you're upset with me," Carin said.

"Do you blame me? I just want to know one thing."

"What?"

"What did the guy think?"

Carin permitted herself a faint smile. "He thinks I'm strange."

"I'll bet." Chris took several steadying sips of wine, then muttered, "The elephant was quite a touch."

"I figured you'd remember it."

"You ought to write Gothics."

"What's a Gothic?"

"It doesn't matter."

She watched him unblinkingly from her corner, then said, "Are you going to stay mad?"

"Honest to God, Carin, I don't know what to do."

"You said you didn't want to be the first . . ."

"I know what I said!"

"Well, now you're not."

"I've figured that out."

"Well?"

"I feel responsible for—whatever you did with that guy."

"You are."

"Thanks."

Chris ordered another glass of wine and consumed it in silence.

"Want to be third?" Carin asked pointedly.

"This is blackmail!"

When they left the restaurant, Carin hooked a hand under Chris's arm and said, "Grandpa's back."

"Thank God."

"*You* don't have a grandpa."

Chris stared down at her until an emerging couple gently pointed out that Chris and Carin were blocking the restaurant door.

In the car Chris asked Carin what time she had to be home, and she hugged him, exclaiming, "Not till eleven. I told Grandpa I've got a rehearsal."

The love affair flourished like a mushroom, in the dark. Dahlstrom's ministry took him north into Michigan with sufficient frequency to permit Carin to see Chris at least once and sometimes twice a week. On those occasions Chris remained with Carin until two or three in the morning. On rarer occasions, yielding to Carin's importuning, he spent the night, stopping at home to shave and change clothes before going to the *Free Press*. But he was never fully at ease sleeping under the Reverend Mr. Dahlstrom's roof, so Carin began spending her grandfatherless nights in Chris's bed. One night he emerged from the bathroom holding an open leatherette pouch. "What's this?"

Hypodermic syringes and ampules glinted therapeutically at Carin. She sprang out of bed. "Since when do you go through my dance bag!"

"I didn't 'go through' it; I tripped over it and this fell out—" He broke off as Carin snatched the pouch from his hand. An ampule fell and Carin knelt, scrabbling at the broken glass. Chris knelt with her. "What's going on?"

"Nothing!" Carin sprang up and disappeared into the bathroom. When she returned, she was empty-handed. She got into bed.

"Carin . . ."

"It's late."

Chris turned out the light and got into bed.

"I'm not a junkie," she muttered.

"I didn't think you were. But naturally I wondered . . ." Carin rolled away from him and settled down to sleep at the edge of the bed. "Okay," he said and forced himself to close his eyes. A few minutes later he was drawn back from sleep by a soft voice.

"I *have* to take it."

"What?"

"Insulin."

Chris sat up. "For what?"

"What do people take insulin for?"

"Diabetes?" She was silent. "Is that it? You're diabetic?"

"Yes."

"And you didn't want me to know?"

"Of course not."

"For Christ's sake, why?"

"You think I go around telling everybody?"

"I'm not everybody."

"I don't tell *any*body."

"Why? It's nothing to be ashamed of."

"I know, but—people don't understand. They think there's something wrong with you. Like you're sick." She looked up at him. "Do you know anything about diabetes?"

"No. I know people have to take shots. And . . ." He stopped.

"And what?"

"That's all."

"Bull. You've heard about blindness, right?"

"I—I think maybe I've heard something about that . . ."

"That's why I don't tell people. I'm not going to spend my life convincing people I'm not going to go blind and drop dead in front of them. I'm a dancer; they're supposed to be healthy. *I'm* healthy."

"Of course you are."

"The rest is nobody's business."

"Did you think I was never going to find out?"

"No."

"Then weren't you being a little unrealistic?"

"What was I supposed to do: break down and confess? It's not the biggest thing in my life; I can handle it—because I learned how. But I don't want to have to teach every person I meet. Can't you understand?"

"Yes." A moment later he said, "Shall we go to sleep? You've got class in the morning, and I've got to go to work."

"You'd better get a book," Carin sighed.

"What kind of book?"

"About diabetes. Then you'll know."

"What?"

"Everything. Diabetics don't live forever."

"Nobody does."

"Get a book," Carin said wearily. Chris touched her. They curled around each other. "I'm sorry I got so uptight, but—people get funny when they know. My mother *still* hasn't adjusted," Carin murmured.

"To the diabetes?"

"My dancing. She doesn't say anything anymore, but I know she's afraid I'll go into shock onstage sometime."

"Are *you?*"

"The thought's crossed my mind. Often. It would be . . . Don't tell anybody."

"Whom would I tell?"

"I don't know, but don't."

"You know I won't."

"See?"

"What?"

"Once you know about it, that's all we talk about."

"Bull."

"You going to forget about it?"

"No."

"Shit."

"I'm going to find out about it; *then* I'm going to forget about it."

She fell silent; her breathing became deep and regular. Chris assumed she was asleep; then she murmured, "I wouldn't marry anyone with diabetes."

"I would."

"Big problems later," she mumbled sleepily. "Pain in the ass."

"Some marriages are a pain in the ass from the first day—with no excuses."

"True," she murmured.

She said no more. Within moments they were both asleep.

Ironically it was Chris who wound up in the hospital. A series of articles on loansharking had unexpected results: a broken nose, broken arm, multiple cuts and bruises. Also a raise, public attention, Traynor's intensified interest and such awesome concern from Carin that it blew the slim cover that had theoretically concealed the sizzling affair from Mai and Doug Bradley.

Mai's response was realistic. She waited until Doug's bowling league night, then, alone with her daughter, said casually, "You know, you might want to talk to Dr. Rothberg."

"I feel fine."

"I'm not talking about that. Maybe you ought to think about birth control."

"Motherrrr . . ."

Mai noted, not without a surge of affection, that the little admonitory song hadn't changed since Carin's eighth year. "I'm serious, honey."

"Motherrrr, I'm a *dancer.*"

Mai observed that she wasn't quite sure what that was supposed to mean.

"Dancers don't get pregnant."

"Oh," Mai said uncertainly. "I still think you ought to talk to Dr. Rothberg."

"You're not listening! I already have."

"Oh."

The next night Doug was less malleable. "You're still in high school."

"So?"

"He's a grown man."

"You'd rather have me running around with grungy kids, smoking dope?"

"This is infatuation!" he snorted.

"You bet."

"You admit it?"

"Absolutely. *Boy,* am I infatuated!"

"There's a difference, you know—between infatuation and love."

"What's the difference?"

"Love—well, love lasts. It gets deeper."

"I love him."

"There'll be a dozen after him!"

"No!" Carin protested, tears glistening. "I don't *want* any more. Chris is *it!*"

A few days after Dahlstrom's death, Carin showed up at the *Free Press*.

"You're early," Chris said. When Carin stared at him, pale, he pushed himself back from the desk and stood up. "What's wrong?"

"I'll wait for you," she said.

"No, you won't," he said, "I'll leave now."

In his car he said, "The reservation's at six-thirty."

"I don't want to go to a restaurant."

"Where do you want to go?"

"Your place."

He twisted the wheel.

"Sit down," he said. She sat on the couch, her legs curled under her. Chris said, "I'm going to have a drink." She nodded. He opened the doors to his pullman kitchen and looked back at her. "Want a tomato juice?"

She shook her head. When he returned to the couch, she shifted her legs to make room for him. He put a hand over her feet. "I know how you feel. It's almost as if one of your parents died." He forced a smile. "You lost your cheerleader."

"It's not that."

"What is it?"

"I'm rich." He looked at her. She nodded. "Grandpa's will. He left me some money."

"How much?"

"Two thousand dollars. A little more, actually."

"I knew he was a neat guy."

Carin began to cry. Chris slid along the couch and held her in his arms. When the tears had stopped, she went into the kitchen. Returning with a plume of paper towel, she wiped her face and sat down in a chair facing the couch. Chris rose. "No, stay there." He sat and waited. "I'm leaving," Carin said.

"For where?"

"New York."

"When?"

"Tomorrow."

The ice rattled in Chris's drink. He put the glass down. "Well."

"Yes."

"Did you come for an opinion?"

"No."

They were silent, then Carin said, "I love you."

"I love you." Chris picked his glass up. He brought it to his lips, then put it down without drinking. "Why tomorrow?"

"I don't want any hassle."

"You think I'm going to hassle you?"

"My folks will. You know what they'll say."

"Maybe you ought to listen."

"I thought you weren't going to hassle me."

"Didn't realize I was."

"I'm scared, Chris."

"That's why you have to leave tomorrow?"

"That's why I don't want anybody to argue with me."

"If you're so unsure of yourself . . ."

"I'm not unsure. I didn't think I'd ever have the chance—and now I do."

"Thanks to Grandpa."

"Yes, thanks to Grandpa. He knew what I wanted." She scanned his face. "So did you."

"Yes."

"So—it's okay? I mean, with us?"

"No. It's terrible." She scowled and turned away. "What did you expect me to say?"

"Exactly what you're saying. But I couldn't leave without telling you."

"Thanks." Carin sniffled and applied the towel to her eyes. "You want some more towel?"

She shook her head and mumbled, "I'm sorry, Chris."

He rose and paused, and when she simply blew her nose into the paper towel, he crossed the room, stopping in front of her to ask, "What do you want me to say?"

" 'I love you.' "

"I love you," he assented. "Now what?"

"Make love to me."

"And then?"

"Say good-bye. For a while. Not long, probably."

He knelt in front of her and took her hands. "Not that I'm going to squeal on you, but how do you plan to engineer this dramatic escape?"

She pointed at her dance bag. "Open it." He opened the bag. Lying on the damp dance clothes was a blank form. "Mom made me put the money in the bank today. I'm going to take it out tomorrow morning."

"And then?"

"I'll be on the first plane to New York."

"And then?"

"I don't know. I'll register for ballet classes and find a hotel . . ."

"Don't you think you ought to plan it a little?"

"It's planned."

"What hotel? What classes?"

"Miss Nicholas told me about some schools."

Chris returned to the chair and knelt in front of her again. "You're going to think I'm trying to keep you here . . ."

"Please don't."

". . . but there's got to be a better way to do this." She shook her head and reached for the withdrawal slip. "What happens when you don't go home tomorrow night?"

"I'm leaving a note."

"Carin . . ."

She stood up abruptly, nearly knocking Chris over. "Don't tell me I'm a kid!" Chris got to his feet, and Carin put out a protective hand. "It's got to be this way. I know what'll happen if I talk to Mom and Dad. They'll ask me to wait. Or they'll *make* me wait."

"You're not a slave . . ."

"I'm seventeen. That's a slave. They can keep me here till I'm eighteen."

"What's so terrible about waiting a few months?"

"I'll *never* go!"

He studied her reddened face, then asked quietly, "How do you know?"

"I know! Dad'll want me to use the money for college. Mom'll want me to save it in case I get sick." She began undressing.

"What're you doing?" Chris asked.

"I want to make love till it's time to go home."

"Like a last meal?"

She continued undressing. "We'll be together again—for good." When she was naked, she opened the convertible couch, lay down on it and turned to Chris. He came to her and sat on the edge of the bed and she asked, "Aren't you going to get undressed?"

"In a minute." He brushed her hair back from her face, and looked at her body. The birth-control pills she took had filled out her breasts. They would never be large, but they contrasted markedly with the breasts Chris had seen the first time she undressed in front of him. He stroked her breasts and her little waist. He touched the tuft of silky hair that had frightened him so much the first time he had seen it. That part of her would never look more than twelve or thirteen, he reflected. But he no longer felt guilt. At the moment, he realized, he felt an unaccustomed panic.

Carin reached for his shirt, trying to unbutton it. He shook his head and she fell back against the pillow. "I don't blame you for being mad at me."

"You think I'm mad?"

"I wouldn't blame you."

He shook his head again and muttered, "I'm not absolutely sure, but I think I'm going to cry."

Suddenly Carin was sitting up, her arms around him, hugging him, crying bitterly against his chest. He lay down next to her, dry-eyed; her outburst had stilled his. They remained there, he fully clothed, until Carin stopped crying. Then she fell asleep, and a few minutes later Chris dozed off too. He awoke nearly two hours later when he felt Carin move. She was sitting up, blinking at the dark window. "What time is it?" she asked.

He looked at his watch. "Almost nine." She shivered. "Get under the covers," he said.

"Only if you will." He nodded. She started to slide under the covers, then stopped. "But you have to get undressed."

He rose and undressed. When he got into bed, she bestrode him at once, her hands on his shoulders, as if to hold him down while her slim hips pumped her wet and him dry. After they had made love, Carin fell asleep again. Chris held her, her head on his shoulder, her sticky pudendum clasped to his thigh like an avid mouth, and stared into the darkness. When she stirred, she asked again, "What time is it?"

"Eleven."

She sat up with a little gasp. "I've got to go home."

They dressed in silence. As they were about to leave, Carin paused to look around the room. "It won't be long," she said.

"Till what?"

"We're together again. You'll see."

In the car Chris asked her, "What if I came along?"

"To New York? That's crazy. You've got a job here . . ."

"I think *you're* crazy, but you're going."

"That's different. I've got nothing here . . ." She glanced across the drafty front seat of the convertible. "You know what I mean. No work. No future. But you've got a career."

"It may surprise you, but there are several newspapers in New York."

"And none of them know who you are. You'd have to start at the bottom again." Row houses swept by, semi-detached, faced with artificial brick and aluminum awnings. "You're not giving up your career for me," Carin said grimly.

"And you're not giving up your career for me."

Used car lots flanked the road; miles of once-loved Fords and Chevies, poised seductively under fluttering foil bunting, winked and grimaced like antiquated trollops at the dashing convertible. Finally Chris said, "So—what happens to us?"

"We see each other as often as we can, and we think, and plan—and figure something out."

"What?"

"I don't know. You know I'm not very smart. I can only handle one thing at a time, and now it's time for—my chance."

"Your chance."

"Yes." A mile later she murmured, "That doesn't mean I don't love you." He nodded. "I do." He nodded. "Very much. Especially now."

When they arrived at Carin's house, he sat stiffly behind the wheel as Carin knelt on the seat, took his face in her hands and kissed him, her tongue licking gently at his lips. She often kissed him that way when they made love; Chris's lips tightened. She turned and slid out of the car.

"Jesus," he murmured. She stopped. "You're really going to do it. All of a sudden . . ."

"It's not all of a sudden! It's what I've been waiting for—every day of my life since I was six." Cords of muscle stood out in her slender neck. "I just couldn't before. Now I can."

"And everything else just . . ."

"You think this is easy for me? I'll die without you. I don't know how I'm going to stand it. I may be back in a week."

"Or you may not."

She leaned weakly on the car. "Or I may not."

"Your mother's looking out the window."

She straightened abruptly. "Don't do anything. Don't say anything. Just—look natural." She smiled and waved into the car. Chris managed a faint smile. Carin walked casually to the house, turned for another wave and went in.

Halfway to the city the road misted in front of Chris. He turned on the windshield wipers; they grated on dry glass.

FIRST VARIATION

TEN, two, three, four
Grand Rond de Jambe

The week that followed Chris's arrival at Forty-eighth Street was, as Carin confided to Diane one morning, "the most perfect week of my life." This extravagance of perfection consisted of an intense romance with Chris and New York, from the high brow of the Statue of Liberty, Masaccio at the Met, Mondrian at MOMA and Fragonard at the Frick to the low brow of plaster-of-Paris madonnas, painted like harlots and hawked in pidgin Spanish by Old Testament patriarchs on Orchard Street, the hitch kicks of the Radio City Music Hall Rockettes, the mute legerdemain of the magician at the base of Walter Scott's statue in Central Park, who chose Carin from the crowd to assist him with a card trick, and the macho rush of a pickup football game in the Sheep Meadow with Chris dashing back and forth, waving his arms and yelling, "Here!" at the panting Saturday jock who was quarterbacking his team while Carin cheered from the sidelines—all of it sandwiched neatly between Carin's daily classes, ballet in the morning and jazz at six.

On what was to have been the last night of Chris's visit, after a flurry of orgasms, Carin cried, "Stay!"

Chris raised his cheek from her thigh; normally, immediately after orgasm Carin's clitoris was too sensitive to be touched, but, obeying her strident command, Chris slid forward and reapplied his tongue to the still-unsheathed organ. When she jumped, he peered up over foreshortened abdomen and breasts. "You said stay."

She curled downward to put her arms around him. "Here. In New York. Don't go home. *Please,* Chris. I love you!"

"But what about your job?" Diane asked.

"There're plenty of newspapers and magazines in New York," Chris said. "More than in Detroit."

Terry put a plate of toast on the table. "But Carin said you were a star in Detroit . . ."

"Maybe I'll be a star in New York someday."

As Terry sat down, his chair clipped Diane's ankle; she yelped and grabbed at it. "Sorry!" he exclaimed. When she glared unforgivingly at him, he said, "You know, that ankle could be fixed. They rebreak the bones . . ."

"Over my dead body."

"It works."

"Once was enough, thanks."

"Did you break it dancing?" Chris asked.

"Not exactly," Diane replied, and went quickly on. "When was this momentous decision made?"

Carin put her coffee cup down to reach for Chris's hand. "Last night."

"It was obvious," Chris said. "If I'd left today, that would've been it. After this show Carin'll probably do another, or she'll get that audition with Jeffrey . . ."

"Joffrey," Carin said.

"Joffrey. Anyway, she's made her move; it was time for me to make mine."

Diane spooned up a dollop of marmalade. "Sensational!"

"I'm afraid we'll have to stay here till we find a place of our own," Chris said.

Diane's chair scraped back from the table with a shriek of tortured wood. "Whattaya mean, a place of your own!"

"A place to live."

"You've *got* a place to live."

"We can't stay here."

"Why not?" Diane scanned one face after another in search of reason, fixing finally on Carin, who avoided Diane's scrutiny by picking up her spoon and attacking her Granola. "Isn't anyone gonna answer me?"

Chris tried to sidestep a lengthy debate with, "We can't do anything till I go back to Detroit and clean things up there."

"And Carin'll be in rehearsal, and on the road," Terry said. "So what's the hurry?"

Chris glanced at Carin. "I guess there isn't any hurry." He turned to Terry. "But that'll mean I'll be here while the girls are in Philadelphia."

"Oh, not to worry!" Terry trilled. "We took the roommate's oath to keep our hands off each other's men." He bestowed a benevolent smile on Carin. "He'll be as safe as if he were in a monastery. Safer," he amended after a moment's reflection.

Waiting in front of Traynor's desk, Chris tuned in to the ragged syncopation of the bells against the steady tattoo of the teletypes.

The percussive music tugged at him, friendly and evocative. He closed his eyes as if that might shut out the siren sound, then opened them when he heard a half-sigh, half-groan that informed him Traynor had looked up.

"You're back," the familiar voice rasped.

"Just for a couple of days." Bushy eyebrows bristled, and the teletypes drummed insistently in Chris's ears. "I'm leaving tomorrow."

"For where?"

"New York."

"Why?"

"I've got a job."

"Doing what?"

"Writing."

"On a paper?"

"Yes."

"Which one?" The teletypes went wild: Buddy Rich on type bars and bells. "Which one?" Traynor repeated.

"You wouldn't know it."

"Il Progresso? El Diario?"

"It's in English."

"How many guesses do I get?"

"The *East Sider.*"

"A neighborhood paper?"

Buddy Rich was really cooking.

"They do some interesting things," Chris said.

"I'll bet," Traynor said, and heaved himself erect. "Have you had lunch?"

"No."

"Got time?"

"Sure."

Chris, intimidated by its gilt-edged reputation, had never been in the London Chop House before. Apparently Traynor suffered from the same inhibition, since neither the maitre d' nor the waiters seemed to know him. When Chris opened the menu and blanched, Traynor peered over his half-glasses and said, "Order anything you want; this is an occasion."

"What's the occasion?"

"Editor Prevents Reporter From Making Asshole Of Himself," Traynor replied in headlinese. Chris felt a prickle of heat under his shirt. "What'll you have?" Traynor asked.

"I don't know," Chris said, trying to focus on the four square feet of menu in his unsteady grasp.

"You like mulligatawny soup?"

"What is it?"

"Spicy," Traynor said, "Indian."

"I think I'll have a shrimp cocktail," Chris said.

"Make that two," Traynor told the hovering waiter, then turned back to Chris. "Then?"

"That's plenty."

"Two minute-steaks," Traynor instructed the waiter. "How do you like yours?" he asked Chris.

"Medium rare."

"The same. And a couple of salads."

"Roquefort, French, Thousand Island, oil and vinegar?" the waiter intoned. Traynor raised his eyebrows at Chris.

"French," Chris said.

"And Thousand Island for me," Traynor muttered. When the waiter had gone, he said, "They call it Russian in New York."

"What?"

"Thousand Island."

"Oh?"

"Didn't you eat out?"

"Not very much."

Traynor sat back, his rumpled bulk incongruous against the restaurant's decorous glint and bustle. "So . . ." he sighed.

"I've *got* to go to New York," Chris said.

"Maybe we ought to have a drink," Traynor mused.

"No."

"Some wine?"

"No thanks. You have some."

Traynor took a package of cigarettes from his pocket and studied them. "Someday," he said, "somebody's going to do a great story about the day these bastards said, 'Okay, everybody wants filter tips. Now all we've got to do is blend a tobacco that'll kick all the tar and nicotine right through the filter."

He coughed cavernously as he lit a cigarette, and Chris asked, "If you feel that way, why smoke?"

"I'll tell you." Traynor coughed a skywriter's puff of smoke and resumed. "Because I'm an asshole too." He entrusted the weighty bulk of his upper body to the table. "But not as big an asshole as you. Want to explain why you've decided to jettison your career?"

Chris felt an unpleasant warmth again. "I have to live in New York."

"Why?" Traynor took another puff of his cigarette; smoke crept across the table like ground fog, slithering around the plates and glasses.

"I think it's time." Chris said.

"It's not." Traynor inhaled more smoke and coughed again. He took a sip of water and ground his cigarette out in the ashtray midway between himself and Chris, then settled back and waited for Chris's response.

"I'm almost thirty," Chris said.

"You're the best I've got," Traynor said. Chris felt a thrill of pleasure and looked up at Traynor. "That's right. You want more money?"

"No."

"Better assignments? More by-lines?"

"Please, Mr. Traynor . . ."

"Call me Jim."

"I've got to go."

"To the *East Sider*?"

"I know it doesn't sound sensible . . ."

"Asinine! If you told me you were going to the *Times* or the *News,* even the *Post,* for Christ's sake . . ."

"That'll come."

"If you stay *here*—and build a body of work and a reputation! Who the hell's going to take you off a neighborhood throwaway!" Traynor paused for breath, pulling air into his lungs in noisy inhalations.

Chris shoved a spoon back and forth, then said, "There's another reason . . ."

"That girl." Chris's head snapped up. "The dancer you wrote about."

"How did you—"

"Murph knows, Stu knows, everybody knows, for Christ's sake. They saw her at the paper, they saw you in restaurants . . ."

"Then you understand."

"The hell I do. She *wants* you to do this to yourself?"

"She's worried . . ."

"So am I, pal." Traynor fumbled for a cigarette, brought it to his mouth, then flung it, unlit, into the ashtray. "Listen, I'm going to tell you something. *I* probably would've left years ago, but my wife's mother was sick." He waved an impatient hand. "People go and stay for a lot of peculiar reasons. The point is, I figured you'd go someday. I was prepared to lose you. To the *Times* maybe, the *Washington Post,* the *L.A. Times*—but the fucking *East Sider*? That's unacceptable!" He was overcome by a fit of coughing. He spilled water as he grabbed at his glass and gulped down a remedial swallow.

Chris waited until Traynor had regained his breath. Then he said, "I have to do it now, and the *East Sider* was the best I could come up with."

"Did you try the *News* or the *Times*?"

"Of course."

"Who'd you see?"

"I don't know. Personnel."

"Asshole! I could've sent you to an editor."

"You'd have done that?"

"No. What'd they tell you?"

"They get a lot of applications—from reporters all over the country."

"I'm surprised they didn't offer you clerk—or copyboy!"

"They said I'd have to wait in line for *that*. They've got Ph.D.s running copy."

"And that didn't tell you something?"

"I need a job."

"You've *got* a job. You're moving. Beautifully. You didn't have to run copy *here* . . ."

"I appreciate everything you've done. More than I can say." He couldn't look at Traynor.

"Fine. Then hang in. In a year or two New York'll be begging for you."

"I can't wait," Chris said quietly.

"This'll teach me!"

"What?"

"If I hadn't sent you on that goddamn conservatory story, you'd still be sane—and working for me." Chris laughed. "You think it's funny? I invested a lot of time in you."

The laughter died. "I know you did. That's why I wanted to see you today. To try and tell you—how I feel."

"Sentiment's for sob sisters," Traynor snapped. "I need newspapermen. The *real* kind—who can write declarative sentences. In English!" He brandished a hand. "Do you know what's coming out of our institutions of higher learning? Functional illiterates! I don't know how you slipped through the system, but you did, and you landed in my lap." He flung his napkin on the table. "The *East Sider*! Jesus Christ!"

In palmier days the huge hall had housed every conceivable manifestation of ethnic joy. Clarinets had bayed numbing chains of fifths as generations of Greeks, Poles, Armenians, Lithuanians and Serbo-Croats whirled around the room, arms linked, feet stamping, in celebration of christening, communion, graduation, engagement, marriage and other assorted rites of passage.

But times, and accents, had changed; Latino had replaced Levantine and Slav, and *cuchifritos* shouldered aside *dolmathes*. *O tempora! O Morales!* The neglected banquet hall had saved its Corinthian pilasters and baroque cherubim from the wrecker's ball by converting to use as badly needed rehearsal space, and for the past twenty years television programs, Broadway musicals and occasional motion pictures had laid out miles of masking tape to diagram their sets on the parqueted floors.

The dancers labored in the center of the space under Sonny's narrow scrutiny, while his assistant Andrew clapped his hands and counted loudly to the music being extracted from a scarred Knabe by the rehearsal pianist. When the music stopped, the dancers waited, arms akimbo, sweat streaming, as Sonny closed his eyes and flipped his hands about in front of him in an effort to pluck the next steps out of the air.

After a few moments Carla, an intense young woman with the compact body of a welterweight, took a step away from her colleagues and fixed her gaze on the assistant stage manager, who was bent over a table near the piano. When her surveillance failed to attract his attention, she cleared her throat and said, "Fred."

Fred looked up, met her glance, consulted his watch and turned toward the distracted choreographer. "Uh—Sonny . . ."

"Not already! Jesus!" Sonny glared at the dripping dancers. "If you were as conscientious about your work as you are about your union rules, you'd all be stars. Take a break."

The dancers, accustomed from childhood to the scorn of teachers and choreographers, turned, unoffended, and wended their way to the far end of the room, where dance bags, pocketbooks, sweaters, leg warmers and various other personal paraphernalia carpeted the floor. As if by carefully choreographed arrangement, they flopped among their jetsam, so neatly entwined that every head was cradled on an obliging stomach, chest or thigh. Within moments the dancers looked like a basket of sleeping puppies, their only motion a little wave of adjustments for greater comfort and better fit.

At the assistant stage manager's table Sonny lowered his voice. "Is Carla the deputy?"

Fred nodded, and Sonny turned to examine the litter on the floor until he located Carla. As he studied her still form with undisguised hostility, Fred offered a hesitant, "It's not her fault, Sonny. Somebody's gotta be Equity deputy . . ."

Fred's admonition withered as Sonny turned his practiced basilisk stare on him. Then he and Sonny spun toward the dancers as Diane screeched, "We're gonna have a wedding! Opal just told me." A snub-nosed girl who had been lying next to Diane sat up, redfaced, and tried to grab her arm, but Diane lumbered on, a bulldozer in heat. "She and Ernie got engaged last night!"

The woolly plain blossomed dancers as arms and legs unbraided and the collective sat up with a jubilant shout. A lanky boy near Opal hunched his shoulders and laughed while his neighbors pounded him on the back. Diane, in her element, raised her arms to still the clamor.

"Okay, okay, settle down."

"I second the motion," Fred growled from the table, where he was busy with his paperwork again.

Diane resumed, a decibel lower. "Okay, we've got some serious business to take care of. Opal says they want to get married before we leave town. When's our next day off?"

"Saturday, the fifteenth," Carla said.

"Anybody got any conflicts?" Diane surveyed the group.

A fragile girl who looked even younger than Opal responded timidly, "My mother and I were going shopping . . ."

Exercising her legendary gift for hair-triggered frontier justice, Diane directed Cynthia to bring her mother to the wedding. "Any other problems?" she asked, looking around. There were none and the steamroller rolled on. "Okay, we'll vote on the honeymoon. They've only got one day, so it can't be too complicated."

"What about Opal and Ernie?" a voice asked.

Diane eyed the questioner distastefully. When you're on a roll, her philosophy dictated, unbroken rhythm is everything. "What about 'em?"

"Well, it's their honeymoon."

"Of course it's their honeymoon. Why do you think we're going to so much trouble?" She turned back to the group.

"Shouldn't they decide what they're going to do?" the questioner persisted. Diane turned to stare in disbelief at this *lèse majesté*. The questioner blanched but made one more attempt. "It's only fair . . ."

"Fair?" Diane demanded. "We're gonna take a vote! Could anything be more democratic than that? Nominations are in order for the honeymoon," she said to the group.

"How about Atlantic City?" a girl asked. "That's where we went when Wendy and Al got married."

"That was a two-day honeymoon," Diane said. "This has gotta be someplace closer."

"Anybody remember Rocky Candido's wedding?" a boy asked. "He and Mary Ann only had one day, so we chipped in for a bus and went to Coney Island. It was outta sight."

Diane looked at Opal. "How does Coney Island sound?"

"Very nice," Opal said shyly. "We were just gonna go to an Italian restaurant near Ernie's place . . ."

"And you acted like we were interfering!" Diane shot at her critic, and turned back to the betrothed. "Wouldn't you rather have a real honeymoon at Coney Island?"

"Sounds great to me," Ernie said. "Only reason we were going to this place near me is a bottle of wine don't empty the bank account, and the ziti's pretty good."

"Forget it!" Diane said. "Anybody in this company gets married, they go first class. With everybody chipping in, you don't have to worry about the tab."

"Nathan's," a voice cried.

"This time of year?" a girl exclaimed. "We'll freeze our asses standing at those counters!"

"But Diane said first class," the sponsor of the proposal argued, "and nobody beats their franks."

"No sweat!" a boy interjected. "Nathan's has a room in back, with chairs and tables—we can sit down and everything!"

Diane's voice topped the hubbub that followed. "Okay, hold it! How many say Nathan's?"

A forest of hands went up, including Opal's and Ernie's. Diane turned a scornful gaze on her erstwhile critic. "How fuckin' fair can you get!" She beamed at the group. "I guess that settles it." Her benign gaze came to rest on Opal. "And I happen to know a brilliant designer who might consider making your wedding gown. For next to nothing!"

Opal stared into the mirror in misty-eyed disbelief. Carin and Diane, seated on Terry's bed, burst into applause, but Terry, perfectionist, hovered next to Opal, hands aloft, fingers drumming anxiously on empty air, eyes sweeping his pinned and basted creation from top to toe.

"That's *it!*" Diane cried, but Terry shook his head.

"Not . . . quite . . . yet." He dove at an offending panel, whipped straight pins out of the glistening silk, molded the panel more tightly to Opal's flank, then replaced the pins with the deft thrusts of an acupuncturist. Opal remained mesmerized by the glowing bride in the mirror, and Terry stepped back to survey her once more.

The reverent silence was broken by Diane's temerarious question to Opal: "What do *you* think?"

"I can't believe it!"

Terry's gaze remained fixed on the wedding gown. "If I'd had a little more notice . . ."

"I don't know how it could be any better," Opal sighed. "I've never seen anything like it."

Opal's latter sentiment was beyond dispute, her former eminently debatable. Years of cavorting about stages in Lurex costumes had left their mark on Terry. Any tendency he might have had toward understatement had long since disappeared, and this creation would have confirmed the view of anyone entertaining doubts about Terry's future as a dressmaker.

The color was right—white, after all, can only be qualified by the narrowest of degrees—and the silk that had been appropriated from the Treasure Chest was unexceptionable, but in Terry's relentless search for "some pizazz," the gown's neckline skidded to a precarious halt just short of Opal's mons, revealing considerably more bridal terrain than was customary. The sleeves offered a startling contrast to the pink expanse of Opal between them. "I thought Taglioni would be appropriate," Terry murmured reverently, and Opal, Carin and Diane nodded in unison, understanding perfectly. In the middle of the nineteenth century, Maria Taglioni reigned supreme, *prima ballerina assoluta* of the world, and fashionable women affected the bell-like sleeves of her *Sylphide* costume. The Taglioni sleeve came down through the years, emblematic of a delicate by-gone era, and though its reappearance in any period was not uncommon, Opal's wedding gown probably marked its first use—outside, perhaps, of Las Vegas—as a frame for a Flash Gordon jumpsuit of white peau de soie, skintight at the thighs, flaring dramatically at the calves and disappearing entirely over significant expanses of the wearer's chest, abdomen and back.

Since Opal, Carin and Diane had spent their youths wrapped in costumes little different in kind or quality from those that had corrupted Terry (most dance costumes being designed to be seen at a distance), they came to this moment prepared.

"Unreal," Opal whispered.

"Next to her, Ernie's gonna look like shit," Diane averred.

"Maybe we can do something about it," Terry replied thoughtfully. "A matching jacket or something." He tugged gently at a seam. "How's that fit?"

"Perfect."

He pulled harder. "Not too tight?"

"She's not going to be doing *grands pliés* in it," Diane chided.

"It's her wedding night," Terry shot back.

"For that she'll take it off!"

"I hope I don't ruin it on the honeymoon," Opal said.

"Just stay away from the mustard and sauerkraut," Diane advised.

"Okay," Terry said to Opal, "turn around and I'll get you out of this." As he carefully removed the row of pins that tracked the division of Opal's buttocks, he asked, "How's Sonny behaving?"

Diane answered for Opal. "Guess!" She fell wearily back on the bed.

"He's always mad about something," Opal complained.

"Every time he looks at me my knees lock," Carin said.

"For your sakes I was hoping he'd mellowed," Terry muttered through pins.

"Oh, he has!" Diane said with a jaunty wave of her hand. "He's now the mellowest cobra in show business."

"Typical nelly faggot," Terry observed, removing the last pin and splitting the seat of the jumpsuit like a lobster. "Stay away from 'em," he confided paternally to Opal, patting her bare bottom. "If you *do* hang out with gays, stick to the butch types like me."

"Butch!" Diane hooted.

"Bitch," Terry growled, and turned back to Opal. "Okay, sweetie, see if you can work your way out of it—reeeal easy."

As he held the jumpsuit by the shoulders, Opal slid her arms out of the sleeves and made a gingerly exit from the tightly pinned legs. The quartet, focused on the task at hand, didn't notice Chris in the doorway, stopped in his tracks by the tableau that had greeted his arrival: Opal, pink as a pupa, emerging from the silken cocoon in Terry's hands, Carin and Diane lolling on the bed, as easy with Opal's nakedness as they would have been with their own. In the vested suit he had chosen for the trip from Detroit, Chris felt, and looked, like an overdressed Martian, space- and time-warped into a pop Eden. His alienism was confirmed as Opal turned, saw him and dove at the bed to roll herself in the cover.

"Chris! Get out!" Carin screeched, and Chris backed out of the room. Following him into the corridor, Carin planted herself amid his luggage and demanded, "What'd you do *that* for?"

"I just got off the plane! How was I supposed to know you were in the middle of some kind of religious ceremony."

"Well, you shouldn't've just stood there."

"Terry was standing there! And Diane's always walking around naked."

"That's entirely different."

"Oh?"

"Of course. We're . . ."

"Gypsies."

"No! Roommates." She looked down at the maze of luggage.

"I always seem to arrive at the worst possible moment," he said.

"No." She stepped over a battered Tourister and put her arms around him. "It's just that Opal's terribly shy."

"So I noticed." She kissed him, quietly, persistently, until he permitted the tip of her tongue in his mouth, then she pressed her cheek against his and murmured, "I couldn't wait for you to get back."

"Four days . . ."

"It felt like forever. Man, do I love you!"

"Man, do I love *you.*"

"You ready for a wedding?"

"Anytime you say."

She giggled. "Not me. Opal."

"The girl in there?" He gestured toward the door. She nodded. "Great body, but I'd rather marry you."

"Opal and *Ernie!* They're getting married this Saturday and we're invited to the wedding. It's going to be something *else!*"

ELEVEN, two, three, four
Attitude Croisée

CAUTION! CHILDREN!

The warning was spelled out in bold black letters on the bright orange butt of the bus. On the bus's flank a calmer legend read OCEANSIDE SUMMER DAY CAMP, OWNER AND OPERATOR, and in the panel over the broad windshield the destination roll had been cranked to CHARTER.

The bus driver, an elderly black man, tall, bald and gaunt, wearing a look of long and silent suffering that matched his threadbare uniform like a carefully selected necktie, leaned against the side of the bus and turned his face toward the wintry sun, enjoying its unexpected warmth. His eyes closed and his face creased in a smile that failed to alter its melancholy cast. Then, abruptly, his eyes opened and he cringed involuntarily against the bus. Cavorting like a comedia dell'arte troupe in its most imaginative motley, an exultant band of gypsies, surrounding a radiant Opal and Ernie, had burst from the Municipal Building's staid brass doors and were pouring down a broad flight of stone steps. The driver's spatulate hands flattened protectively against his bus as the tidal wave hurtled toward him, capped by a splash of opalescent foam: Opal and Ernie in their matching silk ensembles.

In a moment the driver was engulfed and the bus rocked with the impact of the festive wave as Diane, shrill, ecstatic and bossy, shepherded her unruly charges aboard. Two male dancers in heavy leather—black for this formal occasion, over ruffled dress shirts and Red Baron scarves—donned crash helmets and mounted a brutish Harley and a coltish Kawasaki that were parked in front of the bus. Two of the young women accepted helmets and straddled the bikes, pillion behind the bikers. The motorcycles roared into life, accelerating Diane's efforts. She pushed, pulled, exhorted, threatened and, when someone dared to pause on the bus steps, applied a prodding shoulder. When it was Terry's turn to mount the steps, however, the flow was broken by a quick smile and approving pat on the rump from Diane. "Your creations," she said in response to his questioning look. "They're a smash. *You're* a smash! Well, I don't have to tell you—you saw everybody cream when Opal and Ernie showed up. I mean, talk about an entrance! Those outfits were fuckin' blinding!"

"Excuse me, lady." Diane turned to the bus driver. "You know, you're payin' by the hour . . ."

"So?"

He indicated the line of passengers waiting behind Terry.

Diane's eyebrows arched. "We're on holiday, driver," she intoned in her stuffiest Kensington, "so we'd rather not be rushed."

"You're the one was hustlin' everybody into the bus!" he replied. "I figured I'd give you a hand."

"I can cope."

The bus driver shrugged. "It's your money."

"*Our* money." The accent was Oxonian now. "We're chipping in, so naturally anyone who disturbs our harmony will be risking a *grand battement* in the balls."

"You eat with that mouth?" the driver asked, but Diane's reply was preempted by an impatient "Whattaya say, Di!" from somewhere in the waiting line. Terry took the pinch on his gluteal as Diane's cue to him to move, and a few minutes later the bus and its escort of motorcycles rumbled away from the curb.

The little convoy sped down the East River Drive and nosed into the Brooklyn Battery Tunnel. On the Belt Parkway the motorcycles began buzzing around the bus, passing it, falling back. crisscrossing in front of it in hairbreadth passes that brought earsplitting cheers from the occupants of the bus.

A hoarse bellow clambered above the general tumult. "Where's The Mouth?" Another stunt by the bikers brought the bus driver's foot down on the brake, flinging the revelers against the seats in front of them as the bus lurched and the driver repeated, "The Mouth! The Garbage Can! Where is she?"

"Are you by any chance referring to me?" came a reply from the momentarily silent bus.

The driver glanced into the rearview mirror, said, "Yeah," and motioned Diane forward with his head, then tightened his grip on the wheel and winced as the motorcycles stunted across his field of vision inches ahead of the bus.

His foot hit the brake again, and Diane, making her way down the aisle, had to grab at a seated dancer to keep her feet. "Will ya cool it?" she barked at the driver.

"Cool it? Oh, yeah! I'll cool it all right! Get your ass up here, sweetheart, or this trip's comin' to a screechin' halt!"

Diane arrived at the front of the bus and put a hand on the back of the driver's seat. It was Diane's custom, whenever her life-style was called into question, to adopt the loftiest English accent she could effect, on the theory that her critic might take her for a madcap heiress. Diane knew from her careful study of the "Late Show" that madcap heiressing was an honorable profession practiced in the 1930s by Katharine Hepburn, Carole Lombard, et al, and that genuine madcap heiresses were never criticized for their foibles because they were ipso facto forgivable, even lovable. If some thoughtless TV programmer buried *My Man Godfrey* or *The Philadelphia Story* in a four A.M. wasteland slot, the film was guaranteed one sleepy but determined viewer, and at moments like this Diane called on her long, groggy hours of research to save the situation. "You wished to speak to me?" she drawled, world-weary as Hepburn, insouciant as Lombard, English as crumpets.

The driver kept his eyes on the road, his hands tightly on the wheel, his foot poised to slam on the brakes again. "You in charge o' this zoo, right?"

"Everyone here is a free agent."

"Bullshit. You was tellin' everybody what to do outside the Municipal Building." He hit the brakes, and Diane clung desperately to the back of his seat as the motorcycles swooped in front of the bus again. "You get the picture?" the driver barked. "Either everybody settles down," he freed one hand from the wheel for a fraction of a second to gesture at the road ahead, "includin' Evel Knievel and his pal, or I'm reroutin' this bus to Bellevue, which is where you maniacs belong!"

Diane retracted her Hepburn hip and abandoned her Lombard pout. Clearly the bus driver wasn't a Late Show aficionado and wouldn't know a madcap heiress if one flung herself characteristically into his lap. The accent was Texas again. "Now calm down . . ."

"Calm down!"

"They're just feeling good, that's all. It's a wedding party."

"Gonna be a funeral party if everybody don't settle down. I mean it, lady. I ain't rackin' up this bus for no bunch o' nuts look like they left over from some Vietnam demonstration. Tell 'em to cool it or this is the last stop—*right here! End o' the line!*"

"Okay, okay. I'll tell 'em. You just keep on truckin' and leave the gypsies to me."

"The *what?*"

"Nothing! A joke. They're just ordinary, nice people—and oh God, are they gonna behave!"

It took Diane the better part of five minutes to fulfill her pledge to the driver; then she sank into an empty seat with the kind of sigh Vercingetorix must have emitted after an especially hard day at Alesia.

In the row behind her, Susan, a perky dancer with the face and moves of a cheerleader, slid lower to prop her knees against the seat in front of her. Her skirt slid up her thighs. Dennis, a sharp-featured boy sitting next to her, glanced at the Ace bandage wound tightly around one knee and asked, "What happened?" She pushed her skirt over the Ace and glanced anxiously around the bus to see if anyone else had noticed. Dennis understood and lowered his voice. "When'd you do it? Rehearsal?"

"A week before we started." she whispered. "In class."

"I didn't notice the Ace at rehearsal."

"And you're never *gonna.* That's all I need. Sonny'd fire me the first time I missed a step. You know how he is."

"Does it hurt?" Susan rolled her eyes. "Then you oughtta see a doctor."

"I did. The day it happened."

"What'd he say?"

Susan replied in an arid professional drone. " 'Miss Curtis, if you don't stay off that knee for at least a month, you could ruin it for the rest of your life.' "

"Gee! Maybe you should listen to him."

"After what I went through to get this job? I auditioned three times!"

After a moment's reflection Dennis said, "Yeah. What'd you tell the doctor?"

" 'Sure, Doc, great idea. I'll sell one of my minks and live off the proceeds till the knee comes around, but in the meantime gimme a shot of cortisone and an Ace.' "

Two rows behind Susan and Dennis, Carin broke off her examination of the Brooklyn waterfront to turn to Chris. "It's working out perfectly." His puzzled look drew, "All the places we went, we never got to Coney Island."

"Oh. Yes."

An abrupt change in Carin's expression as she looked past Chris toward the aisle turned him around. There was something about the young man with the dark hair, dark eyes and dark smile that nettled Chris. It was, Chris decided, the smile.

"I've never met your friend," Gino said to Carin.

When Carin didn't respond immediately, Chris turned and looked at her. "This is Chris Stevenson," she said, then offered a reluctant, "This is Gino di Vito."

Chris found Gino's hand in front of his face. "How do you do," Gino said, with precisely the smile Chris had selected as the focus of his discomfort.

"Hi," Chris said, shaking hands.

"Enjoying your visit?" Gino asked, absorbing the swaying motion of the bus with a hand on the back of Chris's seat.

"It's not a visit," Chris said.

"I heard you were here on vacation."

"Not anymore."

"Oh. You've decided to stay in New York?"

"Yes." The silence that followed was unbroken by Chris, unappreciated by Carin and, to all appearances, unnoticed by Gino. "You from Detroit?" he asked, his smile unwavering.

"Yes."

"Same as Carin."

Chris's reply was delayed by a brief image of Carin at rehearsal, happy, relaxed, chatty. "Yes."

"Boston."

"Pardon?"

"That's where I'm from."

"Oh."

"Quite different. At least, that's what Carin tells me."

Chris looked at Carin. "You've been in Boston?"

"No," Carin said, feeling, oddly, as annoyed at Chris as at Gino. "It just sounded different."

Very chatty.

"It's Harvard, and all the other schools," Gino said. "There's always something going on. History, too, I guess. You know, the Revolution."

"Mmm."

"I guess we'll be seeing you in Philly."

"I don't know if I'll be able to get away."

"That busy?"

"I'm starting a new job."

"What about weekends?"

"It's a newspaper."

Gino put a hand on the seat in front of Chris and bent closer, encircling him. "Oh? Which one?"

"You wouldn't know it."

"There aren't that many. I read the *Times,* for the theater stuff . . ."

"It's not that kind of paper."

"Oh? What kind is it?"

"It's called the *East Sider.*"

"A neighborhood paper?"

"Sort of."

"East Side news? Like local murders?"

"That's our side of Manhattan, dummy." Gino turned. Diane, finally alert to a looming reef, had risen and moved up the aisle to Carin's row. "They have jewel robberies on the East Side."

"Is that what you'll be writing about?" Gino asked Chris.

"No. The dailies cover that kind of news. We concentrate on the human-interest stuff."

Diane leaned close to Gino, her chin just above his shoulder. Feeling her breath, he turned to find a deadly smile an inch away. "Shouldn't you be in the back of the bus trying to feel somebody up?"

Gino's smile mirrored hers. "Is that an offer?"

"No, an order."

She stepped aside, clearing his path. He turned back to Chris, unruffled, said, "Nice meeting you. You really ought to try to get to Philly. The city's a bummer, but an out-of-town tryout's quite an experience," and squeezed past Diane to return to his seat.

The arrival of the wedding party was trumpeted by a succession of deep-throated *vrooooms* as the bikers skidded to a halt at the curb in front of Nathan's, disengaged their clutches and revved their raucous motors.

The bus sidled up to the curb behind the bikes, its air brakes soughing, then the driver cut his motor and slumped back. For a moment he was motionless, then compressed air gasped again as he levered open the doors. "Coney Island!" he called, adding a private, fervent, "Thank God!"

His announcement was superfluous: the orange bus was already emptying a glittering stream of celebrants in front of a block-long ziggurat of stands and counters topped by a long green sign identifying all below as Nathan's Famous (apparently it was beneath the emporium's dignity to specify Famous *what).*

The gypsies were well rehearsed: money had been pooled, plans laid, signals called—by Diane, of course—and now the wedding guests spread out along the line of stands according to assignment, some in the hot-dog line, some in the shrimp, some in the chow-mein sandwich. Nothing had been left to chance. One dancer was deployed to the gallon jug of mustard, where her only task was to pump a yellow dollop on each frank as it was passed by human chain from the counter to her station.

Thus an operation that might have taken half an hour and threatened the peace, perhaps the sanity, of both servers and served, was over in minutes, and the wedding party, laden with greasy booty and waxy buckets of New York State champagne that had made the trip from Manhattan with them, poured into Nathan's back room, a utilitarian space furnished with picnic tables and benches that bore the stains and scars of countless encounters with the culinary proletariat. Ancient ads, some for products that had long since ceased to exist, and flyblown wooden menus covered the walls. One wall featured a jukebox, garish, battered and silent. A handful of diners who had been listlessly munching their rations of junk food before the arrival of the wedding party hastily dabbed condiments and saturated fats from their lips and, choosing discretion over valor, abandoned the room to the newcomers. Only two "civilians," an elderly couple layered in sweaters and too bemused to budge, remained behind to watch the merry roister.

At the table of honor a teary Opal, high on her first marriage and fourth glass of campagne, clung to a flushed Ernie, who kept reaching for her hand under the table and guiding it proudly to his priapic lap. Next to Opal and Ernie, Diane reigned over the feast, Mistress of Misrule, waving, shouting into the hubbub, pouring champagne, issuing terse commands, seeing to the well-being of the bridal couple.

"We're out of champagne here!" she barked. "Champagne for the bride and groom!" Suddenly her forefinger, trembling with indignity, was leveled at one of the dancers across the room. "Okay, Dennis, I saw you put the bottle on the floor!" Dennis looked innocent. "Right there, Buster, next to your chair." Dennis looked down. "That's it. Let's have it."

Dennis sheepishly retrieved the bottle, then tried to atone for his sin by clambering to his tabletop and crossing the room in a series of deft leaps from table to table. His apology was accepted as the guests responded with laughter and applause. The only naysayers were the last civilian couple, who recoiled in horror as he bounced past their paper plates. Arriving at the table of honor, Dennis jackknifed from the waist and poured wine for Opal and Ernie. Straightening, he managed to turn a pirouette without tumbling off the table, and ended in a sweeping *grande révérence* to the bravoing gypsies.

The offended couple bustled out of the room, their comments drowned in the ovation for Dennis. As Dennis turned to start back across the tables, Diane snatched the wine bottle from his hand. "Anybody else hoarding?" Her narrowed gaze scanned the group like an X-ray.

A chorus of offended *no*s came back, and Diane relaxed, nodding satisfaction as Terry, seated beside her, refilled her wineglass from the confiscated bottle. Dennis, hopping back across the tabletops, teetered when he reached his table, drawing a frightened squeak from an overstuffed woman with lacquered face and hair seated next to his empty place on the bench. Recovering his balance, he dropped into his place and smiled an apology at his neighbor. "Sorry, Mrs. Moore."

Mrs. Moore, the mother Diane had instructed Cynthia to bring, leaned close to Dennis, laid her hand on his and squeezed. "I wasn't worried about me." She poked a pudgy finger into his thigh. "Those legs—dancers can't go around falling off tables . . ."

She broke off as Dennis's eyes clouded and his shoulders hunched in a fit of coughing. The spasm doubled him over the table and Mrs. Moore bent closer to pound him on the back—a mistake, since she was the source of his distress. The rising temperature in the crowded room had begun to release some of the more noxious elements in her makeup and hair spray, surrounding her with a powerful chemical aura. Life within this ethyl-alcohol cloud seemed to have immunized her, but Dennis was susceptible. So, apparently, was her daughter, whose perpetually pink-rimmed eyes and dazed expression could now be explained by any discerning member of the group: Cynthia was contact-high on her mother's emanations.

Dennis drained his wineglass in a desperate attempt to break the anaphylactic barrier in his windpipe, then groped blindly for the paper-napkin dispenser on the table.

"Here you are, dear," Mrs. Moore purred, plucking a napkin from the dispenser and pressing it into Dennis's hand.

Dennis, still immured in Mrs. Moore's force field, dabbed at his eyes with the napkin, then, with a strangled "Excuse me," rose and plunged into the narrow alley outside the back room. There, surrounded by the shrimp tails and corncobs of Nathan's Famous garbage, he soothed the swollen membranes of his throat and lungs with deep, refreshing drafts of comparatively untainted air.

In the back room Mrs. Moore, three sheets to the wind on Taylor's New York State, whirled on Cynthia, who had taken advantage of the momentary diversion to snatch a few french fries from the bucket in the middle of the table, and was now trying to sneak one from her plate to her mouth. "You want a faceful of zitses?" Mrs. Moore seized the contentious sliver. "Not to mention a couple more ounces on the hips!" She poked at Cynthia's flank. Whether from grief or allergy, Cynthia's eyes grew redder and moister. "I saw Mr. Frye looking at your hynie when you came out of rehearsal yesterday," Mrs. Moore declared. "We're going to get that excess baggage *off!*" With which she pushed Cynthia's plate firmly across the table, and Cynthia sat back, pink, damp and expressionless again.

When all the food and most of the wine had been consumed, the dancers gathered around the jukebox, scanning the rows of misspelled, discolored cardboard tabs on the front of the box. Voices were raised and fingers thrust as the relative merits of the Stones and Stevie Wonder were debated. Finally compromises were reached, quarters were pooled and the emaciated jukebox was fed. Its response was a shudder, a groan and a feeble light show: only a few of the bulbs under its plastic skin were still alive. But its tinny speaker blared at the requisite sound level, so the gypsies bustled about, shoving tables and benches toward the walls.

When several couples sprang into the space that had been cleared and began to dance, they were halted by an imperious bellow from Diane. "Hold it!" Diane raked the frozen landscape with a searing regard. "Haven't any of you animals ever been to a wedding party before? The bridal couple first!"

The couples on the dance floor fell docilely back. Diane turned her gaze, benign now, on Opal and Ernie, and swept a hand toward the waiting space. Ernie rose and bowed to his bride, and Opal got up with a giggle, wobbled and reached out to Ernie for support. Still giggling, Opal allowed Ernie to lead her to the dance floor, where she was instantly enmeshed in the swift rhythms looping out of the jukebox. No sentimental waltz this, moaned by an accordion, clarinet and fiddle: like everything else in the Opal-Ernie nuptials, their dance was an antithetic parody of the "normal" rituals of a wedding day. Their bodies jerked and ground to the music, and soon sweat glistened on their foreheads. They spun and turned and leaped, never touching each other, seldom looking at each other, until Ernie approached Opal, turned her away from him, put his hands on her waist, murmured, *"Plié"* and, when she had obliged, brought her to a seat on his shoulder. The onlookers cheered and, encouraged, Ernie muttered, "Fish," at Opal, then dropped the shoulder on which she was perched. She fell in a graceful arc, her body curved like a bow, and Ernie bent and caught her when her chin was an inch from the floor. With her legs extended toward the ceiling, she opened her arms, and Ernie, her torso wedged firmly between his chest and a thigh, opened his. The crowd went wild, and Diane yelled, "Hit it!"

The guests who had been chased from the dance floor poured back onto it. Arms flew, legs flailed, joy reigned. A boy, seeing Susan seated on one of the benches that had been pushed aside, darted to her and grabbed her arm, but she sat back, resisting. When he peered at her, puzzled, she put a hand on her stomach and said, "I ate too much."

"We all did," the boy replied, and tugged again. She shook her head and frowned, pulling her arm free. "What's wrong?" the boy asked.

"You gotta know? Cramps. Okay?"

"Okay."

The boy's embarrassed retreat took him to Cynthia and Mrs. Moore. The moment he was gone, Susan winced and pulled a nearby bench closer. Supporting her bandaged knee with a hand, she propped her leg on the bench and carefully adjusted her skirt to conceal the Ace.

Cynthia's mother beamed as the boy rejected by Susan drew Cynthia to the dance floor. Now only Susan, Mrs. Moore, Chris and Carin remained on the sidelines, and Carin was tugging at Chris's arm. "You really think I'm going to make an ass of myself in front of a bunch of professionals?" Chris demanded.

"Nobody's watching."

"*I* am," Chris muttered as a boy ripped off a triple pirouette in front of him, "and there's no way I'm going out there." He studied Carin as she watched the dancers. "But you go ahead."

"I don't like to dance alone," she said, her eyes on the dance floor.

"Who can tell?" Chris asked, but Carin shook her head. A moment later Chris said, "Looks like your problem's solved."

Terry was standing over them, smiling down at Carin. "Do you mind?" he asked Chris.

"Mind!" Chris said. "It's an act of mercy." Terry's quizzical look drew, "Carin'll explain," from Chris. "Out there," he added, nudging Carin. She rose quickly, and in a moment she and Terry were dancing as enthusiastically as the rest of the wedding party. Sitting back, Chris found Mrs. Moore bestowing a friendly smile on him from across the room. She nodded toward the dance floor and arched her eyebrows invitingly.

That's about my speed, Chris thought, and, pretending near-sightedness, reached for his wineglass. A wave of revulsion reminded him that he was far beyond his normal quota, and he quickly put the glass down and tried to focus on the dancers. But he couldn't: the image refused to resolve, even when he blinked his eyes several times. He drew the back of a hand across his eyes and peered at the dancers again, but Taylor's esters, or perhaps Mrs. Moore's, were working on him, and the double image remained. Reconciling himself to the blur, he called on his journalistic objectivity to study the scene before him.

Pushing aside the irritating otherness of the gypsies—or of himself—he observed that what they were doing on the dance floor was by any standard remarkable. Admiration chipped at resentment as he saw Diane, dancing with Dennis, execute a half-turn that fit her contours to Terry's, so that in what magicians would term a sweet move, Dennis and Terry changed partners. Gyrating bodies closed around Carin and Dennis, and Chris continued to avoid Mrs. Moore's importunate gaze by staring at the lively floorshow.

Inside the pulsing mass there was another swift shift of bodies, and Carin found her movement conforming to Gino's. She faltered, missing a beat in the music, then, annoyed at herself for continually giving him the satisfaction of reacting to his genial challenge, fell into sync with the music and him. But as the mass continued to shift, one of its edges was rent and Carin caught a glimpse of Chris watching her through the gap, a fixed smile on his face. The conjunction of Chris's gaze and Gino's at the spot where Carin danced formed a trine of such unpleasant portent that Carin spun away from Gino in a half-turn that left her partnerless. Unperturbed and patient, Gino danced around her, moving in again to face her.

Nearby, Terry yelped as Diane's movement, suddenly arhythmic, drove a sharp elbow into his ribs. "What're you . . ." he began, and broke off as Diane compressed her lips and eyelids, directing his attention to Carin's predicament. Nodding, Terry improvised steps that brought him squarely between Gino and Carin. Gino tried to circle Terry, but Terry was fixed to Carin as with epoxy.

Chris, still watching with a thin smile, looked up as the air around him turned caustic. Mrs. Moore, her bosom trembling above Chris like a threatening shelf of snow, was smiling down at him. "Notice anything?" she purred. "Except for that girl, we're the only two who aren't out there."

"I can't."

"Why not? I'll bet you're a terrific dancer."

"Oh, I am, but . . ."

"But what?"

"I have a venereal disease. The doctor's advised me to avoid all close physical contact."

Mrs. Moore emitted an appreciative guffaw, enveloping Chris in an astringent cloud. Then she and the frenzied Corybants disappeared behind a veil of tears as a fit of coughing seized Chris.

The frail winter daylight was dying, and the brutal pinks and magentas of Coney Island Avenue's neon facades were struggling to take up the slack when the wedding party issued from Nathan's back room, in high spirits and full career. The bus driver, pensively nibbling a hot dog at one of the sidewalk counters, came stiffly erect as the flying wedge burst from the alley, paused, then veered in his direction. Diane, riding point as always, was the first to arrive. "Whatcha doing?" she demanded.

"Eatin'." His guarded gaze moved around the semicircle that pinned him to the counter.

"Why didn't you come in with us?" a boy asked.

"Wasn't invited."

"What kind of shit is that?" Diane snapped.

"It's your party," the bus driver said.

"You were in the bus too," Diane replied.

"Drivin', that's all."

"Aw, for Christ's sake!" Diane raked the group with an angry regard. "How come nobody noticed?"

"Same reason you didn't," Gino said.

Diane turned back to the bus driver, who watched her, blinking slowly, the last morsel of meat and bun pinched gingerly between thumb and forefinger.

"Well, I'm sorry," she said. "We blew it."

"No problem," the driver responded. "I ate."

"But we had champagne."

"Couldn't have had none anyway. I'm workin'."

"Where's the bus?" Gino asked.

"Parkin' lot a coupla blocks down. Cop wouldn't let me wait in front. Want it?"

"For what?" Gino said. "We're just getting started."

"I bet," the driver replied, the terse syllables afloat on a cold tide of Schopenhauerian gloom, like a hair in a glass of milk.

"C'mon along," Gino said. When there was no reply, he sweetened the kitty with, "It's gonna be wild."

"No doubt," came the philosophical reply.

Ockham's razor flashed as Diane retorted, "Balls!"

"You got a point," the driver observed, and, crumpling his napkin and hitting an overflowing garbage can with a smooth fadeaway shot, offered his arm to Diane and leaped into the abyss with Kierkegaardian daring: "Let's go."

A cheer went up from the gypsies, and they moved off like a pack of demented but amiable children. Making their way through one of the concession-lined aisles behind Nathan's, they paused before a barker with a standing scale, a faded sign and three shelves of plaster-of-Paris horrors.

"Here y'are!" the barker shrilled. "Guess y'r weight, y'r age, y'r date of birth. Ev'ry one a winner. If I fail, you get one o' these charming novelties." He waved a hand at the deplorable statuary. "If I succeed, a unique consolation prize. Nobody goes away empty-handed! Step up, little lady—write y'r date of birth on this piece-apaper. If I fail to guess it accurately, you win a delightful novelty."

Possessing no special powers or perceptions, the barker had nonetheless placed himself in what a computer programmed for game theory might term a Win-Win situation: pitting oneself against the barker required an investment of fifty cents; beating him garnered a prize that had cost him twenty, assuring him a 150 percent profit when he lost.

None of the gypsies had studied game theory, but the "charming novelties" offered no incentive, so they stood silent, held only by an academic interest in the barker's showmanship. He beckoned to Cynthia, but she giggled and backed into her mother.

"Just the month and day of y'r birth. I won't give away the year. Couldn't do that to a lady." The crowds were slim this chilly night and there was growing urgency in his appeal as his eyes scanned the group. "Y'r weight! Y'r age! Y'r date of birth!"

C'mon, ya bastards, let me lose, he thought, then singled Terry out.

"You, sir, y'r age within two years! If I fail, ya get one o' these lovely novelties for y'r lady."

There was a happy shout from the gypsies around Terry, and they pushed him forward. He tried to dig his heels into the rutted cement beneath him, but several of the dancers united to push him into the circle of light around the barker, where he tried to summon an air of dignified disinterest as the barker scrutinized him, the stubble around his pursed lips standing erect. Since the consolation prize only cost him three cents, there was greater profit in being right than wrong; besides, there was such a thing as professional pride, so he squinted at Terry, trying to sort out the confusing signals. Finally he extended a hand, placing his fingertips on Terry's arm—a move that, in his opinion, lent class to his act. After another freighted pause, he muttered, "I would sayyyy . . . thirtyyyyyyy . . ."—the beginning of a long hoot skirled from the gypsies—" . . . three! How's that, sir? Within two years?"

An abrupt "Yes" from Terry, and he darted back into the group. But he was thrust back toward the barker by his cackling confreres. "Wrong! Wrong!" the gypsies howled. "We won! Let's have the prize!"

"Wrong on which side, sir?" the barker asked Terry.

"Both sides," Terry said, trying to join in the general mirth.

"*Both* sides!" the barker replied with professional good humor. "The gentleman says both sides—too young *and* too old!" He weighed his options: losing could encourage more players, and four or five times thirty cents was decidedly preferable to one forty-seven-cent score. On the other hand this group might only be good for a one-shot. It was decisions like this, the barker decided, that separated the men from the boys in his profession. A last sweeping look at the group advised the barker that there was at least one more mark in the crowd: better to lose, with grace and humor.

"All right," he said with an affable grin, "Both sides. Everybody knows a lady's entitled to fib about her age."

Before the words were out of his mouth, he sensed he had stepped off a cliff. Why and precisely how was a mystery to him, but of one thing he was certain: the temperature had just dropped twenty degrees and the jolly circle around him had turned into a noose. In the chilly, threatening silence he recalled jungle movies in which rows of glowing eyes like these had peered out of the foliage at the doomed hunters.

It don't make sense, he told himself, *they can't all be fags; some of 'em are* girls . . .

His thoughts trailed off, then resumed, galvanized.

Holy shit, they're all *queer, even the broads! Transvestites! Cocks and knives in their panties!*

He knew that a piercing "Hey, Rube!" would bring help from his fellow concessionaires, but—he tried to peer into the shadows beyond his circle of light—it looked as if there were a hundred of them, every one of them teed off.

No sudden moves, he thought, and reaching slowly to the shelf behind him, located a mauve plaster-of-Paris dog, which he thrust at Terry.

"Here you are, sir," he said with what he hoped was genuine warmth, and sufficient emphasis on the *sir,* "y'r prize: a beautiful doggie . . . *dog!* Whattaya think of that?" He turned back to the group, oozing affability. "You see how easy it is? I don't feel lucky tonight. Oh, no, not lucky at all. Better get in while the dice are cold

f'r me. Who's next? Y'r weight, y'r age, y'r date o' birth . . ." The
noose was loosening, the sullen, glowing eyes growing dimmer as the
group backed slowly away. "Y'r place of birth . . ." The menacing
figures dissolved into the surrounding gloom, leaving time and space
for reflection.

How can such good-lookin' broads be men? the barker asked
himself.

Nothing in his philosophy equipped him to understand that he
had violated a sacred taboo: only a gypsy mocks a gypsy.

Susan's scream was loud enough to surmount the general din as
the little cars careered around the oval, their antennae spitting
sparks at the electrified screen overhead. Each vehicle bore two
screeching members of the wedding party, bent on a spine-cracking
collision with any car that crossed their path, but the car containing
Susan and the bus driver was in the hands of a man who had been
straitjacketed for years by a professional ethic: bus drivers, after all,
cannot respond to the challenges and affronts that whip other drivers
into cathartic frenzy; they must swallow their bile and sacrifice their
competitive instincts to the safety and comfort of their passengers.
But now, in the crackle and crash of the bumper-car concession, the
Oceanside Summer Day Camp driver was liberated at last. Every
remembered road hog, every unanswered challenge loomed before
him again as he selected his target, maneuvered through the traffic
with murderous precision and slammed into his quarry.

Susan, who had chosen the bus driver as her bumper-car-part-
ner for his conservative utterances on the bus, clutched her bandaged knee in a protective embrace and bellowed, "Please! Take it
easy!"

But the bus driver could hear only his demons. A deft twist of
the little steering wheel spun his car back into the flow of traffic, and
grinning fiendishly, he hunched forward over the wheel, avoided a
check by one of the other cars and drew a bead on his next victim.
Susan, reverting twenty years, began a Hail Mary in Latin.

The situation was reversed in Diane and Terry's car: Diane
drove and Terry cringed. "Holy shit!" he screeched, clutching his
plaster-of-Paris dog as Diane, only slightly less manic than the bus
driver, wrenched her wheel and rammed the car occupied by Carin
and Chris. Heads snapped in both cars and Carin and Diane howled
with delighted laughter.

Chris fought to regain control of his car, but a violent blow
from the side set it spinning. He caught a glimpse of a triumphant
grin as a silver vehicle piloted by Gino hurtled away.

Wrenching the steering wheel in the direction of the spin, Chris
found traction and set out in pursuit of the silver car. Carin had
turned back to shout a challenge through cupped hands at Diane

and Terry, who were being repeatedly rammed as they struggled to reenter the flow around the oval. Unable to make herself heard, Carin twisted front again just as Chris reached his objective. The unanticipated crash flung her against the battered padding in front of her. Recoiling in pain, she spun toward Chris, who was bent over the steering wheel, his hands white-knuckled, his mouth set in a grim rictus.

A loud electrical whine rose above the general clamor as Chris jammed the accelerator into the floorboard, shoving the silver car out of the traffic flow. In the rammed car Gino fought to spin his car away from the insolent constraint, but Chris had caught him athwart and the wheels of Gino's car were locked in a long sideways slide.

Chris's car continued to whine in protest at the demands he was placing on it, but momentum helped it propel Gino's car into a corner of the oval, where it slammed clangorously into the wall under a sign that read KEEP MOVING IN SAME DIRECTION—NO HEAD-ON COLLISIONS.

The shock that raced through both cars snapped Carin's chin into chest muscles still throbbing from the first collision. She exclaimed and turned back to Chris as he kept Gino pinned to the wall, despite the rising protest from his overburdened motor. Behind them other cars, unable to negotiate the turn through the corner, piled into them in a succession of bone-jarring crunches.

"Chris!" Carin yelled, pulling at his arm, but the muscles under her fingers were rigid and unresponsive, and the foot on the accelerator threatened to drive it through the floorboard as the pileup spread out on the track like an overachieving amoeba.

Two attendants sporting grimy sweat shirts and several days of stubble raced across the floor, dodging the few cars that were still moving. Arriving at the edge of the pileup, they grabbed at the outermost cars, pulling them free and sending them back on course with a kick and a curse. Coming finally to Chris's car, they seized it and pulled, but Chris remained hunched over the steering wheel, his foot frozen on the accelerator. The electrical whine rose to a hysterical pitch.

"Get your foot off the pedal!" one of the attendants yelled, but Chris was immutable, and Gino remained pinned in the corner. The attendant leaned over the cockpit, the tip of his nose in Chris's ear. "Hey! *You!* Let up on the pedal before I break y'r goddamn leg!"

"*Chris!*" Carin screeched into Chris's other ear, and suddenly the whining stopped as he sat back and looked at Carin, expressionless. The only sound in the oval was the low hum of the motors in the moving cars, the occasional crackle of sparks between their antennae and the overhead screen and the hiss of their wheels as they spun around the track in a somber pavanne. The convoy of bumper cars revolved like a space station, slowly, majestically—no collisions, every eye on Chris's car, heads rotating to keep it in view as the cars wheeled around the oval.

"Whattaya think y're doin'?" an attendant demanded of Chris, but he was silent, ungirt. The attendants swung his car toward the slowly wheeling traffic. One of them planted a sole on the rubber bumper that encircled the car, counseled, "Take it easy! You don't have to kill anybody. Save that f'r y'r *own* car," and shoved.

Chris's car rolled a few feet and stopped.

The attendant turned to his colleague, arms outspread in an elaborate display of irony. "First the clown won't let up on the pedal, then he don't wanna touch it!" He swung toward Chris. "Hey, you! Motherfucker! Drive or get outta the car."

Chris wondered whether the parade of cars would swerve suddenly and swarm around the bellicose attendant as the gypsies had encircled the Weight-and-Age concessionaire when he insulted Terry. But the courtly pavanne continued unchanged, impassive heads swiveling to keep the drama in view.

Chris turned slowly from Carin and put his hands on the wheel, and the little car moved forward with a listless disinterest that mirrored the mood of the gloomy round it joined.

"Okay," one of the attendants shouted to the group, "you can bump again."

Like the Weight-and-Age concessionaire, like every seasoned member of the fraternity of shills, the bumper-car attendants were ardent students of the Zeitgeist. Accurate measurement of their little arena's temper could mean the difference between profit and loss: satisfied customers were repeaters, good for three or four consecutive rides, and it had been a slow day until this bunch showed up.

A plaintive note warped the attendant's voice. "Okay, bump!" But no one bumped. The stately revolution continued, tranquil and joyless, and the baffled attendants stared at each other. Then, bowing to the inevitable, they cut off the electricity in the overhead screen and the impotent cars rolled to a stop, their antennae erect but juiceless.

Two factors put a curfew on the honeymoon: an early rehearsal the next morning and, of equal consequence, Coney Island's curtailed off-season schedule that confined operations to weekends, and then offered fewer delights for fewer hours.

On the bus the gypsies made one of their practiced adjustments from hyperactivity to none. Seconds after the bus had pulled out of the parking lot, they were sprawled in their seats, pillowed on each other, practicing the art of expeditious sleeping that had been perfected on countless tours. To passing cars the bus looked empty, except for the rigid figure of the driver in front and the two stiff silhouettes in the back: Chris and Carin, awake, erect and miserable all the way to Manhattan.

Alone in their room at last, they lay silent and still awake in their bed until Chris muttered, "Don't think it's him—that guy—whoever he is. It isn't. It's them. All of them. It's like they're swallowing you up. Sometimes you disappear completely—even here at home."

Carin sat up. "I know you feel left out."

"Who wouldn't?"

"The bus driver." As Chris sat up she said quickly, "Chris, this is what I came here for."

"To be swallowed up?"

"No. To be part of this. You could be, too." He shook his head. "You don't want to be."

"That's right. I don't want to be."

"And I'm happy," she said, tears welling.

"You don't look very happy."

"You know what I mean. I told you in Detroit: I've been waiting all my life . . ."

"For this."

She lowered her head and nodded. "What'll we do? You quit your job, you left Detroit . . ."

"I had a reason."

"Do you still?" She waited, tears spilling with each blink.

"Yeah, I guess so."

"Please."

"What?"

"Don't give up on me. Not—not yet. Just be patient."

"For what? *Till* what?"

She turned to him, her words hurried. "Till I come back from Philadelphia. Then, we'll both be working, and we can find a place of our own." She sat taller, buoyed by her inspiration. "Yes! Then it'll be *our* life. Just ours. Okay?"

She was very close, peering up at him, radiating hope and urgency. "Sure," he said. "Okay."

"You mean it?"

"Yes."

With a little gasp she put her arms around him and pressed her cheek against his chest as she had so many times in the past. And as he had so many times in the past, he wondered at the strength in her slender arms.

TWELVE, two, three, four
Brisé Volé

"Terry . . . ?"

Diane peered into the inert gloom from the doorway, her rain-coat dripping puddles on the linoleum, then turned on the over-head light, crossed to the stove and squinted into the oven. As she straightened, Carin came into the kitchen, the runoff of her raincoat swelling Diane's puddles.

"He's not here," Diane said.

"He didn't say anything to me this morning."

"Me either."

"Maybe he decided to go out."

"He'd've called us at rehearsal—or at least left a note. He was gonna fix dinner . . ."

"He probably left something." Carin headed for the stove.

"I looked. The oven's empty."

Carin stopped as she heard a door open.

When Carin and Diane arrived in the living room, they found Terry rooted just inside the front door, mesmerized. He wore no raincoat, and the water that streamed from his jacket, jeans and shoes spread a sheen on the floor around him, giving the impression that he had paused to receive a rather pleasant revelation while walking on water.

The rain had played havoc with his always precariously poised coiffure, and broad patches of scalp glistened between sodden streaks of hair; but the face below shone beatifically.

"Holy Christ! He's stoned!" Diane cried. "And he's gonna catch pneumonia!" She rushed to him and put a hand on the shoulder of his jacket. "What'd you do, swim home?" She grabbed his arm. "Okay, let's go. In the tub!"

But she couldn't budge him: he remained stationary on his little lake, receiving more good news from the cosmos. Accusation banished sympathy as Diane dropped his arm. "Where'd you find the bread to get this mellow!" Terry just smiled. "If you took the grocery money . . ."

"Terry Mitchell is not stoned." His voice was as soft and bemused as his expression.

Diane glared at him. "You're on *some* kind of trip."

Terry began to sing languidly, in a sweet countertenor. " 'My Rio, Rio by the sea-o! Flying down to Rio where there's rhythm and rhyme . . .' "

Carin had drifted across the room to join Diane in her mystified perusal of Terry; Diane turned to her. "He's snapped. I'm serious! That can happen. From too many jumps. It's not just hard on the knees; somebody told me it jars the brain . . ."

She stopped to listen to the blissful murmur issuing from Terry. "Not stoned . . . not bananas . . . not Nut City . . ."

"Then what the fuck *are* you?" Diane demanded.

"Employed."

The splendid silence that followed was punctuated by the steady dribble of water from the three stationary figures. Then Diane's arms and voice rose. "In what?"

"Not Bloomingdale's, baby."

"A *show?*"

"Hard as it is to believe."

"Whattaya mean hard to believe!" Diane screeched. "Who's the one who said you're the most valuable fuckin' commodity in show business! Who? *Who?*"

"You. You," came the quiet reply.

"Well? Was I right? Never mind! Tell me later. You can't knock 'em dead if *you're* dead."

This time Terry moved when Diane tugged. Streaming rainwater and joy, he let Diane and Carin lead him into the bathroom and begin to peel him like a banana. When one of the sleeves of his jacket snagged on a tightly clenched fist, Diane pried two fingers open: he was clutching the mauve plaster-of-Paris dog he had won at Coney Island. "Leggo," Diane commanded.

"Never," Terry sighed.

"Gimme the goddamn dog." He shook his head. "Why not?"

"He got me the job." He brought the dog to his lips and kissed it. "My good-luck charm. Eternal youth. Whither I goest, thither goest Fido—forever."

"Okay, okay, you can let go of him for a minute. Look—see? I'm putting him right here on the sink. He'll be waiting for you when you get out of the tub. Attaboy."

The last of Terry's clothes came off, and the girls plunged him into a bubble bath hot enough for therapy, frothy enough for Jean Harlow.

Stretched out under a creamy layer of soap, with his hands folded behind his head, he looked as if he had been planted in a giant frosted cake. He smiled vacuously at Diane.

"Okay," she said, "now that you're out of immediate danger, you want to explain?"

"What is there to explain?" he asked, without displacing the smile. "I told you—I'm a professional dancer again. The final ended an hour ago."

"But that's impossible," Diane said, lowering the toilet seat cover to provide herself with a chair.

"That's what *I* thought," Terry replied.

"I don't mean that! You'd've told us if you made a final!"

Bubbles flew as Terry shook his head vigorously. "Not this time."

"Since when do we have secrets from each other!" Diane demanded.

Terry's response was quiet and very firm. "I didn't want to have to go through any explanations when I got eliminated." He shook his head again, in wonder now. "Only I didn't get eliminated." A bubble dislodged itself from the soapy frosting. He waited respectfully as it wafted to a suicidal meeting with the ceiling, then repeated," "I didn't get eliminated," very slowly, as if trying to force-feed the datum into a disbelieving computer. Then he snuggled a little deeper into the warm cake and said, "It's called *Hosanna!*, and we go into rehearsal next week . . ."

The end of the sentence was preempted by Diane. Unable to hold back any longer, she launched herself from the toilet, landing on her knees on the bathmat, her arms around Terry. Bubbles flew up like mute fireworks, and Terry yelped, "Your clothes!"

"How can they get any wetter?" Diane cried. "Besides, they're wash 'n' dry. And so am I!" Then, for want of a better way to express her feelings, she began to shriek—long, mindless, free-form howls. Her forthrightness was contagious: in an instant Carin was on her knees next to Diane, her arms around her roommates. Lined up at their enameled priedieu, the two girls whooped together. Then Terry's disembodied head tipped back on the frosting and he joined the merry caterwauling, his voice weaving obbligatos a full octave above his roommates.

A few minutes later Terry was removed from the bubble bath and lovingly patted dry. Then the roommates retired to their various rooms to prepare for a victory dinner at Joe Allen's. When Chris got home, he found the household in semi-full regalia and full cry. Despite his hostility toward Carin's clubby gypsy world, he liked Diane and Terry. In a way they were aspects of the very thing that had first attracted him to Carin and still held him firmly in thrall. They were part of her otherness, incubus to her succubus: he was neatly sand-wiched, and in unthreatening moments it was a pleasant sensation. For their part Diane and Terry had no desire to exclude Chris from their rites; to the contrary, they were determined to absorb him, as they had absorbed Carin and had themselves been absorbed in their turns. As for the incident at Coney Island, they bore no grudge; Chris had exacted a vengeance on Gino of which they privately approved. For them, Chris was the protagonist in the little drama, and while they were aware of the strained relations between Carin and Chris, they rooted for reconciliation—and absorption.

At Joe Allen's Diane raised a glass of house wine and said, "To us."

"To us," Terry and Chris and Carin said. Each glass touched three others: twelve chiming clinks, and they drank.

"To Terry," Diane murmured, and the glasses came up again. When they had clinked and drained their glasses and refilled them, she said, "What'd I tell you? You can't keep a good man down!"

"You can't keep a good man down!" Terry echoed.

"Now I'm gonna tell you the best thing about this whole thing," Diane announced. "I am never—not *ever*—gonna have to listen to that darling-I-am-growing-old bullshit again!"

"Never!" Terry belled. "It's gone. Forever! Hell, I didn't feel this young when I *was* young."

He jumped as Diane rapped his knuckles with a soup spoon. "You forgot already! You *are* young, you dumb son of a bitch! That's like the whole point of this goddamn celebration!"

"I am a young, dumb son of a bitch," he said slowly.

"Correct. Not to mention rich."

"Rich?"

"Add it up! With all four of us working, we're up to our ass in moolah!"

"I am a *rich,* young, dumb son of a bitch," Terry said softly.

"The kind of money we're gonna be dealing with," Diane said, "we can—we can *redo the bathroom!* Now picture this: four sinks! I said four! In a row. No standing in line outside!"

Terry sat back, overwhelmed by the majesty of Diane's concept. "God! Four sinks. No waiting."

Diane raised her glass. "To four sinks, no waiting."

"Four sinks, no waiting," Terry said, raising his glass.

"Four sinks, no waiting," Carin said, raising her glass.

The glasses chimed nine times.

SECOND VARIATION

THIRTEEN, two, three, four
Jeté

Diane kicked off her shoes and stretched out on the narrow twin bed, trying to conform to the inadequate space left by the open but unpacked suitcase at her feet. Linking her hands behind her, she rolled her head back and forth on her palms as she watched Carin make repeated trips from the open suitcases on the other bed to the closet and dresser. When she finally spoke, her voice was a sleepy whisper. "Where do you get the energy?"

"The longer I wait to unpack, the harder it'll be." Carin took a stack of tights, leotards and leg warmers out of one of her suitcases and headed back to the dresser.

Diane's eyes closed, but her lips moved. "Once I waited a week."

"To unpack?"

"Mmm hmm. I figured the show was a bomb and I'd only have to pack everything up again." She was silent, and Carin assumed she had fallen asleep, but after a moment her lips moved. "I was right."

Carin frowned as she continued unpacking. "Is that going to happen to us?"

"*Quién sabe?*" the slack lips murmured.

Carin paused to study Diane's face for a moment, her hands full of underpants, then she asked, "Don't you care?"

Diane's eyes opened abruptly, and she stared at Carin as if her roommate had uttered an obscenity even Diane had never heard before. Then her words knifed through the stuffy hotel-room air. "Have you taken leave of your senses?"

"Well, you don't *sound* like you care."

"Oh, I wouldn't mind at all, if I hadn't formed a few bad habits—like eating and wearing shoes . . ."

The telephone rang, and Diane came up on an elbow with a groan. "Why are hotel phones always so goddamn loud?" Scooping the receiver from its cradle, she cooed, "Philadelphia Lying-In," listened expressionless to the caller's response, then rasped, "Oh, wonderful! Just what I needed!"

She mouthed "Gino" at Carin, then exclaimed into the phone, "What're you, on uppers? We're wrecked! . . . Okay, okay, okay, I'll ask, but I know what the answer's gonna be."

Cupping the mouthpiece, she turned to Carin. "Guinness wants to know if we'd like to go out for dinner. On *him,* presumably. Then him on *you,* presumably. Or maybe on both of us. Gino thinks big." Carin shook her head. "Yeah, I know: no to the last two parts—but what about dinner? We can always stiff him after he's paid the check. Not that I'm voting yes to *any*thing, you understand . . ."

Carin was shaking her head again. Diane nodded and uncupped the phone. "Guess what, cookie—I was right." She listened, settling back on the bed with a sigh, then intoned a weary, "Hold on," and covered the mouthpiece. "He wants to talk to you." She extended the phone to Carin. Carin shook her head and foreclosed further discussion by returning to her bed to resume unpacking.

"She's busy, Gino," Diane said. "Unpacking! In case it escaped your notice, we had exactly ten minutes in this fleabag before they hustled us off to rehearsal, and that was this morning. We've got like a lot of things to do, and then we're gonna crash . . ." She broke off as several thumps overhead threatened to demolish the ceiling. "Oh, no, we're not," she moaned into the phone. "The hotel seems to have booked a couple of Sumo wrestlers over our heads." She ducked as another crash shook the ceiling.

In his room Gino, lying on his bed in a pair of trousers, the phone propped between ear and pillow, one leg dangling over the edge of the bed, smiled, raised the dangling leg, and hammered the heel of his yellow Frye boot into the threadbare carpet again. The room shook and Gino's smile widened.

"Well, listen," he said into the phone, "if you've got *that* kind of a problem, you might as well come out to dinner."

Downstairs, Diane hesitated, then covered the phone and twisted toward Carin. "He says we might as well go out to dinner till things quiet down upstairs." Both girls winced as two loud blows rained down from above. "Jesus!" Diane said into the phone, "it sounds like somebody's getting murdered. I'll call you back . . ."

"What for?"

"We've gotta get this settled. I'm gonna tell the hotel desk what's going on here."

"I wouldn't do that," Gino snapped back.

"Why not?"

"Well—it may stop."

"And it may not. It could be heavy humping."

Gino raised his leg again as he replied, "How long can *that* go on?"

"Depends. If they're sex maniacs like you . . ." Diane broke off suddenly, and her gaze shifted upward.

"Hello?" Gino said.

Diane was silent, her eyes on the ceiling, her gaze darkening. Then she said, "Listen, Gino, Carin's waving at me. She wants to make a call—so I gotta hang up."

"But . . ."

"I'll call you right back. What's your room number?"

As Diane waited for Gino's reply, she reached for the room key on the night table next to her and examined the inch-high *803* etched into the plastic tag attached to it. "Would it by any chance be nine-oh-three?"

In his room Gino's poised leg sank soundlessly to the floor, but his grin was intact as he replied, "You're in the wrong business, Di. You should be a private dick."

"So should you!" she shot back. "The public one's gonna wear out."

He tendered a lifeless, "Ha ha."

"And now that we've established how thin the floors are in this hotel," she concluded, "do you think you could jerk off more quietly?"

Extending the telephone like a morsel of spoiled food disdainfully pinched between thumb and forefinger, she centered it over the cradle and opened her fingers; it fell neatly into place and Diane lay back on the bed, her eyes closing.

There were no more calls that evening, or thumps. The two girls ordered bowls of vegetable soup from room service. The soup was thin and tasteless, and Carin and Diane debated augmenting their order with another call to room service. But the likelihood that the new order would be just as unappetizing turned them back from the phone. They settled for filling the soup with the hard bread and soft Saltines that had accompanied it.

When they had finished the meal, by mutual consent and without discussion, they began to prepare for bed. Carin bathed first, and when Diane came out of the bathroom in an oversize T-shirt, Carin was under the covers. Diane sat on the edge of her bed and looked across at Carin.

"Want to watch TV?" Carin shook her head, and Diane turned out the light on the night table and slid into bed. After several moments of silence she observed, "It's getting me down."

"What is?"

"Thinking about all the people who breathed this air before we did."

"We could open the window."

"Uh uh. I looked out: there's an alley down there with like twenty garbage cans in it—full! Which means they're gonna start throwin' those cans around at six o'clock in the morning."

"Then the air conditioner."

"I turned it on while you were taking your bath. It sounds like a head-on collision."

"Hold your breath," Carin said dejectedly. "We'll only be here a month."

"Yeah."

The girls fell silent. Then there was a muffled sound from the room above.

"Oh, oh," Carin said.

Diane sat up. "He wouldn't dare. He wouldn't *dare!*"

The girls listened. There was only silence. Diane lay down again. A minute later she broke the stuffy silence with, "But he's not going to forgive you."

"*Me!* For what?"

"Tarnishing his record."

From the sound of Diane's voice, Carin imagined a smile on her face. She glanced toward the ceiling, and after another long silence asked, "Is it true?"

"You haven't noticed a slight interest on his part?"

"I mean, his name."

"Gino?"

"His gypsy name."

"Oh. Guinness."

"Yes. The way he got it—is that true?"

"Yep."

"He was on the road with a show?"

"Uh huh."

"And he made it with seven of the girls?"

"Out of eight. One of the girls was ugly. A terrific dancer, but ugly."

After a reflective silence Carin said, "No, it can't be true. It's one of those stories."

"Why?"

"Look how well we all know each other in this company. We haven't even been together six weeks and it's already like a . . . like a . . ."

"Family."

"Yes."

"So?"

Carin came up on an elbow. "There's no way he could go through a whole company like that and keep it a secret."

"Who said it was a secret?"

Carin sat up. "Some of them *knew?*"

"*All* of them knew. Like you said, it's a family."

"Now wait a minute. You're trying to tell me that every girl knew she was one of *seven?*"

"No. The first girl knew she was one of one, the second girl knew she was one of two, the third girl knew she was one of three. . . . Gino doesn't believe in hiding his light under a bushel. Besides, nobody cared much. It was out-of-town . . ."

"Impossible."

"What?"

"It's just impossible. I bet if you checked with anybody in that company, you'd find out it's one of those show business stories that gets blown up till . . ."

"You're talking to number seven."

The bulky drapes, weighted with decades of dust, didn't quite meet, and the gap between them admitted a dirty sliver of light. Carin had been watching motes drifting sluggishly through it; now they seemed to stand still, as if the dense suspension of which they were part had thickened.

Finally she said, "And you knew about the others?"

"I told you: the standby hairdressers knew."

"Then . . ." Carin stopped.

"Why?"

"Yes."

Diane pushed out her lower lip and reflected. Then she said, "You don't know what it's like yet."

"And I'm not going to find out!"

"I mean being out of town. It's—I don't know—different. After a week or two nothing's real—except the show and the hotel and the other people in the company. The rest of the world sort of disappears. When people call you up from New York, you have to remind yourself who they are. And you get lonely. You know, working all day, and then coming back to an empty hotel room . . ."

"But you're alone lots of nights in New York."

"I'm telling you, it's different on the road. There aren't any rules, so you—*want* things more." Carin thought she could hear the smile again as Diane went on. "I was falling in love with the nozzle on my goddamn douche bag! Seriously. It was like the middle of the second week, and one night about eleven o'clock I realized it was the third time I'd douched that day. What brought it to my attention was that I was coming. So I said to myself, 'Maybe there's a better way.' "

"But why Gino?"

"Curiosity, maybe. . . . Yeah. Curiosity. You know: where there's all that smoke there must be a helluva fire."

"Is there?"

"Curious?"

"No. But—knowing about all the other girls—wouldn't that turn you off?"

"On."

"It turned you *on?*"

"Of course. Wouldn't you like to ball Warren Beatty?"

"No."

"Bullshit. Everybody wants a celebrity fuck once in a while." Carin didn't respond, and Diane went on confidently. "He'd been after me since the second day of rehearsal. One night after the show, he tried again, and I said, 'Okay, Superman, let's get it on.' Lemme tell you, it was better than the douche bag." She heard Carin turn over. "You'll see," she said softly.

"I don't want to be in the Guinness Book of World Records."

"I mean, out of town," Diane said. "It's different. Nothing's real. Nothing's the same. It's weird."

"You sound like you like it."

"I think I do. It's part of the fun. Sometimes."

When there was no response for five minutes, Diane turned on her other side, but, facing the window, she could see the galaxies of motes drifting past the muddy light seeping through the gap in the curtains. They served to remind her of the viscous mess she was inhaling with each breath, and she rolled over to face Carin's bed. Another faint sound from the room above raised her blind gaze to the ceiling, but she resolutely brought her cheek back to the pillow and, driving the thought of Legionnaire's Disease from her mind, closed her eyes.

FOURTEEN, two, three, four
Chassé

The theatrical unions, facing reality, stretch their normally stringent regulations to the literal and figurative breaking point during the last critical days before the first public performance of a new theater work. The technical rehearsals of *Ante Meridian* consumed two devastating days and nights in which most of the tortured cast, staff and crew of the show saw little but the inside of the theater, sprawling on any available flat surface backstage or folding themselves into the empty seats out front to snatch a few minutes' rest between calls to take their places in the slowly rising edifice onstage.

Everything had to be rehearsed over and over, in the slowest of slow motions, as *Ante Meridian*'s various elements—sets, lights, costumes, music—were glued to the naked skeleton of the scenes that had been rehearsed in stark rehearsal halls.

Halfway back in the gloomy house, a large tabletop had been laid over several rows of seats, and the director and his staff were lined up in the row of seats behind it, consulting and conferring over the array of scripts, lighting diagrams and floor plans spread out before them. The tabletop was big enough to accommodate an additional assortment of stained coffee containers, overflowing ashtrays and bags and boxes of greasy fast foods. At the top of the table loomed its nerve center, the controls and microphone of a venerable sound system that carried the instructions of director, lighting designer, set designer, costumer and choreographer to the waiting minions on the stage.

Long debates would precede each order, boomed from scratchy speakers in the flies, and long delays would precede the execution of each order. Then endless revisions would amend the order or finally revoke it, and the tedious process would begin again.

As the actors rehearsed a scene, the dancers, in their oldest sweaters, most raveled tights and leg warmers and least valued sneakers, draped themselves in and over the orchestra seats, awaiting the next call to inaction on the stage, where they would perform one step at a time as lights were set and scenery moved for the first creaky time.

Onstage, where everything had stopped for the thousandth time this day, the stage manager called the assistant stage manager to the wings and engaged him in close, inaudible colloquy. The ASM nodded and picked his way down the railless stairs that had been set over the orchestra pit. Moving up the aisle, he peered into the darkness toward the sprawled shapes of the dancers and said, "Carin Bradley."

A shape sat up. "Yes?"

"Sonny and Mr. Kagin want to see you," the ASM said, and Carin's ragged outfit suddenly felt clammy to her. At this point in the proceedings, none of the performers relished individual summonses. "Where's Gino di Vito?" the ASM asked.

"Here," a shape answered, straightening.

"You too," the ASM said. "They're backstage, in Dressing Room D."

"Who's Mr. Kagin?" Carin asked.

"The company manager," the ASM replied.

"Shit," Gino said quietly.

"What's wrong?" Carin asked as she and Gino hurried along the dank backstage corridor.

"I don't know," Gino answered, his grim gaze front.

"Maybe nothing," Carin said, and silently retracted the statement as Gino's eyes swept toward her. "You think we're fired?" she asked tremulously.

Gino's black gaze thrust forward again, knifing into the gloom like headlights. "What else could it be?"

"But why us?"

Gino stopped, and Carin followed his glance to the facing *D* on the chipped dressing room door. After a moment Gino said, "Well, whatever it is, standing here isn't going to make it go away." He pushed the door open.

The dressing room was as shabby and cheerless as the hall, institutional-green paint peeling from its walls, most of the bulbs around the makeup mirror missing or inoperative. The makeup table had been converted to a desk for Phil Kagin, a beefy, red-faced man in a suit that looked two sizes too small, and he and Sonny, his expression no surlier—or less surly—than usual, occupied the battered wooden chairs nearest the makeup table.

Phil waved a chubby hand in which a cigar stub looked permanently wedged toward the remaining two chairs in the room. "Siddown," he said with a smile that teetered between amiable and deadly.

Carin and Gino hesitated, then took the proffered seats as if they were electric chairs and waited, silent, their eyes shifting back and forth between Phil's frightening bonhomie and Sonny's terrifying inscrutability.

"Sonny's got something to say to you," Phil muttered.

Carin and Gino's oscillating attention fixed on Sonny. Sonny didn't look at them. He stared into space, distant, apparently bored, as he spoke. "We had a meeting last night, and everybody agreed." Carin stopped breathing; asphyxiation was no longer an unacceptable option. "The second-act opening isn't going to work, and we've finally put our fingers on the reason."

Of course, Carin thought. *Me. No talent. I could've told you that weeks ago and saved everybody a lot of time and money.*

"Too big," Sonny said, "no focus. Something's gotta go."

Me, Carin's conscience screamed. *Fire me! Send me back to Detroit. It's not too late to save the show!*

"So we're going to try it as a *pas de deux.* Simple, focused. Just two people onstage."

Air trickled into Carin's lungs. Detroit receded. Gino's words were a whisper. "You mean us?"

"You're the ones Sonny sent for, aren't you?" Tobacco-stained teeth appeared as Phil's smile widened; it *had* been amiable. How could anyone have read anything hostile into that warm and generous smile?

"I'm not sure what I want to do yet." Sonny was addressing Phil; in the hierarchical order of this meeting, Carin and Gino clearly came last. They understood; they didn't mind. "And I won't be till I get the bodies in the studio . . ." Now his gaze shifted to the bodies. "But I *am* sure it's going to be more balletic than anything else in the show."

Oh. Sense. Order out of chaos.

"A lot of lifts, and you two are the strongest I've got technically." Sonny rose, his movements at forty still buttery. "Meet me at LuLu Temple at three. I want to try and get the number in by opening night."

"In Phila*del*phia?" Carin gasped.

The eyes that turned toward Carin were as expressionless as a turtle's. "Sure."

"But—that's tomorrow night."

"If I can create it, you can learn it. Unless you'd rather not . . ."

"I can learn it."

A thin smile fought for possession of Sonny's lips. "Of course you can. Whatever it is, it'll be better than what we've got now, and we can fix it after the opening."

"What about the set and orchestration?" Phil asked. "Our copyists' bills are already through the roof."

"I'll use the same set and orchestration for now," Sonny said. "No choice."

"And after?"

"We'll see what everybody thinks of the number. If it works it'll be worth some extra money."

"What extra money? This show's so far over budget—"

"Why don't we wait and see how the new number looks," Sonny said, his eyes hooded. "If the show looks good, we can afford anything. If it doesn't . . ." He left the rest to Phil's crowded memory and moved toward the door.

"Uh—Sonny . . ." Sonny turned and looked at Gino. "What about billing?"

Sonny scowled. Phil shifted, his buttocks spilling over the edges of his overburdened chair, and looked at Gino. Carin caught her breath, and Gino stared woodenly at Sonny, his question still before the house.

Finally Sonny answered. "That's up to Phil." He seemed to address the door as he turned back to it. "But I certainly hope nobody's going to make waves."

He went out, and Carin said, "Nobody's going to . . ." but Gino turned to Phil and asked, "Are we going to get billing?"

"Sure. In the program." The amiable smile had reappeared.

"And ads?"

The smile disappeared. "No way."

"You heard what Sonny said . . ."

"It's not negotiable," Phil said evenly. "If you don't want the parts, lemme know right now so I can tell Sonny."

Carin reached for Gino's arm, but he had waited too long for this moment and rehearsed it too often. "If you're gonna list us in the program, that's not chorus; we should have white contracts."

"You gonna teach me my business, Gino?" Phil took two documents from the makeup table. "What color would you call these?"

The black and white printed forms ignited a glow in Gino's eyes, and his hand shot out. Phil let the hand tremble under the contracts for a moment, then dropped them. Gino snatched the papers back, devoured the print greedily and looked up. "It's twenty-five more than we're getting now."

"That's right."

Carin wanted to whoop for joy. And leave with Gino. Instantly.

"Sonny's using the same orchestration," Gino said.

"Yeah."

"That mother's almost six minutes long, and it's gonna be just the two of us out there, eight times a week."

"So?"

"So eight performances into twenty-five is like three dollars more a performance."

Phil's grin was genuine. "I never heard of a dancing school that taught business administration, but you must've found one."

"I'm serious, Mr. Kagin."

"So am I, pal. I'm not in the habit of negotiating with gypsies."

"But we're *not* gypsies! We're principals now."

"Not yet you ain't. Not till you sign those papers. And if you don't want to . . ."

"Sure I want to, but they've gotta be right. And fair." Gino turned to Carin, who was staring at him aghast. "How much do you weigh?"

"Listen, Gino . . ." Carin said quietly, as if somehow she could have a private conference with him.

"How much do you weigh?" Gino demanded.

"A hundred and five."

Gino turned back to Phil, all business. "Okay, let's round it off to an even hundred."

Phil was trying to rekindle his soggy cigar. "Okay, fine, let's. It'll make her easier to pick up."

Gino pounced. "That's exactly what I'm talking about." Phil's cigar sputtered and caught, punctuating Gino's headlong flight with little smacks. "Sonny said there were gonna be a lot of lifts. You heard him, right?"

Phil exhaled a thin, irregular trickle of smoke. It smelled sour, and Carin had to fight a sneeze. "Right, I heard him." Phil settled back, the damp butt held delicately in front of his face, the debate oddly enjoyable.

"Say there's a dozen," Gino said. Phil nodded graciously. "Twelve times a hundred; what's that?"

The cigar popped and threw off a tiny spark. "You're the one with the head for figures."

"Twelve hundred pounds!" Gino announced. "That's what I've gotta lift every time we do that number. On matinee days, *two thousand four hundred* pounds. That's more than a ton!"

"That's how you judge a work of art? By *tonnage?*" Despite the note of shocked disbelief, Phil was grinning with delight.

Gino rose, his squared shoulders and clenched fist reminding Carin of the revolutionary hero in an overwrought Soviet ballet she had seen on public TV.

"I've *got* to, Mr. Kagin! How long does a dancer last? Ten years? Fifteen? Twenty at the outside. And that's barring injury."

Phil rose. "Yeah, I see what you're driving at, but . . ."

Sensing foreclosure, Gino spoke as rapidly as he could. "No, you don't!" He thrust a hand at Carin. "She's got maybe ten years on me. I don't mean age. Girls last longer because they don't have to do all those lifts. Every lift takes a few minutes off a guy's career."

"Now, hold on . . ."

"You don't have to take my word for it; ask anybody. Even Sonny. The first thing that goes is the back, and when that happens . . ."

"Whattaya want, Gino?"

The question was so unexpected that it was several moments before Gino could offer a tentative, "Fifty a week. Not counting the extra seventy-five if you convert to run-of-the-play."

The light in Phil's cigar and expression died simultaneously, and Gino took this as a cue to plunge ahead. "Before you answer, lemme just say one more thing. Sonny's gotta make the number from scratch, right? How many times do you think I'll have to lift Carin in rehearsal? A hundred times a day? At least. That's ten thousand pounds! Times two days' rehearsal . . ."

"*Okay!* I got the point. Jesus, you shoulda been a longshoreman."

"That's what I'm saying," Gino replied. "I am."

Phil's face loomed close, smelling of cigar and certitude. "Wrong, Mr. di Vito. You know what you are? A little *pischer* with a lot of *chutspah*. You understand any of that?"

"Well . . ."

"It means you got a lot of nerve." Carin sank deeper in her chair, devastated by this defeat snatched from the jaws of victory. "But I'm gonna let you in on a secret: I got a soft spot in my heart for nervy *pischers,* so you get thirty a week over minimum. And don't bother to break down the extra five bucks, because I can tell you: it's sixty-two and a half cents more per performance, or five point three cents per lift if Sonny choreographs a dozen of 'em. Also, don't bother to argue, because you've heard my final offer."

"This is *plus* our out-of-town money . . ."

"It's plus your out-of-town money—and if I hear one more word on this subject, I can assure you somebody else is gonna have the pleasure of shortening his career by lifting this little lady."

"Okay."

"Gimme." Phil was reaching for the contracts. Gino surrendered them. Phil laid them out on the makeup table and picked up a pen. "Sign here."

"Change the numbers first." Phil looked up at Gino for a moment, then bent over the makeup table. "On both of them."

Phil squinted at Gino again. "Whadja think I was gonna do?" He winked at Carin. "When you get outside, give y'r partner a kiss; he got you a raise too. Same as his. Y'see, I also got a soft spot in my heart for ballerinas."

Phil changed the salaries on the two contracts and gave the pen to Gino. Gino signed with a self-satisfied flourish and handed the pen to Carin, who quickly scribbled her name at the bottom of her contract.

"Thanks, Mr. Kagin. We both appreciate this," Gino said and, taking Carin's arm, whisked her out of the dressing room before anything could happen to burst the bubble. In the corridor Gino and Carin took two steps, then turned and stared at each other in rapturous disbelief.

"Thirty dollars a week!" Carin gasped.

"Never mind *that!* White contract! That pink contract you signed last month was chorus. We're principals!"

"Principals!"

She flung her arms around Gino and he picked her up, swinging her in a jubilant arc, then suddenly stopped and put her down. "Hold it! Now that I know every lift is worth five point three cents, I can't just *give* 'em away." Carin laughed. "But I'll take that kiss Mr. Kagin told you to give me."

In the dressing room Kagin, shuffling invoices on the makeup table, looked up at the sound of a sharp burst of laughter from the corridor. He shook his head.

"*Pischers.* They'd've done it for a *dollar* over scale. They'd've taken a *cut.*"

As he went back to the invoices, he paused to glance at his image in the makeup mirror. "You know what? You're getting soft in your old age. Like every other *schmuck.*"

FIFTEEN, two, three, four
Divertissement

The masthead of the *East Sider* listed a president and publisher, editor-in-chief, managing editor, copy editor, entertainment editor, circulation director and a number of contributing editors. In fact its staff consisted of its publisher and two journalists who, under various pen names, performed all the chores on the masthead.

The publisher was Ian Roberts, a thirty-two-year-old go-getter who had wedged a foot in the door of New York's fourth estate during one of the city's newspaper strikes by rushing into print with a jerry-built journal devised to satisfy New York's craving for print during the blackout.

With the settlement of the strike, his stopgap paper had become the *East Sider,* a purveyor of "News and Information to the Young, Upwardly Mobile East Side Consumer."

Its news and ads were designed to reinforce the Bloomingdale aspirations and Maxwell's Plum mythos of the young consumers warehoused in Bauhaus barracks on the upper East Side. It was the *East Sider*'s mission to point these strivers at the merchants of food and entertainment vying for their custom up and down Lexington and Third and Second. The *East Sider* chronicled its readers' adventures; it told them who they were and, more important, *what* they were; it gave them to understand that they were loved, that their heartbeat was *the* heartbeat, that their pulse thundered in board rooms and executive suites, cueing moguls, initiating campaigns, inspiring products, prompting geriatric politicians and communicators to mimic their clothes and hair styles and language. Once a week the *East Sider* was there, on the doorstep of every Olympia House and Royal Arms, to remind its readers that their dreams were spinning through computers, nearing completion, on their way!

Ian was the paper's president and publisher, editor-in-chief, managing editor, copy editor and circulation editor—under various names, of course.

Moira Scanlon, six years out of the Columbia School of Journalism, was entertainment editor—as herself—and a battery of contributing editors, as Rose Kibbe, Miguel Figueroa, Arthur Ogden and assorted other figments of Ian's imagination. Chris, in addition to being Christopher Stevenson, was several other contributing editors of both sexes and nearly identical journalistic styles.

The *East Sider*'s editorial office converted to Ian Roberts's apartment at night when, devoid of its editorial staff, it opened its arms—and convertible couch—to the ambitious young publisher.

There were three desks in the "office," one for each of the protean editors. Chris's and Moira's were separated only by enough space to accommodate an outsize wastebasket that serviced both desks. Ian's desk, in deference to his station, had several square feet to itself across the room.

Moira had copper hair, Irish-white skin and black-Irish eyes, which, in a parting gesture to the concerns of her college years, still peered at the world from behind large blue Gloria Steinem shades.

As Chris picked his way through the *East Sider*'s editorial maze, Moira looked up and said, "A woman called you. Twice. It sounded important."

Halfway out of his coat, Chris paused. "Did she leave a name?"

"No."

"A number?"

"She said she'd have to call back." The phone on Chris's desk rang. "That's probably she. I told her you'd be back at four."

Chris dropped his coat on Ian's convertible couch, squeezed into the narrow space behind his desk, picked up the phone and heard Carin's excited voice exclaim, "Chris?"

"What's wrong?"

"Nothing!"

"But you called twice, and the way you sound . . ."

"I had to tell you! Sonny turned the big chorus number into a duet, and I'm on a white contract—with a raise! It was going to be twenty-five a week, but now it's *thirty*—and it'll be seventy-five *more* if they convert to run-of-the play. I don't know what that means, but that'll be a total of a hundred and five more than I signed for—and my name'll be in the program—"

"Hey! Slow down."

Carin laughed. "I'm sorry, but I'm on a break and all I've got is five minutes."

"At the rate you're going you could recite *Paradise Lost* in five minutes."

Carin laughed again. She was wedged into a phone booth in

rehearsal clothes, her hair matted on her forehead, a soggy hand towel wrapped around her neck. She slid forward on the little seat and pushed her knee up against the inside of the booth next to the phone. "Sonny's choreographing a *pas de deux,*" she said, willing the words to a more moderate rate. "On me! We've been working since three o'clock, and we'll probably work all night . . ."

"A *pas de deux* for one person?"

"What?"

"You said Sonny's doing a *pas de deux* on you."

"Oh. I've got a partner, of course." She laughed. "I can't lift my*self.*" She bounced ahead. "But the first six minutes of the second act is nothing but *us!*"

"Who's 'us'?"

"My partner and me."

"Who's your partner?"

"Gino. Sonny needed a strong boy because of the partnering. But we're principals, Chris! With program credit and more money and everything!"

"Fabulous. Fantastic! I'm proud of you."

"Thanks."

"No more chorus line for you!"

"Oh, we've gotta do all the chorus numbers too, and we still dress with the rest of the kids. It's not like our names are up in lights outside the theater—but we've got our own number, just the two of us."

"When?"

"Tomorrow night."

"Wow!"

"Yeah." It was as if a plug had been pulled: the energy was suddenly gone and the words came slowly, almost lifelessly. "Scary, huh?"

"Not for you. Listen, I'm supposed to cover some half-assed charity thing tomorrow night, but I'm sure I can get somebody to cover for me."

He twisted toward Moira but was turned back by, "Are you talking about coming here?"

"Isn't that what you're calling about?"

"No! I just wanted to tell you the good news."

"But tomorrow's going to be the most important night of your life . . ."

"And it'll be a miracle if I even remember the steps!" She pushed herself straight on the little seat, listened to his silence for a moment, then said, "I want you to see the number when it's finished and I'm good in it." Again she heard only silence. "You can understand that. You know how you are about never letting me read your first drafts."

"Yeah. Right. I understand."

"Do you?"

"Sure. I'll come to Philadelphia when things have quieted down."

Carin's relief was audible. "We'll have more time then, anyway. Once we've opened there's a limit on how much time they can rehearse us."

A placid neutrality deadened Chris's reply. "Fine."

The large door across the hall from the phone booth opened and Gino emerged, signaling to Carin.

"My break's over, Chris. I've gotta run."

"Sure."

"I'll call you tomorrow night—after it's over."

"Right. Do that. I'll be anxious to know how it went."

"So will I."

"Carin . . . ?"

"Yes?"

"You're going to be exhausted. Take care of yourself. You know what I mean."

"Yes, yes. Love you."

Chris hung up and sat back slowly, his eyes distant. In the last three weeks before he came to New York, one of the things that had alerted him to possible danger had been the loss of a pronoun in Carin's letters: her customary closing, "I love you," had lost its *I* and been replaced by a jauntier—and less committed?—"Love you!" At first he had accused himself of paranoia, but on reflection he had decided that "Love you" was definitely a way of *not* saying "I love you," and consequently meant less. Chris's final conclusion was that "Love you" was employed either before a timid *amoureuse* had found the courage to add the fateful *I,* in which case it was a favorable sign, or after ardor had peaked, in which case it was definitely a warning signal. One of the things that had pleased him about his decision to come to New York was that it had restored the crucial pronoun to Carin's amatory vocabulary. Until now.

He was awakened from his revery by a movement in his field of vision. He focused on it. Moira had taken off her glasses.

Sonny, in his customary skintight stretch pants, Byronically flared shirt and soft character shoes, was sprawled in a chair against one wall of the big room. Like the New York rehearsal room, it served as a banquet hall when LuLu Temple was functioning normally, but the Shriners who had reveled there had left a blander impression on the space than their spicier New York counterparts.

Pale lime pilasters with Ionic capitals on placid cream walls gave the room a proper Philadelphia Federal feel. The space was open, clean, cool. It had no mirror, but its floor was the requisite

wood, not cement, or plastic over cement, or even wood over cement, all sternly proscribed by the dancers' union. Two or three
hours of rehearsal on an unyielding surface could produce shin
splints, a crippling pain in the tibialis muscles that flex the foot. In
every city on the pre–Broadway tour route, there were rehearsal
venues that had long since been labeled acceptable or unacceptable,
and LuLu Temple with its obliging old floors was one of Philadelphia's certified spaces.

The folding chairs that normally filled the space had been
stacked against the walls, and now, at midnight, nine hours after
Sonny had begun creating the new number, he was sprawled in a
chair which he had unfolded against one of the room's two long
walls. In a second chair his assistant, Andrew, had assumed an identical position, legs thrust straight out in front of him, heels on the
floor. Carin and Gino had taken advantage of the break to stretch
out on the floor, folded towels under their damp heads. Sonny
puffed slowly on a cigarette, Andrew sipped disinterestedly from a
stained coffee container, and in a far corner of the room the rehearsal pianist was slumped over the room's resident grand piano, his
head on his forearms, as if someone had shot him at his post.

For a minute only Sonny's smoke and Andrew's coffee cup
moved, then Andrew turned and looked at Sonny. When Sonny
returned the glance, Andrew nodded, and Sonny sighed and stood
up.

Though their eyes were closed, Carin and Gino interpreted the
sigh and rustle, and rose. Carin wiped her face with the towel that
had been bunched under her head and tossed the towel at an open
chair near Andrew's. It fell across the chair with a soft sigh that
mimicked Sonny's, then Carin and Gino waited in the oppressive
silence for the next instructions to their aching muscles.

Sonny looked across the room at the piano, then gestured to
Andrew. Andrew crossed the room and touched the pianist on the
shoulder. The musician snapped erect, smiling sheepishly, turned to
the three feet of manuscript accordioned out on the piano's music
rack, blinked to clear the sleep from his eyes and waited, like Carin
and Gino, for the next instruction.

Sonny's eyes narrowed and his hands moved vaguely in front of
him. Another minute passed, then Gino glanced toward one of the
room's big windows as something rattled against it. "Starting to
rain," Gino said vacantly.

"Uh uh," Andrew said. "Sleet." He moved to the window and
peered out. "It's trying to turn into snow."

"What time is it?" Gino asked.

Andrew glanced at his watch. "Five minutes after twelve."

"What if they turn the heat off?" Gino asked. "In a place like
this it might go off automatically and the union says the temperature's gotta be at least sixty-five degrees . . ."

"It's okay," Andrew said. "I checked with the janitor and we'll have heat." He smiled wearily. "You don't think we'd do *that* to you, do you?"

Sonny's head came up and his hands fell to his sides.. "Bad news," he said softly.

Gino slumped. "You want to see it from the top." Sonny nodded. "With the lifts?"

"It's the only way I can tell what we've got," Sonny said. Gino responded with a resigned nod and moved toward the back wall of the room, followed by Carin. At the piano the accompanist leafed backward through the manuscript's folds until a single thick block of paper faced him from the music rack. He put his hands on the keyboard and waited. Then Sonny chanted, "Five, six, se-ven, eight," and the pianist began to play and Carin and Gino began to dance.

Before the night was over, they would dance another six hours, with periodic breaks to keep their muscles from shredding or imploding into marbleized knots.

Slowly, painstakingly, painfully, the *pas de deux* took shape. From the distance at which an audience would watch, the dance would look effortless, the two bodies gliding smoothly through space, Carin floating above Gino in airy lifts, but from Sonny's closer vantage point a parade of paradoxes was visible: Gino's bunched muscles threatening to burst through their flimsy confinement of skin as he pumped another hundred and five of the thousands of pounds he would thrust aloft in the course of this long Arctic night; his blunt, proletarian hand seeking a point of purchase under the gentle curve of Carin's breast or on the smooth inner surface of her thigh, one edge of his palm wedged, for her safety, into the narrow security of her crotch; the complete interdependence of these completely independent bodies; the total and necessary awareness of each other somehow coexisting with each one's unimpaired awareness of self; the steady barrage of inhuman physical demands flowing into inhuman grace; and the overriding paradox of the innocence of these Herculean labors coexisting with the immanent eroticism of this *pas de deux*.

Or any *pas de deux*. Instinctively, and in Sonny's case theoretically, these four dancers knew that most dance—primitive, folk, classical, modern—eventually addresses itself to the basic configuration of one male, one female, face to face, one on one; and at that moment dance and life merge. Two hundred dancers on a stage—or in a jungle clearing—a dozen dancers, six, four, even three, are involved in a social or theatrical or religious experience, but when one man and one woman separate themselves from the group and confront each other, another fundamental mechanism of life is engaged. The dancers touch each other in ways and places that, apart from dance, are reserved for the bedroom or the doctor's office, and in the case of the most formal dance duet, the *pas de deux,* with its courtly (for which *courtship* may be read) entrée, sensuous adagio, increasingly agitated and exultant variations, explosive coda and languid bows, the ascending action, climax and dénouement of sexual encounter is limned as in no other work of art.

So through the night the dance was molded. Ritualistic as an Utamaro shunga, innocent as a Persian miniature, blunt as a blue movie, it emerged like a piece of sculpture struggling slowly out of the shapeless stone in which it had been imprisoned.

Two bars, four bars, eight bars at a time, the dance grew to the accompaniment of the piano and the sleet trying to lash its way into the steamy room.

It seemed to Carin and Gino that for each eight bars that stuck and became part of the dance, eight hundred were danced. As the rehearsal grew long, tempers grew short. For a period of almost an hour, nothing looked right to Sonny. He would create steps, the dancers would dance them, and he would reject them, angry at the dancers for not bringing the steps to life, angry at himself for creating such lifeless steps.

Unfortunately for Carin and Gino, nothing could be accepted— or rejected—until it was tried not once but several times, until they had mastered it so it could be objectively judged; and that meant the steps couldn't be marked, they had to be danced full out, by muscles that were teetering on the edge of spasm and collapse.

Not once in the long night did it occur to Carin and Gino to say, "No more. Not one more step." Their combined ages added up to less than forty-five years, but between them they had trained their bodies for nearly thirty of them. For this. Precisely this night, this agony. If blood had burst from their toenails and trickled from their ears and noses, they would have mopped it up, dismissed it as a minor aberration and pressed on. Stopping now would have meant turning their backs on every *plié,* every *tendu,* every pulled muscle and stretched tendon, every blister and bunion, every Saturday class attended while the "real" kids played, every curfew observed while Johnny Carson provided their coevals with a welcome excuse to stay up. Giving up now, with glory in their grasp, would have meant that all that sacrifice had been for nothing. Unthinkable. Tonight was for *them.* At last. They danced.

Before she had left the theater for LuLu Temple, Carin had drawn up a mental equation that took into account every factor she could anticipate, the length of the rehearsal, the amount of energy she would expend, the food she would consume, the emotional cost of the experience. The conclusion of her calculations was inescapable: to avoid any chance of the nightmarish shock that had nearly overcome her at the *Ante Meridian* audition, she would postpone her next insulin shot until the rehearsal was over. What Carin had neglected to factor in was Sonny's desperation; the rehearsal was running far longer than she had believed it could. She had gambled on four or five hours of exertion—maybe six. But eight hours had passed. Ten. Without insulin, while her laboring muscles poured acid wastes into her bloodstream, and every cell in her body gave up potassium to neutralize the acid, and water to help her overburdened kidneys flush the poison from her system. She recognized the symptoms: raging thirst and the feeling in the last ten minutes before every break that her bladder would burst. She was becoming dehydrated, as she had years before at the Detroit Conservatory. She had no idea how much longer Sonny would rehearse them, how much longer she could hold out, gamble . . .

At three-sixteen in the morning, Gino raised Carin over his head in a dizzying lift. Her strength was as important to it as his, but her strength was ebbing, the room was tilting, spinning. She sagged, weak and heavy, and his hands, running sweat—his, not hers; she was bone-dry now—lost their grip on her waist. She tipped, Gino tottered, Sonny and Andrew leaped toward the reeling dancers. Carin's body slid through Gino's hands and hurtled toward the floor. Gino crumpled, trying to fall with her, under her to take the force of her fall with his body. Her torso fell on Gino, her legs hit the floor with a crash. Sonny and Andrew knelt beside the fallen dancers, nudging them gently to sitting positions with a rush of soft, cooing concern, as one would console a baby who had fallen.

"Don't get up," Sonny urged as he and Andrew ran their fingers over the two bodies, probing for injury. Everything seemed intact, but the solicitous prodding continued. Limbs were slowly moved and flexed, aided by six supporting hands. Then slowly, carefully, Gino got to his feet. He twisted his head on his shoulders and raised his arms; he bent from the waist until his forehead grazed his knees, and when he straightened, he was smiling with relief.

Now the three men helped Carin to her feet. She took an unsteady step, winced and raised her foot from the floor as if she had stepped on a burr. Instantly the three men were kneeling again, their attention fixed on her foot. Sonny's hands cradled Carin's ankle as a veterinarian might tend the fetlock of a Derby winner. As Sonny gently moved the joint, Carin winced again, and at a quick glance from Sonny, Gino and Andrew rose, each taking one of Carin's elbows.

"It's all right," Carin said, but Sonny retained his grip on her ankle, and the hands at her elbows didn't move. "Honestly," Carin said. "It just got twisted a little. All I have to do is walk on it."

Sonny looked up at her, frowning.

"Really," Carin said, and Sonny slowly released her foot. Still slung between Gino and Andrew like a horse in a hammock, Carin wiggled her foot, then lowered it to the floor.

"You can let go," she said. But Andrew shook his head and he and Gino continued to support her as she took a tentative step.

"Easy," Sonny said. "Don't rush it."

Carin nodded and moved forward with her retinue, Sonny backing up in front of her, his eyes alternately on her foot and face. Carin forced a smile. "It's fine."

"Can you *relevé*?" She nodded at Sonny. "Let's see."

Slowly, still supported, she rolled from her heels to her toes, then raised the uninjured foot to *passé* so that the whole weight of her body was poised on the affected leg. She lowered her heel to the floor, then *relevé*ed to half-toe again, more quickly and surely now. She nodded. "It's fine."

"You're sure?"

"You think I'd take a chance with my ankle?"

Gino and Andrew released Carin's elbows. She hesitated for an instant, then took a breath and rose to half-toe with a resolute smile.

"*Glissade,*" Sonny said. She began one. "No," Sonny said, "to the left."

Carin had tried to push off from the left, in order to land on the unaffected right ankle, but Sonny's instruction had reversed the movement, forcing her to land in *plié* on the twisted ankle, not from a jump but from a soft, gliding step that would test the ankle without threatening it with destruction if Carin were concealing pain.

The experiment worked: by a massive act of will Carin landed softly, without strain, and to demonstrate the soundness of her ankle, continued left in an *enchainement* of *glissades*. Her determination would have carried her into a wall if Sonny hadn't shouted in time. Then he said, "One *jeté*. A little one."

Carin *jeté*ed, landing in a soft, successful *plié* on her left foot.

"*Okay!*" Sonny said. "Let's take five so we can all pull ourselves together."

Moving slowly, steadily, with a fixed smile on her face and no sign of a limp, Carin picked up her dance bag and left the rehearsal hall. In the corridor she summoned her last strength for an unsteady trot to the rest room where she hastily unlimbered a hypodermic, filled it with half her usual morning dose and injected it through her tights into her thigh. Letting the empty syringe fall, she leaned back against the wall and closed her eyes. The rehearsal hall was well stocked with sugary snacks. She had avoided them all night; if *this* gamble failed, they were there. Anyway, she had gone as far as she could in this direction: if she went into shock now . . . but she wouldn't. Somehow, she would get through this night—to tomorrow—to that theater . . .

"Carin?"

She opened her eyes and looked at the door. Gino's voice asked, "You okay?"

"Sure. Why?"

"Well—it's been fifteen minutes—almost twenty. Sonny sent me out . . ."

Fifteen minutes! She pushed herself off the wall and was relieved to discover that she felt steadier, stronger. She bent to pick up her dance bag, saw the empty syringe, kicked it under the door of a booth and reached for the door with a smile.

As she and Gino reentered the rehearsal hall, Andrew noted her steady progress and improved color, and turned to Sonny with a sigh of relief. "Could *that* have been a disaster!"

"Better believe it," Sonny murmured back. "There's no time to replace her."

At three forty-seven that morning, the dancers resumed their labors, to a cautionary litany from Sonny: "Careful. Just mark it for now. Don't dance full out till I tell you to."

Fifteen minutes later Sonny had forgotten his caveat—and Carin's fall—and was snapping, "How can I see what I've got if you don't show it to me!"

Fortunately for Carin, her guess in the rest room had been the right one: the level of acids and sugar in her blood was dropping, the suicidal disorientation of her vital organs had been reversed and, healthiest sign of all for a dancer, she was sweating again; waste was being eliminated by a normal, healthy process. As for her ankle, taking a leaf from the dancers' homeopathic pharmacopeia which prescribes a hair of the dog for everything short of shattered bones, Carin was "dancing the injury out."

At five forty-five Carin and Gino showed Sonny everything he had choreographed to that point. As exhausted as they were, the repetition was as important to them as to him, since in less than sixteen hours they would be performing these steps onstage in front of an audience, and just as actors wake in a cold sweat from a nightmare of forgotten lines, dancers live with the terror of a memory lapse that could leave them bumbling or frozen in full view of God and the *New York Times*. Where actors memorize with their minds, dancers must memorize with their bodies, imprinting a sequence comprising thousands of coordinated movements of feet, legs, body, arms, shoulders, neck and hands on the muscles that will perform them. Only repetition—by those muscles—encodes the data so that the sound of the music will trigger the movement without conscious mental command. Thirty years of practice had trained Carin's and Gino's muscles to record the data quickly and recall them on command, but there were literally tens of thousands of kinetic messages for the dancers' exhausted muscles to memorize for these six minutes of choreography—and one night in which to pull off this mnemonic stunt.

The long sequence ended abruptly on an unresolved chord and

movement, with Carin aloft in a lift, the pianist simply stopping mid-phrase to spare his throbbing fingers a single unnecessary collision with the keys. Carin slid down the front of Gino's body, landing flatfooted and graceless, in contrast to the smooth control that had preceded this moment.

The dancers waited, gasping for breath, their hands on their hips, their faces blank with exhaustion, while Sonny strolled thoughtfully, casually to the furthest corner of the room, Andrew padding at his heels. When Sonny spoke, his words were for Andrew only. "What do you think?"

"Gorgeous!"

"I want the truth!" Sonny's face was expressionless, but his snarl was venomous.

"I'm telling you the truth, Sonny. Can't you see it yourself?"

Sonny sagged into the corner, bracing himself in it. "I can't see anything. My eyes won't focus." He drew a hand across them and Andrew was alarmed to see a tremor in it. His response was not only low but gentle.

"Of course not. Do you know what time it is?"

"I stopped looking at my watch hours ago."

"Maybe you should." Sonny was silent, staring blankly out of the corner. "Even if you *do* finish, how are they gonna dance it tonight? They haven't had any sleep since the day before yester—"

"I'm going to finish and they're going to dance it! Tonight."

"Why, Sonny?" Sonny stared out of his corner, cornered. "Would it be such a tragedy if the number didn't go in tonight?"

Sonny's reply was small and hard as a diamond. "Yes."

"Why? We've got *some*thing to open the second act with. Okay, nobody likes it, and the critics'll say it stinks, but we've got four weeks to replace it with this."

"I've got tonight. Period." Andrew stared at him. "Wally's after my ass."

Andrew shrugged. "Producers are always nervous before the out-of-town opening. No matter what they say, they don't really know what they've got . . ."

"What he's got is Bob Fosse's phone number. So if the Philadelphia critics roast the show, I'm out!"

"Because you didn't let him fill the show with fat-ass hookers!"

"Maybe, but he's walking around telling everybody the second-act opening's killing the show." His eyes swept toward Carin and Gino, waiting where he had left them, heads bent, eyes half-closed, like bulls whose shoulder muscles have been minced by the picadors to keep their horns down. "Well, he's not going to have that excuse. He'll see his new second-act opening tonight—so if the show rolls over and dies, he'll have to look for another patsy. I'm not going to oblige him by committing suicide in Philadelphia."

"Suicide in Philadelphia is redundant," Andrew muttered.

Sonny turned to the pianist, who was staring disconsolately at his hands. "How much more music is there, Gil?"

The pianist unfolded a yard of manuscript. "About a minute and a half."

Sonny looked up at his dancers. "Got your breath?" They nodded without looking up. "Okay, we're heading for the finish line. Another two hours at the most."

Sonny was true to his word. Two hours later, as Philadelphia's early risers groped for their throbbing alarm clocks, the pianist's hands slid numbly from the keyboard, Gino eased Carin down from the last lift of the *pas de deux* and Sonny ran toward the two dancers with his arms outstretched. Since Carin had sagged against Gino, Sonny was able to enfold both dancers in one embrace.

"You'll . . . get . . . all . . . wet," Carin gasped, but Sonny hugged her harder, pressing her against Gino.

"Thank you," Sonny said.

"It . . . looks . . . okay?" Gino asked.

"Fabulous!" Andrew cried.

Now the brutal night's final hurdle faced the dancers: eight long blocks between LuLu Temple and their hotel. At this hour there would be no cruising taxis, and Carin and Gino would be exposed to icy winds on dangerously weakened muscles. Sixteen hours of agonizing work could be wiped out by one crippling spasm.

"Get changed," Sonny said.

"Into what?" Gino asked, waving weakly at the chair over which he had laid his street clothes: a pair of jeans, a plaid shirt, a denim jacket; yesterday afternoon the weather had been mild.

"What've *you* got?" Sonny asked Carin. She indicated a little pile of denim and a light raincoat on another chair. Sonny stepped close to Gino and measured himself against him, then glanced at Andrew, who was standing near Carin. "Change into what you've got," he said to the dancers.

"But . . ." Gino said.

"Change," Sonny ordered.

Carin picked up her towels and clothes and left the room. Gino peeled off his soggy T-shirt. Carin reappeared at the door, saying, "The room where I changed—it's locked. Everything's locked."

"Change in the hall," Sonny replied.

"It's freezing out there," Andrew observed.

"I'll change in the hall," Gino said, reaching for his street clothes.

"Nobody'll change out there," Sonny said, unbuckling his belt and peeling off his trousers.

"What're you doing?" Carin asked.

Sonny tossed his pants to Gino. "Gino'll wear these, over his clothes." As Gino bent to pull off his tights, Sonny said, "They should fit over your jeans. I'm a couple of sizes bigger than you." He nodded at Andrew. "Give Carin your clothes."

As Andrew pulled off his shirt, Carin said, "But how will *you* get back to the hotel?"

"Joggers," Sonny said, taking off his shirt. "Nobody'll look twice."

"You'll catch pneumonia!" Carin exclaimed.

Sonny snapped, "Get out of those wet clothes!"

Gino was wriggling out of his dance belt. Carin turned away from the three men and pulled off her shirt and tights. "Be sure you're completely dry before you get dressed," Sonny commanded.

Carin applied her towels to her glistening body, but they already contained as much moisture as they could hold. A voice said, "Here." She half-turned: Gino was proffering a towel. "Thanks," she said and took the towel, careful not to look down. He smiled, careful not to look down. She smiled, reflecting that, no matter what else he might be, he was a perfect partner, considerate, strong, unselfish, tender, like—like Nureyev on that little screen twelve years ago, with Fonteyn—a dream prince. . . .

As Carin toweled herself dry, Gino dressed across the room. When the two dancers had put on their street clothes, they were pulled and prodded into additional layers of shirts and pants, topped by every coat in the room.

That morning in Philadelphia, there *was* no morning. Night, trapped in a surly vise between city and lowering clouds, remained stolidly in place. The bulky figures that lumbered out of LuLu like Michelin logos bent forward against the sleet that slanted meanly down, irascibly refusing to convert to gentle snow. Two blocks from LuLu a pair of eccentric joggers in underpants sped past Carin and Gino with a jaunty wave. At the next corner Carin faltered: the glacial rain had eaten through two layers of denim and, despite Sonny and Andrew's sacrifice, her calf muscles were tightening ominously. Assailed by the same symptoms, Gino slid an arm around Carin's padded shoulders, and the ponderous mass waddled on.

In the gloom of this stubborn night, the deserted lobby of the hotel looked especially drab, but to the dripping dancers it was Eden. They shook themselves like dogs, spraying frigid water over shabby armchairs, but there was no one behind the front desk to protest. A trail of water ahead of them attested to the prior arrival of the joggers; Carin had half-expected to encounter them a block from the hotel, frozen in mid-stride, two ice monuments to Hanes. "Welcome to the glamorous world of show business," Gino muttered. Carin shuddered. He put his arms around her and growled, "Just what we needed: sixteen hours in a goddamn steam bath, then a brisk swim in the Arctic Ocean. You know what's gonna happen when we go to sleep?"

"Knots." Gino nodded grimly, and Carin looked at him, pale. "What'll we do? We've got to be in that theater in a few hours . . ."

"I'm getting into a hot tub."

"You'll wake up your roommate. The tech rehearsal probably lasted till two or three in the morning."

Gino shook his head. "No problem. No roommate. I always take a single on the road." Carin remembered why. "You worried about waking Diane?"

"Sure. If I start running water in the tub . . ."

"Come on up to my room. You won't be keeping me awake 'cause we're both in the same boat." She didn't move. "I said boat, not tub. Look, even if it *were* a pass, who's got the strength?"

Carin managed a smile, but she shook her head.

In the elevator two buttons were pressed in silence; then as the battered door slid shut and the elevator began to move, Carin slumped against the wall and closed her eyes. Gino leaned against the opposite wall, studying her. "You going to be able to sleep?"

Her eyes opened. "I don't know. I wish Terry were here."

"Terry?"

"You know, my roommate. He gives unbelievable massages."

"So do I."

The elevator stopped with a bump, and the door clattered open. On the dingy wall opposite the open door a tilted sign proclaimed 8. Carin, still slumped against the wall, stared blankly at the rakish 8. Gino waited a requisite moment, then pressed the Close button. Perhaps out of exhaustion, Carin offered no protest as the door slid shut and the elevator resumed its ascent.

In Gino's room, Carin, still roly-poly in her layers of insulation, lumbered into the bathroom with her dance bag and closed the door. Gino stared after her a moment, then peeled his protective layers, got into a short flannel robe and sat down on the bed, gently massaging his heavy calves.

In the bathroom Carin unwrapped herself, twisted the worn handles in the tub and, as a torrid geyser splashed on stained porcelain, dug into her dance bag. Extracting the leatherette pouch, she sat on the edge of the tub, filled a syringe with short-acting crystalline zinc insulin and shot the silvery specific into her thigh. It had been five hours since the injection in the LuLu Temple rest room; Carin was herself again, in charge. She knew what to do. Like dance, diabetes had become a ritual to be observed, unswervingly, unquestioningly.

When the syringe was empty, a practiced flick of her wrist withdrew steel from flesh. Then she looked around the bathroom, unraveled a foot of toilet paper, wrapped the disposable syringe in it and aimed the soft packet at the wastebasket. Arm cocked, she paused, reconsidered and tucked the incriminating evidence into her dance bag for discreet disposal later. She buried the pouch at the bottom of her dance bag, swung her legs over the edge of the tub and lowered herself into the salubrious broth.

When the water stopped running, Gino called, "Everything okay?"

The response came one slow, enraptured word at a time. "Nothing has ever felt better in my entire life."

Gino smiled. "Good."

As he resumed his slow, contemplative massage, Carin called to him, "Don't worry, I won't be selfish. I know you hurt as much as I do."

"I'm okay."

"No, you're not. I promise I won't take more than five minutes."

"Take as much time as you want."

He lay back. When he hauled his legs to the bed, he grimaced. Thirty seconds later he was asleep. When Carin emerged from the bathroom wrapped in a towel, he sat up with a guilty start, trying not to blink and squint.

"You fell asleep."

He shook his head and said, "No," but he looked at the window to gauge the time. The window was no help: the morning was still being held at bay. He turned back to Carin, who was holding out a soggy bundle.

"We forgot something. How am I going to get down to my room? These things feel like they've been soaked in ice water. If I put them on again, I'll need another hot bath when I get downstairs."

Gino got up, swinging his legs carefully to the floor. "You don't have to go downstairs." Carin looked at the double bed. "Anyway, you don't have to worry about it till after the massage." He waved a hand over the bed. "Stretch out. I just want to get in the tub for a few minutes."

"You could lend me a shirt and a pair of pants. That'd get me downstairs."

"Sure. After my bath and your massage." Before she could respond, he asked, "Did you leave the water in the tub?"

"No."

"Why not? It's the same sweat." He went into the bathroom. Carin stood numbly for a long moment, then lay down on the bed.

When Gino came out of the bathroom in his robe, toweling his hair dry, Carin's eyes were closed. He paused as he saw her, then moved quietly to the edge of the bed and looked down at her. A moment later he picked up a blanket at the foot of the bed, drew it gently over her and smiled as he was reminded of something.

What precisely? Oh, yes. One of those old-time movies from the Thirties. Like so many of his fellow gypsies, Gino was addicted to "The Late Show." *The guy—Clark Gable or William Powell or somebody like that—had the hots for the girl,* Gino recalled, *and when he finally got her alone in his room, she fell asleep, and he could've jumped on her bones, but he didn't. He pulled the cover up over her very carefully, so he wouldn't wake her up, and then the picture dissolved to the next morning: birds were singing, the guy was stretched out on the couch and the girl was still a virgin. Fuck that,* Gino thought, *she's ready. So am I.*

Carin opened her eyes and looked up at him. "What're you smiling at?"

"I just had one of those *déjà vues.*" But he pronounced it *déjà vous,* which converted it from "already seen" to an oddly appropriate "already you."

"I'll bet," she said, sitting up.

"You fell asleep."

"No, I didn't." But she too glanced at the window. When she turned back to him, there was a note of panic in her voice. "What'll we do if we can't sleep? Sonny keeps saying the number goes in tonight, no matter what."

"You'll be able to sleep after I've worked those knots out. Turn over."

Once again fatigue overruled protest, and Carin rolled over on her stomach. Gino seated himself astride her legs and tugged at the towel that encased her. She came up on her elbows and twisted her head to look at him. He merely shrugged and waited. After a moment she plopped wearily down again, and Gino opened the towel and slid it from under her. As his strong, gnarled hands began to knead the long muscles of her back, she winced, and he said, "Relax." He probed again, finding points of tension as hard as stone. She jumped and he said soothingly, "Yeah, I know. Try not to tense up." He stroked her back with his palms, long comforting caresses. "Breathe."

She took several deep breaths and gave herself to his hands. Whatever his motive—and Carin had no doubts about it—he hadn't lied about his skills as a masseur.

He had already touched her in all these places innumerable times during the rehearsal. She was naked under his hands now, but with the exceptions of the hourly rests, two brief food breaks and the walk to the hotel, her body had been in his hands since three o'clock yesterday afternoon, and they had been face to face and naked at LuLu half an hour ago . . .

Gino's hands worked their way down her back to her buttocks.

Though he had had even less formal education than most dancers, he had discovered and read mythology on his own, and now, as he kneaded Carin's buttocks, separating them to reveal flashes of anus and vulva, he wondered if this was what had turned Pygmalion on as he worked Galatea's clay.

There might be two therapies in order this dark morning, but massage was emphatically first since tonight was no less important to Gino than to Carin. Gino worked himself lower on Carin's legs and began massaging the backs of her thighs, expertly seeking and finding the tormenting ridges. Carin twitched and moaned, but she asked no quarter and Gino gave none. Sometimes, though, when Carin's moan was especially sharp, Gino murmured, "I know." But the expert punishment continued: Gino needed a partner onstage tonight.

When Gino had done the backs of Carin's calves, she muttered, "Unfair."

"What?"

"You need it as much as I do. More. You've been carrying me around for sixteen hours. You must be dead."

"We'll switch around in a while. Turn over."

The musty room was very still; they had arrived at the Rubicon and both knew it. Carin didn't look up this time. She simply lay on her stomach, her eyes half-closed, and searched inside for the springs and levers of indignation—or at least injunction. When she couldn't find them, she turned over.

Since Gino was kneeling at her feet, he picked up her ankle, cushioning it on his palms. Carefully closing a hand on it, he flexed it and looked up at her. She smiled down at him. "It's okay."

"Are you sure?" He flexed it more strongly, and she winced and sat up. "Shit," Gino said softly.

"Honestly, Gino, it's all right. My whole body's stiff. If you twist my right ankle, you'll get the same reaction. I'll be fine tonight."

"We're lucky as hell."

"God, don't I know it! After all these years . . ."

"I mean your ankle." Guilt colored his words. "I was sweating and I couldn't get a good hold . . ."

She put her hand on his. "It wasn't your fault. I've had worse falls."

They sat silent a moment, staring at each other, then Carin lay back and waited. For the rest of her massage. She knew Gino wouldn't stint. They were servants of a ritual neither would violate: the massage once begun would be finished. After that. . . . Nureyev leaped across the little screen, Carin's first *danseur noble,* her first Tartar; he took Fonteyn's little waist in his powerful hands, he turned her like a shiny bauble, he lifted her like a weightless toy. Perfect partner, gallant prince. . . .

Carin closed her eyes and surrendered again to Gino's hands as they worked their way up the front of her legs, from toes to feet to ankles to knees to thighs and hips and abdomen, Gino inching north until he bestrode her thighs, naked under his robe, his sex lying unapologetically on hers, his fingers probing the hollows in front of her shoulders.

"Too heavy?" he asked.

Now! Her chance to unhorse him and escape. But at the rehearsal their positions had been reversed: Gino had thrown himself beneath her, to cushion her fall. He was a gentle and considerate partner. *You can tell everything about a boy by the way he partners.* Nureyev and Fonteyn looked at each other in closeup on the little screen, defining love forever . . .

"No."

So the *pas de deux* which had begun eighteen hours earlier in the neo-classic cool of LuLu Temple ended in the heat of Gino's bed as he took off his robe and came up to his knees. Freed of Gino's weight, Carin's legs slid on the sheets, opening under him to a wide second position. His *allongée* brought him back to her, and his poised flesh entered hers with all the accumulated tension, mutual awareness and shared exhilaration of the last eighteen hours. He pressed into her with the certitude and authority vested in him—and her—by ten thousand generations of men and women, squared off, like Carin and Gino, in the basic configuration of dance and life: one male, one female, face to face, one on one.

Later, when Gino asked, "Is it all right to come in you?" Carin said, "Yes."

"You're sure?"

An important question. On the list of no-no's, pregnancy ranked near the top of the scale, along with torn ligaments and compound fractures.

"It's okay. I'm on the pill" *Because of Chris. Oh, Jesus!*

But her guilt drowned in his orgasm, which triggered hers.

Then they slept without separating.

SIXTEEN, two, three, four
Développé en arrière

Gino spent his teen years on the south side of Boston, in the Italian section. Very few Southie girls aspired to be ballet dancers; none of the boys did. Except Gino.

Gino's mother and father were The Dancing di Vitos—even to him. When he brought a friend home from school, he wouldn't say, "This is my mother and father," he would say, with a note of pride that was lost on his Southie friends, "This is The Dancing di Vitos."

In the Thirties or Forties, the di Vitos' acrobatic ballroom dancing might have taken them to the Latin Quarter, Chez Paree, the Coconut Grove or even the Starlight Roof, in the nimble and prosperous footsteps of the Castles, the DeMarcos and Veloz and Yolanda, but when they began their career, in the Fifties, the road to fame and fortune dead-ended in a numbing succession of roadhouses, VFW halls and blue-collar nightclubs where the patrons drank beer and made attenuated kissing noises every time Sally di Vito opened her legs.

Those shabby temples of proletarian pleasure comprised the only world Gino knew for the first twelve years of his life. Home was whatever rooming house or plasterboard motel was most convenient to the current gig. Education was principally overheard conversations, at rooming house or motel in the daytime, in nightclub or beer hall at night. Gino knew the name of every heavyweight contender before he knew who had discovered America. Periodically Gino's lack of formal education would riddle Sally with guilt, and a frenetic period of tutoring would begin. Seizing on whatever came to hand— newspapers, racing forms, magazines—Sally would rise early, roust a grumbling Gino out of bed and cram him with miscellaneous data. Once she filched a dictionary from behind the bar of the club in which she was working and tried to teach Gino spelling, beginning with *aardvark*. These didactic orgies were, for Gino, blessedly brief. As he pored over his peculiar textbooks, he knew that the day wasn't far off when Sally's aching body would rebel against being forced out of bed for the day's lessons, and Gino's life would return to the comfortable troglodytic routine which precisely paralleled his parents'.

Since a sitter was precluded by the di Vitos' standard of living, little Gino was excluded from—and spared—nothing. He kept his parents' hours and lived their life. He arrived at the job with them, waited in the dressing room if there was one, or in the kitchen or at the bar, while his parents performed, shared their pizza or burgers at two A.M., retired with them at dawn and rose with them at three or four in the afternoon—when Sally wasn't playing her dominie role.

Gino's real education took place in the dressing rooms, kitchens and murky backstage corridors of the clubs in which Sal and Sally worked. (For a short time the act was *called* Sal and Sally; it didn't help.) While the di Vitos danced, Gino probed the netherworld that was as familiar and comfortable to him as the raft and river were to Huck Finn.

A waiter introduced him to cigarettes at six, a drummer to joints at eight; he often sipped beer from half-empty glasses that were brought back to the kitchen; and when he was nine, Sally opened a backstage door to find her son seated on a wooden chair, staring in puzzled fascination at the hennaed head of a chorus girl bobbing up and down over his lap. The chorus girl, on a high, on a bet, on her knees in front of the little boy, her attention fixed on the fellated object, thin and stiff as a pencil, never heard Sally's swift approach, silent as a falcon's stoop, or saw her bend and whip off a stiletto-heeled shoe. As Gino watched, frozen with interest, Sally swung the shoe like a hammer, and when the heel, reinforced with a core of steel for The Dancing di Vitos' act, thudded into the base of the chorus girl's skull, her busy mouth popped open, her head flew back, she stiffened, and fell like a stone.

"Put your wee-wee away," Sally said as matter-of-factly as if she had just taken her little boy to the bathroom. In its tumescent state this took some doing, but Sally helped, then led her son away. By four that morning The Dancing Di Vitos had put a hundred miles between themselves and the scene of the double crime. When Gino had been tucked into bed, Sal observed that the chorus girl might have clamped her jaws shut when the shoe struck; had Sally thought of that? Sally shuddered and said no. The next day, after a discreet phone call to a trustworthy busboy, Sal reported that according to preliminary reports, the chorus girl might never be the same again. "I certainly *hope* not!" Sally muttered righteously.

A few weeks later Gino was fitted with a little tuxedo, and the two Dancing di Vitos became three. The act was no better, but at least Sally knew that while Gino was onstage he was safe from marauding chorus girls—and boys.

Because he had never known any other life, Gino took whatever came as a matter of course. On the rare occasions when he encountered what he thought of as "real" children—that is, children who lived in one place, slept in one bed in one house, and went to school—he stared at them uneasily. If they spoke to him, he was afraid to reply. He had the illusion that he spoke another language—Nightclub—and if he tried to communicate with these strange domesticated children, they would laugh at him.

Once, when the di Vitos were appearing at an American Legion hall, the commander of the post showed up at their rehearsal with his daughter. She was Gino's age and size, and promptly trotted across the room to stare at him, round-eyed. When she smiled and spoke to him, his only response was to stand on his head and walk on his hands, that being the most eloquent thing he could say in his language. The little girl, thinking he was making fun of her, burst into tears, and Sal, seeing a night's pay suddenly in jeopardy, slapped Gino. Gino simply stared at his father, red-faced, while the commander, his arm around his unhappy child, waited for additional satisfaction. With one eye on the commander, Sal continued slapping Gino's face. The operation was conducted in businesslike silence, except for the sharp sound of the slaps, Sal swinging away, his hand describing a longer arc with each blow, Gino unflinching, his body tilted toward the blows to keep him on his feet, the commander waiting for a sign that satisfaction had been exacted. When tears filled Gino's eyes, then spilled on his crimson cheeks, the commander turned and led his affronted child away. That night after the performance, Sal let Gino order the pizza. Gino ordered the works and threw up on the street outside the pizzeria.

During the di Vitos' final two years on the road, Gino eschewed further contact with "real" children, settling happily for the raunchy camaraderie of the adults whose world he inhabited. Chorus girls from Florida to Minnesota continued to compete in the Defloration-of-Gino Sweepstakes, with Gino's increasingly enthusiastic cooperation. Because it was impossible for Sally to police every moment of her son's life, the sweepstakes was won by a twenty-three-year-old exotic dancer (Consuelo, *née* Barbara Ann) when Gino was twelve. Since he was still prepubescent, hence orgasmless, hence infinitely arousable, the congress lasted the better part of three hours, to Consuelo's astonished delight. She cried when the di Vitos moved on to the next stand and began an earnest search for another tireless twelve-year-old.

To compensate for the continuing absence of formal education in their son's life—Sally had finally reconciled herself to her tutorial shortcomings—Sal and Sally embarked on a campaign to teach Gino everything they knew about their art. That added up to a daily dance class: tap one day, acrobatic the next, adagio the next, ballet (or Sally's version of ballet) the next.

The arrival of Gino's manhood was announced to Sally by a thirty-year-old chorus girl in Oklahoma City.

"I'm pregnant."

"Whattaya want, a medal?"

"Child support."

"Go to the welfare."

"It's Gino."

"What's Gino?"

"The father."

Sally rose. "He's thirteen fuckin' years old!"

"You just summed it up, Sally. In a nutshell."

"You know what you can get for raping a thirteen-year-old?"

"You got it backward, Sally. Men rape women."

"And whores rape kids!"

"This 'kid' knows what he's doing."

"So does his mother." Sally lifted a foot and slid off a shoe. The same stiletto heel. She hefted it. "You know what this is?"

The chorus girl retreated a step. "I got something coming, Sally . . ."

Sally advanced, brandishing the shoe like a gun, its heel pointed at the chorus girl. "You bet you do—an' you're gonna get it."

The chorus girl backed toward the door. "The son knocks me up, the mother tries to kill me!"

"The bitch fucks children! The mother gets revenge." Sally raised the shoe. The chorus girl shrieked and fled.

That night The Dancing di Vitos left Oklahoma City—and the road.

"How're we supposed to earn our living?" Sal demanded.

"God will provide," Sally said, finding sudden, unaccustomed solace in religion.

"He's *been* providing—and he's ready to provide again, in the Café Elegante in El Paso, next Tuesday . . ."

"No more clubs!"

"We gotta eat."

"We'll eat. In one place. Fifty-two weeks a year."

"What place?"

The response was instantaneous, and it surprised even Sally. "Boston."

"Why Boston?"

"Why not?"

Sal had no defense against Sally's logic, so The Dancing di Vitos canceled the Café Elegante and headed for Boston. Sally's newfound faith in God led her to South Boston—"There's plenty of Italians, and churches; just look around"—where, after several nerve-racking weeks, they invested their life savings ($2,708.43) in a storefront space that became Sal and Sally's Dance Studio—Tap, Acrobatic, Ballet.

Blue-collar Boston took slowly—and suspiciously—to Terpsichore, but the di Vitos lived behind the studio, so the overhead was low, and, most important, there were no marauding chorus girls or boys, and for the first time in his life, Gino could attend a real school, with real teachers and real kids.

The di Vitos had been in residence a week before Sally could get up the courage to escort her son to the neighborhood school. What would they think of this strange thirteen-year-old gypsy boy who could turn somersaults in the air but had never even attended kindergarten? What would they think of his *mother?*

Sally looked at the pale, sullen face of the boy walking beside her. She reached for his hand: it was as clammy as hers. Neither of them said a word during the ten-minute walk, and when they sat before the registration secretary, embarrassment enjoined them from looking at each other.

The interview went as badly as they'd foreseen, with the secretary finally confessing that she didn't know whether Gino belonged in the seventh grade or the second; she'd have to arrange a meeting with the principal.

Gino was finally assigned to the fifth grade, where he loomed over his ten-year-old classmates like a sullen Everest. He tried to hide his shame with lofty disdain, and if he hadn't been obliged to respond to his teachers, would have affected an unintelligible accent to explain his incongruity and discourage fraternization. His final recourse was to slump loutishly with his fists doubled challengingly on the desk in front of him as his classmates stared.

Most of Gino's teachers ended by ignoring the churlish promontory in the middle of the room, but Miss Rossi thought she could see through Gino's facade. Unfortunately, Gino was just one of a tidal wave of problems washing over Miss Rossi and her colleagues in the beleaguered school system, so Gino's facade remained unpierced.

Remedial classes took up some of the slack in Gino's education, but during the two and a half years of Gino's formal instruction, the only peace, pleasure and reality he found was in Sal and Sally's studio, to which he repaired the moment he was released from the confinement of the classroom. Hurrying home, he would wrap himself in the comforting clasp of tights and leg warmers and join whatever class was in progress. There his real education continued at a feverish pace. At night he worked alone in the studio, devising tricks and routines, trying to master the movements he had seen on TV or at the movies.

The skinny boy in the mirror put on mass. He grew tall and hard and adept. On his sixteenth birthday he told Sal and Sally he only wanted one present: their agreement that tomorrow, and forever after, he wouldn't have to go back to that school. Or any school where the students sat down. Having met society's demands for two and a half years, Sally surrendered without a struggle, and Gino's education began in earnest.

For months it had been apparent to Gino that not all the precious secrets of dance were locked behind the doors of Sal and Sally's studio, so his horizon expanded to other dance schools and other teachers.

His new teachers were astonished to discover that the cocky newcomer who could perform some of the most hazardous moves in the ballet book didn't know the name of a single one of them. When the teacher asked for an *entrechat quatre,* Gino simply stared; when his classmates soared aloft in the movement, Gino said, "Oh," and performed a *six.*

Some of his movement was ragged, or brusque, or gauche, but in the next three years Gino learned his ballet French and acquired some of the polish he would need in New York. Like Carin, he found that New York bristled with well-trained dancers ready to serve their art for carfare and lunch money. When it became apparent to him that, because his formal ballet training had begun late, he would never attain the degree of turnout and finesse demanded by a classical company, he turned his attention to modern dance and, finally, to Broadway. There he found a home.

Technically stronger than many of his fellow gypsies, he could meet the demands of any Broadway choreographer, and with all his faults, he came as close to a classical style as any Broadway show demanded. Most important, Gino projected a strength, a maleness, that was all too rare when he began his Broadway career. The mintiest Broadway choreographers abhorred male dancers whose movements onstage were as effeminate as their own, so Gino quickly became the Broadway chorus beau ideal.

Perhaps his fabled sexual exploits were designed, at least in part, as a form of advertising, to enhance and expand his professional image. When he began his formal ballet training in Boston, he quickly discovered the social advantage of being the only straight in a class full of nubile girls; it was easy enough for someone as streetwise as Gino to translate that personal plus into a professional one.

When the dance boom effaced the stigma that had frightened heterosexual men away, Gino's machismo became less distinctive, but by then his reputation was firmly established, onstage and off.

And now, in his new show, he had cut another notch in the belt above his formidable gun.

SEVENTEEN, two, three, four
Renversé

Though the little traveling alarm clock trilled timidly enough, Diane sat up as if a cannon had gone off. Then, clutching her back with a groan as her muscles reminded her of yesterday's labors, she reached for the clock in slow motion. Before she was halfway to it, the trill had hiccupped to silence.

She stared uncomprehendingly at the clock, then, turning gingerly to the other bed, asked, "What time did you . . ."

The bed was untouched, sheet and blanket folded crisply back, waiting.

Moira cranked a page out of her typewriter and muttered, "Thirty."

Chris looked up. "Finished?"

Moira added the page to several others and tapped the stack smartly on her desk to even it. "Another masterpiece. You'll be overwhelmed."

"The 'Elaine's' piece?"

She read from the top of the first page. " 'Mecca for Models, Movie Stars, Media Maestros and Manicotti.' "

"How about a little alliteration?"

She slid a corner of the stack into a stapler and bopped the handle. "Don't blame me, Mr. Stevenson. Talk to our esteemed editor. He's the one with the alliteration fetish." She dropped the article next to her typewriter and pushed away from her desk. "Elaine invited me back. She said I could bring a guest—on her."

"The power of the press."

"Interested in lunch?"

"Me?"

"Sure. I don't know when I'll be able to make a gesture like this again."

"Maybe you ought to save it for a big night."

"The way our generous publisher staffs this paper, by the time I get a night off, Elaine won't remember me. What do you say?"

Chris tapped a pen on his desk, then replied, "Sure, why not?"

"Where's Elaine?" Moira asked.

"Not in yet," the waiter said.

"When'll she be in?"

"Nine or ten tonight." Chris laughed. Moira glared at him, then turned back to the waiter. "Can you call her?" He shook his head. "Why not?"

"She's sleeping."

"Oh. Well . . ."

"We'd like a table," Chris said. Ignoring Moira's apprehensive glance, he took her arm and steered her in the waiter's wake.

When they were seated at a table, Moira said, "I don't have enough cash!"

"I do."

"*I* invited *you*."

Chris spread his hands. "Fate."

"Forget it, Chris. When you see the prices . . ."

"I've got twenty dollars on me. We'll eat light."

"I've got about five dollars."

"Fine. All we have to save is bus fare."

"I'll pay you back."

"No, you won't."

The prices proved less forbidding than Moira had predicted: she had done her research at night, when the dinner menu was in effect. There were even funds for wine—two glasses each. By the time coffee was served, Moira was relaxed and, for her, expansive.

"Here's what I think we ought to do," she said. "Organize."

"What?"

"A strike."

"Against the *East Sider*?"

"Against Ian. That masthead's a fraud."

"Hold it . . ."

"I'm sure the public would be interested in knowing who Rose Kibbe and Miguel Figueroa are. Off with our masks! Off with the boss's mask!"

"Hold it! I just came to the paper, remember?"

"Where's your pride? Where's your proletarian fire?"

"Burned itself out on campus eight years ago."

Moira's eyes widened. "Campus radical?"

He frowned. "I watched."

"Where?"

"Well, Kent State . . ."

"Oh, wow, as we used to say."

"I didn't *go* to Kent State, I just happened to be there—that day—and I covered it for a Detroit paper."

"You were already on a paper?"

"Campus correspondent—at my *own* school."

"Which was?"

"Michigan."

"Not exactly the University of Leningrad."

"Compared to Kent State, it was Bible school."

"Columbia wasn't," she said, the rumble of ancient battles echoing pleasantly. "SDS."

"You?"

She smiled. "Everybody's supposed to be mellowed out and laid back nowadays. At least we cared about things. Mind if I smoke?"

"You smoke at the office."

"That's different."

"How?"

"At work it's *sauve qui peut*—and I can't write without smoking—but this is social, and if the smoke bothers you . . ."

"It doesn't."

She lit a cigarette and reached for her wineglass. It was empty. "Can we afford any more wine?"

"Sure, if you don't mind walking back to the office—or stiffing the waiter." She sighed and relinquished the glass. Chris pushed his across the table to her. She shook her head. "Go ahead, I don't want any more."

"No, thanks. I don't like white. Too acidy. Gives me headaches."

He indicated her empty glass. "What about that?"

"Red's different. A complete food. *Bon pour le sang.*"

Chris grinned. "Where'd you study your oenology?"

"In France."

"In fact?"

"Half. I lived there—and I studied—but not oenology."

"What'd you study?"

"*Civilisation française.*" She made a face.

"Bummer?"

"It's a course the Sorbonne gives for foreigners. Full of bored rich kids looking for an excuse to hang out in Paris, expatriates in the market for busywork, remittance types trying to justify their existence . . ."

"Was this before or after your radical career?"

"During. You won't believe it, but that's why I went to Paris."

"Shopping for radicals?"

"Shopping for radical*ism*. The 'real thing.' By the time I'd finished my junior year, SDS was turning into an unfunny joke, so I headed for greener pastures."

"Don't you mean redder ones?" She smiled. "Why France?"

"Remember Danny the Red and the *Enragés?*"

"My favorite group. I've got all their albums."

"Daniel Cohn-Bendit and the students. If the Communist party and the unions hadn't sold them out, they might've taken over the whole country."

"And torn down all the Keep Off the Grass signs. And then what?"

"Probably chaos. But I tended to be rather undiscriminating at twenty, and I figured the old revolutionary fire was still smoldering somewhere in France."

"In *Civilisation française* 101?"

"I told you I was undiscriminating. Besides, it was the only Sorbonne course open to me when I arrived."

"Did you ever locate your smoldering fires?"

"Sort of."

"Which brand?"

"It's hard to label."

"Maoist?"

"More like Jesuit."

"I didn't know the Jesuits had jumped the fence. I'd heard a few of them were climbing it . . ."

"He was a priest."

"Who?"

"A friend of mine. I lived with him for almost a year."

Chris whistled appreciatively.

"What's that for?"

"The priest. That's ten points on anybody's scale."

"I only get five points."

"You never went all the way?"

"I went all the way the day I met him. But he was defrocked."

"Before, after—or during?"

"Before. Remember the worker-priests?"

"Sure. Some of them turned out to be more worker than priest."

"He was one of those."

"Where'd you meet him?"

"At the Sorbonne. He was teaching philosophy. A very hot course. I audited it, and one of the students introduced me to him. We went to a *rhumerie* in the *quartier,* and I got my mind blown—among other things."

Chris laughed.

"You should have heard Jean-Louis on Marxist eschatology."

"That's a contradiction in terms."

"Exactly what I would've said in my SDS days." She ground her roach-short butt into the ashtray, fumbled a cigarette out of her pack, lit it hastily and resumed as she waved the match out. "But, look—when God got booted off His throne, what did the Left stick up there? A new god, called History. A new name for the same old con game. God is dead—and now the heroic Soviet worker is sacrificing himself for History! His grandchildren will reap the fruits of his sacrifice in some distant Proletarian Paradise." Smoke and laughter gusted from her as she slapped the table hard enough to make the dishes bounce. "Perfect! Substitute *the future* for *heaven* and you've got Marxist eschatology. Substitute *history* for *divinity* and you've got Marxist theodicy. Substitute *Das Kapital* for the Holy Book and you've got Revelation . . ."

Chris laughed. "You make the Kremlin sound more Catholic than the Vatican."

"Well, what does it sound like to you? That's what I found in France. Can you imagine what it meant to someone who thought she was throwing off the shackles of Blessed Sacrament High School when she joined SDS? When you put them side by side, you can't tell a cardinal from a commissar. All I did at Columbia was trade catechisms!"

"What do you believe in now?"

"Separate, simple facts, one small truth at a time. That's why I came back and studied journalism."

"And took a job at the *East Sider*? I'm sorry," he said quickly. "That was a cheap shot."

"No, it wasn't," she said equably. "You work there too." He nodded. "Why?"

"It was the best I could get for now. Your reason too?"

"In a way. I wanted to be independent."

"Of what?" She stared at the table, and when she finally looked up with a faint, neutral smile, Chris veered to, "Isn't it hard?"

"Sure. Isn't it hard for you? Ian's a certifiable barbarian."

"No, I mean your—attitude about things. I think people have a very strong yearning to live in an orderly universe. It almost seems to be instinctive, genetic. Look at all the time and energy that's gone into trying to construct one unified system after another. No one's immune, not even scientists."

"I know."

"Well, don't you ever feel unsure of yourself?"

"Sure. I miss the good old days when I had all the answers."

"And now you've got . . ."

"All the questions. And a lot of options." She stubbed her cigarette out. "It's not a bad feeling. A little lonely sometimes. A little scary. But exciting." She slid a cigarette out of her pack and lit it.

"You know you smoke too much?"

Smoke trickled from her nostrils. "Yes."

"How do compulsions rate in your canon?"

"Not very high. I think free will's a fact."

"Do you believe in exercising it?"

"Sometimes. But I haven't decided yet."

"Decided what?"

"Which is an exercise of free will: smoking or not smoking."

"So you sit there like Buridan's ass . . ."

"Smoking myself to death." She ground the cigarette out in the ashtray.

"I guess we should get back to the office," Chris said.

"Why?"

"That's what we're paid for."

"We're paid to write. I've written. You saw it."

"That doesn't do me much good."

"What've you got left?"

"*What's Up* and a piece on Christmas vacations."

"I'll help you with the Christmas story."

"You've got your own . . ."

"*I'm* busy, but Rose Kibbe's sitting around with nothing but time on her hands. If you play hooky with me today, I'll pitch in for you tomorrow."

Chris studied her. "You may have solved a problem for me."

"The Christmas piece?"

"No. Distraction."

"You *are* distracted or you *want* to be?"

"Want to be." He stood up. "Where to?"

"My place?"

The hotel room was empty when Carin darted in, swathed in Gino's robe, her clothes held gingerly before her in a soggy bundle. The hiss of the shower drew her glance toward the closed bathroom door. She took a deep breath, glanced up at the ceiling, then dropped her wet clothes on a straight chair near the door, moved slowly to her bed and sat on the edge of it.

She was immobile for several minutes, then, slowly, she extended her left leg and flexed her foot, her eyes on her ankle. Flex, point, flex, point. She raised the leg so that it soared straight up from her hip, and flexed her foot again. This time she winced and quickly took the strain off her ankle by breaking the straight line of the leg with a bent knee. Taking her foot in her hands, she brought the abused ankle close to her face and examined it as she massaged it anxiously.

The hissing stopped, and Carin quickly lowered her leg. When Diane came out of the bathroom in a robe, Carin was staring blankly into space.

Diane stopped. "Well!" Carin looked up. "The motherfucker *did* it!"

Carin's windpipe knotted. "Diane . . ."

But Diane was looming over her, emanating shampoo and warm terry cloth. "The bastard worked you all night! How does he expect you to drag yourself onstage tonight?"

Carin exhaled slowly. "Oh."

" 'Oh'?"

"Oh, *well*. We'll get through it. If we can remember it."

"Six minutes?" Carin nodded. "In one rehearsal? Holy Christ! Sonny must be some kind of genius. Or some kind of sadist. From three o'clock yesterday till now? That's twenty-two hours . . ." She broke off.

Carin looked up at her. "What's wrong?"

Diane was silent for a moment, then she said, "Nothing. I just recognized the bathrobe. Welcome to the Guinness Book of World Records."

Moira poured two cups of coffee and indicated the tray. "Help yourself. If you'd rather have refined sugar . . ."

"No, this is fine," Chris said, filling a teaspoon with ragged brown crystals.

Moira sat at one end of the couch, her stockinged feet curled under her, and Chris settled into the other, looking around. "You must know where the body's buried."

"What body?"

"At the *East Sider*. Or you're a better negotiator than I am."

"The *East Sider*'s not paying for this place."

"But *you* are."

"With a little help from my friends."

"Nice friends!"

Moira shrugged. "It's not as interesting as it sounds. Money from home."

"Your parents?"

She nodded. "You see how deep my scruples go. *I'm* a remittance type."

"There's nothing noble about living lousy."

"Do you live lousy?"

When he didn't respond, she leaned over the coffee table and opened a cigarette box. "Sorry, I didn't mean to pry. Occupational hazard."

"You weren't prying; it's a logical question. No, I don't live lousy . . ." He paused.

She lit her cigarette and exhaled a banner of smoke. "But you'd like to live better."

"Yes."

"Where do you live?"

"On West Forty-eighth Street."

She stared the length of the couch. "Where do you find an apartment on West Forty-eighth? I thought that was strictly commercial."

"There are brownstones west of Eighth."

"I thought those were all . . ." She stopped.

"Some of them aren't."

"Do I sound as tightass to you as I do to me?" Moira asked.

"No. I know what you mean. It's not a neighborhood I'd normally choose."

"What made you choose it?" When he was silent, she stood up and said, "I've got a perfect antidote for my dumb questions: Hindemith—*The Four Temperaments.* You know it?"

"Yes."

"You like it?"

"Very much."

As she ran a finger along a line of albums, Chris said, "My God, you've got a lot of music."

"One of my passions. My first degree was in music."

"Your *first* degree."

"Doesn't mean a damn thing." She put a record on the turntable and returned to her end of the couch as music filled the room. "I can't sing or dance or play an instrument. All I can do is listen."

"Some speakers!" Chris said.

"A gift."

"From the family?" She nodded. "Where are they?"

"Mamaroneck. That's about twenty-five miles north of here."

"Rich people?"

"Medium. *I'm* not. They are."

"But sometimes they share the wealth."

"Enough to keep me above the poverty level."

"But they're the ones you want to be independent of."

"Yes."

She lit a cigarette. Chris sipped his coffee, then said, "Mind if *I* ask a dumb question?"

"Why should I have a monopoly?"

"What made a rich kid turn radical?"

"Where *were* you? At its peak the movement had a higher per capita worth than Greenwich, Connecticut! I knew a girl who went down to Mexico to live in a cave, and her mother had a kitchen installed. Go ahead, laugh, but that's what killed the movement. I think the only working-class types that ever got into it were FBI. That's what made them so obvious."

She cradled her cup in both hands for a sip, and the cigarette protruding from the fingers of her right hand wove a woof of blue smoke into the pale warp of steam rising from the coffee. Hinde-mith's Melancholic Variation snaked out of the speakers, lean and assertive, to add gray strands to the tapestry of smoke and steam.

Chris felt warm and comfortable. Perhaps it was the coffee. "I live on West Forty-eighth," he said, "because the girl I came to see lives on West Forty-eighth."

"Is that the girl who called this morning?"

"Yes. A lot of dancers live in that part of town."

"She's a dancer?"

"Yes."

"Exotic!"

"She's not an exotic dancer."

"I didn't mean that! I meant it's exotic to be a dancer. What was she doing the first time you saw her?"

"Dancing."

"Did you fall in love with her on the spot?"

". . . In a way."

" 'How can we know the dancer from the dance?' "

Chris grinned. " 'Labour is blossoming or dancing where the body is not bruised to pleasure soul.' "

" 'Nor beauty born out of its own despair, nor blear-eyed wisdom out of midnight oil,' " Moira replied.

" 'O Chestnut tree, great-rooted blossomer, are you the leaf, the blossom or the bole?' "

" 'O body swayed to music, O brightening glance, how can we know the dancer from the dance?' I rest my case," Moira said.

"You rest Yeats's case."

"Wouldn't you like to be a dancer if you could?" Moira asked.

"Would *you?*"

"Oh, God, yes! But I'm so klutzy."

"It's hard work."

"I know. And hazardous. That's what makes it glorious."

"Being a writer is hazardous too," Chris muttered. "Hostile crit-ics, irate readers, cretinous editors, paper cuts . . ."

Moira smiled. "Without the rewards."

"Rewards?"

"Handsome young men falling head over heels in love with them. And that miracle that happens when they go out on stage: defying gravity with thousands of people cheering them on . . ."

"You're talking about superstars."

"Your girl friend isn't a superstar?"

"On Forty-eighth Street?"

"She's probably young. How old is she?"

It was a moment before Chris replied, "Eighteen." Moira's glance traversed the couch again. "I know," he said.

"What?"

"There's something silly about me and an eighteen-year-old girl."

"I didn't say that."

"But you thought it."

"No, I didn't. But apparently *you* did." He put his coffee cup on the table. "What're you so self-conscious about? You can't be more than twenty-eight or nine, and to those of us who've passed the big three-oh, that's not old."

"It's not her age—or mine."

"Then what's the problem?"

"Nothing." He stood up. "I ought to go."

"Where?"

"Home."

"I wasn't listening this morning—I mean, I wasn't trying to listen—but it sounded like your girl friend is out of town."

"She is."

"Then what're you going to do at home?"

"Read."

"What about dinner?"

"I'm sure there's something there."

"There's something here. And I happen to know you emptied your pockets to pay for the lunch I lured you to . . ."

Chris laughed. "Will you relax? It was a great lunch. A great day."

"How about a great evening?" She amended it to, "A great dinner. I cook better than I write, I promise you."

"I think you're a very good writer." He grinned. "And an authentic radical."

"Then why not stay for dinner?"

The performance in Philadelphia that evening was as unreal to Carin as her audition had been. By prearrangement she and Gino met onstage two hours before curtain to try to reconstruct the dance they had learned the night before. The rehearsal pianist pounded out the music from the pit, Sonny stood in the front row beating time with his hands, shouting counts and imprecations, and Andrew danced a few feet away from the performers, his movements designed to cue theirs. Carin and Gino had to stop repeatedly, and once Gino got into a shouting match with Sonny about precisely what step came next. Andrew had made a few notes in his own verson of Labanotation, but the cruel fact was that the only record of what had been created a few hours earlier existed in the two aching bodies moving in puzzled fits and starts. At one point Carin simply knelt on the stage and burst into tears. When Sonny vaulted onto the stage and ran to her, she looked up at him through streaming eyes and begged him to let the second act open with the group number they had rehearsed for weeks.

She gasped as Gino dug his fingers into her arm and exclaimed, "No! We can do it!"

"Of course you can," Sonny said.

Carin was startled. She had seen many expressions on Sonny's mobile face, but this was the first time she had seen a look of fear. "Just a couple more days," Carin pleaded.

"No!" Sonny shrilled. "The critics are coming tonight. In an hour!"

"They can come back."

Sonny knelt next to her, forcing her to look at him. "They can't come back. It's now or never. For the show. For *you.*" Carin simply stared at him, pale and damp. "You want to get fired?"

Carin shrugged helplessly and sat back on her haunches. "I can't remember it, Sonny. Neither can Gino. Or Andrew. Or you."

"You just need the music."

Carin nodded weakly at the pit. "He's playing it."

"It's not the same! When you hear the orchestra, it'll be different. It'll all come back to you."

"Yeah," Carin murmured. "The *old* number, that's what I keep remembering." When Sonny began to reply, she covered her face with her hands and burst into tears again.

"Lemme try," Gino murmured, and Sonny and Andrew withdrew to the wings, where they hovered, their pale faces floating in the shadows.

Gino knelt in front of Carin and put his hands on her shoulders. He waited until her sobs had diminished to sniffs, then he said, "We'll remember the steps." She shook her head. "Then we'll fake 'em."

She stared at him through red-rimmed eyes. "For six minutes?"

"We'll remember most of it, and if we get stuck we'll improvise till we get to the next part we remember." He tried to smile. "When in doubt, *bourrée* out."

"It's going to be a disaster, Gino!"

"There's a worse disaster." She ducked her head, but the words she was trying to avoid caught her. "Getting fired."

"If we mess up we'll get fired anyway."

"Not if we try. That's all Sonny wants. He knows what we're going through. He'll be suffering with us."

"There's a difference. The audience can see *us.*"

Gino took her hand and held it for a moment. His eyes were fixed on the scarred floor between them, and his voice was softer and gentler than Carin had ever heard it. "Please."

"What?"

"Please." He looked up, and Carin caught her breath. Pink with embarrassment, he was fighting tears. "Please. It—it'll never happen again. Never. You don't know—this is your first show, but I've been waiting . . ."

"Don't, Gino!"

His hand tightened on her. "You've got to, Carin. It's not a question of whether we can or not—we've *got* to, because this'll never come again. Never . . ."

He stopped, staring wretchedly at the floor, and grunted, "Shit!" through clenched teeth, furious at his tears, shocked at the sound of his pleading. He tried to rise, but this time it was her hand that held them together, pulling him back to his knees.

"It's okay."

He looked at her, his face wet and twisted.

"It's okay," she repeated softly, "I'll do it. We'll do it. If we stink, we stink. What can they do? Climb over the footlights and lynch us?"

Gino's relief was so vast he clutched at his chest and took several fast, deep breaths. "Fuck 'em," he said finally with a shaky smile.

"Fuck 'em," Carin smiled back. But her knees wavered as she rose, and she had to fight an impulse to throw up. Sonny and Andrew drifted a few steps out of the wings and stopped, afraid to ask.

"We'll do it," Gino said.

"Probably lousy," Carin said, but Sonny was in front of her, pulling her into his arms.

"You'll be fabulous," he said. "You'll remember everything."

She began to nod, but stopped because the forward motion of her head was tipping vomit from her throat to the back of her tongue where she could taste it. She breathed a silent prayer: *Please, God, let it be stagefright. Just stagefright.* It was. For the moment she had beaten off her diabetic demon.

Sonny looked at the pit. "Start from the top." He turned back to Carin and Gino. "Just mark it for now. Andrew'll be right next to you. Whatever you forget, he'll remember. And tonight he'll be dancing in the wings. If anything happens, just look at him."

Moira took the bowl from the counter, handed it to Chris with a long wooden spoon and said, "Okay, if you insist. Here."

The kitchen was compact and efficient, the appliances of much more recent vintage than those on Forty-eighth Street. Chris took the pot to a small table, sat on the stool next to it and looked at Moira, who said, "Just stir." Chris stirred, and Moira resumed her labors at the sink.

"You look out of character in that," Chris said, waving the spoon at Moira's frilly apron.

"Why?"

"Rich, radical journalist . . ."

"First of all, I'm not rich . . ."

"But that's the way you grew up."

"No."

"Did you cook at home?"

"No."

"Who did?" Moira bent to adjust the flame under a pot. "Your mother?"

"No."

"You paid someone."

"A maid."

"You were rich."

"Why this obsession with money?"

"Is that what I sound like?"

"Yes."

"Sorry." He reflected, then explained. "I guess it's the contrast."

"With Forty-eighth Street?"

"Yes."

"This is a very ordinary building in a very ordinary neighborhood."

"I know. It's the difference in—life-style."

"You don't sound too happy."

"It's momentary." He glanced at his watch.

"Got a deadline?" Moira asked. "Dinner's almost ready."

"No problem," Chris said. "I was just wondering what time it was."

"In Philadelphia? The same as here." The stirring stopped. "You mentioned Philadelphia this morning—on the phone." Chris put the wooden spoon on the table, and Moira came quickly from the stove, wiping her hands on her apron. "I'm sorry, Chris. I'm giving you a hard time and I don't know why. It's just that you're obviously going through something, and I'd like to offer you that distraction you said you were looking for, but I'm not sure I know how."

"You're doing fine," he said quietly.

A few minutes later they carried serving dishes to a table at one side of her living room. As Chris sat down, Moira went to the record stack. "What kind of dinner music do you like? Heavy? Light? Mozart, Smokey Robinson, Debussy . . . ?"

"Not Debussy."

"Okay."

"Anything else."

She pulled a record from the stack, slid it from its jacket with two fingertips under its label and a thumb on its edge to keep her grease out of its grooves, put it on the turntable and came back to Chris as *The Fireworks Music* burst from the speakers.

After dinner Moira offered Chris a Calvados. "Apple brandy," she said, "from Normandy. Peasant stuff, kind of raw and fiery."

He nodded. "Remarque used it in a lousy novel, as a macho symbol. The more effete characters drank *creme de menthe,* as I recall." Moira laughed. "I'll have the manly stuff."

As Moira poured the brandy, she said, "I drink too much, on the theory that I'm more articulate when I'm a little bombed."

"The *East Sider*'s Coleridge."

"I said bombed, not stoned. I've always wanted to try laudanum, though. It sounds so—writerly."

As they faced each other from the corners of the couch again, the sharp aroma of apples misting warmly up from their snifters, Rampal's golden flute pouring layers of creamy sound into the room, Chris studied Moira. She was taller than Carin, rounder, softer. And harder. Her vulnerability was different from Carin's. And who was to say who was better educated. Carin had been specializing for fourteen years and had attained a level of proficiency that still stunned Chris when he saw her move . . .

Why am I comparing them? he asked himself irritably.

He took a long sip of Calvados, and its crude warmth restored his humor. "What happened to Jean-Louis?" he asked.

Moira stared into her glass, turning it slowly between her palms. "Shall I withdraw the question?"

"No. I got pregnant. He was gung-ho about it. I wasn't."

"Why?"

"Something strange had begun happening to me. I mean, before I found out I was pregnant. I got the first inkling when I found myself slowing down in front of the American Express office and McDonald's to listen to those flat Middle Western accents. All of a sudden they sounded kind of—wonderful."

"Latent Americanism."

"Not so latent."

"You were ready to forgive us?"

She shrugged. "It occurred to me that any society that invented Saran Wrap and nectarines couldn't be all bad. I began to see enormous virtues in first-class plumbing, shopping centers and 'I Love Lucy' reruns with bowls of Wise potato chips and Planters peanuts—the greasy kind."

"You can take the girl out of the middle class, but you can't . . ."

"Bet your ass!" She tipped her snifter and swallowed twice, then declared, "I'd also had it up to here with French kitsch. Don't get me wrong: I hadn't turned off on kitsch per se . . ."

"Not if you were hanging around McDonald's."

"Precisely. I decided if kitsch was my birthright, it might as well be a Fourth of July parade in Mamaroneck as the *Garde Républicaine* at the Opéra." She tilted her glass again.

"You were pregnant . . . ?" he prompted.

The glass came down. "Oh."

"I don't mean to be nosy."

"Yes, you do," she said, affably enough.

"Occupational hazard."

"When Jean-Louis realized I wasn't exactly overjoyed about the pregnancy, he thought it was an attack of middle-class morality and proposed on the spot. That's when I told him what had been happening to me."

"The McDonald's syndrome?"

She nodded. "I told him I just couldn't see myself spending the rest of my life in France, no matter how much I cared about him. Eventually it'd—turn bad, and I didn't want to do that to him."

"But why couldn't he go back to America with you? Wouldn't that have solved the problem?"

"He didn't want to live in America any more than I wanted to live in Europe. He was completely European. He knew it, I knew it."

"You had a problem."

"Yes, because I really was madly in love. Living with him was like a marvelous movie: exciting, emotional, fictional." She chuckled mirthlessly. "Poor man, he could never be the person I'd invented. *He* was my revolution." She looked at Chris. "Does that make sense?"

"Yes."

"And the revolution was over. The only problem was . . ."

"You were pregnant."

"When he realized I was going home no matter what, he asked me to stay in France till I had the baby and leave it with him."

"He wanted it that badly?"

"No. He knew what I was planning to do."

"Abortion?"

She nodded. "Guess what? He didn't believe in it. Morally. After that long philosophical journey, after all the risks and changes, he had an orthodox Catholic attitude toward abortion. He admitted it, he said he couldn't understand it, but he also said he couldn't deny it or ignore it."

"It was his child."

"Yes, that was part of it. Now, for the first time, abortion wasn't a theoretical question: we were talking about his child, and suddenly he couldn't distinguish between abortion and murder. There was no way he was going to let me terminate that pregnancy."

"Where's the child?"

"I went to Switzerland."

"For the birth?"

"The abortion."

"He gave in?"

"He didn't know. Till it was over. By the time he found me, I was trying to pull myself together in Zermatt. Catholic conditioning dies hard."

"Well, he'd been a priest . . ."

"I'm talking about mine. Maybe it was postpartum depression—they say you can get it after an abortion. All I know is I crashed. When he showed up, I was in no condition for a battle . . ." She rose abruptly. "What the hell are we talking about!" Hurrying to the kitchen, she refilled her snifter to the halfway point, then turned to Chris with the bottle of Calvados. "You?"

He shook his head. She put the bottle down and returned to the couch with a muttered, "As you can see, Irish sentimentality becomes maudlin with very little prompting, so do me a favor? Don't prompt?"

"Sure."

They sipped their brandy, listening to the music until Moira asked, "What about you?"

"What *about* me?"

"That girl." The Calvados sloshed in her glass as she gestured. "The beautiful dancer."

"Who said she was beautiful?"

"All dancers are beautiful, by definition. Unless you want to debate it with Yeats."

"No. She's beautiful."

"And you love her."

"Very much."

"You going to marry her?"

It was a moment before he responded. "I think so."

"You're not sure you want to?"

"It's not that."

She waited, inhaling the fumes of her brandy, watching him from her end of the couch, composed again.

Finally Chris said softly, "Maybe she's *my* revolution."

"There's nothing wrong with marrying your revolution. It just didn't happen to work out in my case."

"Or Yeats's. He never married Maud Gonne."

"She had her own revolution." Moira took a sip of brandy, then said, "You like Yeats."

He smiled. "How can you tell?"

"You bothered to memorize him."

"So did you."

"I used to belong to the Cuchulain Circle."

"A Yeats society?" She nodded. "At Columbia?"

"Well, near Columbia. It met in a local bar."

"Oh."

"We'd convene on an ad hoc basis—like every night—and get

bombed on beer, or try to, and recite Yeats at the tops of our voices till the neighborhood regulars who'd been hanging out in the bar for years threatened us with annihilation if we didn't shut up."

"You know something?"

"You don't have to say it: you sympathize with the regulars. In retrospect so do I, but at the time we looked on it as a major civil rights issue." She lit a cigarette and observed, "It could be started up again."

"The Cuchulain Circle?"

"Yes."

"I'm not sure I want to die for Yeats in a bar."

"We could move the meetings to a safer spot. Like here. Any night you'd like. I told you it was ad hoc." Chris glanced at his watch, and she asked, "What's happening?" He looked up. "In Philadelphia."

"Oh. A new show. It's opening tonight." He looked at his watch again. "Just about now."

"With your dancer?" He nodded. "Shouldn't you be there?"

"She asked me not to come. Nerves."

"That's understandable. But she won't be nervous *after* the performance, and if you left now . . ." She paused.

"Only one problem," Chris said, and patted a trouser pocket.

"That's my fault. If I hadn't dragged you to Elaine's . . ."

"Will you forget it?"

"No!" She got up and left the room. When she returned, she was clutching a little stack of bills.

He stood up, red-faced. "What're you doing?"

"It's a loan."

"No!"

"Are you going to be sexist about this?"

"It's not sexist! I don't want to take your money."

"I told you: it's a loan. You can pay me back Friday."

"And till then?"

She aimed a thumb at the bedroom door. "There's more in there. And Mamaroneck. Take it." She pushed the money toward him. He stared at it. "Damn it, Chris!"

He took the money.

She went back to the couch, retrieved her glass from the coffee table and raised it to him. *"Bon voyage."*

"You probably think I'm childish—or crazy," Chris said.

"No. It's nice to be in love. Even the lows are a kind of high." She glanced at him. "Don't you think so?"

"Yes. Where did you put my coat?"

"Oh. Just a minute." A moment later she was back with his coat. He tried to take it from her, but she held it up to help him into it.

"There are limits," he said and took the coat from her.

"Sexism dies hard."

"Like Catholicism." He reached for her hands. "You were right."

"Of course I was. She'll probably be relieved when you show up in Philadelphia, no matter what she said."

He shook his head. "I'm talking about the evening. You said it would be great. It was. It is. It's nice to be here with you."

"It's nice to be here with you."

The record ended, the turntable clicked off, the room was oppressively silent.

"Go ahead," Moira said.

"I'll pay you back Friday."

"Don't worry. I'm rich, remember?"

He smiled, kissed her cheek at the corner of her mouth and went quickly out the door. Moira returned to the coffee table, picked up her glass and tapped it with a fingernail. It gave off a shimmering note. She drank enough brandy to raise the note a third when she tapped it again.

Throughout the first act Diane maintained a discreet distance from her friend. All the gypsies were acutely, painfully aware of what Carin and Gino were going through, and like the teammates of a pitcher with a chance for a no-hit game, they said and did nothing to remind their colleagues of what was happening.

Carin was beyond exhaustion. During the first act she had performed twice with the rest of the dancers, sung in several group numbers, milled about the stage in crowd numbers (once as a boy) and raced up and down the backstage stairs for five costume changes, pausing only to throw up in the fourth-floor bathroom each time she passed it, and nibble some candy to replace the sugar she had vomited. The urine test she gave herself after the first act came up Fresca, her word (coined at the age of twelve with a self-congratulatory giggle) for sugarless. Her prayer had been answered: the atrocious assault on her mind and body was nothing but abject terror. She fought back tears of joy and retched dryly over the toilet again.

When the tinny backstage squawk box called places for the second act, Diane, seated next to Carin at the long makeup table, shifted her glance in the mirror to meet Carin's gaze. Even with its coating of garish makeup, Carin's face was ashen, and her eyes were as round and vacant as Orphan Annie's.

Diane permitted herself one cautious gesture: without taking her eyes from Carin's frozen image in the mirror, she extended a finger and touched Carin's arm. If Carin felt the touch, she gave no sign. After a moment Carin rose and hurried out the dressing-room door. For the second time that night her costume didn't match every other costume being yanked on in the girls' dressing room. At this moment in her life, as never before, she was alone.

No, she reflected as she ran down the long, stony flights of backstage stairs, not quite alone. There was Gino. He was alone too. They were alone together. No, not quite, she thought as she came to the stage and saw Andrew, in white leotard and tights so they would be able to see his body moving in the wings.

Carin grasped the edge of a velour leg and *plié*ed to a deep first position, her crotch on her heels. She repeated the movement several times, then rose and began a series of slow *tendus*. The movement was unnecessary—her legs were still warm from the first act—but the movements, repeating precisely the first movements Carin had ever done in a dance class at the age of six and had done at the beginning of every dance class in the twelve ensuing years, provided a continuity she needed at this moment.

Dimly, from the other side of the thick house curtain, she heard the first notes of the second-act overture, and behind her, deeper in the murky wings, she saw Gino, one hand on a fly rope, lowering himself into a deep *plié* in first position. He repeated the movement, then began a series of slow, careful *tendus*.

The last bars of the overture introduced the motif of the dance music that would open the act. The instant the motif sounded, Carin and Gino stopped moving.

The stage manager whispered "Go" into his microphone; there was a thud as the electrician pushed a long lever on his board, and the stage glowed amber and pink and blue.

Gino moved to the leg where Carin was standing. Like Diane, he touched Carin's arm. She looked up at him, then stared back at the now radiant stage.

The stage manager murmured another "Go" into the microphone, a hefty stagehand hauled rope and the house curtain rose with a melancholy sigh.

Carin tasted vomit and wondered how there could be any left. She felt for the little bulges of candy in the pockets she had secretly sewn into her costume.

Gino pulled himself erect, taller than he was, taller than his conformation meant him to be. His upper body was afloat now, attached to his hips by no more than skin. The two dancers hyperventilated, pulling outsize drafts of air into their lungs, the last untortured breaths they would know for six minutes—six minutes that could change their lives, answer their questions, vindicate or mock them . . .

Thirteen, two, three, four; *fourteen,* two, three, four; *fifteen,* two, three, four; *sixteen,* two, three, four . . .

The dancers ran onstage, and Diane, in costume for her next

entrance, slid into their place in the wings, fighting for air as desperately as they. As she watched, her body moved, mimicking Carin's and Gino's, reducing the *pas de deux* to a tense miniature above the velour leg that hid her from the audience. Between two downstage legs a brighter mirror shone as Andrew flailed about, a living Teleprompter, dancing Gino's steps for a few moments, then Carin's.

Onstage the two glistening bodies obeyed last night's instructions. As each moment came, the memory banks in the dancers' muscles delivered up the data that had been filed during the long, steamy night in LuLu Temple. There were moments that didn't qualify for the dancers' highest grade, "Clean," and once Carin turned left when she should have turned right, but Gino compensated with his next step and they moved in unison again.

After four minutes fatigue became a factor, and both dancers began to lag behind the music, but the conductor, forewarned by Sonny, slowed the orchestra's tempo until the dancers were in sync again. The change, Sonny hoped desperately from his post at the rear of the house, would be imperceptible to the audience and the critics.

In the wing opposite Diane's post, another pair of shadowy figures crouched above a velour leg: Cynthia, in costume for the next chorus number, and behind her, Mrs. Moore. Cynthia sniffled, then sneezed softly as her mother leaned close to hiss into her ear, "That could be you out there if you weren't such a goddamn shrinking violet! You can dance circles around that pushy little bitch!"

Cynthia's shoulders rose, two bony, ineffective earplugs.

In the last minute of the dance, Carin's data bank ran dry and suddenly she was standing motionless on the stage, staring at Gino. In the rear of the theater, Sonny staggered against the director, clutching his chest. Knowing that coronaries are extremely rare in dancers, the director remained focused on his own anxious thoughts. The next day one of the critics would dwell at some length on "the enormously effective moment when, in the midst of the whirling, leaping beginning of the second act, all motion suddenly ceased, and the two dancers simply stared at each other, rendered human and vulnerable—and all the more touching—by this simple, brilliant choreographic device." But that praise was more than twelve hours away, and as Carin stood frozen on the stage, Sonny clutched at this chest and saw his life pass before his eyes.

Carin's immobility brought Gino to a standstill, and the break in the continuity of the movement snapped the tape that was running in his head. Long before scientific minds had postulated that the human mind recalls data sequentially, like a tape on forward, dancers, singers and actors were led to that conclusion by the fact that often when their memories failed them in the middle of a dance or song or speech, the only way to recover was to rewind the tape, so to speak, and start again at the beginning, arriving at the critical moment without interruption. Countless times in her life Carin had backed up to perform a double-time, silent-movie version of the dance she was working on until she arrived at and rocketed past the trouble spot. She had seen singers back up, too, to sing a piece from the beginning in rapid falsetto, sounding precisely like a tape on fast forward, until, on safe ground again, they could slow to a normal tempo and sound.

But Carin and Gino knew that onstage, in front of an audience, with music thundering ahead in the pit, there was no rewinding, no quick recapitulation to close the frightening gap. Carin and Gino, like legions of petrified dancers, singers and actors before them, were denied the natural solution to their eternal problem.

So the two young dancers stared at each other, their minds blank, as an eternity of eight bars ticked away. Then Gino saw something beyond Carin in the wings: a slender ghost, Andrew in his lifesaving white leotard and tights, waving his arms and legs in a pattern that fit the music issuing from the pit.

In a split second Gino was dancing, his movements emphatic, exaggerated. The *épaulement, port de bras,* gliding *chassé* and quick *échappé* bridged the synapse in Carin's memory and suddenly, smoothly, she was dancing in unison with Gino. Only the coda of the number lay ahead, and with relief in sight, both dancers felt a powerful surge of energy.

At the end of the number, the audience responded enthusiastically, but the only knowledge Carin and Gino had of it was the *rowwwwwwr* that issued from the squawk box on each landing as they hurtled up the stairs to their dressing rooms. In less than three minutes there would be a street scene in which Carin's and Gino's costumes had to match those of their colleagues, who were already milling in the wings.

The dressing-room doors were open, and in each one a dresser waited, hands outstretched to strip the dripping costumes from Carin and Gino and fling fresh attire on their steaming bodies. Gasping from their labors and the dash up the stairs, the dancers drew wracking breaths that could be heard from one dressing room to the other. Then, still zipping zippers, they nearly collided as they emerged from the dressing rooms and started down the stairs, impelled by the shrill music blaring from the squawk box, alerting them to the fact that they were twenty-four bars from their cue to stroll nonchalantly across the stage.

As they came onstage they glowed like porcelain dolls, and Sonny made a mental note to cut them from the street scene in the next performance if the sweat couldn't be toweled off in time.

EIGHTEEN, two, three, four
Frappé

At the end of the performance, there were five curtain calls, the audience's response lashed along by the show's brightest up-tempo number, thunderously reprised from the pit. The cast grinned vacuously at the audience, their eyes shiny with relief and exhaustion, and waved their clasped hands over their heads in a victory gesture that was at the moment nothing more than a wan hope. The audience response sounded enthusiastic, but the more experienced members of the cast knew that an opening-night ovation, in New York or out of town, was *de rigeur,* and only the neophytes muttered, "Listen to that—we're a hit!" out of the corners of their gaping smiles.

Five curtain calls, Sonny mused from the back of the theater as the house lights brightened and the first-nighters plodded up the aisles, wrestling with their heavy winter outerwear. *I've seen better and I've seen worse. But I think the new number works.*

He glanced at the director, who was deep in earnest, inaudible discussion with Wally. Wally's pinky ring glittered as he waved a hand to make a point.

If the show falls on its ass, he can't blame it on me, Sonny assured himself; *he didn't like the second-act opening and I gave him a whole new number overnight. There isn't another choreographer in the country who could have spit something out that fast. And that good. Okay, so they blew eight bars, but the rest of the number* worked. *Let him fire Al. Or George—nobody's gonna tell me that's a Tony-winning score!*

His reverie was interrupted by Wally's beckoning finger. "C'mon over. We're gonna have a meeting."

Three minutes after the house curtain fell, the girls' dressing room received the full force of the tension that had been building for

two and a half hours. Slender bodies in various states of undress
whizzed randomly about the room, like subatomic particles in a
cyclotron. Wardrobe mistresses careered through the maze, clipper
ships in full sail, costumes on hangers billowing about them as they
hurried toward long rows of pipe racks. Greasy faces confronted
themselves in the makeup mirror that ran the length of the room, as
orange, pink and blue pigments were transferred from cold-creamed
skin to soggy slabs of Kleenex. Over this colorful explosion hung an
equally gaudy canopy of screeches, chatter, hoots of laughter, howls
of joy and bursts of song.

Carin's tissue turned her face into a cubist mask, the features
jumbled by multicolored smears of greasepaint. Carin sneezed into
the tissue and raised her gaze to look at Mrs. Moore, who was standing behind her, beaming at Carin's reflection in the mirror.

"Well!" said Mrs. Moore. Carin resumed wiping the makeup
from her face, her eyes on Mrs. Moore's genial image, as the pillowy
shape exclaimed, "Fantastic, that's all I can say! How you even remembered the steps. . . !"

A faint smile defined Carin's mouth among the jagged lines of
makeup. "I didn't. Sometimes I was improvising. So was Gino."

"Well, no one would ever have known it. Least of all the
audience."

Carin nodded. "They were nice."

"They certainly were." A pudgy, heavily ringed hand fell on
Carin's shoulder. "Whatever happens to the show, you'll certainly
come out of it with flying colors." Mrs. Moore's teeth glittered in the
mirror as her smile widened. "And I'm not saying that to make you
feel good. Ask Cynthia. I was saying exactly the same thing in the
wings all during the number."

"Thank you, Mrs. Moore."

Mrs. Moore managed another half-inch of smile and moved
away. Diane, who had stopped removing her makeup to observe the
encounter from her vantage point next to Carin, leaned over and
peered at Carin's back. "What're you looking for?" Carin asked.

"The knife. Go ahead, laugh, but if Cynthia turns out to be
your understudy, you'd better hire a food taster." Diane turned to
her right and reacted with surprise as she saw Susan, seated next to
her at the makeup table, carefully wrapping an Ace bandage around
her knee. "What'd you do to your knee?"

"Nothing new. It's been like this for weeks."

"I never saw the Ace before."

"Damn right. I was afraid Sonny'd fire me if he spotted it during rehearsals." As she tugged the bandage tight and fastened it with
two metal clips, she added dryly, "But we're open now, so I can
come out of the closet. Besides, it hurts too much not to."

"Maybe I ought to follow your example," Diane said. Susan
looked at her, and she raised a leg to flex a foot between them. "I

ought to keep an Ace on this foot, but I'm always afraid to. Like you. If people get the idea you're injured . . ."

"When did you do it?"

"Oh, years ago." As she stared at the foot, still poised at eye level, her gaze clouded and it was a moment before she resumed with, "An old war wound. When I'm alone, I wrap it up in a special bandage."

"Better than an Ace?" Susan was clearly and instantly interested.

"It's a regular Ace, but I used to know a Zen freak—macrobiotic, the whole *shtick*—and he claimed he could cut healing time in half by drawing something on bandages and casts."

"I've got a friend who's into pyramids. I stuck my knee under his. It didn't do much."

"This is like a mantra, only you don't say it; it's drawn on the bandage." Susan stuck her leg out. "Want one?"

"Of course. It can't do less than the cortisone."

Carin watched as Diane picked up a makeup pencil and drew a bright red yin-yang circle on Susan's Ace, then turned as she heard an outcry from the girls seated nearest the dressing room door. Andrew had entered. Though many of the girls were naked or nearly naked, the outcry was not a protest, and no one hurried to don or close a dressing gown. Andrew had entrée to the girls' dressing room: he was a member of the gypsy fraternity, he was Sonny's assistant, and he was gay—three important qualifications. An unannounced entrance by one of the stage managers would have drawn a barrage of dance shoes.

The outcry comprised a chorus of queries, all turning on the question of the hour: how did we do?

Andrew's thin voice rose above the hubbub. "Ronnie's meeting with the brass, but he asked me to tell you he's proud of the way everybody came through." A loud cheer went up, and happy chaos reigned again.

"We still haven't heard where the party's going to be," Diane yelled at Andrew.

"You won't," Andrew yelled back.

There was a distinct edge in Diane's voice as she shouted, "Last time I was in Philly we had a *great* opening night party."

"Must've been a hit," Andrew said flatly, and in an instant silence reigned.

It was broken by Diane. "We're not?"

Andrew scanned the anxious faces, some of them still wearing their twisted cubist masks of cold cream and greasepaint. "I didn't say that."

"Yes, you did." It was Carla, the Equity deputy, at her militant mightiest.

Andrew's response was too calm and too hasty. "We don't know yet. The curtain's only been down for five minutes, for Christ's sake." He started for the door but found his way blocked by two girls, one of them Carla, who, with her arms akimbo, bore more than her usual resemblance to a Golden Glover.

"Ever fucked a girl?" Carla demanded.

"What?" Andrew said, backing a step.

Carla advanced on him, calling over her shoulder, "Somebody lock the door."

Andrew continued his retreat. "What do you think you're doing?"

Carla's chin jutted. "You're about to be raped by eight girls. More, if the singers want to join in."

Andrew backed into a chair. "C'mon, Carla, don't get cute. Sonny's waiting for me."

Diane rose and moved toward Andrew. "Don't *you* get cute, Andrew. We happen to be talking about something important. Like our fuckin' *fate!*"

"You think *my* fate isn't tied up with this show?"

Diane stopped in front of Andrew, her nose an inch from his. "It sure as hell is, so you must've paid a little attention to what the brass were saying out there."

Andrew surveyed the ring of faces tightening around him, then murmured, "I think they're worried."

The frozen moment that followed allowed him to get out of the room, but in the corridor he once again found his way blocked, this time by Mrs. Moore's bountiful shape.

"Oh, Andrew," she smiled. "I was *hoping* we'd have a chance to speak for a moment. I know how busy Mr. Frye's been, but—do you know whether he's been able to give any thought to an understudy for poor Carin?"

" 'Poor' Carin?"

"Dancing on those knees." Mrs. Moore exuded compassion, among her other emanations.

"What's wrong with her knees?"

Mrs. Moore's eyes widened. "You mean—she's never mentioned any—problems?"

"No."

"In that case," she said emphatically, "we'll just forget we ever had this little conversation. For Carin's sake."

She patted Andrew's hand and reentered the girls' dressing room where life of a sort was beginning again. The frozen frame Andrew had left behind him was reanimating, but sluggishly; the room looked like a slow-motion parody of its former self, and the few girls who found the strength to speak conducted their conversations in hushed tones, as though they were in the presence of death—as in fact they might be.

Diane, back at the makeup table, slumped on her tailbone and stared at her naked reflection. In the harsh light of the bulbs around the mirror, her face, cold-creamed clean of its garish makeup, was sallow except for the long pink scar on her cheekbone. She looked tired. And old. She closed her eyes.

Three places to Diane's right, Pam, a tall dancer in her late twenties, was also solemnly surveying her image in the makeup mirror.

"Well, I guess that settles it," she said softly to the image.

Opal, listlessly brushing her hair next to Pam, directed a questioning glance at Pam's image in the mirror.

"I've been fighting the idea of Las Vegas," Pam said, "but . . ." She shrugged helplessly.

"I hear the money's terrific," Opal said.

"If you don't mind two shows a night, seven days a week."

Sharon, seated on Pam's right, said, "I knew a girl who wound up making fifteen hundred a week. Sometimes more."

Opal's eyes widened. "I didn't know they paid *that* kind of money."

"They don't," Sharon said, and began applying street makeup.

"Then where did she get it?" Opal asked.

Carla leaned forward to project her answer over the jars, boxes, tubes and bottles lined up on the makeup table. "The same place you got Ernie." Opal stared blankly. "In the boudoir, sweetie."

Opal looked at Sharon. "You mean . . ."

"She means," Diane intoned, "when you get to Vegas, you find out you can make more money off your feet than on them."

Opal's unblinking gaze swung toward Pam. "That's not what *you're* talking about, is it?"

"Of course not," Pam replied crisply.

"Nobody *ever* talks about it," Diane sniffed.

"Speak for yourself, Di," Pam shot back.

Diane's response was measured and quiet. "I am." She seemed to be addressing herself in the mirror. "I'm not saying I'd go out there *looking* to hook, but when you see that kind of money changing hands, and the time's going by, and you hear another show's closing. . . . Anyway, I'd like to know what's so fuckin' honorable about the unemployment line! At least the girls I know in Vegas are paying their own way, and the smart ones are putting something aside for their old age—which happens to be like thirty-five in this fuckin' business!"

She stared at the image in the mirror. Her hand rose, her fingertips traced the line of the scar on her cheek. "If they'd just let you pick your customers," she said in a voice inaudible to any but the nearest dancers. She stared past the pale, scarred, mirrored Diane at . . .

Liam. Adorable Liam. Excitable Liam. Yonkers Liam, who "worked late" four or five nights a month—and left Diane's bed at midnight to drive guiltily to Yonkers, to Roseanne and Michael and Sean and Margaret. *Paterfamilias* Liam.

Liam was semi-civilian, which in Diane's lexicon meant he wasn't show business but he wasn't *business* business either. He was a photographer whom Diane had met when an agency decided to use dancers for a pantyhose ad. A one-inch notice in *Show Business* and *Variety* had brought a hundred dancers running, and Liam sat atop a ladder in his studio surveying the leggy crop. He picked six for the ad, one of them Diane. When the elect had donned the sheer pantyhose, the room went white with light and Liam waved the girls toward the no-seam. Bathed in candlepower, the little clutch of dancers looked naked. The client settled back in his camp chair and took a sip of Tab, then glanced up as the account executive bent over him to suggest, "Maybe we should ask them to shave."

The client looked at the row of pubic shadows. "Won't they airbrush out?"

The account executive strolled to Liam, whispered to him for a moment, then returned to the client. "Liam says it won't be any problem."

The client nodded toward an empty camp chair. "Then sit down. Have a Tab. Enjoy." He watched as Liam posed the girls on the no-seam; then he leaned toward the account executive. "Good idea to use dancers. More muscle tone than models. Most of the models look flabby, you know what I mean? No matter *how* thin they are. These girls . . ." He contemplated them, silent, pleased with his idea, pleased at this moment with his life. "Not a bad way to spend an afternoon," he sighed to the account executive.

When the session was over, he took the trouble to thank each girl and, with an amiable laugh, told the group that he might never use models again. The girls laughed back and silently, earnestly hoped he meant it. Three hours had netted each of them three hundred dollars. On Broadway or in a dance company, that much money represented a week of hard labor: class, rehearsal, performance.

As Diane was leaving, Liam stopped her to ask if she would be interested in testing.

"Testing what?" Diane asked warily. She was twenty. New York was still *new* York, and she was on the lookout for worms in the Big Apple.

"Testing," Liam repeated. "The agencies send me girls who haven't had much experience, and I take pictures. It's practice, for them and me. And sometimes the stuff is interesting and I can sell it, and we both make money."

"Sure," Diane said. "When?"

"Tonight. Now. I—I don't have anything on the schedule for this evening—and if you're free . . ." He waited, thin and rather scholarly behind his round rimless glasses, under an outburst of curly hair.

"I don't have anything to do tonight," Diane said, and Liam said, "Excuse me a minute," and retired to his small office, where he made the first of what would in the months ahead be many phone calls to tell Roseanne in Yonkers that he had to shoot tonight, so he wouldn't be home till late. *"C'est la vie,"* he sighed when Roseanne began a gentle reproach; then she put Michael and Sean and Margaret on the phone to say good night to Daddy. Margaret could only gurgle and coo, since at ten months she hadn't yet acquired the rudiments of the English language.

Then Liam returned to the studio and led Diane back to the dressing room. Waving a hand at the array of high fashion hanging along one wall, he invited her to put on whatever caught her fancy. "Anything that fits," he smiled, and pointedly left the dressing room.

The twenty-year-old Diane marveled at the dazzling windrows of color and cloth awaiting her decision. She was sure she'd seen that red organdy number in the *Times* Magazine section a couple of Sundays ago. She took the dress off the rack and held it in front of her, turning right and left in front of the full-length mirror. Her jeans and sneakers sticking out from under the frail red hem made her smile, then frown. She put the dress down and took off her jeans. A new problem confronted her: at twenty Diane was already unalterably opposed to visible panty line, so she was wearing no underwear. And the red dress was sheer. On the other hand, so had the pantyhose been, so the photographer wouldn't be seeing anything new. But maybe they didn't retouch the test pictures. She'd better ask. She parted the dressing room curtains, holding a panel of them around her like a wrapper. "I don't have any underwear."

"Pardon?"

"I don't wear, uh, underwear. Because of the VPL. You know, under tight jeans . . ."

"Yes."

She hurried on, relieved but not surprised that he understood. "Well, this dress . . ." She thrust the transparent material through the opening in the curtains.

"See the dresser?" Liam asked.

Diane glanced behind her. "Yes."

"The top two drawers are underwear: pantyhose, bras, panties. Whatever you want. Lots of sizes. All new. And you'll find shoes on the floor near the mirror. Pick a red pair. If they're not a perfect fit it won't matter. Just as long as they look right."

Diane nodded and disappeared, and when she came out, she was red from head to toe.

"Great!" Liam exclaimed and pulled down several feet of fresh no-seam.

Diane posed for fifteen minutes in the red outfit, then changed to a blue one, then an ivory evening gown. As she posed in each of the dresses, Liam circled her, exclaiming, "Yeah! Fabulous! Outstanding! Dynamite!" his camera punctuating his exclamations with sharp clicks.

They took two breaks, and during the second one, as they sprawled in the camp chairs sipping wine and listening to the joyous thunder of two massive KLH speakers, Liam said casually, "How about some beauty?" Diane tightened, wondering if *beauty* were a synonym for another expression she'd learned in New York: head.

"Beauty?"

"Head shots," Liam said.

Diane felt cheated. Liam had seemed so straight and decent. He could have walked into the dressing room while she was changing, but he hadn't. The whole thing had been so businesslike. And now . . .

Liam took a large blowup from the table next to him and displayed it to her. It was a closeup of a tawny model, staring enticingly into the camera.

Diane's muscles relaxed and she sank back into the chair. "Oh. *That* kind of head. A person."

Liam smiled. "Yeah. Like hair, cosmetics. You know—it's not the clothes in this picture, it's the model."

"Sure," Diane nodded. "But I won't look like that."

"You'll look better."

"That'll be you, not me," Diane said.

"It'll be both of us," Liam said, rising.

He took Diane to the no-seam, fired the lights, seated Diane on a stool and handed her a towel.

"Am I sweating?" She brought the towel to her face.

"No. Take off the top of the dress and wrap the towel around you." Diane stared at him, and he went back for the picture he had shown her. "See? Bare shoulders. The frame cuts you off right here." He drew a hand across his chest. "The camera won't show the towel."

He went back to the table and busied himself with his cameras, changing lenses and reloading. Diane lowered the top of her dress and wrapped the towel around her, covering her nipples and leaving the tops of her breasts round and bare.

"Ready?" Liam asked, thus getting full credit for not having turned back.

Diane smiled. Her first impression was reaffirmed: Liam was terrific. "Ready."

Liam took head shots of Diane for half an hour. Under the warmth of the lights and Liam's camera-punctuated litany of praise, Diane relaxed and grew bolder, turning her head freely, tossing her hair, smiling impishly or provocatively into the camera. "Incredible!" *Click!* "Wild!" *Click!* "Sensational!" *Click! Click!*

Liam turned the lights off, and Diane realized she was sweating. She came off the no-seam, turned her back on Liam, unwrapped the towel and carefully dabbed her face. Liam was at the table, pouring wine. "Want to hear something different?" he asked. She wrapped the towel around her and turned to him. He nodded toward the turntable.

"No," Diane said. "Johnny Mathis is fine."

Liam brought the wine to her and touched her glass with his. "Cheers."

"Cheers," Diane said and took a long sip of wine. The heat had made her thirsty.

"Scott was right!" A puzzled look from Diane brought, "The client. He said he never wanted to use models again. Neither do I. It's dancers from now on, man. You people know how to move!"

Diane smiled. "That's all we know."

"It's enough. People think fashion photography is faces and clothes. Forget it. It's movement. Look at any great fashion picture: Avedon, Hiro. Look at the movement! You give me that in every picture. Wait till you see the stuff we're getting."

Diane's head was spinning. The wine. She took another sip. "I *can't* wait."

"You tired?"

"Not at all. This is a piece of cake compared to what I usually do. Does *every*body get a hundred dollars an hour?" There was a note of awe in her voice.

"Some get more. Beginners get less, of course."

"*We're* beginners."

"But there's a pantyhose rate. Because of the semi-nudity. That's why you got a hundred." Diane considered the three hundred dollars she had earned and shook her head in wonder. "Think you could go another half-hour?" Liam asked.

"Whatever you say."

"Okay! I've got a new motor-drive I want to try. It's fabulous—two, three pictures to the frame—like a machine gun. Brrrrrrr! I'll give you some clean no-seam." He went to the set and hauled on the huge roll of white paper that hung above it. When the area in front of his cameras was pristine again, he tore off the scuffed no-seam on which Diane had trod and kicked it aside.

Diane put her glass on the table. "What do you want me to wear?"

"Oh—nothing." He turned to her. "Now it's all movement. All you." She was silent. "You can wear something if you want," he said, "but it'll destroy the line." He waited, his owlish face blank but not unfriendly. Diane reflected. The room had been full of people when they did the ad, and she could see the other girls: in the pantyhose, under the glaring lights, they might as well have been naked. He'd already seen everything, and he was obviously a terrific person . . .

Diane removed the towel, dropped the dress that hung on her narrow hips and peeled off the pantyhose she'd found in the dressing room.

Liam stacked the Supremes and Marvin Gaye on the turntable, and Diane began to move on the no-seam. Liam had guessed right: the Motown sound enveloped Diane, cloaking shyness, obliterating inhibition. The music freed the dancer, and Diane danced. She spun, she contracted, she leaped. Arms flew, breasts bobbed, legs kicked— and Liam's camera clicked and whirred as its motor drive propelled the film past the gaping aperture. When one camera ran out of film, Liam seized another and continued imprinting Diane's naked image on the plunging film. Inside the cameras the tiny white figures sprang through the dark in a series of frozen frames, two pictures to the turn, three to the jump. In fifteen minutes both Diane and Liam were bathed in sweat. She stopped, gasping.

"No! Not yet! Just a few more. You look fantastic like that! If you could see yourself. Shiny. Gilded! Don't stop."

Diane moved, the Supremes wailed. Finally Diane said, "No more. I . . . can't . . ." and sat down on the no-seam, her legs crossed, her head bowed, her hair hanging wet and stringy on her shoulders. Liam turned off the floods and sat down next to her, panting as audibly as she. The Supremes climbed higher.

A few minutes later Liam made love to Diane on the no-seam, and at midnight they left the studio and went their separate ways, she full of Irish sperm, he full of Irish guilt.

For the next two years they were lovers, sporadically, when Liam was able. The first summer Liam took a house in Quogue, and during the week, with Roseanne and the kids in the country, he spent every night with Diane in New York. But Labor Day ended the idyll.

During the second year of the affair, in self-defense, Diane took to disporting outside the relationship. The disaffection began when Liam announced a sabbatical. "I think Roseanne suspects. I'm sure she does. The way she looks at me . . ."

"Where does that leave us?"

"We just have to cool it for a while. Not long."

"How long?"

"I don't know. Two, three weeks maybe, a month. Till we—till she stops suspecting. You understand—I don't want to hurt her. She doesn't deserve *that.*"

"Sure."

A week later Diane spent the night with an actor who was waiting tables at Joe Allen's until the summer-stock theaters geared up.

A month later Liam was back, repentant, desperate, devoted. The renunciations and reunions became the focal point of Diane's life. She had never had a "mature" love affair before. It made her feel alive and important, like a character in almost any of her "Late Show" movies. There was drama in her life at last, pain, sorrow, meaning, danger—everything a simple Texas girl of twenty-one could hope for in her first great love.

Shortly after one of their reunions, as they were making love in the studio, Liam was interrupted by a call from Roseanne, telling him Margaret had a hundred and four. With both ends of his life in flagrante—delicto in New York, fever in Yonkers—Liam bathed his penis in the studio sink, as he always did after a dalliance with Diane, and rushed to his daughter's burning side. Margaret had to be hospitalized and, as Liam reported to Diane a week later, "We almost lost her!"

" 'We'?" The response seemed insufficient, so she added, "Gee."

Liam nodded gravely. "Maybe it was a warning."

"A warning?"

"You know—a punishment."

"For what?"

"You know."

"Us?" Another solemn nod. "You think God's punishing us?"

"It's possible."

"Why would He take it out on Margaret? *She* didn't do anything."

"God works in mysterious ways."

"When did you get so religious?"

He rose from the couch in which they were nestled and stalked away to the accompaniment of Mantovani's strings. Diane watched him, the dull pain in her chest telling her that she was about to enter a Bette Davis phase again (Roseanne was Mary Astor).

She was right. Once again Liam sank out of sight in a sea of guilt, and resurfaced three weeks later with an empty tank. For both Diane and Liam, the bittersweet passion of the reunions compensated for the pain of the renunciations—indeed, renunciation and reunion were inseparable sides of the same precious coin, though neither of the actors in the trite drama knew it. Once Diane timorously suggested that Liam might feel less guilty if he *left* Roseanne, and he stared at her as if she had addressed him in Bantu. "Leave her? Leave the kids? That's never been in the cards. You understand . . ."

Diane understood and broadened her circle of friends, skin thickening, speech coarsening.

Slowly, ineluctably, an emotional arteriosclerosis set in, as silent and pernicious as its medical counterpart. Their meetings, though no less frequent or fraught, were now steps in an elaborate choreography that tacitly included the invisible, invincible Roseanne of Yonkers and the various intruders in Diane's loins and life. The *pas de trois* became a *pas de quatre,* then a *pas de six,* a *pas de dix.* . . .

As the second year ended, the expanding choreography encompassed Arturo, a hairdresser in Raul's Salon to which Diane repaired for an occasional indulgence. One night, after Arturo had washed, cut and set her hair, Diane invited him out to dinner to help her celebrate the occasion.

"What occasion?"

She touched her newly coiffed hair. "This."

After dinner she took him to Forty-eighth Street. He left before midnight because the eponymous Raul was a) his roommate, b) his boss, and c) jealous.

The fact that Arturo was gay didn't deter Diane: she had long since grown accustomed to occasional encounters with backsliding homosexuals. More important, it didn't seem to deter Arturo.

Weekends were a problem for Diane, however, Saturday and Sunday being *jours sacrés* for family men like Liam and Arturo. On one occasion, coming home late on a Saturday night, Diane bumped into Arturo and Raul emerging from one of Eighth Avenue's raunchier gay bars with a leathery trick.

"Who's that?" Raul asked when Diane had offered a slightly too cheery greeting and gone her way.

"Wash, cut and set."

"Wedge?"

"Sauvage."

"Don't remember her."

"She doesn't come in that often."

A few days later Arturo called Diane. "You'd better see a doctor."

"Why?"

"Do I have to explain?"

"Yes."

"I'm sick."

"What're you talking about."

"Raul and I picked something up on Eighth Avenue."

"That heavy-leather stud I saw you with?"

"I said some*thing.* Penicillin clears it right up. The doctor said it's like getting a cold."

"You son of a bitch!"

"Don't blame *me.* At least I had the courtesy to warn you. I could've kept my mouth shut."

"It's not that serious," the doctor said to Diane.

"I've actually got it . . . ?"

"Yes, but you'll be okay in a couple of weeks."

"What about other people?"

"Other people?"

"That I've—been with."

"You should speak to anyone you've had intercourse with. Definitely."

"Liam?"

"Hi."

"You busy tonight?"

"I'm sure I told you: tonight's a birthday. Michael, the eldest."

"Could we have a drink?"

"I've got to leave early. It's a *kid's* birthday party; it'll be over by seven."

"Just give me five minutes."

"A problem?"

"Sort of."

"It can't wait till tomorrow?"

"No."

"Well . . . come to the studio at five. But I'll have to leave by five-fifteen. I planned my whole day so I could get out of here."

"Fine."

"You don't want to tell me what it is?"

"I'll see you at five."

The model who was leaving smiled at Diane. She was tall, with delicate features and the kind of hair and teeth unknown outside the world of television commercials.

"How much does she make?" Diane asked Liam.

"Her basic rate's seventy-five an hour."

"How much do you suppose she makes a week?"

"I don't know. It depends on how much she works."

"She's gorgeous."

"Yes. What is it?"

"Can I sit down?"

"Of course. I'm sorry. You want a glass of wine?"

"Yes. No."

"Which is it?"

"No." Since her visit to the doctor, Diane had felt unclean. She had gone straight home and scoured all the china and silverware, though the doctor had assured her her roommate had nothing to worry about, and now the thought of contaminating one of Liam's glasses froze her. She stood irresolutely just inside the studio door.

"Are you going to come in?"

"Yes."

She went to a tall canvas director's chair near the no-seam and perched on it. Liam pulled an identical chair to the no-seam and sat down. His stereo, which normally blared from the moment he entered the studio until the instant he left it, was silent. He waited, then said, "I think maybe I can guess."

"I'm not pregnant."

He sat back, his relief undisguised. "You need some money?"

"You have to see a doctor."

The canvas chair felt hard and unyielding against his back. "*I do? Why?*"

"Because we made love last week."

"I know we made love last week . . ."

"And I'm infected."

"With what?"

"Gonorrhea."

He had the odd impression the chair was tipping. Putting a hand on its wooden arm, he pressed down as if to drive its long legs into the floor. "Is this a joke?"

"Am I laughing?"

He stood up. "You've got gonorrhea?"

"Not anymore. The doctor gave me penicillin."

"Are you trying to say I gave it to you? That's impossible! I haven't been with anybody but you and Roseanne in months . . ."

Diane tried to raise a hand, but it was too heavy. "You didn't give it to me."

"Someone else did?"

"Yes."

"Who?"

"It doesn't matter." Her answers were leaden, mechanical, each one ending on a tired falling note.

"If you just got it . . ."

"I had it last week—when you and I made love. If you've made love to your wife since then . . ."

"Oh, *Jesus!*"

"She has to go to a doctor too."

Liam pivoted right, then left, looking for support. He reached out to the director's chair he had vacated, clutching at its arm. Diane would have risen and gone to his aid but strange forces were rooting her in her chair, high above the floor. Liam turned back to her. She managed to spread her hands and say, "I'm sorry," before he struck.

The hard outer edge of his hand sliced into Diane's face like a scalpel, opening the taut flesh over her cheekbone. She toppled backward on the no-seam, rigid as a Barbie doll, jetting blood. Still in the chair, she stared glassily up at Liam, each spurt of blood leaving a crimson stripe on the glossy white paper around her. The stripes began running together, pooling, as if she were afloat on her back in milk.

"What do I tell her!" Liam screamed.

"I'm sorry," Diane murmured, then turned her head and

gagged as blood ran into the corner of her mouth. Blood spurted in a new direction, candy-striping the unsullied side of the no-seam. Liam swiveled right and left again, head twisted, eyes staring, looking for succor, support, revenge. He slashed at the air around him, grunting and cursing, then, finding himself facing the fallen girl, leveled a kick at the nearest leg of the director's chair, splintering it, dislodging the footrest which still supported Diane's feet, though she was horizontal. Her legs fell to the no-seam and Liam kicked again, striking the sole of her foot with the sharp toe of his boot. She had wounded him at his most vulnerable point—his wife, his family—so he sought hers. The boot shot out again, striking her ankle. There was a sound not unlike the splintering of the chair leg, and Diane shrieked and brought her knee to her chest, clutching her broken ankle. The blood from her cheek slithered on the slick paper, framing her head in a bright corona, a red halo.

Liam bent over her, livid, top-heavy. His owlish glasses fell off, landing on her stomach. She stared up at him, open-mouthed, as he bent more precariously forward and screeched, "You *filthy whore!*"

Diane blinked. The corona of lights in the makeup mirror was searing her eyes, bringing a wash of tears to them, and when she blinked, red shellbursts blossomed beneath her eyelids. She groped for a Kleenex and pretended to remove the last vestiges of makeup from her face. The scar on her cheek ached under the soft paper.

She forced her eyes from her own image to Pam's, as Pam, also studying herself in the mirror, muttered, "I'll tell you one thing I'm not going to do: no silicone!" She took a lengthy breath and thrust her breasts at the mirror. "If these aren't big enough for Vegas, I'll stay in New York and—"

"What?" Sharon asked.

Pam's ribcage collapsed like a punctured balloon, and her breasts shrank to hillocks.

By the time Carin and Diane left the dressing room, the ominous word had spread. The backstage corridors were nearly deserted, and the few shadowy figures moving through them maintained a respectful funereal hush.

"Hungry?" Diane asked, and Carin shook her head. "We oughtta do something!" Diane complained. "It's opening night, for Chrissake . . ." She broke off, following Carin's glance toward the boys' dressing room, where Gino, sleek in black leather, had emerged, seen Carin, and was now moving confidently toward them. "Oh," Diane said.

NINETEEN, two, three, four
Echappé

Diane seldom thought about Liam anymore, except on nights like this: alone in a musty hotel room, perched on a narrow bed, her back against a pillow, her knees drawn to her chest, her body wrapped in one towel, her damp hair bound in another, a listless hand groping for the cold hamburger on the room-service tray, her eyes fixed glassily on Joel McCrea exacting black-and-white frontier justice in the glassy cavern of the battered Zenith, her mind drifting back to that terrible, thrilling time of her life.

After Liam and Arturo, there had been Tom. No; Steve. Steve? No; Russ. Russ was definitely next.

Russ was heavy-duty. Real potential. He and Diane had talked about marriage. *After* they had become lovers, so, Diane had reasoned, it wasn't a plot to get her into bed.

Russ could've been it. But Diane got a job in the road company of a solid Broadway hit. That meant a year's steady employment. It also meant a year on the road, far from home, from friends . . . from Russ. Russ assured her it would be no problem: he could meet her in Philadelphia, Washington and Boston during those engagements. It would be fun. It was. Cleveland wasn't. St. Louis was out of the question, so Diane flew to New York the Sunday morning after the last St. Louis performance and rejoined the company in Chicago Monday afternoon. By then Diane knew Russ was going, and by Denver he was gone. Diane would have left the tour and returned to New York, but the damage had been done: Russ was, as he had told her sadly in the last phone call, "involved with someone." "Me," Diane blubbered.

"No," Russ said, "this is different."

Of course it was. Whoever "someone" was, she was a *real* person, with a job maybe, and a permanent address. She was there, in New York, a few minutes away from Russ. She was free in the evenings—who needs a girlfriend who's tied up between seven and eleven every night—and she was probably never tired, and certainly never had to "save" anything for class or performance. . . . Of course.

Diane tried to comfort herself with the thought that ballet dancers had it worse: they were always on tour. It was fine for the male dancers: if they were straight they had their pick of the company's frustrated female complement; if they were gay they could cruise every night, after every performance, no matter where they were. If the groupies weren't waiting for them outside the stage door, they could find ready recreation in the gay bars, quickly and easily located even in the squarest Bible-belt communities. But the girls in a ballet company repaired to their hotel rooms after most performances, to wash tights or darn toe shoes or read. And as often as not, if a girl had tempted fate by setting up emotional shop with a man in New York, by the time she returned from a long tour, she found that her man, like Russ, had fled to an easier, more proximate attachment.

In marked contrast, some of the straight male dancers had honest-to-God families in New York—a wife, children, a car, maybe even a suburban mortgage and crabgrass—glue, in short, to hold a marriage together, even in the absence of one of the partners. But the girls could leave behind nothing more than a husband or lover, loose and randy in New York.

Some of the married male dancers Diane knew went gay on the road or formed no-nonsense, utilitarian relationships with girls in the company, on the clear understanding that the end of the road tour would be the end of the road. Diane knew two girls in a modern-dance company who, faced with the aridity of a tour, always roomed together on the road in homosexual self-defense, then, imperceptibly shifting gears, returned to their customary heterosexual pursuits in New York.

Diane had tried it all: one-nights with the straight men and temporarily gay girls; longer road relationships with the married men; "meaningful commitments" in New York that fell apart under the pressures of her schedule—morning classes, performances six nights a week (when she was working on Broadway), long tours (when she was lucky) on the road.

Like most of her colleagues, Diane lived with the forlorn hope that she would eventually encounter a man patient or understanding enough to adjust the rhythm of his life to hers. She knew the odds were long—and lengthening; and like most of her colleagues, she felt that the alternative—changing the rhythm of *her* life by abandoning dance—was unfair, unacceptable and, thus far, unnecessary. If something had to be sacrificed it wouldn't be the one thing that had provided excitement and reality since those tap-dancing days in the echoing bathroom. In a couple of years—one more tour, one more show, one more opening night—it might be time to hang up her spikes and . . . what?

Maybe she could advertise in the *Village Voice:* "Dancer, formerly unavailable mornings, evenings and altogether for extended periods of time, now available full-time for extended or even permanent emotional engagements. Children acceptable."

No, not yet. Not quite yet.

She looked around the room with a thin smile. "Yeah," she said aloud, "who'd be crazy enough to give *this* up." She picked up the hamburger, took a distracted bite of it and abruptly spat the cold, gristly meat into her palm.

She turned, surprised by the sound of a knock at the door, then rose, dumped the rejected meat on the tray and, clutching the towel around her, made her way toward the door.

"I didn't expect to see *you* again to . . ."—Chris was standing outside the door—". . . night."

"See who?"

"Anybody." Diane could still taste the hamburger's cold lipids. "May I come in?"

Diane clutched the towel closer. "I'm not dressed."

"I wouldn't recognize you if you were." Diane stared at him. "I'm your roommate. Remember?"

"It's different here."

"Why?"

"Well—I'm not alone."

"I know. Carin's with you."

"No. Not tonight." She saw Chris stiffen. "I got lucky. One of the actors." She felt a small wave of relief as inspiration took hold. "Matter of fact, I thought you were him."

"You just said you didn't expect to see anybody."

"Tony's moody," Diane improvised. She even managed a laugh. "Sort of a tomcat. You never know where he'll wind up. But as far as I know, it's still on."

Chris's eyes gleamed from the dark corridor. "Where's Carin?"

"That's what I'm trying to tell you. She's staying with another girl tonight. As a favor. To me." She waited, prayerful that her performance was adequate.

"Which girl?"

Shit! The worst possible question. "I don't know."

"You don't know?"

"She didn't say."

"You don't say."

"No, *she* didn't say. The whole thing happened so fast. I just said I needed some privacy tonight, and she said sure." Encouraged, she essayed another laugh. "You probably thought only guys helped each other out like that . . ."

"May I come in?"

Shit! "I just explained . . ." She knew it sounded lame.

"I'll go as soon as I locate Carin."

"If Eddie walks in and finds another guy sitting here . . ."

"Tony."

"What?"

"The tomcat. His name was Tony a minute ago."

Shit!

"But I see what you meant about the way you girls stick together," Chris went on. "It's impressive. May I come in?" She didn't move, her toweled body blocking the door. "I'd like to use the phone." There was a narrow space between Diane's left flank and the door frame; Chris turned sideways and stepped through it. Diane spun to him.

"Honest to God, Chris, I don't know where she is."

"That's okay, I think I do." He moved to the phone, snapping the TV off on the way. Joel McCrea flickered and died. "What's Gino's last name?" he asked as he picked up the phone.

"Don't, Chris."

"Then just tell me his room number."

Diane hurried to him. "You don't know what she's been through the last two days. That's a *six-minute number* they put in the show. In twenty-four hours! Can you imagine the pressure, the tension?"

"Fuck the tension!" Diane started and recoiled a step. "Fuck the show and Philadelphia and the magical gypsy world that ordinary people like me aren't qualified to understand! You know what you look like to me? A bunch of over-age Peter Pans who think they can get away with anything as long as they refuse to grow up!" An angry hand shot toward the window. "What do you think that is out there? Disneyland?"

"She didn't expect you tonight," Diane said with unwonted timidity.

"Because she told me not to come! And now I know why."

"No, you don't! She was scared out of her mind."

"And that excuses everything. Including what she's doing now."

"I don't know what she's doing now. And neither do you."

"Then give me Gino's room number so I can find out."

Diane compressed her lips and Chris turned disgustedly away. "Arrested development, that's all it is." He prowled the room in a tight triangle, from the bed to the window to the television set. "Nothing's wrong because nothing counts. It's all fun and games. Gypsy games." He found Diane in his path and stopped. "Okay, I've

finally got the message. You and your playmates are right, and the
rest of the world is wrong. Including me." He leaned toward Diane,
and she backpedaled again. "Now that we've got that settled, you
can initiate me into the tribe. What'll it be tonight? Spin the Bottle
or Doctor?" He reached out and twitched the towel off Diane. It
flopped to the floor at her feet, and Diane stared at Chris, naked, her
eyes wide and blank. "What's the matter? Afraid Tony, or Eddie, or
whatever-his-name-is will walk in?"

"No."

"Then what're we waiting for?"

"Somebody to make the first move," she said bleakly. "And
nobody's going to." She bent over and picked up the towel. "Too
bad, in a way. I've had the hots for you since the day you showed up,
but according to the roommates' code, you were off-limits." She
wrapped herself in the towel, tucking it tight above her breasts.
"Come back in a few years, when you're not so hung up on her."

Chris sank into the room's only armchair. A puff of dust rose.
He stared morosely into space. "How could I get so hooked on
somebody like that?"

"Easy. She's a terrific girl. I know you don't feel that way this
second . . ." She paused, waiting for a disclaimer. When none came,
she sat on the edge of the bed, fingered a cigarette out of its pack
and leaned against the pillows that had supported her before Chris's
arrival. A few minutes later she asked, "Want to watch TV?"

He shook his head and rose with a sigh. "I'm sorry," he said.
"About . . ." He indicated her towel.

"That's okay," she replied wearily, "I'm used to it. Professionally." Suddenly a mysterious rage flooded her. "Everybody and his
brother walks through our dressing room! I'm gonna buy a goddamn
padlock!" She jumped to her feet as Chris started for the door.
"Where're you going?"

"Back to New York."

"And then?"

"I'll move my stuff out."

"Nine-oh-three."

"What's that?"

"Gino's room number."

Chris studied her. "I thought you didn't want to tell me."

"I didn't—but if you leave like this, it's all over."

"And if I go up there?"

Diane indicated one of the twin beds. "At least I'll have the
pleasure of lying here listening to Gino get his brains beat out. And
then you and Carin'll have to talk."

"About what?"

"I don't know. What do real people talk about?" Chris shook

his head and reached for the door. "A couple of minutes ago you were desperate to find 'em."

"I forget why." He opened the door.

"What'll I tell her?"

Chris paused in the doorway, his back to Diane, then said without turning, "Tell her I figured she wouldn't mind if I came *after* the show, when the pressure was off. And I hope everything went great tonight. I mean, at the theater."

He pushed into the corridor, thick in his overcoat, and closed the door behind him. Diane remained next to the bed, her eyes on the door, then looked slowly up at the ceiling. She debated, then, lowering her gaze, shook her head angrily, moved stiffly to the television set, snapped it on and flung herself on the bed with such force that the springs twanged. Joel McCrea came thundering over a mesquite-dotted rise.

There was only one ticket window open in the vast station, and the agent behind it looked as if he belonged to a race of night-bloomers with rheumy eyes and mushroomy skin.

"It's a milk train," the agent said.

"What choice do I have?" Chris asked.

"Take the first express in the morning."

"And in the meantime?"

"Go to a hotel and get y'rself a night's sleep. Or tell the bellboy you want a broad." A rheumy eye winked.

"I'll take the milk train."

There was something familiar about the shabby car. Chris was past Trenton before he realized what it was: it smelled like the dank air shaft between his bedroom window and Renée's Advent.

He slept fitfully on the hard seat, waking at each jolting stop. In Penn Station he followed the signs to the Eighth Avenue subway, and when he emerged from his stop at Fiftieth Street, the avenue was uncharacteristically still. An inertia greater than fatigue slowed him as he approached the brownstone on Forty-eighth Street, and when he stood at the foot of its steps, staring up, not even the wind knifing through the deserted street from the Hudson could drive him into the hostile gypsy camp.

Back on Eighth Avenue, he fished a dime out of his pocket, stepped into a graffiti-adorned phone booth, called Information, got a phone number, dialed it and waited, torn . . . driven. A sleepy voice answered the phone. "Yes?"

"It's me."

"My God." He heard scrabbling sounds. "What time is it?"

"Almost five. I'm sorry. I know this is stupid . . ."

"Where are you?"

"In New York."

"I thought . . ."

"I went. I'm back." He was silent. Across the street a stocky woman stepped out of a doorway and leaned into a cruising car that had stopped at the curb.

"Are you all right?"

"Yeah. It's just—I don't want to go home, and I—I was wondering—when's the next meeting of the Cuchulain Circle?"

The sleep was gone from Moira's voice. "In about fifteen minutes. Unless you can get here in ten."

When she hung up, Moira sprang out of bed, tripped on a slipper and caught herself on the dresser as she was about to fall. Cursing softly, she prodded the toes she had stubbed, then limped into the bathroom, where she splashed cold water on her face, brushed her teeth and ran a comb through her hair before she permitted herself to turn on the light over the bathroom mirror for a critical examination.

The flannel nightgown wouldn't do, she decided. Apart from that, it was catch as catch can. She frowned and brought a hand to a throbbing temple. The Calvados. Opening the medicine cabinet, she located a plastic bottle of aspirin. The child-proof cap nearly separated the nails from her thumbs before she finally managed to pop it. She held her thumbs under a stream of cold water to deaden the new pain, then took two aspirin and turned out the bathroom light. A moment later the light was on again. She hadn't moved and her gaze was fixed on the little flying saucer next to the aspirin bottle in the cabinet. After a swift debate she snapped the saucer open and took out her diaphragm. Her hand was so unsteady the creamy line she squeezed around the edge of the device looked like the crimped edge of a tiny pie, and when she put a foot on the rim of the tub and tried to work the folded diaphragm into her vagina, the unprepared sphincter ejected it and it fluttered into the tub like a stricken butterfly. Cursing softly, she retrieved it, and after a few more failed attempts, managed to poke it home. Fitting the nozzle to the tube of contraceptive jelly proved equally difficult, but when the cool cream finally jetted into her it was soothing—and promising.

When she turned out the light and returned to the bedroom to pick out a less dowdy nightgown, she wondered if Yeats had ever come crashing into Maud Gonne's house in the middle of the night.

TWENTY, two, three, four
Failli Tombé

The test pattern glowing from the TV screen endowed the drab room with more warmth and color than it normally possessed. Diane, sprawled on the bed, her hair and body still swathed in towels, the room-service tray next to her, looked like a newspaper photo of a murder victim:

NUDE DANCER FOUND IN SEEDY HOTEL ROOM

The corpse stirred and sat up as the door opened and Carin entered.

"Sorry," Carin said as she closed the door and moved too briskly past the beds.

"What time is it?" Diane asked groggily.

"Early. Go back to sleep." She stopped in front of the television set. "Fall asleep watching?"

Diane shielded her eyes from the test pattern. "Yeah. Turn it off."

As the color bars vanished, Diane caught sight of the gelid hamburger on the tray next to her and pushed it away with a grimace. She reached for a Kleenex on the night table and blew her nose, then lay back to watch Carin undressing slowly, wearily.

"Get any sleep?" Diane asked.

"Some."

"That's one thing you can't take away from Gino." Carin looked at her. "He always gets A for effort." Carin's only response was to pull her sweater over her head and toss it on a chair. "We had a visitor," Diane said.

Bent over, her jeans halfway down her legs, Carin looked up.

"Chris," Diane said.

Carin straightened, suddenly fully awake. The jeans slid to her ankles. "You mean here? In Philadelphia?"

"In this room."

"But—we decided he wouldn't come."

"*You* decided. He waited till the show was over, so he wouldn't make you nervous."

"Where is he?"

"Probably back in New York by now. Moving out."

"You told him where I was?"

"I didn't have to. He's a newspaperman, remember? Used to digging out facts."

Forgetting her fettered ankles, Carin took a step toward the phone and toppled across the foot of Diane's bed. Twisting on her back, she kicked off the jeans, then stood up between the beds and reached across Diane for the phone.

"I wouldn't," Diane said.

"You think it's no use?"

"What're you gonna say to him?"

Backing up, Carin bumped into her bed and sat weakly.

"Maybe I could call Terry," Diane suggested.

"What for?"

"To find out what's happening."

"We know what's happening." Still in her panties and sweat socks, Carin turned down the covers and slid into bed with her back to Diane.

Diane remained silent for what she considered a respectful length of time, then, unable to see whether Carin's eyes were closed, offered a barely audible, "I just realized . . ." and waited.

Carin didn't turn, but a muffled answer floated up. "What?"

"We didn't get any flowers from Terry last night. Not even a crummy telegram. He never forgets an opening. Especially mine; he knows I'd cream him."

"*You're* forgetting something."

"What?"

"He just started rehearsals in his own show."

"Of course! What's the matter with me. He's got a few things on his mind too."

They fell silent. Diane studied Carin's rigid back, then asked, "You okay?"

"No."

Diane sat up. "What're you gonna do?"

"Die."

"Besides that."

"We've got a rehearsal call at four, right?"

"Yeah. Brush-up."

"I thought I'd try to get some sleep till then."

"Okay."

A few minutes later Carin murmured, "You still there?"

"Yeah."

"I don't blame *you*. For what happened. With Chris."

"I tried to make up a whole story. It just didn't work." The next time Diane spoke, she whispered in the event that Carin was finally asleep. "You love him, don't you?

"Chris?"

"Of course. Who else?"

"Yes."

"You crying?"

"Yes."

A few minutes later Diane snarled, "It's Phila*del*phia, for Chrissake!"

"What?"

"You and Gino. It doesn't *count.*"

"Did you explain that to Chris?" Carin asked wearily, abandoning the fetal position to lie on her back.

"I told him how hard you've been working."

"That must've impressed him."

"What was I supposed to say!"

"Nothing. I told you: I'm the one who screwed it up, not you."

"Why?" Diane asked softly. Carin looked at her. "You had plenty of warning. About Gino."

"So did you."

"Me!"

"When you were number seven."

"That was different."

"How?"

"I didn't have somebody like Chris."

"Neither do I."

"You did yesterday."

Why? Nureyev floated across the little screen, but Carin shook her head, rejecting that explanation. *The work. So close. Nobody gets that close. Ever. Even when we make love, Chris doesn't touch me like that, hold me like that, protect me like that* . . . Carin shook her head again. Gino hovered above her lean and powerful, supported on his arms, elbows locked, hips moving. She closed her eyes.

Why?

"Maybe . . ." she ventured, and stopped.

"What?"

"Well—I *like* Gino . . ."

"You can't be that dumb!"

"He's different . . . when you're alone with him . . ."

Diane groaned, and Carin fell silent.

Why? The best she could come up with was: *Philadelphia*—and the fact that in some mysterious way making love to Gino was preserving her sanity. It had something to do with the show, and dancing, and the future. Chris would have been miserable in Philadelphia, an outsider, another problem. Gino was . . . a gypsy. So was Carin . . . now. The whole thing was a process, and Gino seemed to be part of it. And yet . . . Nureyev and Gino collided, the little television screen shattered, the glittering fragments melting together into a single penetrating regard, paler than blue, denser than gray: Chris's silver gaze.

Carin sighed helplessly, and Diane asked, "What can I do?"

"Shut up," a gentle murmur suggested.

The snow finally came, thick and white and powdery, while Carin slept, and after the long night of sullen sleet, the city looked relieved and cheerful as Diane and Carin trudged toward the theater, the fresh snow squeaking under their boots. From a clearing western sky the sinking sun filled Broad Street with rosy, bouncing shards. " 'It's beginning to look a lot like Chrismas,' " Diane sang, then stopped as a frosted newspaper kiosk sparkled at her.

"Interested in the verdict?" she asked. Diane indicated the stacks of papers in the kiosk. The girls veered, and Diane peered into the stand. A pair of eyes framed by wool and fur peered back. "A newspaper, please," she said.

"Which one?" was the muffled reply.

"How many have you got?"

"Three."

"All of 'em."

As a pair of mittens emerged to stack a *News,* an *Enquirer* and a *Bulletin,* the vendor muttered, "You must be in the show that opened last night." Diane looked up. "Lotta kids like you been stoppin' by, and everybody takes all three."

Diane gave the vendor a dollar. As he peeled off a mitten to make change, she balanced the papers on a forearm and leafed to the *Bulletin* review. With Carin craning around Diane's arm to see the review, Diane read for a moment, then uttered a deeply felt, "Yeccch!"

"That's more or less what they all been sayin'," was the philosophical comment from the kiosk. As Diane began to leaf through the *Enquirer,* the muffled voice said, "It don't get any better."

"Wait a minute!" Diane cried to Carin. "Here's something nice about you!" She pointed and Carin craned. "C'mon," Diane said, pulling Carin toward a coffee shop. "We got some time. Let's have a cup of coffee and study the situation."

"Downstairs," the stage doorman said. "In the lounge. You gotta go through the house."

Sonny nodded and, drawing a bead on a caged work light in the center of the stage, felt his way through a crowded wing. Emerging from the wing, he unwrapped a Dickensian muffler as he went to a downstage corner and stepped out on the orchestra rail, a gaunt funambule, arms outstretched, muffler trailing from one hand. Inching around the pit on the rail, he dropped to the orchestra floor and made his way up the center aisle to the lobby, where he trotted down the steps to the lounge, pulling off his sheepskin coat.

At the foot of the stairs, he stopped short, arrested by the four pale faces fixed beseechingly on him. Spreading his hands, he forced a smile. "It's only me."

The director, composer, lyricist and book writer looked mournfully away. As Sonny added his sheepskin coat to the mound of cold-weather gear on the bar that dominated the long wall of the lounge, he asked, "Where's Wally?"

"That's what we'd like to know," the director muttered, trying to adjust his long frame to the shallow leatherette armchair he occupied next to the men's-room door.

"Anybody seen him since last night?" Sonny asked, taking a seat on the maroon leatherette couch that already held the composer, who was leaning back, a hand across his eyes, sighing faintly with each breath.

From his seat on a piano bench across the room, the lyricist replied, "No."

"What about Phil?" Sonny asked.

"I'm sure *he's* seen Wally. He must've got a call the minute the papers came out," the book writer said. His blond, bushy hair and slender frame made him look ten years younger than any of his colleagues, as in fact he was. He had written the first draft of *Ante Meridian* while still a senior at Yale Drama just two years earlier, and now, Sonny noted, he seemed to have been crying: his eyes, normally the only clear ones in the group, were red-rimmed and puffy; his modish three-piece suit looked as if it had been slept in and he repeatedly clasped and unclasped his hands as he glanced toward the stairs from the lobby. Searching his own wounded soul, Sonny managed to find a scrap of sympathy for Brian: it was, after all, his first Broadway show, and from the looks of things, quite possibly his last.

"You've seen the reviews?" Brian moaned.

"Yes," Sonny replied.

"You came off all right," Brian said, and Sonny tried to hide his satisfaction. Of all the show's creators, he had been the least lacerated, as a result, he was sure, of his persistence the night before last at LuLu Temple. An ardent admirer of Noel Coward, Sonny subscribed to the philosophy summed up by his hero when, asked why he, the quintessential Englishman, always sailed the Atlantic on the French Line, Coward replied, "Because, on the French Line, in the event of disaster, there's none of that nonsense about women and children first." Decidedly not the type to lash himself to the tiller,

Sonny had vowed that in the event of disaster this ship would go down without him. That resolution had nearly cost the lives of two dancers, but now, Sonny reflected smugly, Wally would have to look for another patsy.

"I got three calls from New York," the director said listlessly.

"They know already?" the lyricist asked.

"Of course," Al said.

"Fucking vultures!" the lyricist snarled. "Just waiting for bad news."

"We've all done it," the composer sighed.

"Not me!" Brian exclaimed.

The composer didn't remove his hand from his eyes. "You will. When somebody else is in trouble in Philly. You'll get that nice warm feeling, thinking about the fights, the cold coffee and stale sandwiches, the all-night meetings they're having—without you."

Brian looked around the room, ashen. "Everybody's acting like it's all over. We don't know that."

"Don't we?" the director murmured.

Brian sat back, then rose abruptly and darted through the nearest door.

"Hey!" the director yelled. "That's the ladies' room!"

"What the hell difference does it make," the lyricist muttered.

For a long moment the only sound in the lounge was the book writer throwing up in the ladies' room.

"Sounds like he's in an echo chamber," the composer observed without removing his hand from his eyes. "We oughtta make the cast album in there."

"*What* cast album?" the lyricist growled.

The composer dropped his hand and opened his eyes. "The record company wouldn't do that. They've got a hundred thou in this show."

"Ever hear the old saw about not throwing good money after bad?" the lyricist replied. "Not to mention beating a dead horse."

The composer covered his eyes again. Brian emerged from the ladies' room, his eyes redder, his face paler.

"Is it true there aren't any urinals in there?" Sonny asked.

"*They* do it sitting down," the lyricist said.

"How would *I* know?" Sonny replied.

A sound from the lobby snapped every head toward the stairs. Wally appeared. Prepared to grasp at any straw, Sonny noticed that under the circumstances, Wally looked rather natty. *Why would he bother to get dressed up to deliver bad news?* But a glance at Phil lumbering glumly in Wally's wake dispelled Sonny's momentary optimism.

Wally sat in the only empty armchair, and Phil wedged himself into the couch between Sonny and the composer. Wally's pinky ring glittered as he spread his hands. "What can I tell you?"

"Everything," the lyricist said.

Wally rubbed a hand across his smooth cheek. Sonny could smell his cologne all the way across the room. It was, Sonny thought, a surprisingly delicate scent for a man like Wally.

"Are we dead in the water?" the director asked.

Wally looked at him. "What do you think?"

"I've had worse out-of-town openings," the director replied.

"I wish you'd told me that before I signed you," Wally muttered.

Al jumped to his feet. "Oh, I see! It's my fault! I wrote the music, I wrote the lyrics, I wrote the book—"

Wally raised a hand. "Hold it, hold it, hold it! I didn't call the meeting to blame anybody. You can all relax."

Brian sat up, wild hope rejuvenating him. "We can fix it, Wally! I know we can. I made notes last night—every single thing that isn't working . . ."

"I said *relax,*" Wally repeated, and Brian sat back, confused.

"I think he means we can stop working on the show," the lyricist said.

Brian looked at Wally, his eyes wide and wet again. "Is that it?"

Wally nodded, and Brian sank back in his chair, shattered.

Al resumed his seat and said evenly, "I know how bad it looks, Wally, but we're all ready to work our butts off . . ."

"With what?" Wally asked.

"Well, I'm sure everybody's got some idea of what's wrong . . ."

"I'm talking about this." Wally rubbed a thick thumb and forefinger together.

"We're out of money?" Brian whimpered. Wally nodded. "But how *can* we be?"

"Easy. Remember when you insisted on recasting two parts? Remember when you came up with a whole new first-act finale halfway through rehearsals, with a new set, new costumes, new music . . . ?" He looked at the composer. "Wait till you see the copyist's bills. George? You asleep?"

The composer took his hand from his eyes. "No. The light in here hurts my eyes."

"Mine too," Wally grumbled. "I can't wait to get back to New York."

"There must be *some* money left," Brian exclaimed.

"Yeah, sure," Wally said, "but it's not mine, it's the investors'."

"You think *they* want the show to close in Philadelphia?" Brian queried.

"No. But I don't think they want their money squandered on a lost cause."

"Who says it's lost!"

"I do. That's my job. I got a fiduciary relationship with my investors, an' I'm not throwin' good money after bad."

The lyricist looked at the composer, who closed his eyes.

"What about the money we can make in Philadelphia?" Brian exclaimed.

"After those reviews?"

"Three opinions!"

"Did you see the TV reviews?"

"Five—six. I didn't write *Ante Meridian* for the critics; it's an audience show." Wally groaned. "What's the matter?"

"You sure learn fast, kid. Every masterpiece turns into an audience show when the out-of-town critics hate it."

"But . . ."

Wally twisted toward Phil. "What'd we wrap today?"

"Don't ask."

"I'm asking."

"Bupkes."

"What's that?" Brian asked.

"Wally is asking Phil how much we took in at the box office today, and Phil is telling us we didn't do well," the lyricist said.

"A bus-and-truck company of *Babes in Toyland* would draw better," Phil said. "At least the kiddies would come."

"It's the first day," Brian protested.

"I think Wally's telling us it's the last day," Al said quietly.

"Not quite," Wally said. "We'll play out the week."

"What if business picks up?" Brian asked weakly.

Wally leaned forward, an elbow on his knee, his pinky ring gleaming. "Kid, I give you my word of honor: if there's a big spurt at the box office, I'll take the notice down."

Once again, Brian straightened in his chair. "Then we've got to advertise. Radio, TV . . ."

"No."

Brian stared at Wally. "No?"

"That's right."

"But if we don't advertise, what chance do we have?"

"I told you: I'm not risking any more of the investors' money. I got a conscience."

"And a career," Phil said. The others looked at him. "This isn't the last show Wally's going to do. He's going to have to go out there and raise money again."

"So we get short-changed," Brian muttered.

"No," Wally said calmly. "We gave it our best shot."

"One performance!"

"When a show's in this much trouble—"

"Al said we're all willing to work."

"Rehearsals cost money," Wally said. "Changes cost money. Once you're out of town, everything costs money."

"Listen—listen," Brian said. "My mother was here last night. She was bowled over."

"Will wonders never cease," Wally said.

Brian plunged ahead. "And she's got a lot of friends with money. She could make a few phone calls and . . ."

"No," Wally said. "The books are closed. I'm not going out and raise more money on the basis of what we've got here. You can't beat a dead horse."

The lyricist looked at the composer, then turned as he heard a pathetic, "But you *loved* the show!"

Brian was standing over Wally, dripping tears on his double-knit. The group waited for Wally's response. Finally he said, "That's right, I did."

"Well, what happened?"

"I found out I was wrong."

"You're willing to take the opinion of a few incompetent critics . . ."

"How about the audience? Those people going up the aisle all night were voting with their feet."

"No show's perfect . . ."

"Brian," Wally said, "find me one person who thinks I was right about the show. Besides your mother. *One person.* After all these years in the business, I don't need a brick wall to fall on me. I've dug myself out too many times."

Brian made one more desperate sally. "Maybe—if we had help . . ."

Wally looked up. "I told you . . ."

"I mean the other kind. Creative help." He swallowed hard. "I know this is my first show. Maybe somebody more experienced could come in and—kind of punch things up . . ."

"You didn't look around that audience last night?" Wally asked.

"Well, yes, but . . ."

"He wouldn't recognize them," Al said. Brian looked at him. "There were two book writers sitting out there."

"Three," Wally said. "I had premonitions."

"If you want to bring someone in, I'm willing to step aside," Brian said, "I'll share billing . . ." He paused. Wally was shaking his head. "Did you *ask* them?"

"I *brought* 'em to Philly. They all said the same thing."

"What?" Brian whispered.

"Close the show."

A choking sound rattled in Brian's throat.

"Wally . . ." Al said. Wally twisted toward the director. "What about closing now—I mean tonight—cut our losses and go straight into New York. A few previews and we take our chances."

"With no advance, no money for ads, no *show?*" Wally rose and found himself belly to belly with his poleaxed playwright. "I'm sorry, Brian," he said. "Really. I know how you feel and I wish there was something I could do, but believe me, there isn't." He put a hand on Brian's shoulder. "I know you're *not* going to believe me, but it's better this way. The whole thing'll be forgotten in a few weeks." Brian moaned. "You'd rather go into New York and get your head handed to you in the *New York Times*? Of course not. Now you can write another show . . ."

"Never!" Brian screamed and ran through the nearest door.

"Hey!" Wally yelled. "That's the ladies' room!"

"It's okay," the lyricist sighed, "he knows the territory."

As Brian's retching echoed through the lounge, Wally looked at Sonny, staring blankly into space. "You okay?"

Sonny turned, surprised. "About the same as everybody else, I guess."

"You oughtta be proud of yourself." Sonny's mouth popped open but he said nothing. "You did a helluva job on that new second-act opening. I loved it. I'm sorry the New York critics won't see it."

"Thank you, Wally . . ."

"You're putting the notice up?" the director asked Phil.

"It's already up."

Diane stopped just inside the stage door and grasped Carin's arm. Not even Carin's heavy winter coat could protect her from Diane's steely fingers. "Ouch!" she exclaimed, and tried to pull away, but Diane was drawing her inexorably toward the knot of performers clustered in front of the call board. Rising to half-toe, Diane peered between heads, then sank to her heels with a groan.

"What is it?" Carin asked.

"The notice," Diane said.

"The notice?"

"The closing notice. Saturday night."

"You mean we're not going to New York?"

"Merry Christmas, everybody." The group turned. Sonny was standing in the door that led to the stage. He raised a hand as a barrage of voices assailed him. "It wasn't my decision. I'm a hired gun, just like you."

The fusillade of questions struck again.

"Wally'll explain," he said.

"When?" someone demanded.

"He's going to talk to the company onstage at half-hour. Until then . . ."

"No rehearsal?"

"For what?" He looked at Carin. "At least we won't have to go back to work on your number. I wanted to redo half of it." He looked at the ring of stricken faces. "If you've never been to the

Philadelphia Museum, now's your chance. There's a Rodin museum, too . . ."

He was unable to finish the suggestion as a human wave engulfed him, sweeping him aside in a dash for the pay phone just beyond him. The boy who arrived first snatched the receiver from its cradle and groped in his dance bag for a dime as the others jostled into a ragged line. When the boy looked up to ask, "Who's got some change?" a clamorous chorus demanded that he step aside for the properly accoutred. Bracing himself against the phone, he propped his dance bag on a raised knee, dug into it again with a caustic "Thanks a lot!" extracted a dime from the bag and added, "It looks like I'll be able to manage without you."

At the call board Sonny glanced at Carin, the only figure in the corridor apart from himself and the stage doorman not waiting impatiently for the phone. Still clutching her dance bag, she stood woodenly where Diane had left her, nacreous tears rolling down her cheeks.

"Operator," the boy at the phone said, "I'm calling the Koenig Talent Agency in New York, person to person to Mr. Nat Koenig—collect. . . . The number? Oh, Jesus, hang on."

As he rummaged in his dance bag, a voice from the line yelled, "Five-one-five-two-oh-four-two! Tell him you're calling for me, too."

Sonny approached Carin. Mortified, she let her dance bag fall to raise a hand and wipe her eyes. Sonny caught her hand and held it. "Did I tell you how good you were last night?"

She lowered her head and shook it. "Please don't."

"Why?"

"It'll just make me feel worse." Her head came up; the tears were trickling again. "That's it?" she asked. "It's over? They'll never see us in New York?"

"That's the way it looks, unless . . ." He paused and she waited, her eyes on him, her grip tightening on his hand. "Well—they could take the notice down if we start doing a lot of business here, but—I wouldn't count on that if I were you." Carin whimpered and bit her lip, the tears streaming now, and Sonny pulled her to him, hugging her.

"That—that's the first time anybody ever made a dance on me," she sobbed into his chest.

"But it's not the last."

"Yes, it is. I'll never have another chance like this. I knew it was too good to be true . . ." The words dissolved in a fresh torrent of tears, and Sonny led Carin toward the stage, past the line of staring performers.

"Nat? It's Jamie," the boy exclaimed into the phone. "You heard? . . . Yeah, three death notices. We'll be back Sunday morning. Any auditions next week?" The line strained forward to listen.

In a pitch-black wing Sonny held Carin until she had cried herself out. When she finally pushed back from him, he said, "Take my word for it, you'll have plenty of chances."

Wiping her cheek with the back of a hand, she shook her head. "I'll have to start all over again. Nobody's going to make a ballet for me. God—I told my mother and everything! She was going to come to New York for the opening." Tears threatened again, but she fought them back and reached for Sonny's hand. "Sonny—I think you're terrific. I never saw anybody work like that . . ."

"Careful," Sonny said softly, *"I'll* be crying in a minute."

"You should. That was such a beautiful dance."

"I'll make some more. Maybe on you."

"Oh, I hope so!"

"Here," he said. He tipped her face up and wiped it with the end of his muffler.

"Don't! It'll get all wet."

"That's okay. Will you be all right tonight?"

"Yes."

"How's your ankle?"

"Fine."

He smiled. "Bullshit." As she started to protest, he said, "But that's all right: you'll have time to rest it after Saturday. You think you'll remember the steps tonight?"

"I went over them in the hotel room before we came to the theater."

"Tell you what: if you and Gino will come to the theater half an hour early, I'll brush it up with you."

"Oh, thanks. I'll tell Gino."

"Meet me downstairs in the lounge."

"What about there?" She pointed at the stage.

"If Wally sees us onstage, he'll go berserk. The stagehands could charge him for a rehearsal call if they want to cash in before the show closes. We'll be able to walk through it in the lounge; that's all you need." She nodded. He brushed a wisp of hair back from her forehead. "I'll watch tonight. I'll watch *every* performance."

"And give me corrections?"

"Sure." He nudged her toward the corridor. "Go tell Gino about the rehearsal. If he doesn't want to . . ."

"He'll want to." She disappeared into the corridor. Sonny remained still for a moment, then began wrapping his muffler around his neck. He stopped when he heard voices issuing from the shadows above an upstage leg. Taking a silent step toward the inner edge of the leg, he turned upstage and listened. One of the voices was unmistakably Wally's, the other was familiar . . . Of course: Mrs. Moore.

"It's heartbreaking!" Mrs. Moore was saying. "I want to cry."

"Me too," Wally said.

"You poor man! All that work."

"It's worse for the writers. Two years down the drain."

"And the children!"

"The children?"

"The dancers."

"Yeah. I feel for 'em. I know I'm the villain 'cause I had to make the decision to close the show, but I care about those kids."

"Oh, I can tell you do. It's obvious. Cynthia's terribly aware of that. She's mentioned it any number of times."

"Really?"

"Oh, yes. She refers to you as—what's the expression she uses? 'That sweet man'—that's it."

"That's very nice to hear."

"She means it, too. Cynthia may look like a child, but actually she's very mature for her age."

"Uh—what *is* her age?"

"Nineteen." There was a silence, and Sonny took a soft step back into the wing, remaining there, still as a statue, while the colloquy continued. "But, like I said, a very mature nineteen."

"I suppose she's got a boyfriend back in New York."

"Not one in particular. Several." Sonny thought he could hear a smile in Mrs. Moore's words. "Youngsters today are so sophisticated. Not like in my day."

"Or mine," Wally said.

"Oh, Mr. Mack, I hope you're not putting yourself in *my* category. You look more like someone in Cynthia's generation."

"You're being much too generous."

"Well, if I am, let's not tell Cynthia." She giggled. "She thinks you're the most attractive man in the company."

"There must be something wrong with her eyesight. With all those boy dancers around . . ."

"I guess we both know about *them.*"

"That's true."

"I'm happy to say Cynthia's sensitive enough to appreciate that certain something that only comes with maturity. That's why she singled you out."

"Mrs. Moore . . . !"

The giggle rolled out of the darkness again. "All right, don't take my word for it. Ask Cynthia."

"You think I could do that? Go up to a member of the cast and say, 'What do you think of me?' "

"Well, you'd get a very surprising answer if you asked Cynthia."

Now Wally's chortle tumbled out of the wing. "She'd probably faint dead away."

"You're not as good a judge of character as I thought you were, Mr. Mack. Cynthia may look shy and retiring when she's just sitting around rehearsal, but that girl's a ball of fire when she wants to be. A ball of *fire*," she repeated significantly. "I'm sure you noticed her onstage . . ."

"How could I not?"

"Well, that's the *real* Cynthia: peppy, outgoing—a little naughty sometimes . . ." Wally grunted, and Sonny imagined Mrs. Moore poking a playful elbow into his paunch. "But girls will be girls," Mrs. Moore chuckled. "And men will be men. And ever the twain shall meet." There was a silence. Evidently Mrs. Moore was waiting.

"I certainly think your daughter's got a bright future," Wally said.

"Oh, I can't tell you what it means to hear a person of your experience and standing say something like that. But you're telling it to the wrong person."

"Oh?"

"Of course. It would be so wonderful if you'd say that to Cynthia. Can you image what it would mean to her, coming from you? She'd be so—grateful."

"Well, I'd be happy to tell her."

"You're serious?"

"Of course. One of the great pleasures of producing is discovering young talent like Cindy. And encouraging it."

"Cynthia. Cindy's that fat singer."

"Oh, yes—Cynthia. I know who we're talking about: a very gifted young woman."

"Well, you wouldn't believe how happy it would make her to hear that."

"In that case . . ."

"Yes?"

"Maybe she—maybe you and your daughter would like to have a drink with me after the show. Or a bite to eat."

"It may be too late for *me*—I need my beauty sleep—but I'm sure Cynthia would just love it."

"Uh—will you speak to her?"

"Of course. But I can tell you right now what her answer will be: she'd be honored."

"Fine. We can meet at the stage door as soon as she changes."

"The stage door it is." There was a moment's silence, then Sonny heard Mrs. Moore's throaty contralto again. "You can't imagine what this'll do for that girl."

"I think I can."

And they accuse us *of preying on children,* Sonny thought as he slipped into the corridor.

Moira leaned back against the door to widen the aperture for Chris, who was sidling in, a suitcase in each hand. Just beyond Moira, he eased the luggage to the floor, said, "One more," and went back into the corridor. A moment later there were three suitcases on the carpet, and Moira closed the door.

"Come have a drink," she said.

"Do you think I could shower first? I'm still knocked out from that train ride."

"Not another word," she said, reaching for one of the suitcases.

"It's okay," Chris said, intercepting the suitcase, "I've got it."

When he came back to the living room fifteen minutes later, Moira was on the couch, an offering of drinks and cheese and crackers on the coffee table in front of her. As Chris settled into the couch with his drink, Moira inhaled and asked, "What smells so good?"

"Jean Naté."

She sniffed at his shoulder. "I've seen it advertised, but I don't think I've ever smelled it before. It's nice and fresh."

"All the dancers seem to use it . . ." He broke off. Now that he thought of it, the bottle he had hastily tossed into his kit was Carin's. Or Diane's or Terry's. He had discovered the cologne on Forty-eighth Street and grown accustomed to its scent on nearly every dancer he met. When he had asked Diane about it, she had told him they used it after class instead of a shower sometimes.

He made a mental note to get some cologne of his own tomorrow—anything but Jean Naté—and forced himself to concentrate. Moira was asking him a question: "How did it go? At home."

"Oh. Perfect. There was no one there."

"That man who lives there . . . ?"

"Terry."

"You were worried about bumping into him."

"He wasn't there. I just went into our—my room, packed up and got out."

She nodded toward the pair of suitcases near the door. "That's everything?"

"Plus the suitcase in the bedroom—and a few things in Detroit—my books, a typewriter, my car . . ."

"You've got a car?"

"Everybody in Detroit has a car. It's against the law not to."

"What'd you do with it?"

"Lent it to a reporter at the paper. He wants to buy it from me if I don't come back."

"You going to sell it to him?"

"I don't know."

"That means you don't know if you're going back." She waited for an answer, then asked, "True? False?"

"That's right, I don't know." He smiled at her. "I've converted to *your* faith: no answers, a lot of questions and a potful of options."

"How does it feel?"

"Not too hot." He stared at the suitcases. "In the meantime, you're looking at two thirds of my worldly possessions." He took a sip of his drink. "Impressive, huh?"

"People of our persuasion travel light." He looked around the room. "My mother furnished it."

"That's cheating."

"I know. I'm like the road sign in *Gargantua and Pantagruel* that points the way to a city without ever going there itself." She refilled his glass, replenished her own drink, lit a cigarette and sat back with, "Want to tell me what happened in Philadelphia?"

"No."

"Fair enough." She gestured toward the kitchen. "Dinner'll be ready in half an hour."

"I feel so guilty."

"About what?"

"Imposing on you like this."

"Who said it was an imposition?"

"Me. I'll have enough money to move out of here Friday."

"Okay, whatever you say."

After dinner, Calvados on the coffee table, Satie on the turntable, Chris observed, "Maybe it's time for *my* grand tour."

"I'm surprised you haven't taken it already."

"So am I."

"Why didn't you?"

"A lot of reasons. All dumb. I got a job at the *Free Press* the day after graduation. That impressed me so much I put everything else on hold. You think Paris is still there?"

"The last I heard."

"I mean Hemingway's."

"It's hard to find under the Toyotas and *supermarchés.*"

"What's the use of going?"

"When you've got two or three days, I'll tell you."

"Then, on balance, you liked it."

"*Off* balance, I liked it. Paris was a rite of passage."

"I think I'm ready for that."

"You ought to go."

"On what?"

Chris fell silent and Moira said, "If you do go, I'll give you a letter to my friend Larry Rosen. He's got a big apartment near St. Germain, and every Sunday's open house for the Americans in Paris. If the weather's good they start with softball in the Bois, then the afternoon's devoted to cultural affairs. Writers read a couple of chapters they've written that week, a poet recites his latest canto, a singer sings. . . . You like puns?"

"If they're good."

"Well, there was a soprano—big girl—glorious voice—and every week she was sort of the grand finale. One of the musicians or composers would play for her and she'd favor us with an aria or two. Unbelievable on a Sunday afternoon."

"I'll bet," Chris said distantly.

"But one Sunday, after all the other budding geniuses had done their thing, she wouldn't get up. Well—sacrilege! Nobody'd ever copped out before. Everybody started yelling, and she just sat there getting redder and redder, and finally she said, 'If you've got to know, I'm wearing a new girdle, and it's so tight I can't sing,' and one of the writers said, 'Well, your *gaine* is our loss.'" Chris stared into space. "You see, in French, *gaine* means girdle. I guess I should've explained that up front." Moira waited, then said, "Want to go to a movie?"

"What? Oh—sorry. She wouldn't sing, and then . . . ?"

"I suggested a movie. There're two theaters on Thirty-fourth Street."

"I'm sorry, Moira, really. What's the end of the story?"

"*I'm* bored with it. Want to go to a movie?"

Chris stroked his cheek, his eyes half-closed, growled, "What a dumb idea!" and stood up.

"I didn't say it was the greatest pun I'd ever heard . . ."

"I'm talking about moving in here. What the hell was I thinking of!"

She got up. "Will you please relax?"

"No! And I'll be damned if I'm going to share my nervous breakdown with you!"

She willed a smile. "Selfish."

"I'm serious, Moira. I must've been out of my mind to think I could walk in here and dump my trash on you."

"I'm not complaining."

"I am."

He stalked into the bedroom and reappeared hauling a suitcase. Depositing it next to the two suitcases that still stood near the door, he turned to a closet and wrestled the crowded rack for his coat.

"Where do you think you're going?" Moira asked.

"To a hotel."

"You're broke, remember?"

"I've got a few dollars. I can probably get into the Y."

"Listen," Moira said, "if it'll make you feel better, I'll sleep out here on the couch . . ."

He turned to stare incredulously at her. "*You'll* sleep on the couch!"

"Okay, *you* can sleep on the couch . . ."

His hand on her shoulder stopped her. "Moira—listen to me: I'm the one who called up in the middle of the night, I'm the one who walked in here like a zombie and fell into your bed . . ."

"You were exhausted—you'd been on a train all night . . ."

"We didn't even shake hands!"

"The couch," she said evenly. "You can sleep on the couch. I'm not trying to trap you into a new affair."

He yanked his coat out of the closet. "At the Y I can be as boring as I want."

"You can be as boring as you want here. I'm the one who's been forcing all the socializing. Miss Conviviality! Forget it. I've got some work to do. Set yourself up in here, and I'll keep busy in the bedroom. Knock if you want to use the bathroom, I may be *déshabillée* . . ."

"Why are you doing this?"

"I don't know. I like your company. In a couple of days it'll be Christmas. This time of year I always help the needy. Any or all of the above . . ."

"That's repartee. What's the real reason?"

She caught her breath, then exploded. *"Everything* I say is repartee! Hadn't you noticed that? It's the secret of my irresistible charm!" She was gone. Chasing her, Chris had to pull up sharply to avoid ramming into the bedroom door as it slammed in front of him.

"Moira!"

"Go if you want or stay if you want!" came the muffled reply. "I don't feel like begging. It's too—human!"

He stared at the bedroom door.

There was an air of what seemed like relief in the girls' dressing room. With their worst fears confirmed the pressure was off, and the native optimism without which every one of them would have settled long since for the drab security of life behind a desk or counter had reasserted itself. Leaning toward the glowing makeup mirror to convert their faces to the masks of Delacroix orange and Constable blue that would fling their features up to the last row of the balcony, the gypsies bantered animatedly.

A stranger might have thought that the slender filament from which their economic futures hung was still intact. In fact, they were all about to lose their jobs, a trauma that drives blue collar workers to drink, middle-class employees to shrinks and upper-class executives to the brink of suicide on the two or three terrifying occasions it may occur in an average lifetime. These gypsies and their acting, singing, writing and directing colleagues faced the trauma of unemployment and the corresponding humiliation of offering themselves for reemployment twenty or thirty times a year. To them, security—a job, a contract, fringe benefits, pension plans—were words in a nearly unintelligible language.

A part of their courage was ignorance. But only a part. It was also a laudable willingness to place nothing between themselves and life's vicissitudes but the frail shield of their hopes and wits and bodies. They sometimes paused to cast an envious glance toward

their European brethren, comfortably ensconced in the civil service
of subsidized dance companies, but for the most part they swallowed
their anxieties and accepted their lot with the kind of lighthearted
defiance that was on view now as the dancers and singers prepared
without complaint to mount, and beat, a dead horse until the stage
manager turned out the lights, casting them into the raw Philadelphia night to go capering back to New York like the doomed
revelers frolicking over the horizon in the last frames of a Bergman
film.

As Susan raised a knee to unfasten the clasp that held her Ace,
Diane glanced at the yin-yang symbol she had drawn on it. "Did it
help?"

"Not yet."

"It will."

Carin peered across Diane as Susan began unwinding the bandage. "I thought you were going to leave it on now that we've
opened."

"I changed my mind."

"Why?" Carin asked.

"Yeah," Diane chimed in. "What can Sonny do? Fire you?
We've got three more performances."

"I've got a couple of auditions next week," Susan replied,
lowering her voice, "and you know how word gets around."

The three girls twisted toward the door as a cry went up further
down the line. "Joni! What're *you* doing here?"

The young woman who had entered was slim, and her flatfooted gait as she crossed the room to the makeup table was a neon
proclamation of her profession. "Rick and I drove from New York
to see the show," Joni said. "We were going to wait till next
week . . ."

"It's a good thing you didn't," Diane grunted, "unless you're
apeshit about deserted theaters."

"We heard," Joni said, stopping behind Diane's chair.

"Already?" Pam exclaimed.

Joni nodded. "That's why we came. Between us we've got like
eight friends in the show."

"That's what I call loyalty!" Sharon exclaimed.

"Or masochism," Diane muttered.

"The show's that bad?" Joni asked.

"How do *we* know? We haven't seen it," Pam replied.

"The cast is always the last to know," Carla sighed.

"It's really going to close?" Joni asked.

"Didn't you see the notice when you came in the stage door?"
Pam asked.

"How can anybody miss it?" Joni replied. "I'm sorry."

Diane shrugged and resumed her preparation. "That's show
business."

"It sure is," Joni said grimly. She watched Diane make up for a moment, then asked, "What're you going to do?"

"Line A and group B," Diane replied, stretching her mouth to line her lips. Carin directed an inquiring look at her in the mirror. "Line A at the unemployment office," Diane explained.

"There're a couple of auditions next week," Joni said.

"That's group B," Diane said to Carin, and looked up at Joni. "We'll be there, paddin' our bras and shakin' our buns."

"Fifteen minutes, ladies and gentlemen, fifteen minutes," the squawk box announced tinnily and sputtered to silence.

The tempo of the preparation at the makeup table accelerated, and conversation ceased. Joni remained behind Diane's chair, watching her pat powder over the scar on her cheek, then she observed, "It's a shame the show couldn't make it to New York, at least for opening night."

"Specially for her," Diane said, poking her powderpuff at Carin. The puff left a little white cloud in the air. Joni looked at Carin in the mirror, and Diane said, "You've never met, have you?"

"No," Joni said.

"This is Joni Miles," Diane said to Carin's image, then raised her glance to Joni's face hovering over her own in the mirror. "This is my roommate, Carin Bradley. You'll be glad you came when you see her. She and Gino open the second act—they got the only good reviews."

"I can't wait," Joni said, and turned back to Diane's image. "But I was thinking of *you.*"

"I don't have that much to do," Diane shrugged. "Clive Barnes wouldn't even have noticed."

"I was thinking of . . ." Joni stopped. Diane looked up. "What?"

Joni nibbled at her lip. "Maybe I shouldn't tell you. It might just make you feel worse."

"Tell me *what!*" Diane demanded in the tone that brooked no opposition.

"Music to My Ears opened last week . . ."

"I know."

"And the kids had already decided . . ."

She broke off as Diane's chair fell backward. Heads spun, sponges, brushes, puffs, and pencils froze at the pistol shot report. On her feet, eyes welling, Diane reached for Joni's hands. "Not—the Robe . . ." Joni nodded. "Oh, God! Oh, God!" Diane exclaimed, clutching her temples.

Now Carin's chair fell backward as she sprang up, reaching for her friend. "What's wrong!"

Blubbering, Diane allowed Carin to seat her in the chair that Susan had righted. "Oh, God, oh, God!" Diane sobbed. "The Robe!"

"What's she talking about?" Carin pleaded.

"The Gypsy Robe," Joni said quietly. "She was going to get it—and now she won't."

Still lost, Carin turned to her fellow dancers. Pam plucked at the makeup-stained kimono she was wearing. "The first one was somebody's makeup robe—like this—years ago. The gypsies in some show decided to sew a prop on it—something from their show—and the next musical that opened, they showed up on opening night and presented it to one of the gypsies in the new show. You know—for luck. The kids in *that* show decided to sew something from their show on it, and pass it along to a gypsy in the *next* show that opened. Get it?"

"Yes," Carin said.

"That must've been a hundred shows ago," Pam said. "Maybe more."

"And every show added something?"

"Yup."

"How can anybody find room on it—or lift it?"

"Oh, the first Robe's in the Library of the Performing Arts at Lincoln Center."

"So are all the others. I've seen 'em." Sharon said.

"The one Diane was gonna get—that's the current one," Carla said. "Someday *it*'ll go into the museum."

"Boo hoo!" Diane said. It was Diane's habit to laugh "Ha ha," cry "Boo hoo," sneeze "Ah chew," hiccup "Hic," giggle "Tee hee" and clear her throat "Ahem." The fact that she emitted sounds that corresponded to onomatopoetic conventions in no way diminished the sincerity or depth of her feelings. She simply made the kind of noises that customarily appear on printed pages or, classically, in balloons over the heads of comic-strip characters: it was an anatomical matter, having to do with bone structure and resonating chambers, not temperament or affectation.

"Boo hoo!" Diane bawled; Carin put an arm around her shoulders and held her while she moaned, "It's not *fair!*"

Susan leaned toward Diane. "They're gonna call five minutes . . ."

Turning toward her image in the mirror, Diane stared in horror at a fingerpainting by a hyperactive five-year-old.

Sharon rose and moved quickly down the line. "I'm finished. I'll help you."

"Lemme get this stuff off first," Diane sniffled, scooping a dollop of cold cream from the jar in front of her. Smearing it hastily on her face, she snatched up several tissues and removed the technicolor guck with angry little stabs as she muttered, "All my life I wanted to be a star. Okay, maybe it's not gonna happen—maybe I'm never gonna win an Oscar, or an Emmy, or a Tony—but the Gypsy Robe—holy *shit*—that *says* something. It tells everybody, whatever you did with your goddamn life, you were *good* at it. And when the Robe goes into the museum—so would *I!* I'd be part of history!" The disappointment and anxiety she had managed to shrug off in the wake of *Ante Meridian*'s failure surfaced now, full-blown and virulent, as she hurled the sodden wad of tissue at the makeup mirror, where it stuck like a putty nose on the desolate image of her face.

With new freshets of tears threatening to render Diane *hors de combat,* Sharon took matters firmly in hand, tipping Diane's head back and sponging orange stripes of pancake on her cheeks and forehead. "You're not going to make curtain," she said, and Diane sniffed loudly, inhaling the encroaching tears.

A minute later she reached for the sponge with a steady hand. "Thanks. I can do it now."

"It's okay," Sharon said.

"I can do it faster," Diane insisted, and Sharon relinquished the sponge and went to the costume rack, where a nervous wardrobe woman held out a costume. Carin quickly put the finishing touches on her own makeup as Diane's hand darted about next to her and the dressing room's normal bustle and chatter resumed.

Through the explosion she had touched off, Joni had hovered near Diane's chair. Now she moved closer and muttered a guilty, "I'm sorry."

Sniffling and patting, Diane replied,"It's not your fault. Somebody else would've told me. And I'm *glad* I know. It's a goddamn fuckin' honor, even if . . ." Tears glimmering again, she broke off and furiously brushed an eyebrow.

"Can't you get it anyway?" Carin asked.

"Only on opening night in New York," Diane muttered, her nose a few inches from the mirror. "Philadelphia doesn't count." Sitting back to examine her handiwork, she added, "Wait till Terry hears about this." She glanced up at Joni's image. "You know, in all these years he never got the Robe?"

"Are you sure?" Joni asked. "Somewhere along the line, he must've . . ."

"Nope. Not once. And you wouldn't believe how much it bugs him." Joni coughed and stepped back to avoid the cloud of powder that ascended as Diane tattooed her face with a puff. When the cloud dissipated, Diane snapped, "I don't care if he *does* get jealous. Serves him right."

"For what?" Joni asked.

Diane brandished the puff at the mirror in front of her. "What do you see?"

"Nothing."

"That's right: nothing!" The puff swept toward several telegrams Scotch-taped to the mirror in front of Susan. "Not even a lousy wire on opening night. Okay, save the flowers for opening night in New York, but . . ."

"I guess he was too upset," Joni said.

"He didn't know we were gonna bomb," Diane muttered through stiffened lips as she leaned close to the mirror again, applying lipstick.

"I mean about his *own* show."

Diane's head tilted back; her eyes met Joni's in the mirror. "What're you talking about?"

"He hasn't told you?"

"Five minutes, ladies and gentlemen. Five minutes," the squawk box rasped.

Diane's anxiety took the—to her—more acceptable form of irritability. "Haven't you been listening? I didn't even get a fuckin' wire. What happened to his show?"

"Nothing. I mean, the *show's* okay." Joni fell silent, aware that the first-act curtain was in new jeopardy.

"If you're saying . . ." the ashen face in the mirror growled, stopping short of the fateful conclusion.

"Jesus, Di, I'm sorry. I'm bringing you nothing but bad news."

Diane's lips didn't move and the question was barely audible above the dressing room's buzz. "He got fired?"

"The third day of rehearsal. I was sure you knew."

Moira stood in front of the door for several minutes before turning the button in the doorknob to unlock it. It was another moment before she twisted the knob and edged the door open to look into the living room. It was empty. She stepped out of the bedroom, then stopped as she saw the three suitcases still parked near the door. Turning, she surveyed the room again, but there was no sign of Chris. She went to the kitchen, looked into it and returned to the living room, her frown deepening. Circling the couch, she stopped short again: Chris was stretched on it, asleep. As she bent over him, she came between a table lamp and Chris's face, shadowing it, waking him.

Moira's loose blouse had fallen away from her bent body, and through it Chris could see the silhouette of her breast against the glow of the lamp. He caught her hand and pulled her down to him. He would have opened her mouth with his tongue, but it was open already, the tip of her tongue attacking.

Her breast was firm under his hand, larger and rounder than Carin's, and her body as he took the clothes from it was also larger and rounder than Carin's, a woman's body as opposed to a child's, the fluff of pink cotton candy on the mount more plentiful than Carin's pale down . . .

He fought off Carin's agile ghost by taking Moira's sex in his hand: it was as open and willing as her mouth had been.

With Chris above her, Moira wondered if the contraceptive

cream she had inserted last night was still effective. Then she seized Chris's buttocks and pushed him into her.

Still in costume, Diane waited impatiently at the pay phone, the receiver clasped between bony shoulder and ear. She squeezed against the wall to make room in the narrow corridor for the stream of stagehands and musicians making their customary expeditious exit from the theater. A blast of icy air from the open stage door turned Diane around, and she found herself staring into the friendly eyes of a paunchy, balding musician in a raccoon coat.

"Hi, sweetheart," he said, tucking his fiddle case under a furry arm. "Care to have a drink?" She shook her head and he bestowed what was clearly intended to be an ingratiating smile on her. "You'll be gone in a couple of days."

"So?"

" 'For all we know, we may never meet again,' " he sang.

"That suits me," Diane replied. "I'm a Diesel dyke."

As the musician stalked sullenly toward the stage door, Diane slammed the receiver back into its cradle and retrieved her dime. The musician paused at the door for a quick appreciative glance at Joni hurrying in from the alley behind the theater, but relinquished her, and himself, to fate as her husband pushed in behind her, a hand on her shoulder.

Bucking the outbound tide in the corridor, Joni pushed forward, calling, "Diane!"

Diane turned, said, "Hi, Rick," and received a kiss on the cheek from Joni's husband.

"It wasn't the best show I've ever seen," Joni said, "but I certainly wouldn't call it the worst. Isn't there a chance . . . ?" She broke off as Diane's bleak expression registered. "Want me to shut up?"

"It's Terry," Diane murmured.

"I know how upset you are . . ."

"I can't reach him."

"You called?" Joni asked.

"Just now."

Rick looked at his watch "It's only eleven. He's probably out."

"Celebrating?" Diane asked morosely.

"Forgetting," Joni said.

"He can't afford a *beer,*" Diane said, then added an abrupt, "Are you two going back to New York tonight?"

Joni nodded. "As soon as we see the rest of the kids."

As they began the long ascent to the girls' dressing room, Diane said, "I'm going back with you."

"What about the show?" Rick asked.

"No rehearsal anymore," Diane said, speaking slowly to preserve her wind for the climb and the fast change to street clothes. "All I have to do is make it back for the matinee tomorrow."

"But if you keep on calling Terry . . ."

"I know him: when he's down, he won't answer the phone. He'll just sit there eating himself up . . ." She shook her head. "He needs me. If you don't have room, I can catch a train."

"Of course we've got room," Joni said. "I just hate to see you put yourself through all this when you're going to be home Sunday anyway."

"I'll be out of this stuff in ten minutes," Diane said.

There were streaks of pink and purple cold cream in Diane's hairline when she left the dressing room with Joni and Rick ten minutes later. Carin, still in her robe, padded out of the dressing room in their wake, poking at the cold cream in Diane's hair. "It's okay," Diane said, "I'll get it all off in the car. If anybody gets uptight, tell 'em I'll be back by noon at the latest."

Carin nodded and watched as the three bundled figures bustled down the stairs. A draft spiraling up the stairwell made Carin shiver and draw her robe closer around her. As she turned around, Gino emerged from the boys' dressing room. "Oh," he said. "Hi. I was just coming to ask you if we could meet later at the hotel. The guys want to go out and drown their sorrows. I oughtta go along for a beer or two. I'd take you, but they said no girls."

"I wouldn't go anyway," Carin said.

"Shouldn't be too long. I'll call you as soon as I get back to the hotel. Unless it's too late. You gonna stay up?"

"I don't know," Carin replied numbly.

He put his arms around her. "I know you feel lousy."

"Don't you?"

"Yeah. You work your ass off all your life, and then . . ." He shrugged. They stared at each other, disappointment uniting them as sex had early that morning. "Maybe we can do it up at the Ninety-second Street Y or something. Or on TV." She nodded. "Where's Diane?" he asked.

"She went back to New York. Just for tonight."

"I'll call you when I get back to the hotel. Would you like that?"

"I don't know. I think so. I don't feel like being alone."

"Sure." He kissed her lightly, quickly, and headed for the stairs. "This shouldn't take long."

Listening to the diminishing sound of his footsteps, she wondered if she should call Chris—if she dared call Chris. Then she remembered she couldn't call him; she didn't know where he was. She imagined what he would say if she did find him, and the thought sent another shudder through her. As she turned toward the girls' dressing room, the door opened abruptly and she had to step back for a more than usually red-eyed Cynthia, followed by Mrs. Moore.

"Sor-ry!" Mrs. Moore caroled, then, seeing Carin, paused for a stricken "Oh, Carin! What can I say? This would've been *it* for you."

"Excuse me, Mrs. Moore," Carin said, and pushed past her into the dressing room.

Mrs. Moore turned to Cynthia. "Well! That says it all, doesn't it! Can't even be gracious to well-wishers. *She'll* never be heard from again." Seizing her daughter's arm, she steered her across the landing and started down the stairs, the manicured manacle firmly in place. "Talent is fifty percent. *Fifty.* The rest is personality, charm, contacts, who you know and how you behave . . ." She tottered as Cynthia stiffened and stopped, her back against the stairwell's clammy wall. "Do you realize I could've fallen down these stairs . . . ?"

"Whyyyy?" Cynthia wailed. Mrs. Moore tugged at her daughter's arm, but Cynthia braced her feet against the stair. *"Whyyyy!"*

Mrs. Moore glanced nervously up and down the stairs, then bent close to her daughter. "Weren't you listening?" Cynthia sneezed violently, and Mrs. Moore yanked at her arm. "Listen to me! You just saw a perfect example of what happens to performers who can't even bother to be polite to their betters. You think anybody's ever going to notice that little nothing again? She's *finished!*"

"I don't want to go out with him," Cynthia moaned.

Mrs. Moore leaned closer and tears began to drip from Cynthia's assaulted eyes. "Every other girl in this company would give her eyeteeth to go out with him."

"Then *let* them!"

"He's interested in *you.*" The already measured beat of her words grew even statelier. "The producer of this show has singled you out. You think this is the last show he's ever going to produce . . . ?"

A clatter of footsteps silenced her. As several dancers turned the corner above them and trotted past, Mrs. Moore felt her daughter strain, lemminglike, toward them, but her considerable bulk kept Cynthia pinned to the wall until the danger had passed; then she leaned close again and hissed, "Did you hear what I said? You're the only one who's going to come out of this a winner!"

"Of what?"

"Who knows?" As Cynthia gasped for breath enough to respond, Mrs. Moore shot ahead. "All he suggested is a quiet little supper somewhere. What's wrong with that?"

"You know what he wants!"

"Have you *looked* at the man? Answer me! Have you stopped for ten seconds to look at the man?"

"He's old!"

"If he's old, what does that make *me?* Are you trying to insult me? Is that the thanks I get for putting you ahead of everything—for trying to *help?*"

"He's ugly!"

"You call that ugly? Now tell me Cary Grant's ugly. Well, Cary Grant's old enough to be Walter Mack's father . . ."

A fresh tattoo of footsteps counseled flight. Renewing her grip on Cynthia's arm, Mrs. Moore propelled her daughter down the stairs and across the stage. Veering, she steered her charge into a dark wing where stacked scenery shielded the two of them from view and velour legs effectively muffled their voices. Pointing a pudgy finger at the entrance to the stage-door corridor, she said, "He's right out there, waiting for you: Mr. Walter Mack, one of the most distinguished producers in the history of the American theater—a legend in his own time. Next to a glowing review from Walter Kerr, that's one of the greatest honors an aspiring performer could . . ."

"He wears a toupee!"

"So does Fred Astaire!" She gripped Cynthia's arm with such force the girl winced. "Listen to me, you little bitch! I'm not throwing away a lifetime of work because you're too stupid to hear opportunity pounding on the door! Seventeen years of sacrifice! Seventeen years of going without! Of thinking of nothing but you—living for nothing but you! For what? So you can turn into a shrinking violet when the big moment finally comes? Oh, no!" The pudgy finger pointed, trembling. "You're going to walk out there like a star, you hear me? Like a *star,* and you're going to say, 'Good evening, Mr. Mack . . .' "

"And then what?"

"Then you'll go and have a delicious dinner."

"And *then* what?"

The rancid cloud enveloped Cynthia; she could feel her mother's heat, see the tiny deposit of powder in each pore of her nose. "How should I know?"

"You know!"

"Am I asking you to do one thing you don't do with Skip?" Cynthia inhaled sharply and exploded in a fit of coughing that failed to deter Mrs. Moore. "You think I don't notice anything when Skip brings you home from the 'movies' with your hair standing on end and your skirt on backward? You think I didn't know what was going on behind closed doors when you were thirteen—with that Puerto Rican girl you used to bring home from class? I *saw*—with my own eyes—but you were both too busy to notice, so I closed the bedroom door and went out for a walk. Did I say anything when I came back? Did I throw her out? Did I bother you when I found the rubbers in Skip's dance bag or the Ortho jelly in the bottom of your sweater drawer? No! I let you develop in your own natural way. I let you *grow.* And this is the thanks I get!"

Knees buckling, eyes closing, Cynthia clung to the edge of the velour leg. "I can't," she gasped faintly.

"*I* could!" her mother snapped.

"Fine. *You* go out with him."

"Not *now!* Who'd want me now? I'm talking about ten years ago, when men still used to turn around on the street to take another look. Remember when you came home crying because your teacher said no more classes till I paid up all the back tuition? Remember? You thought the world was coming to an end—and it was!"

Aqueous lenses magnified the face in front of Cynthia. She blinked and the swollen image broke and ran. "Yes . . ."

"And remember I told you not to cry, I'd find the money somewhere?" Her nose brushed Cynthia's. "Well, where do you think I found it?"

"I don't know."

"Try Mr. Novograd."

"My teacher?"

"Your teacher."

"He gave it to you?"

"Not exactly gave. No, it was more like—paid. Remember how he used to stare at me in the back of the class? Every time he'd demonstrate a step, he'd look at me for approval. And when we walked out, I could feel him devouring me with his eyes . . ."

"You didn't!"

"Oh, didn't I! Not just one night, for dinner and a little diversion. Mr. Novograd was insatiable!"

"He was seventy-five!"

"At least. With a toupee like patent leather—and false teeth that rattled and smelled like cat food." Cynthia clutched at the leg. "Compared to your Mr. Novograd, my Mr. Mack is Robert Redford! But you got your lessons, didn't you. Every day, every week for five years! Did I say, 'He's old, he's ugly'? No. I closed my eyes and concentrated on *why* I was doing it. And it was easy! You think I wouldn't do it again—tonight—if I thought it would help you that much?" She displayed the tip of a forefinger. "But Mr. Mack isn't interested in me. It's you he's interested in. *You'll* get the benefit. Do I step in and say, 'Leave my daughter alone, you dirty old man'? No. I say, 'Thank you, Mr. Mack. Take good care of her and remember her when it's casting time again.' Because I know what this world's really like—and I want the best for my girl, the best!" Even in the deadening environment of the velvet panels, Mrs. Moore's fervent whisper reverberated. "No matter *what* we have to do to get it. I've done my best; I've given my all. There comes a time when the most caring of mothers has to face reality and pass on the torch. It's your turn now. You may have to go on without me, but you have my blessing—and my love—and my dreams . . ."

Mrs. Moore swayed and clutched at the leg. "Mama!" Cynthia wailed.

Mrs. Moore took a deep breath, put a hand on her heaving bosom, and said, "I'm all right."

"You're not!"

She straightened, an inflated Joan of Arc. "Yes, I am. The doctor said . . ." She stopped.

"The doctor said *what?*"

"Nothing—nothing. I'm fine."

"Mama . . . !" Cynthia keened.

Mrs. Moore took her daughter's hand. "Do you really want to make me feel better?"

Cynthia hesitated an instant, then said, "Yes."

Mrs. Moore patted the thin hand she held. "All I want to know is that you'll be all right—when I'm gone." She felt the welcome signal of Cynthia's tightening grip. "I know we haven't had what you could call a normal mother-daughter relationship. Most mothers are busy living their own lives—but my life has been—you." A fleshy palm stroked Cynthia's cheek. "And it's been worth it. Every minute, every sacrifice. But let's face it, I won't be here forever." She wheezed, Cynthia sneezed, she continued. "And all I want to know is that the sacrifice hasn't been in vain. I want to know you're safely on your way. That's a mother's prayer. You've got the talent, the personality, the charm. All you need is—the break. And in my opinion—for whatever it's worth—the break is waiting for you right out there."

The pointing hand shook violently, and Cynthia seized and kissed it, suffering a long dry slice in her lip on the edge of a jeweled cocktail ring. Later, Wally Mack's wiry pubic hair would open the cut like steel wool; for now, it went unnoticed as Mrs. Moore enfolded her daughter with her free arm and kissed the top of her head. "It's up to you," she said. "I've done all I can. The moment has come to step back and say, 'Go with my blessing. Live your own life.' "

"Mama!" Cynthia wept. Mrs. Moore held her daughter for a long moment, then murmured, "It probably doesn't matter anymore; he may be gone by now." Cynthia's head came up and she found a handkerchief poised to dab away tears.

"I—I'll go," she said.

"Only if you want to." Each word was a prolonged shudder.

"I *do* want to. Mr. Mack—Mr. Mack's very nice to be—so interested."

"*I* think so. If you could've heard the things he said about you . . ."

Cynthia looked at the corridor. "He's out there?"

"I hope so. Just inside the stage door. Wait!" She dabbed again at Cynthia's face. "Maybe you'd better freshen up first. He'll wonder what all the waterworks were for."

"There's a bathroom under the stage."

"Run down there."

"But if he's going to leave . . ."

"I'll go out and tell him you're coming." As Cynthia started out of the wing, Mrs. Moore called softly, "Cynthia—he thinks you're nineteen, so we're going to be very grown-up tonight, aren't we."

Cynthia nodded solemnly and trudged across the stage. When she had been swallowed by the opposite wing, Mrs. Moore permitted herself a moment of exultation, raising her face toward the flies to take a breath that threatened to exhaust the dark void's meager supply of air. Then she felt her way out of the crowded wing and strode into the corridor that led to the stage door.

Naked, on her back on the carpet in front of the couch, Moira raised her snifter to refract the light from the room's only illuminated lamp. Fractured by the swaying contents of her glass, the light broke on her body like amber foam. Lying beside her, Chris took a sip of brandy, then tried to lick the lambent specks from one of her nipples. It crinkled and rose under his mouth.

Still studying her glowing glass, Moira spoke slowly, solemnly. "Do you realize what today is?"

"Saturday."

"And?" He raised his head. "Christmas Eve."

He sat up, folding his arms around his raised knees. "Jesus!"

"An appropriate response." She took a sip of Calvados.

"I haven't even thought about it."

"I have." He looked at her. "My favorite time of year."

"There's no lapsed Catholic like a lapsed lapsed Catholic."

She swam past the bait. "You know what I like best about Christmas? It's so—whimsical: normally sane people dragging messy, living trees into neat, dead rooms and using embarrassing words like *joy* and *merry;* choirs singing in banks, trumpets braying on street corners; janitors and bartenders hanging tinsel—everything you'd be fired, arrested, ostracized or committed for any other time of the year."

"I've finally figured you out," Chris said. "You're a red Roman-Catholic romantic."

"You left out Kierkegaardian."

"It doesn't alliterate. Ian would disapprove."

"Do you think you can reach those cigarettes?"

Chris stretched across the coffee table, snared the booty, delivered it and lay back, studying Moira's profile as the brief flare of a match etched it. There was more to Moira in every way: more flesh than Carin, more face, more physical and mental terrain . . .

He clenched a fist until it ached. *Electrodes that shoot shocks into the soles of my feet every time I think of Carin,* Chris reflected; *maybe that's the solution.*

"You know, we're due at the office in a few hours," Moira said.

"Hey! I've got a terrific idea."

"I know what it is. Forget it."

"We walk into the shop and tell Ian to stick the *East Sider* up his south side."

"I was right."

"So? What's your answer?"

"You're drunk."

"That's right, I am," he said slowly, and sat up. "I'm also dead serious."

She looked up at him. "I think you are." He nodded and gravely emptied his glass. "What'll happen when you sober up?"

"I don't intend to do that."

"Ever?"

"Until we've gone into the office this morning and submitted our resignations. Not just ours but Arthur Ogden's, Miguel Figueroa's, Martin Brazil's, Antoinette Mercer's . . ."

"And then what?"

"Ian pisses purple."

"And what do *we* piss?"

"What're you worried about?" He waved a hand in what he assumed was a northward direction. "You've got Mamaroneck."

"I don't seem to have conveyed my message: the *East Sider* is instead of Mamaroneck; I'm trying to cut that umbilical cord."

"We'll find jobs someplace else." He slid closer, coming to rest next to her with his back against the couch. "You're going to think this is the raving of an amateur alcoholic . . ."

"We Irish consider all non-Irish alcoholics amateurs."

". . . but what if you tried again?"

"Let me explain something to you: the female organ is made of soft tissue; it can stand only so much friction."

"I'm talking about Paris."

She stared at him, the light behind her going amber through her hair as it had through her glass. "Going to Paris?"

"I assume you know the way . . ."

"Yeah, Air France on Fifth Avenue, then . . ."

"I mean it, Moira. I'm serious."

She leaned over the coffee table to put her cigarette out, then sat back against the base of the couch again.

"Bad idea?" Chris asked.

"No."

"Good idea?"

"Strange idea."

"Want to think about it?" She nodded, and ten seconds later he said, "Time's up."

She smiled. "*How,* Chris?"

"My car."

"You think it could make it across the Atlantic?"

"The guy who's using it offered me a thousand for it. I can probably get twelve hundred if I make him a take it or leave it proposition." She stared into her glass. "How long would that last us?"

"About ten minutes." He sagged against the couch. "But I've got some money. For *me,*" she added as he straightened. "I'd pay my own way, and we could fly Laker to London and then take the boat-train to France . . ."

He twisted toward her. "Is that hypothetical?"

"It was when I started the sentence . . ." He reached for her hand. ". . . But unless you plan to stay drunk till the money runs out, how do we earn our livings in Paris?"

"I was hoping you'd have some suggestions." She frowned. "What about that Sunday salon? Are they all remittance men?"

"No. Some of them are working."

"Where? At what?"

"Well, it's easiest for the musicians, of course, and the dancers; they don't have a language problem."

"You speak French. I can manage; and they must have crash courses. Jesus! The *Free Press!*"

"Do they have a Paris bureau?"

"No, but maybe they could use a stringer. I'll call Traynor to-morrow—today! As soon as it's morning." She looked at him. "He was my editor. If he wants to help . . ."

"Chris, do me a favor: tell me—right now—what does all this mean? I'm high—not just on brandy: you could probably talk me into anything tonight. But one thing I really wouldn't like to do is go back to Paris and get screwed up again."

"Maybe you wouldn't like to go at all."

"You're catching me at a weak moment, but . . ." She put her glass on the table and closed her eyes.

"But what?"

"Why do you want to go?"

"Because I can't stand my life in New York, and everything I've ever heard about Paris has whetted my appetite, and maybe if I don't go now I never will."

"And you're dying to get away."

"It's that time of year."

"That's not what I mean."

He studied her, then said quietly, "You think I'm trying to get away from Carin." She nodded. "And if that's part of it?"

"I'm in trouble. Not now. A month from now. Six months from now. In Paris. Twice would be *de trop,* as the French say."

Chris stood up and crossed the room, the hair on his loins matted by her vaginal jelly and juices. Near the suitcases he stopped, rubbing the sharp line of his jaw.

"Sorry to bring up a thorny subject," Moira said from her seat on the floor in front of the couch, "but I can't help worrying about a couple of things, like my sanity and survival." She fell silent, waiting, and when Chris finally turned toward her, she added, "There's a better than fifty-fifty chance you're still in love with her." He shook his head. "You've got remarkable recuperative powers."

He came back to the couch and hunkered in front of her, his penis, still heavily veined from its labors, bent against the rug. " 'How can we know the dancer from the dance?' "

"Simple as that?"

"Yep. I realized it when we were making love. All of a sudden I wondered how I'd feel about Carin if she weren't a dancer—if she were a secretary or a singer, or anything but a dancer. I fell in love with her courage and her virtuosity . . ."

"That's what you were thinking about while we were making love?"

"I'm sorry; there're moments when she's still there. It's only been twenty-four hours . . ."

"That's exactly what I'm talking about."

He touched her face. "I know. You don't just walk away from two years . . ."

"Or run away."

"I'm not. Being here with you isn't running away. I feel like I'm running *toward* something." He glanced at her. "I guess you don't believe that."

"I'd like to."

"Well, all I can tell you is this is where I want to be. And Paris is where I want to go. With you. So what do you say?"

"You're scaring me to death."

"I'm scaring myself a little, too. This free will of yours is a pain in the ass."

"It's also free *won't*, you know."

"I know. I move the affirmative. All in favor . . ."

"I don't want to be your *counter*revolution," she said slowly.

"You're not."

"How do I know?"

"You don't." When she frowned he said, "I don't remember Kierkegaard saying anything about a safety net. You're going to have to jump without it. So am I. No net, no guarantees . . ."

"Just tell me one thing."

"What?"

"If I say no, what'll you do?"

"Go anyway."

"To Paris?" He nodded. "I'm jumping."

Moving creakily, her limbs stiffened by nearly two hours in the backseat of Rick's car, Diane eased herself to the sidewalk and leaned into Rick's open window. "Thanks."

"Tell him Rick and I want him to come over for dinner tomorrow night," Joni said. "We can keep him busy till you get back from Philly."

"Great idea. Thanks."

As Diane turned from the car, Joni said, "You can call me in the morning and let me know if he's coming."

"Right."

Diane heard the car pull away as she wedged her dance bag between belly and scrofulous lobby wall to grope for her keys. When they didn't come immediately to hand, she cursed softly. Locating them at last, she opened the lobby's inner door and began a slow ascent, husbanding her energy for the final flights, but at the first landing an unexamined impulse made her quicken her pace. At the second landing, despite the anguished complaint of her leg muscles, she broke into a trot, and at the third landing, she began a sprint that brought her to her door, lungs so anguished and hand so palsied she was unable to fit the key into the lock. Holding one hand with the other, she brought her whole body forward: the key slid into the lock and the door swung open.

The living room was dark, the only sound in it her hoarse breathing. A light shone from the end of the corridor that led to the bedrooms. Marshaling what was left of her strength, Diane ran through the living room, the corridor and the open door to the lighted room.

The bed was neatly made. Terry's work table was in perfect order, scissors in a line, each spool of thread impaled on its own little sodomizing peg. The sewing machine squatted implacably on its stand, stern and efficient.

Then Diane heard it: horse's hooves, staccato gunshots, barked commands and the unmistakable trashy grandeur of movie music.

Her fatigue forgotten, her smile illuminating the hall, Diane trotted toward Carin's room, bellowing, "I just want to know one thing: were you here at eleven o'clock when the phone rang? Because if you dragged me all the way from Philly for nothing . . ."

She came to a halt just inside the room, her eyes on the window: as she had anticipated, it was open and cowboys were cavorting on Reneé's Advent across the narrow air shaft. But the sling chair in front of the window was empty.

She went to the window, ducked under the open sash and leaned out over the dank shaft. "Renée!"

A silhouette appeared in front of the Advent. "Yeah?"

"Seen Terry?"

"No."

"He wasn't watching?"

"I don't know, I didn't look. You want another channel? This one sucks."

"No, it's okay."

The silhouette disappeared. Diane bent to pull back into the room—and froze. Gunshots echoed from the Advent, hooves thundered, Erich Wolfgang Korngold chords crashed. Then, slowly, Diane's head came up, her eyes bulging, her mouth distended in a mute screech, her back arching, neck muscles straining until her head struck the raised sash.

Then, as if a loose connection in a speaker had been jiggled into place by the collision, a sound emerged from her gaping mouth. Reaching back to her roots, she called upon The Word: *"Shiiiiiiiiiiiiiiiiiiiiiiiiiiiit!"*

CODA

TWENTY-ONE, two, three, four
Fouetté

Heavy-duty flashlights sliced the narrow courtyard into chunky, shifting blocks of blackness. Flat against a slimy wall, as far as she could get from the object that occupied the huddled navy blue shadows, Diane waited, gasping her grief with each broken breath.

Above her the Mondrian pattern of windows giving on the air shaft was broken by irregular shapes leaning out, peering down, calling questions across the sour space.

"Did you see it?"

"No?"

"When did it happen?"

"I don't know. I never heard nothin'."

"Neither did I."

A navy blue shadow straightened and came through the jigsaw of flashlight beams toward Diane. She cringed as if he might swing at her with his nightstick. The policeman was young, with a bushy mustache. "Excuse me."

Diane stared glassily at the center of the courtyard, breathing loudly and with manifest difficulty through her open mouth. The policeman studied her for a moment, then stepped between her and the object of her horrified attention. Her eyes rose slowly to his.

"Sorry," he said.

She made no reply.

"You the lady who called?"

She nodded.

He took out a notebook and pen. The notebook reminded Diane of grade school. She wondered if those were Crayolas in the gun belt that hung on his hips. "Your husband?" he asked, and when she stared at him, he asked it again. "Your husband?" She shook her head. "You want a doctor?"

The mask moved; the mouth closed. A tiny, weird hope wiggled in Diane's chest like the worm in a withered Mexican jumping bean. "A doctor . . . ? For . . . ?"

"For you," the policeman said gently. The mouth sagged open again, the eyes clouded, the mask moved right, then left. "I know this is rough," the policeman said, "but we gotta have information." The mask moved up and down. "He lived here?"

Diane nodded again and whispered, "Up there." She looked up, but dropped her gaze abruptly as if afflicted by inverted vertigo.

"With you?" She nodded. "Your boyfriend?"

A window shot up on the fourth floor and a newcomer asked, "What happened?"

"A jumper," the third floor said.

"No shit! Who?"

"We don't know. Maybe one of those crazy dancers."

"One less all-night party."

"Lady?" Diane tried to focus on the policeman. "Did you hear me?"

"Yes."

"Was he your boyfriend?"

Diane studied the policeman's face. He looked young. Younger than she. And he had a mustache. Some cops even smoke grass, she thought, but why take chances; they all hate gays.

"Lady . . ."

"Yes. He was my boyfriend."

Slumped on a chair in the dark living room, the phone to her ear, Diane looked ten years older than she had a few hours earlier in Philadelphia, as if Terry's departure had left a chronological vacancy that she was already beginning to fill. She made an ineffectual pass at her disheveled hair and said, "I don't know. I just don't know."

Ashen, red-eyed in their hotel room, Carin asked, "Where—where is he?"

"An ambulance came."

The worm wiggled in Philadelphia. "An ambulance?"

"It doesn't mean anything. The policeman said they have to take him to a hospital. To make it official, you know?" She stopped and gasped, "Boo hoo!"

Carin responded with her own lachrymose noises, and for several metered minutes the roommates exchanged only sobs and sniffles. At one point Carin blubbered, "Maybe—maybe we better hang up to cry, and then call each other back."

"Who cares—it's practically like a local call after eleven."

They cried again, trying occasionally to speak to each other, then giving up and giving way to new outbursts. Finally Carin managed to get through, "There—there has to *be* something—you know?" without breaking down. When Diane's only response was more sniffles, Carin added, "Some kind of service."

Diane blew her nose, then said, "Oh. Yeah."

"What is he?" She corrected herself with difficulty. "What was he?"

"A gypsy."

"I mean his religion."

"So do I."

"I guess his family will take care of it."

"He doesn't have any."

"There's nobody you can call?"

"Nobody I know. He didn't have any brothers or sisters, and his mother's dead."

"What about his father?" There was no response. "Di?"

"They don't even talk to each other."

"But he has to know."

A threat of hysteria shook Diane's voice. "You don't understand! He saw Terry on the TV news—being interviewed at a gay-rights march—and he called up like a madman. I was listening."

"But *now* . . ."

"The motherfucker was screaming 'faggot' on the phone." She delivered the *coup de grace:* "He's a cabdriver, for God's sake! He saw the news broadcast in the fuckin' garage—with all his macho buddies! He told Terry he disgraced him!"

"You've got to call him."

This time Carin knew Diane was still there; she waited until she heard, "I don't even know his name."

"Mitchell."

Diane's anguish found its customary outlet in anger. "Nobody but you uses their real name in show business! It's some kind of long name. German or Polish or something!"

"There must be something in Terry's room. His unemployment book. That'll have his real name."

"Mine doesn't."

"Go and look. I'll wait."

"No."

"His father has to know!" Hysteria was surfacing in Philadelphia.

"I mean, no, don't wait. I'll look in Terry's room and I'll find his father."

"Then what?"

"I don't know."

"When will you be back here?"

"Next time I get picked for a show that's playing Philly."

"But we've got two more performances . . ."

"Tell 'em to send a cop and arrest me!"

"I'll explain to Sonny."

"Sharon'll swing for me. And if she can't, tell 'em one less body isn't gonna make their rotten show any worse!"

Carin heard a strangled sound, then a loud "Boo hoo" and said, "They'll understand."

"Jesus, Jesus, Jesus!" Diane sobbed. "If I'd just known about it the day he got fired!"

"I don't understand why Chris didn't tell you when he was here last night."

"I guess Terry didn't tell him."

For a long moment there was no sound from Philadelphia, then Carin asked, "Is Chris there?"

"No."

Carin pressed a knuckle against her lip, then said, "You shouldn't be alone."

"I'm okay." Before Carin could respond, Diane threw in, "I gotta find Terry's father, right?"

"Definitely."

"Okay. I'll call you in the morning."

"Okay." After a long silence Carin said, "You going to hang up?"

"I told the cop he was my boyfriend. I could just hear him and his buddies laughing if I tried to explain." Apparently New York had broken off the edge of the continent: Diane's voice sounded as if it were coming from half a world away.

"You did the right thing."

New York slammed back into the continental shelf, and Diane's voice was near and strong again, giving no quarter, brooking no argument. "Anyway, I *did* love him! Who the fuck did I ever love *more!* Boo hoo! I'll call you in the morning!"

She hung up and bent forward until her nose touched her knees, then emitted a string of fervent boo hoo's as even as matched pearls.

In Philadelphia Carin stood next to the phone for several minutes, staring blankly into the room. Then, without moving, she cried for a few minutes. Then she was immobile and blank again. Then she looked around the room, as if frightened by its now-familiar furnishings. Then she sat down on the edge of the bed, picked up the phone and dialed three digits.

A moment later Gino's voice said, "Hello?"

"Gino . . ."

"Oh, hi. I just got in. I was afraid it was too late to call you."

"May I come up?"

"Hey—I admire your spirit, but we've got two shows tomorrow."

"I've *got* to come up, Gino. Please!"

"Is something wrong?"

"Yes."

"What?"

"I'll tell you when I get there!"

She hung up and moved unsteadily toward the closet, pawing at the blinding tears.

Diane stopped in the dark hall outside Terry's room. Although she had explored the room an hour earlier, it looked different now: foreign, forbidding. She steeled herself, moved across the threshold and stopped with a gasp. Draped in a gaudy, unfinished outfit, Terry's headless dressmaker's dummy managed to stare at her, mocking her as it had mocked Terry. A straight right to the dummy's solar plexis dropped it with a crash, then, whirling, Diane swept the top of Terry's work table clean and turned to survey the room from a wrestler's crouch, ready to trash anything else that had conspired against her roommate.

The chilling sight of Terry's clothes peering forlornly from the open closet cooled her anger, converting steam to water. Weeping bitterly, she shuffled through the shards of Terry's life-in-fashion until she came to the dresser, where she pulled feebly at a drawer. Terry's socks appeared, rolled into neat balls and grouped by hue. Groping beneath the socks, she found nothing.

She closed the drawer and opened the one next to it. It contained a disorderly assortment of papers and souvenirs. A gay-rights button caught her eye and she turned it over. The mauve plaster-of-Paris dog, symbol of Terry's triumph over fading youth, was shoved hastily to the depths of the drawer, where she felt a familiar shape and pulled out Terry's unemployment book. The name "Terry Mitchell" on its first page drew a frustrated exclamation from her. She slapped the book into the drawer and rummaged again, avoiding the dog. An expired passport came to hand. Above a photo of a young Terry, hair abundant and short, eyes bright and confident, something nailed Diane's attention. "Date of birth: May 9, 1932." Diane gasped and said, "1932?" aloud. Then she focused again, on one of the lines above the date of birth: "Thaddeus Miteski."

The passport went on top of the dresser, and Diane plunged into the accommodating drawer again, digging until she came up with an address book. Hasty examination of its *M* pages yielded no Miteski *père,* no Miteskis at all.

Diane frowned, tapping the address book on the edge of the open dresser drawer. The quest had had a salutary effect: her eyes were dry, her mind racing, gears turning smoothly. The *doyenne* of West Forty-eighth Street was back at the helm, the world was tilting slowly to an even keel again.

Suddenly Diane's eyebrows popped up and she nearly tore pages out of the book racing to the tab that read *F.* A finger hurried down a ladder of names, then Diane flipped to the next page: it was blank. Stumped, she glared at the recalcitrant book, then abruptly leafed back to the *D* pages. There, between an enigmatic entry that read simply "Dale (!)" and a businesslike "Dazian's—textiles, 40 E. 29," Diane's search ended: under several heavy pencil slashes the word *Dad* was visible, followed by *Home* and *Garage* and two telephone numbers.

In the living room Diane settled into the armchair next to the phone and tried the home number first. It rang a dozen times. "The turkey could be sleeping," Diane muttered and let it go on ringing. Finally, slamming the phone down, she referred to the address book in her lap and dialed the number next to "Garage." This time there was a response after only two rings.

"Bluebird."

"Bluebird?"

"Yeah, Bluebird. Whattaya want?" The accent was Brooklyn; a latter-day Henry Higgins might have narrowed it to Bushwick. The owner of the accent was sprawled at a battered desk to one side of a gloomy cement room, with disabled cabs strewn like beached whales at one end and a cluster of benches, lockers and vending machines at the other. There was a fine layer of oil over everything, including, to all appearances, the dispatcher's littered desk and the dispatcher himself. Over his head hung a faded sign that warned: *REMEMBER—if it's a front end collision YOU'RE RESPONSIBLE.*

"Uh—I'm calling a taxi company," Diane said.

"Y' got the garage. If y're lookin' f'r a radio cab . . ."

"I *want* the garage."

"What for?"

"I'm trying to reach Mr. Miteski."

"Who?"

"Miteski."

"Stan Miteski?"

"I guess so. He's a driver."

"That's right."

"Oh, good. I tried him at home but there wasn't any answer, so I figured he was working . . ."

"Naw. He was a day man."

"Oh. What time do you expect him in?"

"*No* time. I don't know where you got the home number, but he ain't there anymore either."

"He's moved?"

"Left town. His son died . . ."

"That's what I'm calling about!"

"Y'r a little late."

"What?"

"His son died like eight, nine months ago. Stan came in and told us. No big loss from what I hear."

Diane forced her fist open. There was blood on her palms where the nails had dug in. With a massive exercise of will, she banished the fury from her voice. "Uh—do you know where I can reach the—uh—Mr. Miteski?"

"Sure. Florida," came the amiable reply.

"Where in Florida?"

"That's *it*, lady: Florida. We ain't even had a postcard."

"Do you know anybody who might've heard from him? A friend? Maybe one of the other drivers?"

The dispatcher shifted on his broken swivel chair; it pitched fitfully like an outmatched dinghy in weather. "Lady, you think I got nothin' better to do with my time than keep tabs on the private life of every stiff that shapes up in this place? We got over fifty drivers, an' between you an' me, there ain't five of 'em I *wanna* know."

"But this is very important!"

"Yeah? What is it?"

Diane squirmed, trying to keep her fingernails out of the cuts in her palm. "I told you—it's about his son."

"An I told *you:* it's old news. Stan knows his son's gone, f'r Chrissake."

"This—this is private."

"Suits me, lady. It can stay private." As Diane tried to respond, he growled, "You ain't listenin', lady: I can't help ya. An' I got an important thing or two goin' on here right now. This is a place of business. Okay?"

"Okay," came the faint reply.

The dispatcher jammed the receiver into its cradle with a muttered, "Takes all kinds," retrieved half an overstuffed corned-beef sandwich from its plate of greasy wrapping paper and tipped back in his chair. It yielded with a series of jolts that shivered the dispatcher's heavily larded timbers.

Gino emerged from the bathroom with a glass of water. Pulling his robe tighter around him, he brought the glass to Carin, who was seated numbly on the edge of his unmade bed in hastily donned shirt and jeans. He remained poised above her, studying her pale face as she drank some of the water. When she lowered the glass, he said, "Maybe you oughtta take something." She looked up. "Somebody in the company's gotta have some Valium or a red . . ."

She shook her head. She stared straight ahead, her fingers curled around the glass. Gino studied her uneasily, then sat down next to her on the edge of the bed. A moment later he said, "I can't believe it."

"Neither can I," was the barely audible reply. After another long silence Carin brought the glass to her lips, but her hand was shaking so violently the water began to spill.

Putting a steadying hand on her wrist, Gino said, "You're gonna freak out if you don't take something. You know that, don't you?"

"It's not just that I keep thinking about him—I keep seeing him. Except for Diane, he was my best friend . . ." She bent her head, crushed.

Gino stood up. "That's not going to stop till you're asleep."

"I can't sleep."

"Yes, you can. I'm gonna see if Kelly's got anything. He's a walking drugstore."

"I don't want any grass or blow or anything like that. Then I *will* freak out."

"No, I'm talking about the real thing: downs." He waited, then, taking her silence for assent, took his key from the dresser and went out, closing the door quietly behind him.

Carin sat motionless for several minutes, then rose mechanically, turned and pulled the rumpled blanket down. As she placed a knee on the bed, she stopped. A crumpled length of elastic cloth was coiled on the sheet like a snake. Carin picked up one end of the cloth, and when she raised her hand, it fell to its full length, reassuming its identity as an Ace bandage. Carin stared at her thumb: under it was the yin-yang symbol Carin had watched Diane draw on Susan's knee in the dressing room.

Carin opened her fingers and the bandage coiled threateningly on the sheet again.

Diane frowned, hung up and redialed 215 and the hotel number.

"Eight-oh-three," she told the operator.

"Someone just rang it."

"That was me."

"Well, then you know there's no answer."

"Listen, cunt, I'm only an hour and a half from Philadelphia and I know where your rathole is . . ." The line went dead.

"Man, do I know this company," Gino said. "If you can swallow it, sniff it or stick it up your kazoo, Kelly's got it . . ." He stopped and peered around the empty room. "Carin?" he called toward the closed bathroom door, then went to it and pushed it open. Coming back into the room, he stopped abruptly, his eyes on the bed.

Diane nearly fell as she skidded out of the corridor into the living room. Righting herself, she scooped up the phone and plopped into the armchair. "Yeah?"

"It's me."

"I tried to call you a few minutes ago!"

"I went up to Gino's room. I had to talk to somebody."

"That's what I finally figured out, but by then the operator had a burr under her saddle for some unknown reason . . ."

"What operator?"

"At the hotel."

"Here in Philadelphia?"

"It doesn't matter. I'm just glad you're not alone. For once in his life, Gino can be of some use to somebody . . . Carin?" she inquired of the silence.

"Yes. Did you find Terry's father?"

"Yeah. I mean, no. He's gone."

"Where?"

"It's a long story."

"Can't we find him?"

"No. Looks like it's up to us. And that's the way it oughtta be: we're his fuckin' family."

After a silence Carin said, "Cynthia's out in the hall. I don't know what to do."

"What?"

"Cynthia's out in the hall."

"Why?"

"I don't know. She's just sitting on the floor crying, with her legs wide open and no underpants on. There's blood all over her chin. It looks like somebody socked her in the mouth."

"Guess who!"

"Her mother?"

"Who else. The dizzy old bitch. Don't get mixed up in it."

"But she's just sitting there crying. And laughing, too. And talking to herself. Maybe it's an acid trip . . ."

"Forget it! Tell Gino to put you in bed and hang onto you till morning. *I'll* tell him—put him on."

"No."

"I'm not gonna get salty with him."

"No."

"Well, tell him to do his fuckin' duty."

On his back in bed Gino lofted a leg and examined it. As intricately veined and muscled as an anatomical chart, it pleased him. He stretched it, flexing and pointing his foot to watch the machinery work, then lowered it and raised the other leg to repeat the process. He turned restlessly on his side, twisting and cracking his spine, then flopped on his back again, his hands behind his head, his eyes on the ceiling. He glanced at the inert television set, debated a moment, then opened the drawer in the night table next to him. Extracting a penciled list, he studied it, then picked up the phone, dialed three digits and lay back. After several rings a sleepy voice said, "Hello?"

"Pam?"

"No, Sharon. Pam's sleeping. Hold on . . ."

"That's okay! Sharon?"

"Yeah."

"This is Gino. I'd much rather talk to you."

"About what?"

"I don't know. You and me."

"Have you lost your mind?"

"No."

He heard a fumbling sound, then an affronted, "It's after four!"

"Shows you how long I've been lying here thinking about you."

"Aw, for Christ's sake, Gino . . ."

"I mean it. When we leave here Sunday, that's it. God knows when we'll see each other again."

"So I'm supposed to get out of bed and come up there? Or down there—or wherever you are?"

"I'll come there, if Pam doesn't mind."

"No!"

"Then what're we gonna do? . . . Sharon?"

"I'm thinking."

TWENTY-TWO, two, three, four

Coupé

"He's not here," Moira said.

Bundled in their coats, Chris and Moira stood just inside the door of Ian's bed-sitting-city room. "What're we standing here for?" Chris asked, and the two bulky figures pushed into the room.

Divested of their coats, they sat awkwardly at their desks. Moira picked up a sheaf of papers. "I've got some editing to do, but it seems silly to start anything."

"We'll just wait." He studied Moira. "You're having second thoughts, aren't you."

"Absolutely not. I had my second thought when I opened my eyes this morning. I'm on my two hundredth now."

"Which way is the pendulum swinging?"

"Eastward. How about you?"

"Oh, I've already begun burning my bridges." He tilted back in his chair, his knees against the edge of his desk. "While you were getting dressed, I called Detroit and sold my car. We're modestly rich."

The phone rang and Moira picked it up, flushed, snarled, "Mr. Roberts isn't in yet!" and slammed it down.

"What was that?" Chris asked.

"Some clown said, 'May I speak to the asshole.'"

The front legs of Chris's chair hit the floor with a bang. "That's *me!*" Moira stared. "I mean, it's Traynor—my editor." He punched frantically at the buttons on the phone. "I left a message for him to call me." The phone rang and he nearly broke a finger changing lines. "Hello?"

"Asshole?"

Chris breathed a sigh of relief and sat back with a broad smile. "That's me. How are you, Mr. Traynor?"

"You can call me Jim."

"And you can call me asshole—anytime."

"Fair enough. Lew said you were looking for me."

"Not exactly. I . . ." Chris hesitated.

"Don't tell me: you've decided it's time to come back to your senses, earth and the Detroit *Free Press.*"

"Not exactly."

"Well, fill me in. As you may remember, I'm a pushover for precision."

"I—I'm going to Europe."

"The grand tour?"

"To work."

"Where?"

"That's why I called."

"Oh."

"I was wondering if the *Free Press* needs anybody over there. The paper may already have a stringer; I don't remember . . ."

"That's not my department."

"I know, but I thought you might be willing to—well . . ."

"Why Europe? Is that where the ballerina goes next?"

"No."

"That's over?"

Chris looked away from Moira and said,"Yes."

"I'm sorry."

"No, you're not."

After a moment's silence, presumably for reflection, Traynor said, "Now that you mention it, I'm not. It was distorting your values. The *East Sider*!" he spat. "What happened to that?"

"I'm quitting."

"Can I compete with Europe?"

"No."

"Too bad. Stringer's another step back for you."

"It's better than the *East Sider*!"

"What isn't? I'll talk to Sam Levy."

"That'd be great."

"Don't get your hopes up. Where'll I get in touch with you?"

Chris gave Traynor Moira's phone number and said, "Merry Christmas."

"Want to give me a present?"

"Sure," Chris laughed.

"Quit pissing your life away."

The line went dead, and Chris remained behind his desk staring into space until the outer door opened and Ian inched into the room, half-concealed behind a large bag of groceries.

"Looks like you bought out the store," Moira observed as Ian lowered his burden to the couch.

"Nothing's too good for my staff on Christmas Eve." He waved a hand at the bag. "The first annual *East Sider* Christmas party."

As be began pulling fruits, cheeses and bottles from the bag, Moira sank into the chair behind her desk and said weakly, "Ian, do me a favor: don't turn into a swell guy. Not today. Not now."

Half-bent over the couch, a red Gouda shiny as a Christmas ornament in his hand, Ian asked, "What's wrong?"

When Moira looked helplessly at Chris, Chris said, "We want to talk to you."

"On Christmas Eve? It's party time, man!"

"Ian . . ." Moira said, "it's a farewell party."

"For who?"

For *whom,* Moira corrected silently as she always did in conversations with Ian.

"Us," Chris said.

Ian dropped the Gouda. It sparkled on the couch. "You're leaving?"

"That's right."

Ian looked at Moira. "Both of you?" She nodded. "You mean, walking out?"

"You might put it that way."

"That's fuckin' illegal!"

Chris glanced at Moira, then turned back to Ian. "I—I'm sure we can stay long enough to break in some replacements . . ."

"You're out!" Ian screeched. "As of now! I don't want to see your faces here."

Moira stood up. "Our work's all done. It just needs some editing . . ."

"Oh, I see! You're concerned. How touching. Out! I'll cope, believe me."

As they took their coats out of a closet near the door, Ian stabbed a hand at the bag of groceries and demanded, "Do you know how much I spent on that?"

"I'm sorry, Ian," Moira said. "I really think we ought to stay another week or so."

"Out!" he yelled. "Supper soldiers and sometime patriots!"

"Summer soldiers and sunshine patriots," Moira said.

"Out!" Ian roared.

On the street in front of the apartment building that housed the *East Sider,* Moira shuddered as Chris helped her into her coat. "Hurry," he said.

"It's not the cold; it's the guilt." She looked up at Chris. "Would you believe I feel sorry for the little son of a bitch?"

"Relax, it's over. And we got paid yesterday, so . . ."

"Oooh! Right!"

"What?"

She kissed Chris's cheek. "See you later."

"Where're you going?"

"Shopping. Tomorrow's Christmas, remember? See you at home."

As she started briskly away, Chris called, "Moira!" She stopped. "I don't want anything for Christmas."

"Neither do I." She waggled a finger at him. "I mean it, Chris. Every penny you've got is for Paris. Right?"

"Right. But that's got to be a two-way deal or somebody'll be embarrassed."

"Okay, fine. Paris'll be our Christmas present to each other. You'll need a passport; you can apply for it Monday. There's an office in Rockefeller Center."

She waved and hurried away, her boots Gouda-red against the city's slate-gray snow.

Diane pushed her way through the mass of matinee-bound theatergoers. A bright sun brought Times Square sharply into focus: grubby sidewalk Santas listlessly tolling the needy's sorrow in front of windows full of black-lace crotchless panties; art galleries featuring "Original Oil Paintings," principally of rabbis and ballerinas; hot-dog and pizza stands sending greasy siroccos roiling into the street; record shops competing for the heedless crowd's attention with waves of high-voltage effrontery; souvenir stores urging the tourists to tickle the folks back home with custom-printed headlines on bogus front pages—"YOUR CHOICE OF NAME" FARTS ON SUBWAY; HUNDREDS OVERCOME; porno marquees pledging SENSATIONAL LIVE ACTS INSIDE; radio and rug stores that had been GOING OUT OF BUSINESS! at the same stand for ten years . . .

Through this defile of contemporary culture, Diane made her determined way toward America's Temple of Melpomene. Under a marquee emblazoned with critical praise for *Music to My Ears,* she worked her way against the grain of the theatergoers pushing across the sidewalk. Bursting free on the crowd's western edge, she veered into the alley that led to the theater's stage door.

"Nobody admitted after half-hour," the stage doorman said.

"Charlie, for God's sake, don't you remember me?"

The doorman leaned forward and squinted through what looked to Diane like a pound of glass. "Ever since the cataract operation . . ." he muttered.

"It's me. Diane!"

"Tiffany?"

"Cartier."

"Oh, yeah. Hi, sweetheart!"

She leaned over to kiss him. He slid his tongue into her mouth and pinched her nipple through her coat, but Diane considered it a small enough price to pay for admittance.

In the girls' dressing room a shout went up. "Di!"

"What're you doing here?" a girl demanded. "Your show doesn't close till tonight, does it?"

The room, with its white lights and costumes and babble and smell of makeup, was indistinguishable from the room Diane had left in Philadelphia. The only alien element was Diane, her ashen face reduced to bones, sunken eye sockets and quadrisecting scar, a death's head compared to the vivid masks turned to it from the makeup table.

"I had to come back," Diane announced ambiguously.

"Was it as bad as we heard?" one of the masks asked.

"Pretty bad."

Several voices spoke together, and Diane raised a shaky hand for silence and undivided attention. The response was only partial: curtain was less than twenty minutes away. "Listen—" Diane said, "I heard—I heard I was gonna get the Robe."

"Aw, who told you!" a querulous voice demanded.

"Is it true?"

One of the girls, like Diane, noticeably older than her colleagues, stood up and indicated a massive assemblage hanging on the wall near her chair. Beneath a baffling assortment of cloth and metal oddments, patches of the underlying garment were visible: wherever the memento of a musical had not been appended, signatures sprawled across plain muslin. Diane stared at it, deliberately putting her nails into the still tender wounds in her palm to dam the tears rising tidally from somewhere deep inside. "Yeah," the girl said. "I got it on our opening night, and we decided. . . . Well, I know how bad you feel, but what can we do? There's another show coming in . . ."

Diane swallowed hard. "I didn't come to ask for the Robe. I mean, not for me." She scanned the row of gaudy masks. Puppets would have been more responsive. She opened the jammed fist, then quickly closed it again. Something was dripping from her fingers and she suspected it was blood. *No distractions, please.*

"This is probably gonna stir up a big fuss," she said, "and a lot of the kids'll want to say no . . ." She took a deep breath, designed to smooth the tremor from her voice. "But they can't, see? You don't have to vote on it or anything. It's *settled.* Because—because something happened last night . . ."

Now she had the full attention of the room. No one daubed, no one chatted, nothing stirred. Even the wardrobe women stood frozen, costumes drooping from their outstretched arms like slackened sails.

Moira added the book to the pile on the counter and looked at the salesman. Sore of foot and heart, fed up with Christmas, the salesman murmured, "Anything else?"

"No, that's it."

"Giftwrapped?"

"If it's not too much trouble."

The salesman eyed the stack of books. "Individually?"

Moira was glad to be able to reply, "No, all together."

Mindful of the fact that Chris had left his books in Detroit, Moira had decided on a Christmas gift of the collected works of every poet represented on Doubleday's poetry shelf. Several volumes of biography and exegesis had caught her eye as well, with the result that the distracted salesman was now trying to cope with nearly six feet of stiff giftwrap. "It doesn't have to be perfect," Moira said sympathetically. It wasn't. Reflecting that she had some Christmas wrappings at home, Moira helped the salesman work the bulky package into a shopping bag.

Outside Doubleday's she turned right and paused in front of Hallmark to join a package-laden crowd listening to several Juilliard students plying flute, oboe, cello and bassoon with numbed fingers. Between them and their audience, an open fiddle case was littered with silver and bills. Moira put down her shopping bag and opened her purse. Tipping it toward the glow of Hallmark's window, she located a dollar bill, worked her way through the crowd to drop her offering in the case and returned to the outer edge of the crowd just in time to see a black boy of eleven or twelve, in thin sweater and sneakers, scoop up her shopping bag and scurry down Fifth Avenue, staggering under its weight. "Hey!" she shouted, and he turned on the afterburners. For a moment she stared at the rapidly diminishing figure, too shocked to move, then abruptly cupped her hands around her mouth and yelled, *"Read* them!"

Then she went back into Doubleday's.

Even without the familiar hint of catarrh in the voice, Chris knew whose it was before it had finished wheezing, "Asshole?"

"Mr. Traynor . . ."

"Call me asshole."

"What happened to 'Jim'?"

"He's an asshole."

"Why?"

"Because he's contributing to the delinquency of a minor talent—maybe a major one."

"Levy said yes?"

"Levy said no."

Chris sat heavily in the couch. "But I thought you said . . ."

"I'm cutting my own wrists," Traynor growled.

"How?"

"By making it too easy for you to leave the *Free Press.*"

"I don't understand."

"Of course you don't. Because you're faint of heart and feeble of mind. And callow. You know what callow means?"

"Yes."

"It means you need seasoning. And I give very good seasoning."

"Please, Mr. Traynor."

"You see? There's a perfect example of your callowness."

"I'm sorry."

"Don't apologize. Grow up. That's the cure for callowness."

"I'm definitely going to Europe."

"Don't be too sure."

"Why? Have you sent a trumped-up dossier to the State Department?"

"I wish I'd thought of that. It's probably too late now. Have you got your passport?"

Recalling the end of *The Front Page,* and reasonably certain that Traynor did too, Chris said, "Yes," then added a wary, "Why shouldn't I be too sure I'm going to Europe?"

"Ever heard of the Washington *Post*?"

"Of course."

"Good paper? Good city? The White House, the Capitol, Georgetown, the Smithsonian, Kennedy Center . . . ?"

"Mr. Traynor . . ."

"I told you to call me asshole!"

"Asshole . . ."

"Moved by an impulse I can't explain, I called a friend. He's willing to talk to you."

"Who?"

"The President! You're the new secretary of Health, Callowness and Welfare."

"Are you saying you called the *Post*?"

"I'm *trying* to say it!"

"And they've got an opening?"

"That depends."

"On what?"

"What kind of impression you make on them. Try to stay away from your puerile penchant for ballerinas and world travel; I lied and said you were a mature talent, ready for the big time."

"Jesus . . ."

"Asshole will do. I can't stand fawning."

"I don't know what to say."

"Just don't disgrace me in Washington. And if it turns out you can't stand the big time, come back to Detroit and brighten my drab existence."

"But Mr. Traynor . . ."

"I earnestly hope you're not going to say something stupid."

"I'm afraid I am."

"You'd rather make a sentimental journey to a Mecca that hasn't existed for forty years than work at one of the best newspapers in the world?"

"It's complicated."

"By what?" Chris's silence evoked an ominous "Don't tell me there's another girl." When Chris didn't respond, the embittered voice muttered, "Jesus Christ!"

"Asshole will do," Chris replied wanly.

"It's insufficient!" Traynor roared and hung up.

TWENTY-THREE, two, three, four
Balancé

Diane had been poised at the living-room window, watching Forty-eighth Street, so by the time Carin had hauled the luggage out of the cab, Diane was on the sidewalk in the heavy robe and woolly slippers she wore when the antiquated oil burner in the basement lost too much ground to the weather.

As she bent to pick up one of the suitcases, the robe swung open; she was naked beneath it. "Diane!" Carin exclaimed, and glanced at the taxi driver, seated placidly behind his wheel, eyes front, puffing a cigar stub.

"If he wasn't too lazy to get out of the fuckin' car and help, he could have himself a cheap thrill," Diane said, letting the robe gape.

"But what about *other* people?" Carin asked, gesturing toward an elderly man walking a raw-boned dog half a block away.

Diane brightened. "You think *he'd* help?"

"You'll freeze!" Carin scolded.

"It's colder in there." Diane jerked a thumb at the house and bent over to pick up a second suitcase. The robe gaped wider.

Putting herself between Diane and the driver, Carin pushed withered bills through the window on the passenger's side of the driver's seat. The driver took the money and pulled away with a screech of rubber and, very nearly, Carin's hand. Carin flapped the buzzing fingertips that had been ticked by the departing cab, then, bending to pick up the remaining suitcases, heard a choked, "Merry Christmas."

She looked up. Standing above her, her shoulders sloping toward the heavy bags she held, her navel and pubic hair framed by the edges of the open robe, Diane had begun to cry. As tears flooded Carin's eyes, she said, "For God's sake, let's go upstairs to do this."

Diane nodded and lugged her burden up the front steps. Carin had to turn around and mount the steps backward to accommodate

the weight she carried. Inside the building they stopped at the first
landing to rest their aching arms, and Diane said, "I'm sorry you had
to bring all my junk back from Philly, but I knew Gino would help
you get it on and off the train . . ."

"It was fine," Carin said, "no problem. Let's go."

Puffing and sniffling, they dragged the luggage to the top floor
and collapsed onto the couch. Diane pulled a huge wad of Kleenex
from a side pocket of her robe, extracted several sheets from it and
gave them to Carin, then helped herself. Several sheets of Kleenex
later, Carin straightened on the couch, took a deep breath and
looked at the corridor that led to the bedrooms. "I'm afraid to go in
there."

"It's a bitch."

"Is—is everything still there?"

"What was I supposed to do? Give his clothes to the Salvation
Army?"

"No, no, I just. . . . Well, what *do* you do? When Grandpa died,
Mom's family took care of everything."

"It's all arranged."

"Who arranged it?"

"Who do you think arranged it?"

"Is there going to be a—service?"

"Jimmy Dean should've had such a service! Marilyn Monroe!
The *Pope!*"

"But who's going to come?"

"Everybody. That man was *loved!*"

"How will they know?"

"They'll read the paper."

"There's something in the paper?"

"Of course. I called the *Times,* the *News* and the *Post.* They've
all got obituary columns. And the *News* called me back to find out
what happened. They'll probably do a story."

"Like he was a celebrity?"

"He *was* a celebrity," came the measured response.

Carin sighed and blew her nose. Then she said, "I don't want to
go in his room."

"You don't have to."

"We can't just leave it that way forever."

"There's time. After the funeral."

"When is it?"

"Thursday."

"Not till then?"

"Figure it out. The word's not gonna get around till Monday;
then everybody'll need at least two days to get something special
together . . ."

"To wear?"

"Of course. Anybody shows up in jeans is out on their ass! Two days takes us to Wednesday . . ."

"That's matinee day."

"Exactly. So: Thursday."

Carin tried twice to articulate something, then she blew her nose again, took a deep, audible breath and on the exhalation raced through, "Where is he?"

Diane blew her nose. "At the funeral home."

"Can—can we . . . ?"

"What?"

"See him?"

"*See* him! He's lyin' in *state,* man."

They slumped on the couch for several minutes, their legs stuck straight out in front of them, heels on the floor, in the position that best accommodated their always abused muscles. Then Carin rose. "Might as well unpack."

She bent behind one of her suitcases and began shoving it toward the corridor. It caught on the rug and she picked it up. In the corridor she was able to slide it again. She heard a sound and glanced back over her shoulder: Diane was sliding Carin's second bag into the hall. "Don't bother," Carin said, but Diane persisted, hunching over the skidding suitcase, her head down like a laboring bullock's.

At the open door of her room, Carin straightened and the suitcase Diane was blindly pushing rammed Carin's calves. Her knees buckling, Carin sat down hard on the interloping suitcase and stayed there, her eyes on the room. Diane apologized for the collision, but Carin didn't hear her. "Where is he?" she whispered.

"I told you: there's a viewing room . . ."

"Chris. He hasn't been here at all?"

"Not while I was."

Carin's hand drifted toward the open doorway. "You didn't look . . . ?"

"I've been busy!"

Carin stood up, put a leg over the suitcase in front of her and entered the room. Constrained by a dimly perceived scruple, Diane remained behind the barricade of the suitcases, her view of most of the room blocked by the frame of the door. She saw Carin come and go through the aperture, heard drawers and doors open; then an apparition appeared in the door, hanging on the frame for support.

"There's nothing here. *Nothing.* He's gone."

Diane didn't know what to say. What had Carin expected? She shook her head sympathetically; it was the most she could muster.

Carin turned and examined the room again, her back to Diane. Finally she turned once more to look at her roommate over the little wall of luggage. "*Every*body's gone."

"This is my mother," Moira said.

Mrs. Scanlon was pretty much what Chris had imagined: a bit taller and thinner, but no less patrician. She had what an English novel Chris had read called good bones, and she moved with a bearing that was straight without being stiff. Mr. Scanlon measured up, too: hearty and hefty, with his own Old World echoes of port and gout. Moira's sister and brother were something of a surprise, the sister less fragile and the brother less jock than Chris had envisioned. Apart from that everything was as it should be, including the Irish setter rising occasionally from sleep in front of the flagstone fireplace to wag its tail and stretch and collapse in a somnolent heap again, and the house itself, baronial at the end of a long drive that led from a twisting street crowded with oaks and maples.

"You really quit?" Moira's sister asked.

Moira pursed her lips. "*Quit* may be too mild a word for it."

Mrs. Scanlon frowned and looked at her husband.

"And what next?" Mr. Scanlon asked brightly.

Moira glanced briefly at Chris, then swept a hand at the carpet of tinsel and ribbon and foil under the seven-foot tree in front of the picture window. "Listen, if we don't start opening those presents, you'll have to put our turkey in a doggie bag. We've got to get back to the city."

Early that morning in Moira's living room, protesting loudly that their pact had been broken, Chris had opened the bulky package from Doubleday's.

"It's not very well wrapped," Moira said, "but the salesman had to do it twice."

"Twice?"

"Not important." As the little library emerged, Moira said, "You've probably got most of them in Detroit."

"No."

"And I don't expect you to lug them to Europe. You can leave them here."

He put his arms around her and kissed her. Then he hurried into the bedroom and returned with a small package wrapped in magenta foil.

"We had a deal!" Moira protested.

"Some deal," Chris said.

After breakfast Moira's mother called to make a final plea. "It just won't be Christmas without you."

"I'm sorry, Mom."

"Do you have to work?"

"No."

"Then I just don't understand. If you don't want to bother with the train, Bob can drive down and pick you up . . ."

"The train's no problem."

"Then what is?"

"Well, I've got a date."

"Can't you bring your date up here?"

Moira glanced at Chris, stretched out on the floor, leafing through one of his new books. "I don't know."

"Well, how about calling and asking him? We're not *that* unpresentable."

Moira laughed and said, "I'll call you back." She hung up and knelt next to Chris. "Guess what?"

" 'A shudder in the loins engenders there the broken wall, the burning roof and tower and Agamemnon dead,' " he said, and looked up from the book. *"That's* what."

"Besides that."

"You're ready to apologize for breaking our agreement."

She squatted next to him, naked arms across naked knees, and nodded toward the phone. "That was my mother."

"A summons from Mamaroneck?"

"Yes. The clan always gathers at Christmas."

"Sure. Go ahead."

"No way." He sat up. "I don't want you to get the wrong idea: you're not being trotted out for inspection . . ."

"Are you suggesting I go up there with you?"

"Too hopelessly petty bourgeois?"

"What'll you do if I don't go?"

"Have a terrific day here. So far it's been first rate." He studied her, and she reached across the quiet space between them to put a hand on his hard, bare shoulder. "Forget it."

"No." He stood up. "Let's go."

After dinner, with the family strewn about the living room and the setter sighing and trotting in his sleep on the hearth, Moira sat next to Chris and squeezed his hand. "They're not too bad, are they?"

"Hell, no. They're what a family ought to be."

"If you're into families," Moira said, and looked up as her father heaved himself out of the couch and lumbered toward them, the flickering firelight complicating the design of his plaid pants. With a faint groan he seated himself cross-legged on the floor in front of Moira and Chris and said, "Okay, now—what's next?"

"No food, I hope," Moira said.

"With you," her father said, peering intently from under bushy eyebrows. Chris felt Moira's hand tighten a little on his, then slide away.

"I—well, I'm thinking of going back to Europe."

"No kidding!"

"Yes."

Mr. Scanlon tried to take the strain out of his back by shifting his weight to one hip and putting a palm on the floor next to him for support. "Europe." Moira nodded. "Where?"

"Guess."

"Paris again?" Moira nodded. "Hmm. Eileen?" Mrs. Scanlon looked up from a couch across the room, and Mr. Scanlon motioned her toward them with a toss of his head. She rumpled her son's hair, rose and came across the room. "Sit down," Mr. Scanlon said, and Mrs. Scanlon folded gracefully into a chair facing Moira and Chris. "Guess what," Mr. Scanlon said heartily.

"What?"

"Muffy's on her way again."

Mrs. Scanlon looked at her daughter.

"I'm thinking of going back to Paris," Moira said faintly, then corrected herself with an edge of annoyance. "I'm *going* to Paris."

"For how long?"

"I don't know."

"You don't mean you're going to live there again."

"I don't know."

Mrs. Scanlon glanced at Chris and, out of respect for a guest, limited herself to, "But you might."

"Yes."

"What would you do? I mean . . ."

"I'm not working at the *East Sider* anymore, so I might as well look for a job there. It's not as though I've got anything exciting to do in New York."

"I wish . . ." Mrs. Scanlon said and stopped.

"What, hon?" Mr. Scanlon asked.

"I wish you'd reconsider," Mrs. Scanlon said levelly, her eyes on Moira.

"It's not forever, Mother," Moira said. "If things don't work out I can be back in six hours."

Mrs. Scanlon turned toward her husband.

"Anybody want to take a walk before it's pitch dark out?" Moira's brother called, and Moira jumped up.

"Yes!"

As Diane put the cardboard boxes on the table, Carin looked around the dining room, recalling the first time she had seen it, bulging with food and gypsies. She closed her eyes hard, trying to squeeze the memories back into the dark. Pinwheels whirling under her eyelids made her open them. Diane was offering chopsticks. They had an assortment of them in the kitchen; whenever they ate in a Chinese restaurant, they always wiped their chopsticks carefully on their napkins and took them home with them, four pairs, Carin's and Diane's and Chris's and . . .

"Eat," Diane commanded, poking her chopsticks at the open cartons.

"I'm not hungry."

"You want to have an insulin attack?"

"I'm fine."

"Look at you. Have you been taking your shots?"

"Please—leave me alone."

"Answer me!"

"Yes."

"Yes, you've been taking your shots."

"Yes."

"Then you have to eat too, or . . ."

"You don't have to tell me how to take care of myself; I've had
plenty of practice."

"Sometimes it doesn't seem that way." Diane waited, her
chopsticks still poised like an *en garde* épée. In self-defense Carin
tweezed some *lo hon ji* out of a carton and put it on her plate. Diane
waited until some of the vegetables had gone from Carin's plate to
her mouth before she plunged her own chopsticks into one of the
cartons. "Have some *goon bow chi ding*," Diane commanded. Carin
added some of the spicy chicken to her plate, and finally they ate in
silence. Toward the end of the meal, Diane said, "It's not exactly
your traditional holiday feast."

"It's good."

"That's what I figured. I—I don't have anything for you, but the
stores'll be open tomorrow . . ."

"Forget it."

"I was gonna shop for presents in Philly."

"Don't worry about it."

A few minutes later Diane said, "Usually I like Christmas. A
lot."

"Me too. We used to go to Grandpa's; the whole church was lit
up. It was so pretty."

"Last year we had a tree. And a gypsy party. Terry supervised
the trimming . . . Aw, shit!" She threw her chopsticks down and ran
into her bedroom.

Later, in the living room, Carin said, "I guess it'll be expensive."

"What?"

"The funeral."

"Yeah, sort of."

"How're we going to pay for it?"

"The same way we pay for any gypsy party."

"Everybody'll chip in?"

"Of course."

"Have they agreed?"

"They will."

It was the infirm-of-purpose, give-me-the-knife tone that customarily ended their discussions—or *any* discussion—but Carin
asked, "How much will it be?"

"Don't worry."

"Well, those things can be so expensive. I saw a documentary on TV once . . ."

"I got the cheapest box. It'll look nice; you'll see. The salesman acted like he had the hots for me, and I sort of acted like things'd work out if he played along with us."

"When—when can people start—seeing him?"

"Wednesday morning. Then we'll have a bunch of cars—Rod Schafer's lining that up."

"Cars?"

"For the procession."

"We're going to the cemetery?"

Diane's eyebrows rose. "You think I'd let him go alone?"

They napped in their rooms. When Carin awoke, the pillow under her cheek was soggy, and she realized she had been crying in her sleep. A few minutes later Diane appeared, sat down on the edge of the bed and asked, "Which calamity are you crying about?"

"All of them." She flipped over on her back. "Terry's gone, Chris is gone, I'm out of work . . ."

"What're you gonna do?"

"I don't know. I didn't work long enough to qualify for unemployment. I guess I could be a waitress again, or go back to Detroit . . . Jesus!" she muttered. "I've got to call my mother and tell her. She still thinks she's coming to New York for the opening. I'd better call her today; she was going to go out and buy a fancy dress. Maybe that's what Dad gave her for Christmas."

"What're you gonna do about Chris?"

Carin stared up at her roommate. "What *can* I do?"

"Lie there on your ass," Diane said flatly, "or go and find him."

"Where?"

"Why do I always have to do all the thinking!"

"Okay!" Carin said, and started to flip over on her side.

Diane pulled her supine again. "There's such a thing as the *East Sider*, you know. Want me to look up the number?"

"I know it."

"Want me to dial it?"

"They wouldn't be open today."

"Oh yeah. I keep forgetting it's Christmas. Wonder why." Diane was silent a moment, then added, "You can call tomorrow."

"What can I say?"

"How about, 'I'm sorry'?"

"You think that'll solve the problem?"

"You want to solve the problem?"

Carin yanked the wet pillow from beneath her head. "I don't know *what* I want!"

"If you're gonna tell me you've fallen for Gino . . . !"

"No."

"You gonna see him in New York?"

"No."

Diane's eyes narrowed. "What happened?"

"Nothing. I just don't want to see him." She rolled to her stomach. "I don't want to see anybody!"

"Bullshit."

"Merry Christmas," Moira said to the conductor as he punched the tickets.

His answering smile was faint and tired. "Merry Christmas." He pushed the tickets into the metal frame on the back of the seat in front of Chris and moved down the aisle. Outside the car the lights that pierced the blackness were smeared into comets' tails by the rushing train.

Moira slid a hand under Chris's arm and snuggled against him. Her coppery hair, heavier and coarser than Carin's, tumbled against his chin, smelling pleasantly of the shampoo she and Chris had shared under her shower before leaving for Mamaroneck. "You tired?" Chris asked.

"A little. You?"

"I guess so."

She tipped her head enough to peer up at him. "My family wore you out?"

"No. I meant it: they're very nice."

She sat up. "They're really not bad. Dad's a little too hail-fellow-well-met, but underneath that bluster he's quite sensitive."

"I could tell. And your mother's charming."

"She's fun. Sometimes." She sat back, her eyes on the car's swaying ceiling.

"She doesn't want you to go to Paris, does she."

Moira's eyes shifted toward him. "You know how mothers are . . ."

"I think she knows I'm going too. Or assumes it."

"What if she does?"

"She doesn't like it."

Moira twisted toward him to put a hand on his arm. "It doesn't have anything to do with you, Chris. I give you my word."

"What *does* it have to do with?" The hand left his arm and Moira sat back. Chris smiled. "More impertinent questions. We both seem to do that—very often. Do we have that many secrets?"

The train slowed to a stop. Several passengers got on, all of them carrying shopping bags of Christmas booty. When the train had resumed its lurching journey, Moira turned back to Chris. The expression of resigned sadness on her face took him aback. "*Hey* . . ." he said.

"No," she said firmly, "it's just as well. Maybe that's why I invited you up there. Things just—pop out when you're *en famille.*

Maybe I was hoping they would. God knows I didn't have the guts to come right out and say it."

"Say what?"

"Why Mother's so nervous. I told you what happened to me in Paris . . ."

"Moira . . ."

"No, let me. Please." He sat back, uneasy, regretful, certain that something was about to go badly awry. "It's not very complicated," Moira said slowly. "Or interesting. When I came back from Paris, I went into Payne Whitney." She looked at him. "You know what that is?" He shook his head. "It's a clinic." She smiled thinly. "*Clinic*—that's an expensive euphemism for hospital. Funny farm. Laughing academy." She looked at Chris, asking for acknowledgment.

"You had a breakdown."

She emitted a mirthless laugh. "That's another euphemism. Poor people go crazy; rich people have breakdowns. It sounds so much nicer, doesn't it—like something that might happen to this train: a few days in the shop and it's rolling right along again." She stared front, her head against the back of the seat. "Well, it wasn't like that. I really came apart. Unraveled. After Payne Whitney I went to another fancy institution for six months. That's quite a long time, but my family could afford it. I hope you notice that I've stopped denying we're rich. You can make all the money jokes you want now."

"I don't feel like making any jokes."

When the train leaned forward and slid under Park Avenue, the tunnel amplified its steely clatter so that, to Chris, Moira's lips seemed to be moving in silent prayer. He leaned closer to hear, ". . . shock treatment."

"What?"

"I had shock treatment. It's not as bad as people think. You don't feel anything. I mean, it doesn't hurt. And lithium." She looked at him.

"Lithium?"

"It's a drug."

"I know what it is."

"I was on that for a while. I'm not on anything now."

"Oh." It was the only response Chris could think of.

"I haven't been for a long time."

"That's good. You—certainly seem healthy to me."

"Let's see . . ." Moira said, as if perusing a shopping list in a store she knew she would never be able to visit again. "Does that answer all your questions?" He looked at her. "The degrees. I just stayed in school. Sanctuary." She smiled distantly. "And the *East Sider*. Something stable, dull—unchallenging—when I finally ventured out of the groves of academe." The sad smile focused. "Just what the doctor ordered."

Chris sat back, aghast. "And I came in and busted it up, like a spoiled kid with a Tinkertoy! It's a wonder your family didn't sic the dog on me!"

"They don't blame you, Chris."

"*I* do! Why didn't you tell me!"

"I—I was trying to work up to it, but, frankly, I was having too good a time, and when you start telling somebody about a problem like this, it tends to put a damper on things."

"God damn it, *that's* repartee!"

The train slowed and began picking its way through a thicket of red and green and amber lights.

"Yes," Moira said, "you're right, it is. But I don't know what else to say. I'm nervous about this. It's so unattractive, and we were having such a—glamorous time. It didn't seem appropriate." Chris sat back with a heavy sigh, and she reached for his arm. "Please, Chris, don't feel bad; it's my fault."

"It's nobody's fault. We have to figure out what to do, that's all."

"It doesn't *have* to change anything. I just wanted you to know why Mother was acting the way she was. I knew you were blaming yourself, and . . ."

"And I was right! We're sitting there making jokes about how we kissed Ian off . . ."

"I'd've done it anyway." She leaned close. "I swear! I was so fed up I was ready to go back into Payne Whitney! And I'd got everything I needed out of it. I'd proved my point: I could do something four-square and sensible, five days a week, fifty-two weeks a year."

"I'm not sure your family think it's time to move on."

"It's not their decision to make!" She lowered her voice. "Listen to me, Chris: I don't need the *East Sider*. Christ, *no*body needs the *East Sider*! Okay, I wasn't going to quit this week, but I give you my word of honor: in another month I'd've been gone—whether you ever showed up there or not. Do you think that's all I'm capable of? Grinding out pablum for twenty-year-old toddlers who don't know the difference between their public images and their private parts?"

"No, of course not."

"Then don't blame yourself. Please, I *beg* you . . ."

"Sure. Of course."

She stared down at her hands, then she said, "Going to Europe is no problem. For me. Maybe you don't want to go with me now . . ."

"I didn't say that!"

She looked up. "But I wouldn't blame you for thinking it."

"I'm not thinking it either! Will you quit trying to put words in my mouth—and thoughts in my head."

"I'm not asking you to say I love you—neither one of us needs maudlin reassurance every fifteen minutes. Whatever's happening between us, it's just—happening, that's all. I like it . . ."

"So do I."

"Then please . . ." She choked, cleared her throat angrily and tried again. "Please, Chris—don't take Paris away from us . . ." Her throat closed again and she ducked her head to avoid the wide-eyed stare of a black child in an orange baseball cap who had stood up on the seat in front of them to see what was going on.

They stepped off the train into what looked to Chris like a giant, untended basement, gloomy, gritty and cold. As they hurried along the platform, Chris stole a glance at his companion and decided it was time for, "Well, now I know your guilty secret."

"I would've told you before we left . . ."

"Your name is really Muffy."

"Oh, God!" She looked up: his grin was doing valorous battle with the platform's desolate ambiance.

"Don't deny it. I heard your father say it, and your mother."

"Isn't it hideous!" But she was grinning back.

"A little precious, maybe."

"What it is is disgustingly upper class. When I was taking riding lessons, half the girls in the class were called Muffy. The other half were Missy." She made a retching sound, and Chris slid an arm around her waist. She responded with an arm around him, and, flanked by bulging shopping bags, the broad-beamed unit trudged up a ramp to Grand Central's cavernous main floor, where recorded carols greeted them. As they passed under the giant photomural that arched over the waiting room like a Kodacolor Bridge of Sighs, Moira asked, "Walk or subway?" and Chris replied, "Walk, if you're up to it."

"Absolutely."

At Forty-second Street Moira asked, "How about a paper?" Chris nodded and she bought a *News*.

At home she brewed hot chocolate, then she and Chris split the paper and stretched out on the sofa, propped at opposite ends, their feet in each other's laps. Christmas music that had been recorded on the St. Eustache organ swirled around them.

"What did you say that fellow's name was?" Moira asked.

"What fellow?"

"Your roommate."

"On Forty-eighth Street?" She nodded. "Terry Mitchell. Why?"

She pulled a page from the section of the *News* she was reading and pushed it toward him.

TWENTY-FOUR, two, three, four

Grande Révérence

Whether out of respect for Terry or fear of Diane, the gypsies had adhered strictly to Diane's dress code. To the "civilian" mourners honoring the funeral home's dead, the ragtag line waiting outside Reposing Room Three may have looked like an extras' audition for a Fellini film, but the gypsies considered their dress and demeanor respectful, and respectable, to a fault.

Granted, there was a sprinkling of feathers and beads in the line, but, in honor of the occasion, the embellishments were without exception of a somber hue. Granted, too, varicolored tights protruded from beneath the hems of many of the female mourners' weeds, but this was after all a weekday, and most of the celebrants of this solemn rite were on their way to or from a dance class. Besides, while the word had spread that Diane's fists were cocked for anyone gross enough to show up in ordinary, everyday apparel, no restraint had been placed on the gypsies' native sense of drama and individuality. As on the occasion of Opal and Ernie's wedding, the only way to dress was up, and up the dancers had dressed, each expressing his or her grief in his or her way. By Thursday morning not a thrift shop in Manhattan had had a black veil left, and now as the line shuffled slowly into Reposing Room Three, the veils had reappeared, adorning one grieving head after another, regardless of sex. There had been a run as well on feather boas and Art Deco accessories in general, out of respect for Terry's fondness for the period, and now the boas drooped from divers shoulders, again regardless of race, creed, age or sexual preference.

Some of the mourners, former lovers of the deceased, wept openly, drawing scandalized stares from passing civilians, but for the most part the gypsies waited decorously, murmuring quietly to each other, standing silent, alone with their thoughts and memories or sucking furtive tokes out of cupped hands to steel themselves for their first confrontation with death.

Inside Reposing Room Three the line snaked along one wall, coming at last to the bier where, under a neon cross—the funeral home's *mauvais goût,* not the gypsies'—the deceased reposed.

The Gypsy Robe took up so much of the casket there was barely room for Terry; only the upper half of his face was visible, peeping over a tin trumpet, tap shoe and stuffed rabbit that had been stitched to the robe's collar by former laureates. The acquisition of the Robe had been far harder than Diane had anticipated. If it had been a simple matter of lending the Robe to Diane for the funeral, there would have been no argument.

"Whattaya mean *keep* it!" one of the girls in the *Music to My Ears* dressing room had demanded.

"It goes *with* him," Diane had replied, inching her feet apart to take her customary fighting stance.

"It doesn't belong to us," the current *Music to My Ears* honoree exclaimed, brandishing a hand at the Robe again. "I got it, and then we were going to give it to you, and then you'd have to give it to one of the gypsies in the next show that opened . . ."

"You don't have to tell me the rules," Diane snapped. "I've been around since they invented the fuckin' wheel."

"Then you know," another girl said.

"Tell you what I know," Diane growled, widening her stance. "There's nobody in the United States of America who deserves that Robe the way Terry does."

"Fine. You can have it for the funeral, then you'll return it."

"It goes in the ground," Diane said, "Like him: forever."

"Look, Di, we know how you feel about Terry, but this Robe's gotta go in the museum with all the others . . ."

"It's *his,*" Diane screamed. "I'm not pulling it off him after the service!"

"Fifteen minutes, ladies and gentlemen," the squawk box said, "fifteen minutes to magic time."

A girl reached for a powder puff. "Nobody leaves this room till this is settled," Diane growled.

The line moved slowly, each mourner pausing to peer over the tap shoe and stuffed rabbit for a last look at Terry. Then the line moved past Diane and Carin, posted just beyond the bier, dressed fittingly, if a bit outlandishly, in two black dresses that had once been designed for Diane by Terry.

That morning, naked in her room, Carin had held one of the dresses up. "I don't know . . ."

"Whattaya mean, you don't know!" Diane, naked, the second dress draped over her arm, had demanded.

Carin separated her hands, spreading the dress out. "What did he make this for?"

"Halloween. It was a costume party, and I wanted to go as a witch."

"You want me to go to his funeral as a witch?"

"I'm not telling you to wear the goddamn hat!"

"Well, why should I wear *this?*"

"It's beautiful! It's silk, for Chrissake. And it's black. Terry didn't make very many black things; it wasn't his style." When Carin continued to eye the dress suspiciously, Diane muttered, "Did we agree we were gonna wear Terry Originals to ,he obsequies?" Diane had read a booklet given her by her admirer at the funeral home.

"But they have to be right."

"You don't think that's right?" She whipped the other dress off her arm and pushed it into Carin's hands. "Okay, you take this one and *I'll* wear the witch dress."

One of the boys in the line leaned over to kiss Terry, but the stuffed rabbit was in his way. He reached into the casket to move the rabbit and Diane hissed, "Get y'r hand outta the box!"

The boy withdrew his hand as if the rabbit had nipped it and dismounted the bier to extend his sympathies to Diane. "I'm sorry, Di. But you oughtta move the bunny."

"It's there for a reason," Diane snapped.

"But what if somebody wants to kiss him good-bye? You can't get near the bottom of his face."

"There isn't any."

"What?"

"That's where he hit. I told you: the bunny's there for a reason."

"Oh, Jesus, Di, I'm sorry."

"Forget it. It—it's nice that people want to kiss him; they just can't, that's all . . ." Her eyes were so red she looked as if she was about to cry blood; the boy moved on.

Reposing Room Three's exit was flanked by two funeral directors, their striped pants and cutaway coats in marked—more accurately, violent—contrast to the motley that was passing between their twin pillars of rectitude. As a mourner left the room, the eyes of the funeral directors met behind him in a look that mingled dismay and disdain. Then the taller of the two officials leaned across the doorway to whisper, "Have you had a chance to take a good look at the outfit on the departed?"

"Before I opened the room," his colleague replied with a nod.

They were silent as another mourner went through the door. Then the taller director said, "I suppose we ought to be used to anything these days, but *this* . . . ! It's a carnival!"

His colleague rolled his eyes toward heaven. "Father, forgive them, for they know not what they do."

The witch dress, it turned out, was the more conservative of the two outfits Diane had selected from her closet, but Carin hadn't been able to summon strength for a second confrontation with her roommate, so she stood near the casket now, red-eyed, in a broad-shouldered black satin dress Joan Crawford had worn in one of her steamier roles, accepting the condolences of the line of similarly Decoed mourners, many of whom had appeared with her in *Ante Meridian.* Carla, the once and future Equity deputy, stood on half-toe to embrace Diane, then took a step and put her arms around Carin.

And there he was. Over Carla's shoulder. Looking alien as always, and splendid in his dark gray business suit, with the sharp planes of his Modigliani face framing his silvery eyes.

Feeling Carin stiffen, Carla stepped back, releasing her. "Sorry. It's these wrestler's arms of mine . . ." She trailed off and followed Carin's gaze. Remembering the tension at Opal and Ernie's wedding, she squeezed Carin's hand and beat a hasty retreat. As Chris stepped forward to Carin, Diane watched, too, her disinterested hand in the grasp of a weeping boy.

Carin and Chris stared at each other. "Are you all right?" Chris asked.

"More or less."

"I'm sorry," Chris said. Carin nodded. "I really liked him. I know I didn't at first. I didn't understand, but—I do now." He went silent, then began, "I . . ." but the weeping boy, releasing Diane, flung himself on Carin, hugging her and bawling as if the casket contained Judy Garland. Chris glanced at Diane, then, feeling the pressure of the line coming from the bier, went quickly between the disapproving stelae at the exit door.

Eight male gypsies moved smoothly under the casket, accustomed to much more cumbersome burdens. At the curb one of them murmured, "Se-ven, eight," and they swung the casket from their shoulders and slid it into the hearse. Diane stood anxiously by, nibbling at a fingernail, her authority momentarily preempted by an officious funeral director. As the doors of the hearse slammed shut, one of the pallbearers took Diane's arm. Sightless, she let herself be led toward the vehicle into which the mourners were streaming; then she heard a murmur of voices and felt a new grip on her arm. Extracting a tissue from a pocket of the witch dress, she blew her nose and the world swam back into focus. A familiar face was smiling down at her, black and narrow, framed by close-cropped gray hair around a shiny black tonsure.

The bus driver! Diane looked up. The sign on the big orange bus said, CAUTION! CHILDREN!

Diane looked back at the bus driver. "My God! It's you!"

"Sure, sure," the bus driver crooned, patting her hand.

Diane turned to look at the boy who had led her from the hearse. "I figured we'd get the same bus we used for the honeymoon," he said. "Saved finding a whole bunch of cars."

"Of course!" Diane said. "Great idea. This is exactly the way Terry would've wanted it."

She looked at the bus driver, and he squeezed her hand, smiling mistily. "This fella tol' me all about it. I felt terrible, jus' terrible. We didn't start off all that good, las' time, but by the time we got back to Manhattan, I felt like we was fam'ly. Tol' my wife all about you kids. 'Crazy,' I said, 'but nice as they could be. Wouldn't hurt a fly.' "

Crying, Diane kissed him; then he put a hand under her arm and tenderly helped her aboard.

The hearse drove fast, but the bus kept up. This time their route led westward, through the Lincoln Tunnel and across the industrial flats of New Jersey. The funeral director who had sold Diane the coffin had recommended the cemetery: "Perpetual maintenance at minimal cost."

As the black hearse and orange bus crossed the tightrope of the Pulaski Skyway, the bus driver glanced into his rearview mirror. While the gypsies' demeanor was seemlier than it had been the last time he had seen them, their attire showed the old fire, and the bus driver half-expected them to burst into boisterous song after the interment, like a brass band on its way back from a New Orleans graveyard. He picked out the pretty blond girl and her boyfriend who'd made all the trouble at the bumper cars. But they weren't sitting together now. Problems. Still. The boy kept looking at the girl, but she wouldn't look at him.

When the hearse led the way into the cemetery through rusty gates, Diane looked suspiciously around, and by the time the hearse and bus had stopped a few yards from a mound of freshly turned earth, Diane was bristling.

"The son of a bitch said it was a first-class cemetery!" Diane hissed into Carin's ear as they clambered off the bus.

"It doesn't look too bad," Carin said.

"What about *that!*" Diane waved a black-silk witch's arm at a forest of tanks and pipes and chimneys belching smoke and noxious gasses. The cemetery abutted a petroleum-cracking plant, and, in fact, Carin found it difficult to draw a deep breath. "Terry believed in clean air!" Diane raged. "He took me to a clean-air concert once. Pete Seeger sang!"

"Diane . . ." Carin said, tugging at her sleeve.

"I'm not leaving him here!" Diane snarled. "He'll suffocate."

There was a quick parley, then a small delegation of the mourners took Diane and Carin aside while the grave diggers watched,
leaning on their shovels and marveling.

Within the little circle of the conference, Carin, in tears, asked,
"Where can we take him?"

"I don't know," Diane said, "but he can't stay here."

The group stared helplessly at Diane. Suddenly she said, "How
about taking him back to Forty-eighth Street?"

"Up five flights?" a dismayed pallbearer gasped.

"You wanna leave him in the basement?" Diane demanded.

"I want to leave him here," the boy replied, and Diane doubled
her fists.

"It's illegal," a girl said. "You can't keep him at home."

"Just till I find the right place . . ."

"Look!" Diane turned. One of the boys was pointing south,
away from the cracking plant, and the view beyond his finger was an
acceptable vista of fields with a row of trees on the horizon. "That
isn't bad at all," the boy said.

Diane squinted critically at the view, as Berenson might have
squinted at a quattrocento lunette, then she looked at the grave.
"Which way will he be facing?"

"Let's ask," the boy said.

The delegation marched back to the fascinated grave diggers.
"Which way does he go in?" Diane demanded. The grave diggers
stared. "Can he face that way"—she pointed at the fields—"with his
back to *that?*" She aimed a thumb at the cracking plant.

"Any way you want," one of the grave diggers said. He indicated the hole at his feet. "It goes both ways."

Diane nodded, and the relieved pallbearers hurried to the
hearse before she could change her mind. When the casket had been
placed on the rim of the grave and the mourners had gathered in a
circle, Diane nodded at a tall girl in a white pre-Raphaelite dress
Diane had found in a thrift shop and bought for this austere purpose. The dress was short on the girl, and summer-weight, so that
she shivered in the December wind that rolled across the noisome
flat as she opened a guitar case, slung the guitar's shoulder strap
around her neck, strummed a chord and began to sing. The mourners lowered their heads.

"'My Rio,'" the girl sang slowly, in a high clear voice, "' Rio
by the sea-o! Flying down to Rio where there's rhythm and rhyme.
Hey feller, twirl that old propeller. Got to get to Rio and we've got to
make time.'"

One of the grave diggers put his palms on his shovel handle and
laid his forehead on the back of his hands. His rounded shoulders
shook and he emitted helpless little squeaks and buzzes. The bus
driver, standing near him, sidled closer and bent over him "Hey,

buddy . . ." The grave digger looked up, bubbling stifled laughter. "How'd you like a knuckle sandwich," the bus driver snarled.

Diane was the last to leave the grave. Carin tried to pull her along when the group moved toward the bus, but Diane snatched her arm back with a harsh, "Go and wait for me. I want to be sure they put him in facing the right way." When Carin hesitated, Diane barked, "Go ahead," and Carin hurried to join the others at the bus.

"You can go," one of the grave diggers said.

"Put him in," Diane replied.

"Usually the family goes before we lower . . ."

"Put him in."

The grave digger shrugged and took one end of the sling.

"Careful," Diane said as the coffin jounced into the hole.

"That's why we like everybody to leave," one of the grave diggers grunted.

"I have to perform in front of people," Diane shot back.

When the casket had come to rest at the bottom of the grave and the grave diggers had withdrawn the sling, Diane made an abrupt move. Something clattered into the grave. One of the grave diggers moved forward to peer over the edge. "Cover him up," Diane snapped. When the grave digger hesitated, she said, "It's nothing—a dumb little plaster dog. Not even worth a nickel, so don't take it out when we leave."

"I wouldn't think of it," one of the grave diggers said and shoveled a spadeful of earth into the grave. Diane waited until the dog had disappeared, then went to the bus where the mourners were huddled in a group, watching her.

"Come on," she snapped, "let's go," and there was a rush to board the bus. Carin found herself next to Gino. He looked at her, but she looked away.

Gino grabbed a chrome rail and swung gracefully aboard the bus. As he made his way up the bus's crowded aisle, he was stalled for a moment next to an aisle seat from which Chris stared up at him. He looked down, coolly accepting the challenge in Chris's eyes. The aisle cleared ahead of him, but he remained where he was until a girl behind him pushed and said, "Come on, Gino, let's go. You're holding up the parade."

He unlocked his gaze from Chris's and moved to the back of the bus, where he took the empty seat Pam had reserved with her dance bag. As he settled into the seat, Pam reached for his hand and moved close, fitting her body to his.

Diane dropped wearily into the seat at the front of the bus that had been reserved for her and Carin. As the gypsies continued to file aboard, Diane looked past Carin at the cemetery and frowned: from this angle the cracking plant loomed over the arid necropolis.

Carin raised a blocking hand. "Don't look."

Diane sat back with a groan. "I thought that funeral director who recommended the cemetery was a nice guy—friendly, horny but kind of cute. Would you believe I was gonna deliver? I hope he calls. You know what he'll get?"

"Forget it."

"The perpetual maintenance better be the real thing. I'm coming out to check."

Opal and Ernie were the last mourners to board the bus. As the driver levered the door closed and started the motor, they paused next to Diane and Carin. Diane looked up with a wan smile and said, "I guess this bus has memories for *you.*"

Opal took Ernie's hand. "Sure does."

Ernie leaned over Diane. "Hat's off, Di. If he'd been the President of the United States, he couldn't have had a more beautiful send-off. Not too hokey, and not too ordinary."

Diane pressed his hand. "That's the effect I was striving for."

"Well, you hit it. Right on the money!"

Diane sighed. "I hope so. They're standing there waiting for you to make decisions you never had to make before, and you wind up guessing—and hoping."

"Well, you guessed right. Terry would've loved it."

Diane shook her head. "No. He hated funerals. The only one he ever went to was his mother's, and it wrecked him. He wouldn't have come to *this* one if he could've got out of it."

Opal and Ernie exchanged a melancholy look, then he took her hand and they moved up the aisle, steadying themselves as the bus lurched over a hump designed to slow traffic entering the cemetery.

"He was so scared of dying," Diane murmured to Carin. "That's why I don't understand . . ."

The bus passed through the cemetery's rusty gates and picked up speed.

"You know," Diane whispered, "he was over forty. *Well* over forty."

Carin's head snapped toward her. "Terry?" Diane nodded. "No, he wasn't."

"Yes, he was. I saw it in his passport when I was looking for his name."

"Over forty . . . ?" Carin shook her head in disbelief.

Diane stared forward through the bus's big windshield. "You know something else? I'm not twenty-nine, I'm—"

"Shut up." Though the command was delivered in Carin's soft, childlike voice, it had absorbed, perhaps by osmosis, some of Diane's mettle. "It doesn't matter."

Diane continued watching the road rush toward the bus. "You're right; it doesn't. When you're eighteen."

Carin looked up. Chris was standing in the aisle. "May I talk to you for a minute?" he asked.

"Certainly," Diane said, before Carin could respond. She stood up. "I need the little girls' room."

"There isn't any on this bus," Carin said.

"That's *my* problem." Diane slid into the aisle, yielding her place to Chris, and moved toward the back of the bus.

Chris waited for a sign from Carin, but she seemed absorbed in the industrial blight outside the window. After a moment he sat down. "It must've cost you a lot."

Carin looked at him. "You know how we do things."

"Everybody chipped in?" She nodded. "I guess that's one of the advantages."

"Of what?"

"Belonging to the club."

"Please, Chris, not now. Not here. It doesn't matter anymore anyway." She looked out the window.

"Doesn't it?" He was surprised. He hadn't expected to say that. But he felt obliged to amplify it; Carin was looking at him again. "I—I meant what I said in the funeral home. I think I'm beginning to understand." He hadn't meant to say that either. He had only come to the funeral out of respect for Terry; he had promised himself he would avoid any unnecessary contact with Carin, and he certainly hadn't intended to go to the cemetery. It was the familiar schoolbus that had drawn him; before he had known it, he was aboard.

He looked past Carin at his reflection in the dusty window, trying to read something in his own expression, but it was as mysterious to him as to Carin. He shifted his gaze to her. Yes, she looked puzzled. Why shouldn't she? "I'm leaving," he said abruptly.

"You've already gone."

"No—I mean, I'm leaving New York."

She nodded. "It's best."

"What?"

"You belong at the *Free Press.*"

"I'm not going back to Detroit."

"Oh? Where're you going?"

"Europe." Suddenly it sounded pretentious to him, sophomoric.

"Europe?"

"France. Paris." It was getting worse.

"To work?"

"I don't know. I'm going to try to get some work over there."

"You're going to stay?"

"I don't know. Listen . . ." She listened, but he didn't know what he had intended her to listen to. He frowned and chewed the inside of his cheek. Then he knew. "I'm sorry."

"About what?"

"What happened in Philadelphia."

"You're apologizing to *me?*"

"Yes. I should've understood." She shook her head and looked down. Her lashes were very long and thick. He had noticed that in the drugstore near Wayne State. "I see . . ." He paused. She looked up. There were moments, like this one, when she still looked like the sixteen-year-old girl who had arranged to have herself deflowered. For him. He pushed the past away and tipped his head toward Gino at the back of the bus. "I see it's off."

"It was never really on."

"Are you saying nothing happened?"

"No."

The bus swung onto a highway and picked up speed.

"What if . . ." Chris asked, and stopped, wondering how he had meant to finish the sentence. She was looking at him again, waiting again. Her hands, slender and pale and more childlike than any aspect of her but her mount, were folded in her lap; the rims of her eyes were red, but the whites were clear again, as unmarked and vulnerable as a child's. He could smell Jean Naté.

"What if what?" Carin asked.

He responded without thinking. "We tried again." It was like automatic writing. Despite the fact that his heart was pounding, he felt oddly disassociated from what he was saying, as if the noxious fumes at the cemetery had induced an intense high.

Carin stared at him, her mouth slightly ajar. He could see the edges of her even teeth and a pink glint that must be the tip of her tongue. He tried to picture Moira, but he couldn't focus on her. He tried to conjure up the pleasant aroma of shampoo that rose from her heavy hair, but the Jean Naté intervened. He wondered if *he* weren't a candidate for Payne Whitney. *Forget it,* he told himself, *you can't afford it*—and nearly smiled. "Well?" he asked, without planning to.

"I don't know."

"You don't want to?"

"I didn't say that."

"I still love you." He stared past her at his image, aghast now. Moira's point on the train had been well taken: he had never mentioned love to her, nor had the word crossed her lips. When she had insisted they were both above it, he had wondered whether that was more repartee, like her airy answer when he had asked her once where her philosophy left God, and she had replied, borrowing the words of the mathematician and astronomer Laplace when asked a similar question by Napoleon, "I have no need of that hypothesis." Or maybe her disclaimer was pride, cushioning her against his silence. In any event, it had surprised him, and worried him a little. He had never thought about whether he was or wasn't in love with

Moira; it hadn't been a factor. She and Chris were, as Moira had insisted, what they were; no more, no less. But did Moira really feel that way? And why had he just said "I love you" to Carin so easily, so naturally? *Because,* he thought, *I mean it.*

Something turned anxious and unwieldy in him. Moira loomed, vulnerable. Dangerously vulnerable. In the dusty window beyond Carin, he saw the malicious boy with the broken Tinkertoy.

"You don't have to say anything," he said abruptly.

"But . . ."

"No, really. We—I don't have the right. Let me call you. Tomorrow maybe. Or the next day."

"Sure. Okay. But . . ."

"That's the best way. The only way."

She nodded, uncomprehending.

TWENTY-FIVE, two, three, four

Battement

Moira knew something was wrong when she walked in the door. There was no music wafting from the speakers; only one light burned, dim and insufficient, in the sizable living room; and the little library of books she had given Chris for Christmas was neatly stacked on a table. This morning the books had been strewn blithely about the room, some prone on their open pages, waiting for Chris to return and stretch out with them on the floor. Now the room looked terribly formal, as if awaiting a prim ceremony, and the primmest element in it was Chris himself, seated on the couch in the dark suit he had worn to the funeral.

"Well," Moira said. She took off her coat and jammed it into the closet near the door. "One more coat and we won't need hangers," she observed as she came to the couch. She stood over Chris, studying him. "You won't believe it," she said, "but I had a feeling. All day long I kept wondering what it was like for you, seeing them again . . ." She let the thought drift away, and waited.

"Sit down," Chris said.

"Where?" she asked.

"It's your house."

"It doesn't feel like it."

She considered the couch, then opted for an armchair facing Chris across the coffee table. He lowered his face into his hands. "You look like you need sympathy," she said.

He straightened, drawing a breath. "No."

"Was it tough?"

"Yes. I really liked Terry. Now that I think about it, he was one of the most thoroughly honest people I've ever met." He paused, then said, "I wish *I* were."

"Here comes the bad news," Moira said. She tried to smile, but her lips wouldn't cooperate. The resultant rictus conveyed no specific emotion; she simply looked ill.

"Maybe it's good news."

"For whom? Or, as Ian would say, for who? Repartee," she observed flatly. "I can't seem to break the habit." She shifted in the chair, extending her legs and crossing them at the ankles. "I gather we're not going to Paris."

"*I'm* not."

"I knew you'd sober up." He looked at her. "Thanks for not waiting till we got to Paris."

"Jesus, Moira, I'm so sorry."

"That's *your* repartee."

"You don't think I mean it?"

"Sure, I think you mean it. But I also think it's unnecessary."

Chris rose and stalked toward the shelves crowded with books and records. "Is it? I've been so fucking unfair to you!"

"Chris, do me a favor . . ."

"Will you please let me accept the blame!"

"Sure, if it'll make you feel better. But please don't pretend you're doing it for me."

He stared at her across the dark room. "You're so goddamn smart."

"Oh, I don't think so." Her voice threatened to break, but she steadied it with, "I hope you're planning to take those with you." She was nodding toward the neat stack of books.

"Why are we being so sophisticated?"

"I don't know what *your* reason is, but *I'm* trying not to scream." He hurried toward her. She raised a hand. "Whatever you do, don't do that." He stopped several feet from her, swaying slightly. "Are you going back to Forty-eighth Street?"

"No. I'm going to use the money I got for the car to rent an apartment—somewhere."

"Somewhere?"

"I'm not sure where. I—I've got to make a couple of calls."

They were silent, then Moira said, "You're all packed, aren't you."

"Yes."

"Don't let me hold you up."

"Can't we talk?"

"About what?"

"Okay: my guilt."

"I'd rather not."

"What about you?"

"You want to hear how awful I feel? That's just male ego."

"I want to know you'll be okay."

She smiled. It was real. "You want a safety net? We work without one, remember? The Flying Romantics."

"I *made* you jump!"

"Will you stop it, Chris?" The edge was undisguised. "I've grad-
uated from Payne Whitney. It's not a crutch anymore, or an excuse.
If I can survive a year with Ian, I can survive anything." As he
started to respond, she said, "Yes, that's repartee, but I've never
been so serious about anything in my life. I'm not going to pay you
the compliment of coming apart, or promising not to. Whether I
fuck up or buck up, it's my life again. You've lost your journalistic
privileges: no more questions." She was breathless. She looked
around. Chris was familiar with the gesture: she was looking for a
cigarette. Apparently she changed her mind. She turned back to
Chris and waited.

"I'll get my bags," he said. She nodded. He went to the bedroom door and stopped, a hand on the knob. "If I hadn't gone to the
funeral. . . . I didn't realize till I saw her . . ."

"This is what I'd rather not talk about."

"But you were the one who sent me to Philadelphia!"

"That was before I fell in—" She broke off, closing her eyes,
clenching her fists, then resumed without opening either. "Chris—
this is very bad for me. *Very.* You'll have to take my word for it."
She opened her eyes.

"Yes," Chris said, and went into the bedroom. A moment later
he emerged with two suitcases, set them down near the door and
went back into the bedroom. When he returned with the third bag,
Moira was still standing in the middle of the room, but she was
crying now, silently and copiously.

Chris dropped the suitcase and took a step toward her, but she
raised a hand. "I meant it. Do me the courtesy of allowing me my
feelings without interference, just as if I were a great big grown-up
person."

His head bobbed once in a tight nod, and he picked up the
suitcase. Propping the front door with it, he worked his coat out of
the crowded closet. Several coats fell. "Leave them," Moira said. He
shoved the remaining suitcases into the hall and followed them out.
When he picked up the first suitcase, the door slammed shut. Moira
remained where she was for a moment, then turned from the door
and cursed softly: he had left the little library on the table.

The room was small; Chris had asked for the least expensive
one in the hotel. There was barely space for him and his three suitcases, but he anticipated a short stay; perhaps he wouldn't even have
to unpack. He sat on the edge of the bed, read the printed instructions for direct dialing, dialed an area code and number and waited.
When he heard the catarrhal rasp, he said, "Asshole One? This is
Asshole Two."

TWENTY-SIX, two, three, four
Relevé

Carin looked up from the sling chair. The face was entirely unfamiliar. Diane's smile glowed next to it. "This is my roommate Carin," Diane said, prodding the stranger into the room.

He was young and rangy, the new breed of dancer, taller by a head than the generation of male dancers that had preceded him. His walk and demure demeanor marked him, to Carin's practiced eye, as both dancer and homosexual.

"This is Carin's room," Diane said to the newcomer. She waved a hand at the open window. "Unobstructed view of an Advent. It belongs to a girl in the next building. Her old man's got all kinds of dough, but she's one of us, so she leaves her window open and takes requests." The hand that had introduced the window singled Carin out of the room's other artifacts. "Carin allows virtually unlimited TV-watching privileges." The voice hardened. "Right?"

On her feet now, Carin was staring at the newcomer.

"This is Ozzie Russell," Diane said. "We met in class this morning, and guess what."

"He needs a place to live," Carin said tonelessly.

"Right! How about that!" Diane turned and clapped the candidate on the back. "Ozzie's brand new in New York. Just arrived. Like a few months ago," she said to Carin, and turned back to Ozzie. "From where?"

"Chicago."

"Chicago! I played there. Twice! And Carin's from Detroit. That's like right next to Chicago, isn't it?"

"Diane . . ." Carin said.

"Chicago, Detroit and Texas!" Diane trilled. "Sounds like a pretty good combination to me."

"Diane, do you think I could talk to you?"

"Sure."

"Alone."

"Oh—sure. Ozzie, why don't you wait for me in the living room. Take a look at the dining room and kitchen while you're out there. Do you cook?"

"A little bit."

"O-*kay*. We share all the chores here."

"Oh, I'd expect to do my share."

"That's what I like to hear. If you'll just wait for me out there . . ."

"Sure."

He went out, and Diane turned to Carin with a spacious smile. "Did you hear that? Cooks and everything. Understands our philosophy . . ."

"You never said a word."

"I just met him today, in class! What was I supposed to do—send you a telegram?"

"You're going to put him in Terry's room?"

"You want him in yours?"

"I'm serious, Di."

"So am I." The manic note was gone. "We've gotta do something; you know that."

Carin sat heavily on the edge of the bed. "I know."

"Then what're you giving me a hard time for?"

Carin stared at the floor. "It's like going out to get a new dog when the old one dies."

"What'd you say . . . ?"

The naked menace in the question brought Carin's head up. As many times as she had been berated by Diane, she had never seen hatred in her roommate's eyes before. "You know what I mean," Carin said limply.

"Like hell I do. Are you accusing me of forgetting about Terry?"

"Well, what does it look like? If this boy moves in, we'll have to clean out Terry's room. You said we didn't have to yet."

"What did you do today?"

"Do? I took a class."

"And then what?"

"Came home."

"Well, I took a jazz class . . ."

"I know."

"And then I went out and got a job."

"In a *show?*"

"You should live so long. I'm waiting tables at a place called Murphy's. You know it? It's on Columbus Avenue."

"No."

"Well, that's where you'll find me six nights a week—till Dame Fortune smiles again."

"Diane . . ."

"Don't apologize."

"I wasn't going to."

"Oh? Why not?"

"It just hurts, that's all. I can't even walk past Terry's room, and the thought of going *in* there to . . ."

"You think it doesn't hurt me? But guess what. *Diane Cartier is gonna survive.*" She took several deep breaths and went on. "You think I'm looking forward to Murphy's?"

"Of course not."

"I was born to dance!"

"I know."

"*Born to dance*—not dish up slop for creeps who just want to pinch my ass and stiff me. Murphy's is survival!" She swept a hand toward the living room. "So's Ozzie. Nobody takes Terry's place. Ever! Not for one second. But Ozzie's one third of the rent—*so I can hang in.* And *you* can hang in. Here—where we belong—*till it happens.* And when it does, *we'll be ready.* Understand? Whenever it comes—whatever it is—we'll be ready! Well?"

"I understand."

"Tell me I'm gonna forget Terry! I'm gonna beat the fuckin' system that *beat* Terry! You call that forgetting?"

"No."

"Okay. We'll take a vote. All those in favor of letting Ozzie move in . . ."

"Aye," Carin murmured.

The doorbell rang faintly. "I'll get it," Diane said, and hurried out. A moment later she was back, blusterless. "It's Chris." Carin didn't move. "Go talk to him." It was gentle suggestion, more plea than demand.

Carin rose and went to the living room. Chris, still in his coat, was standing just inside the door. Ozzie rose nervously from the couch and said, "Listen, I get the feeling you don't want . . ."

"No," Carin said distantly, "it's okay. We decided we'd like you here. You and Diane can start clearing out Ter . . . the room."

As Ozzie hurried into the corridor to the bedrooms, Chris asked, "Terry's replacement?"

"No one replaces Terry," Carin said evenly.

"But I thought . . ."

"He'll be living in Terry's room. We need the money. For the rent."

They were silent. "May I come in?" Chris asked.

"Of course."

He went to the couch and started to sit. "Take off your coat," Carin said.

Chris put his coat over a chair and sat on the couch. Carin pulled a chair to face the couch and sat down. "I'm sorry to walk in on you like this, but I wasn't sure you'd talk to me if I called," Chris said.

"It's okay. You want anything? Coffee? A Dr. Pepper?"

"No. I—just came to tell you what's happening." He paused. She waited. "I'm leaving."

"I know. For Europe."

"No, that's changed. I decided it—wasn't a good idea. I'm going to Washington."

"What for?"

"I've got a job. A *good* job. On the *Post.*"

Her spine bent; she leaned forward in the chair. "Oh, Chris, that's wonderful!"

"Yeah, I think so too. Traynor arranged it. Remember him?"

"Of course. I knew he wouldn't let you waste your life."

"No matter how hard I tried." He smiled. She didn't smile back. "I wasn't talking about us."

"You shouldn't have come to New York. Not to work on the *East Sider.* It was wrong."

"Well, that's over now. I've got a terrific job—better than the one I had at the *Free Press.*"

"I'm so glad." It was clear she meant it. "When do you go?"

"Tomorrow."

"Wow."

He remembered how her *wow*'s had frightened him when she was sixteen. Neither of them spoke for almost a minute; then Chris said, "The reason I came—Washington's a great city . . ."

"So I've heard. Just imagine the kind of stories you'll be writing! You'll probably meet the President!"

Chris smiled. "It's the news capital of the world."

"I'll buy the *Post* at the out-of-town newsstand in Times Square and look for your name—like I used to."

"Washington's got a lot of things going for it. Kennedy Center . . ."

"I know."

"Several theaters. I don't know if they've got a ballet company, but . . ." He paused and looked at her. He could see the edges of her teeth again, and the pink glow of her tongue.

"What're you saying?"

"Come along."

"To Washington?" He nodded. "With you?" He nodded. "To live?"

"It won't be like this, but—I hear Georgetown's like the Village, only cleaner and classier . . ."

"Chris . . ."

"We could get married. We *should* get married. I love you." Her mouth gaped wider. He smiled. "It's a known fact. Does it surprise you?" She shook her head. "Does it interest you?" She nodded. "It's not as though I were trying to pull you back to Detroit," he said. "That was moronic. You have to be where the action is—*your* kind of action. Well, from everything I hear, Washington has both kinds of action—yours and mine. It's liable to be—perfect." He sat back and waited, his heart thumping. He wished for once that he smoked, so he could do something that looked nonchalant and self-assured. Maybe that was why Moira smoked . . .

"Chris . . ." Carin was saying.

"Yes?"

"I don't know what to say."

"I know I've been acting like an idiot—since the day I met you: yes, no; now, never; go, stay. . . . But I think I've finally got my act together. I'm not following you around anymore. I'm living my own life, the way I ought to be living it. I'm sure you can see that."

"Yes. I'm very proud of you."

"Anything else? Anything more?" His heart pounded.

"Yes. I love you."

It was barely audible. Remembering Moira's upraised hand, he didn't rush at Carin. "Well?"

"You want me to come with you tomorrow?"

"More than I can tell you."

"It's gonna work out great!" Diane announced as she and Ozzie came into the room.

"I'll be back tomorrow with my stuff," Ozzie said.

"The room'll be ready," Diane said. She introduced Ozzie to Chris. "Chris used to be one of our roommates . . ." She broke off, looking from Chris to Carin, hoping for amplification or emendation.

"I'll see you tomorrow," Ozzie said.

"Right." Diane walked him to the door, then came back and stood above Chris and Carin. "See you later," she said, and left the room.

"It's so much," Carin said.

"I know."

"What do we know about Washington?"

"Nothing. That might be the best part of it: we'll be tourists for a while." When she didn't answer, he managed a smile and said, "Want to meet the President?" When that got no response, he said, "Even if they don't have a ballet company, I'm sure they've got classes and things like that. All the important companies dance at Kennedy Center."

"I know."

Chris rose. "I have to go tomorrow, no matter what. No more *East Sider,* no more Forty-Eighth Street. For me." She nodded. He reached into his pocket and put something on the coffee table between them.

"What's that?"

"A plane ticket. To Washington. Merry Christmas." Carin stood up. "If you can't use it tomorrow—well, there's no expiration date on it. I'm taking the two o'clock shuttle. There's a shuttle terminal at LaGuardia; any cabdriver knows where it is, but I could pick you up."

"Let me think."

"Sure. Want me to call you in the morning?"

"No. If I can come, I'll be there."

"Like a perfume commercial? Running toward each other in slow motion? Isn't that a little melodramatic?"

"It's easier."

"Than what? Saying no to my face?"

"I don't know what I'm going to say. There's been so much. *Too* much. Philadelphia . . . and Terry . . ." She shrugged helplessly.

"I understand. I'll be at the Eastern shuttle at two."

She nodded, and now for the first time he went to her. He took her hand, and when she permitted that, he put a fingertip under her chin and raised her face toward him. She let him kiss her gently, for a long moment, but when he stepped back, her expression hadn't changed. He took his coat from the chair where he had dropped it and left. Carin stared down at the airline ticket.

TWENTY-SEVEN, two, three, four

Tour en l'air

Carin stretched long and looked at the window. It was no help: the gloomy air shaft always gave back midnight. Twisting, she fumbled for the clock on the night table, then sat up abruptly. She had overslept; it was nearly eleven. She had missed class, she had . . .

Something else on the night table stopped her: the airline ticket, bright and sizable, like the ticket of her childhood that allowed unlimited rides at the amusement park.

She sat up in bed, letting the covers slip. Naked, legs jackknifed against her breasts, arms around her shins, chin on her knees, she stared into the future. Memories, hopes, calculations, fears slid by. Pains resurfaced. And dreams. Chris hovered, his silvery gaze compelling, his swollen flesh crowding her vagina again, his still, sleeping presence making a fortress of this bed. Voices murmured and shouted: her mother's, her grandfather's, Miss Nicholas's, Mrs. Rome's, Diane's, Terry's, Sonny's, Gino's, Chris's . . .

The dome of the Capitol shone, Kennedy Center towered, the Potomac gleamed. The Hudson glowered, Broadway sneered, Eighth Avenue snarled. She looked around the room. The furnace was still on strike; she pulled the covers up around her like a pup tent, but continued to shiver.

She listened: no sound, neither the Advent nor Diane. She looked ahead again: no picture, neither Broadway nor Lincoln Center. No Joffrey, No ABT, no Balanchine. A swinging door flapped, stale aromas wafted: the restaurant on Columbus Avenue—the heavy plates, the hunched diners, heedless unless hungry or horny. She looked back, further: Chris again. Loving, steady, patient—*there*.

She released her knees: her feet sought the floor on their own initiative. They circled the foot of the bed and took her to the closet.

Though bare, they rose almost to full *pointe,* jacking her up six inches, while her hands, equally independent, sought something on the closet shelf. Straining fingers closed on air. Heels dropped, knees bent, and from the *plié* Carin sprang straight up, toes automatically pointing. At the top of the *temps levé,* her hands shot out, hooked a handle and, as she descended to a soft *plié,* the suitcase tumbled down on her. She ducked her head to take the impact on her forearms, and the bag fell to the floor at her feet.

She stared at it, comprehending at last her body's commands, then shook herself, doglike, to try to wake up. Looking toward the closed door, she wondered whether she would need a robe to go to the bathroom. What time had Ozzie said he was coming?

The door opened. Stretching and yawning in one of her outsize T-shirts, Diane mumbled, "Didn't you hear the phone?"

"No. I'm sorry if it woke you. Is it Chris?"

Though Diane was erect, her eyes were closed. Both she and Carin had slept soundly last night, their first unbroken sleep in days, and neither was fully awake. "No," Diane muttered, "Joffrey."

Carin straightened, drowsiness purged. *"Mister* Joffrey?"

"Somebody *from* Joffrey." As Carin raced into the corridor, Diane's knees buckled and she sat on the edge of the bed.

The receiver was hanging from the edge of the table, swinging gently. Carin snatched it up and jumped onto the couch, her legs folded under her. "Hello?"

When she returned to the bedroom, Diane was stretched out on the bed, eyes closed, mouth open, bum bare. Carin shook her and, as always, Diane came up fighting. Ducking an elbow, Carin screeched, "An audition!"

"What . . . ?"

"An audition!"

Diane's eyes opened. "For Joffrey?"

"Yes! Saturday! They're starting to audition again, and they heard about my reviews in Philadelphia . . ."

Diane was on her feet, smothering further communication in a massive embrace. She rocked back on her heels, trying to lift her roommate from the floor, and when she failed in that, settled for pounding her repeatedly on the back, in tempo with hoarse cries of, "I knew it! I knew it!"

"Easy!" Carin gasped. "So far it's just an audition."

"With your talent that's all you need. Wooooooooooooo!" She twirled Carin in a circle, repeating the Valkyrien cry each time she was able to replenish her supply of oxygen.

"Oh, God!" Carin yelped, coming to a halt that nearly capsized them both.

"What's wrong?"

"I haven't been on *pointe* in three months!"

"You never forget. It's like riding a bike."

"I've got to be good enough to get into the company!"

"You can take a class this afternoon."

"But Saturday's only five days away."

"Take *two* classes."

"That's *ten classes!*"

"Honey, if you can't pull yourself together in ten classes . . ."

"I'm talking about paying for them."

"What're you worried about?" It was "Late Show" insouciance, the calm assurance of a madcap heiress.

"What am I *wor*ried about! I came back from Philadelphia with nothing! I don't know how I'm going to come up with my share of this month's rent."

"Not to worry." Katharine Hepburn, definitely. "You seem to forget that I am now gainfully employed."

"You think I'm going to let you wait on tables to pay for my ballet classes?"

"Would you do the same for me?"

"Listen . . ."

Katharine Hepburn metamorphosed miraculously to Edward G. Robinson at his surliest. "Would you do the same for me?"

"Of course."

Katharine returned. "Then it's settled. And if it bothers you, when you sign with Joffrey, I'll live off you for a while. See how simple life is when you don't complicate it?"

Carin looked at the clock. "Ooh! Maybe I can make Madame Eugenia's one o'clock." She circled the foot of the bed in a dash for the closet and fell headlong. Diane vaulted the bed to help her up.

"I'm okay," Carin said, but Diane was staring down at the obstacle that had floored her roommate.

"What's that?"

"My suitcase."

"I know that! What's it doing *there?*"

"You can go ahead of me," Chris said, and a grateful commuter picked up his canvas carry-on and squeezed past Chris to give his ticket to the waiting Eastern agent. The agent tore a strip from the shuttle ticket and indicated the baggage X-ray a few feet away. The commuter flung his bag on the conveyor belt that fed the X-ray and marched through the Friskem.

Chris looked up and down the long corridor that fronted the Washington and Boston shuttle gates. Unlike Chris, most of the travelers scurrying to and fro were encumbered by no more than light carry-ons or briefcases.

The agent leaned toward Chris. "Are you planning to take the two o'clock shuttle, sir?"

"Yes."

"Then I'm afraid you'll have to board."

Chris looked at the clock over the agent's head. It read 1:56. "According to that, I've got four minutes."

"But you've got to go through security—I can't get your bags on this plane as it is."

"Wait!" The distant figure struggling with two familiar suitcases was conspicuous among the lightly accoutred commuters—and unmistakable. "One minute!" Chris shouted at the agent and dashed down the hall, shouting "Hurry!" Panting, he accelerated, and as he pulled up next to the bent figure, he gasped, "You weren't kidding about that perfume commercial . . ."

The traveler looked up, startled. There was no resemblance. None whatsoever. Except in the luggage—and the coat, perhaps. Chris stumbled back a step. "I'm sorry . . ."

Still eyeing him suspiciously, the young woman dragged her suitcases to the Boston shuttle gate.

The face in the mirror stared back, its pallor accenting the pink of the lips, the blue-white clarity of the eyes that were fixed on the eighteen-year-old girl in dark leotard jungle-camouflaged with stains of sweat, damp tights, tattered leg warmers from knee to ankle, and frayed Capezio Tekniks.

The eyes in the mirror darted sideways as the teacher, a dreadnought in gypsy—*real* gypsy—skirt and blouse, prowled along the line of straining dancers at the *barre*, prodding, pointing, hectoring in a stentorian voice and impenetrable Russian accent.

"Annnd *relevé!*" the teacher bellowed. Carin clenched her teeth and rocked up to full *pointe*. The *pointe* shoes closed on her toes like iron maidens despite the soft bed of lamb's wool packed into their boxes.

The teacher paused two dancers away to poke a boy in the ribs and roar, "Pullllll *op!* . . . Stre-e-e-e-etch!" she bawled at the student next to Carin.

Carin's eyes roved to the clock above the mirror. It read 1:59. As she watched, the minute hand jumped to the top of the dial.

"May I eenquire vot ees so eemporrrtant op therrre?"

Carin winced and dropped her gaze. "Nothing."

"You veesh class vass over, maybe."

"No, Madame."

The teacher didn't move. "And *développé!*"

As Carin's leg rose, quivering, tears began to spill on her cheeks.

"Hurrrts, huh?"

"Yes, Madame."

"Ees sup*pose* to!"

Satisfied that she had succinctly summarized this dancer's—any dancer's—life in art, Madame Eugenia stalked away through a thicket of wool: tights, sweaters, leg warmers, stained and tattered as overloved teddy bears.

Carin blinked repeatedly to break the shimmering barrier between herself and the vital image in the mirror at the front of the room. The barrier broke: distortion vanished, order reigned again. *Just this audition. If I flunk it. . . .* She made herself a promise, reasonably sure it was a lie. Time is every dancer's enemy, but Carin knew that for her the clock ticked backward, subtracting precious minutes, hours, years perhaps. In a few months she would be nineteen. Her diabetes would be ten.

An intense act of will brought her back to the dancing figure in the mirror. The head at the tip of the gently waving stalk looked small—too small, Carin decided. Rivulets of sweat ran down muscle-shored channels in the long sweep of neck which had been attenuated by nearly thirteen years of stretching toward an unattainable victory over gravity. Below the neck, the swelling female softness was in striking contrast to the flat abdominal muscles wedged into narrow loins. At the acute angle where hip and leg met, the leg swept skyward, the long adductor, sartorius, rectus and tensor muscles discretely limned under the stretched fabric of the tights.

The leg trembled, reached higher. At the end of it, above Carin's head: the striving foot. Cruelly arched, against nature, against sense. Pulsing in space. Vibrant.

Russian Research Center Studies   60

One Hundred Thousand Tractors

One Hundred Thousand

The MTS and the Development of Controls in Soviet Agriculture

TRACTORS

ROBERT F. MILLER

Harvard University Press, Cambridge, Massachusetts   1970

© 1970 by the President and Fellows of Harvard College
All rights reserved
Distributed in Great Britain by Oxford University Press, London
The Russian Research Center of Harvard University is supported
by a grant from the Ford Foundation. The Center carries out
interdisciplinary study of Russian institutions and behavior
and related subjects.
Library of Congress Catalog Card Number 70–95929
SBN 674–63875–1
Printed in the United States of America

Preface

For nearly thirty years the keystone of the entire Soviet collective farm system was the network of machine-tractor stations (MTS). Despite its prosaic title, the MTS played fundamental roles in the development of the political, administrative, and ideological, as well as the economic foundations of Soviet agriculture. Now, years after the demise of the MTS system itself, its influence can still be discerned in the structural and operational patterns of the agricultural system. Therefore, the story of the MTS, in addition to being of considerable historical interest in its own right, offers many excellent vantage points for studying the overall development of Soviet rule in the village. Many general and specific problems of the Soviet political system can be profitably examined by using the MTS as a focus and a source of data and illustrations. The present study sets for itself this dual task of analyzing the history of the MTS and relating it to major issues of Soviet politics and administration.

One of the broad questions of the Soviet system treated as an underlying theme of the book is the continuing interplay of economic, political, and ideological factors in the formulation and conduct of policy. The history of the MTS is particularly rich in illustrations of this complex interaction. The persistent tensions between economic and political desiderata in agricultural policy were a direct product of the model of economic development adopted by Stalin.* Essentially following the theory of "primitive socialist accumulation" developed by the discredited leftwing economist Evgenii Preobrazhenskii, the Stalinist modal placed the agricultural sector in the role of an internal colony to be exploited for the rapid growth of the heavy industrial and defense sectors.

* For an outstanding discussion of the debates on the model of economic development see Alexander Erlich, *The Soviet Industrialization Debate, 1924–1928* (Cambridge: Harvard University Press, 1960). For a definitive treatment of the specifically agricultural applications of the debates and the contemporary situation in the Soviet village, see Moshe Lewin, *La Paysannerie et le pouvoir soviétique, 1928–1930* (Paris: Mouton et Cie., 1966).

The corollary of severely restricted investment in agriculture meant that a good deal of reliance had to be placed on political pressures to supplement economic incentives for the extraction of the "surplus" produce of the peasants. The MTS, perhaps more than any other Soviet institution, embodied this combination of economic and political pressures. Although conceived originally in primarily economic terms, the stations operated as administrative and political agencies as well. A major goal of the book is to analyze these different roles in depth and to assess their relative importance in the total scheme of agricultural controls. This necessarily entails extensive descriptions of the economic and technical aspects of MTS operations in addition to the political and administrative aspects which are the main concern of the book.

Besides these broad questions of the interaction of economics and politics the book examines a number of more specific problem areas: namely (1) the functions of ideology in the Soviet domestic decision-making process, (2) the principles and practices of Soviet public administration as applied to agriculture, and (3) the development of patterns of Party control in the countryside. The complex of factors involved in the decision to abolish the MTS are also treated as a separate problem area.

The structure of the book basically follows this topical rubric. Part I deals with the historical background of the MTS and its subsequent evolution in Soviet practice. Chapter 2, which is a brief chronological survey of major MTS developments, sets forth the basic periodization followed in the topical discussions of Parts II and III. Part II is devoted to administrative aspects of the role of the MTS, and Part III is devoted to the involvement of the MTS in the system of Party controls in the village. Part IV includes the discussion of the liquidation of the MTS and the general conclusions of the book. Finally, in a brief Epilogue there is a synopsis and evaluation of major developments in Soviet agriculture since the abolition of the MTS.

The first of the specific problem areas, the functions of ideology deserves special treatment in the case of the MTS. In many respects the MTS idea was without precedent in socialist agrarian theory, although certain vague hints can be found. The European social-democratic theorists had attributed an extraordinary role to modern farm machinery, particularly the tractor, for the economic and sociopsychological transformation of the peasantry. This idea was accepted as an article of faith by no less a realist than Lenin himself in his long-range planning for agricultural modernization. Chapter One describes some of the more important European Marxist formulations on the "agrarian question" and the efforts of the Bolsheviks to put them into practice before the beginning of mass collectivization. Early setbacks compelled Lenin and his colleagues to work out some of their own theories and programs under which various forms of cooperation occupied a central position.

The theory of the MTS was eventually constructed on the basis of these early formulations. Chapter 3 is concerned with the development of the ideological model of the MTS-kolkhoz relationship and its subsequent influence on concrete agricultural policy. The discussion attempts to draw certain conclusions on the modes of influence of ideology in the decision-making process from the experience of MTS theory.

The second major problem area, principles and practices of Soviet public administration in agriculture, is the subject of Part II. The problem is handled on two levels: that of the individual station and that of the nationwide MTS system. Chapter 4 concentrates on the internal structure of the individual station and the formal and informal roles of the managerial, technical, and operating personnel. Attention is given to the patterns of change in the internal role structure during successive stages of agricultural policy. The chapter also devotes considerable attention to the changing qualitative characteristics of MTS personnel and their implications for MTS operations.

In Chapter 5 the focus shifts to the MTS network as a subsystem of the general agricultural administrative system. The chapter analyzes the major legal and financial arrangements which were evolved for the regulation of MTS performance and the relationship between the MTS and the kolkhozes. An effort is also made to analyze the function and effects of repeated administrative reorganizations in terms of both the formal principles and informal practices of Soviet administration. Where the evidence is fairly strong, the influence of high-level political infighting is also taken into consideration. Some suggestive illustrations of the Soviet approach to administration are afforded by tracing the course of the prolonged rivalry between the MTS and the raion land organs (raizo) for managerial authority in the kolkhozes.

The third major problem area, the relationship between the MTS and the system of Party controls in the countryside, occupies the longest section of the book. The seven chapters of Part III deal with the nature of Party leadership in the rural raions, the complex division of labor between the local Party and administrative organs, and the special relationship between the raion Party committees (raikoms), the MTS, and the kolkhozes in the management of agricultural production. A central question is the nature and scope of Party activities in and around the MTS and the extent to which the MTS themselves functioned as agents of Party-political control in the village. Part of the answer is sought in data on the changing characteristics of Party leadership personnel attached to the individual stations.

Part IV contains an analysis of the decision to abolish the MTS and some general conclusions on the factors involved in Soviet domestic decision-making. An effort is made to relate these factors in a loose paradigm which suggests possible comparisons with other decision-making systems.

Finally, in an Epilogue, I have tried to assess the most important developments in agricultural policy and politics in the decade following the abolition of the MTS, tracing elements of continuity with problems and practices of the MTS era.

The main outlines of the history of the MTS have been sketched before by both Soviet and Western writers. The principal Western survey of the MTS is that by Roy D. Laird, Darwin E. Sharp, and Ruth Sturtevant, *The Rise and Fall of the MTS as an Instrument of Soviet Rule* (Lawrence, Kansas: University of Kansas Publications, 1960). This book provides a useful summary of the major subsystems of the MTS. Its chief drawback is its brevity, which does not permit an appreciation of the developmental aspects of the MTS and the important changes that occurred during its thirty-year history. Perhaps the best of the many Soviet historical surveys is that by Iu. V. Arutiunian and M. A. Vyltsan, *Istoricheskaia rol' MTS i ikh reorganizatsiia* (Moscow, 1958). Although this book was obviously written as a rather hasty justification of the decision to abolish the MTS, it contains much useful information, and its authors are acknowledged specialists on the economic history of agriculture in the Soviet period with numerous important works to their credit.

In addition to these general surveys certain individual aspects of the role of the MTS were given scholarly attention in the Western (mainly economics) literature on Soviet agriculture during the lifetime of the MTS. Good examples are the sections on the MTS in Lazar Volin's *A Survey of Soviet Agriculture,* Agriculture Monograph 5 (Washington, D.C.: U.S. Department of Agriculture, 1951), pp. 55–69; and Naum Jasny's monumental work, *The Socialized Agriculture of the USSR: Plans and Performance* (Stanford, California: Stanford University Press, 1949), esp. Chap. 12. There have also been a number of worthwhile non-Soviet treatments of the rural Party and government organs, including some which touch upon the role of the MTS in the system of local controls. Examples are Merle Fainsod's *Smolensk Under Soviet Rule* (Cambridge, Massachusetts: Harvard University Press, 1958) and Sidney Harcave, *Structure and Functioning of the Lower Party Organizations in the Soviet Union* (Maxwell Air Force Base, Alabama: Human Resources Research Institute, 1954), not to mention the myriad general textbooks on Soviet government and politics.

All of these studies are useful as far as they go. In general, however, the historical surveys lack sufficient analytical depth, and the selective studies are too narrowly focussed, to provide a comprehensive perspective on the overall patterns of Soviet rule in the countryside and the position of the MTS in these patterns. It is my fervent hope that the present work will help to fill in many of the gaps in our knowledge of this perennially critical area of the Soviet system.

The book is the product of an extensive rethinking and reformulation of a Ph.D. dissertation in the Department of Government at Harvard University, completed in the spring of 1964. Five years of teaching, research, reading, thinking, and conversation about the Soviet system and about political science in general have inevitably caused me to change a number of my original assumptions, criteria of judgment, and, indeed, some of my conclusions. The loss in timeliness of the subject matter has, I think, been more than compensated by the additional insights gained — in part from personal experience in American agriculture which has heightened my appreciation of some of the problems of Soviet farmers. Mechanical breakdowns, delays, and mistakes of judgment are, alas, not unique to Soviet agriculture. I have found myself approaching the completion stages of the study with a good deal more humility than I did when first considering a topic for my dissertation.

The list of persons and institutions to which I am indebted for assistance at various stages of my project is a long one. Among the individuals to whom I owe particular debts of gratitude Adam Ulam occupies a special place. As a teacher, adviser, critic, friend, and occasional tennis partner, he has invariably been able to provide just the right mixture of advice, encouragement, and humor to make the problems I encountered in my work seem manageable. Merle Fainsod has offered valuable comments and suggestions at various stages of the dissertation and the book. Jerry Hough has given me many useful insights into local Party and governmental relationships from his vast store of knowledge of the Soviet industrial scene. I should also like to thank John H. Kautsky of Washington University (St. Louis) and Howard Scarrow and Charles Levine of the State University of New York at Stony Brook for their comments on sections of the manuscript. Finally, I wish to express my thanks to the Soviet scholars who aided me with their advice on research problems and generally facilitated my work in the Soviet Union. Although we did not always see eye to eye on interpretations of data, their help was highly professional and in the best traditions of international scholarly cooperation. Responsibility for the assertions and interpretations made in the book is, of course, solely my own.

Among the institutions and agencies which have given me support I am particularly indebted to the Inter-University Committee on Travel Grants for their administrative and financial assistance in connection with my research in the USSR. The Foreign Area Training Fellowship program made it possible for me to write up my findings and complete my dissertation before embarking on my teaching career — a boon for which I shall always be grateful. Throughout my career as a graduate student and fledgling scholar I have been indebted in one way or another to the Russian Research Center at Harvard University. The Center has provided me with generous support in finances and facilities at various stages in the preparation of the manuscript. I am especially grateful to Helen Parsons for making my many, but all too brief, periods of association with the RRC pleasant and fruitful. Rose DiBenedetto deserves a special word of thanks for her patience and cheerful diligence in typing the final draft of the manuscript.

Finally, I should like to express a few words of appreciation to my wife, Ellen. Although she helped with some of the typing of early drafts, her main contributions were in less tangible matters. Most of all I am grateful for her kindness, fortitude, and resourcefulness in making life pleasant no matter what the external circumstances. Without her, I can truthfully say, this book would not have been written.

Contents

xiii

Figures

Tables

Part I Historical and Ideological

Foundations

If tomorrow we could supply one hundred thousand first-class tractors, provide them with fuel, provide them with drivers — you know very well that this at present is sheer fantasy — the middle peasant would say: "I am for the kommunia" *(i.e., for Communism)* . . .

Lenin

1 The Prehistory of the MTS

Among major Soviet economic and political institutions the machine-tractor station (MTS) was certainly one of the least directly foreshadowed in the theoretical and programmatic literature of Marxian socialism. Indeed, the MTS idea was an answer to a problem that, according to Marx, was not supposed to exist by the time a society was ripe for a socialist revolution: namely, the problem of the social, economic, and psychological transformation of a traditional peasant majority. This is not to say that the MTS concept was un-Marxian. On the contrary, the MTS clearly represented an adaptation of Marxian concepts to Soviet conditions. In particular it reaffirmed the Marxian faith in the socializing power of modern machinery.

Marx, no less than the Manchester Liberals he criticized, was decidedly a child of the Industrial Revolution. He shared their unbounded optimism over the material progress and radical social transformations made possible by modern science and technology. His examination of the history of the English Enclosure Acts and the concentration of farm ownership which ensued had led him to the conclusion that the laws of capitalist development applied with no less force to agriculture than to industry. Indeed, he felt that capitalist development in the two sectors was necessarily simultaneous and complementary. The countryside provided the urban industrial sector with labor, foodstuffs, and raw material, and the towns furnished the countryside with machines and manufactured goods in return.[1] In agriculture as in industry, he saw as an inevitable tendency the crowding out of the small-scale, independent producer. Those peasants who remained on the land would be reduced to the status of rural proletarians, not essentially different in life-style and attitude from their urban brethren of the same class. By the time capitalist socioeconomic conditions had been driven to the point of revolution by their own inner

3

dynamic, he predicted, the peasant question would have ceased to exist. In *The Communist Manifesto* Marx had proclaimed his disdain for the "idiocy of rural life." This would remain his basic attitude toward the peasantry as a potential element among the social forces in the coming proletarian revolution. True, in his *Eighteenth Brumaire* Marx would devote considerable attention, and even a little sympathy, to the actions and the fate of the French peasants during the rise of the Second Empire. But here, too, the prevailing tone was essentially one of contempt — he characterized French peasant society as constituting a social entity only in the sense that "potatoes in a sack form a sack of potatoes." [2] History had doomed the peasants to inevitable extinction, and there was little point in giving them serious thought in the scheme of socialist revolution.

For political and perhaps temperamental reason, Marx's alter ego, Friedrich Engels, was less inclined to dispose of the agrarian question contemptuously. In his "Anti-Dühring" Engels took special pains to discuss the increasing tensions between town and country resulting from the top-heavy concentration of scientific, technological, and cultural development in the urban centers.[3] He came to the conclusion, not unimportant despite its obvious-ness, that the peasant, even as rural proletarian, was doomed to an inferior state of existence and, hence, consciousness under capi-talism. The implications of a sizable, relatively conservative mass, standing outside the mainstream of revolutionary development, were of course tremendous, especially when practical political strategy became an important issue.

By the end of the nineteenth century the agrarian question had indeed become a matter of more than theoretical interest for the European social democrats. The German Social Democratic Party was already a strong contender for political power, and Engels, as its elder statesman, found it necessary to help formulate a workable peasant policy. In one of his last major works, *The Peasant Question in France and Germany*, he attempted to come to grips with the problem of peasant psychology and its antisocial-its bias, which he attributed to a "deep-rooted sense of property." [4] Engels asked what social democracy could legitimately offer the peasant to overcome these prejudices or at least to neutralize him in the coming struggle for power. It could guarantee him against forcible expropriation, but it could hardly promise support for his private farm in a future socialist state. Engels was confident that sooner or later the peasant would see for himself that only large-scale, cooperative farming on a mechanized basis could save him from ruin. To facilitate the learning process, Engels suggested the retention by the victorious socialist state of large estates, which would then be transformed into model cooperative farms. The latter would, it was hoped, attract the peasants to socialism.[5] Lenin attempted to carry out such a program immediately after the Bolshevik Revolution.

In the meantime the contemporary agricultural cooperative movement was treated as a particular bête noire by the orthodox European social democrats. They repeatedly called attention to its basically capitalistic modes of operations, fearing that it might actually hinder the ultimate social transformation of the peasants by keeping them in an intermediate stage of "group capitalism" and protecting them from the worst evils of an atomized society under capitalism. Thus, Engels would write, in a letter to August Bebel which is often cited by Soviet authors as a direct foreshadowing of the MTS concept, that cooperative production was at best a way station on the road to socialism in agriculture.

Marx and I never doubted this. But the matter should be so arranged that society — consequently, in the initial stage the state — will retain for itself the ownership of the means of production and, thus, the private interests of the cooperative associations would not gain sway over the interests of society as a whole.[6]

That the superiorities of heavily capitalized collective farming would be overwhelmingly convincing to the peasants Engels obviously took for granted. To him this was hardly a problem! The real task was to ensure that the activities of the cooperatives were properly channeled into the mainstream of the socialist economy. His solution was to maintain state ownership of the main means of production — the land, machinery, production buildings, and so forth. As Soviet experience would show, the problem of inducing the peasants to join cooperatives, especially those sponsored by the socialist state, was itself far from simple. The entire formulation of the question pointed up the extreme rationalism of the orthodox Marxists, a rationalism they shared with the early theorists of capitalism from whom they had borrowed so many of their doctrinal principles, a rationalism that ill prepared them to cope with the complex motivational structure of the peasantry.

Indeed, the obvious incorrectness of Marx's predictions on agricultural evolution became a serious issue among leading socialists toward the end of the century. Prominent agrarian theorists, such as Eduard David and Werner Sombart, were asserting that the intensiveness of small-scale farming and the seasonal nature of agricultural work suggested that the role of the machine in agriculture had been greatly exaggerated by Marx. It seemed that entirely different economic laws were operating in the agricultural sector. The implications were tremendous for Marx's theory of the inevitable proletarianization and revolutionary awakening of the peasant masses and, consequently, for the prospects of revolution itself. For orthodox revolutionary Marxists, especially those from predominantly rural Russia, these were obviously vital questions.

The challenges to Marx on the agrarian question did not long go unanswered. Some of the most prominent leaders of the social democratic movement, for example, Karl Kautsky and Emile Vandervelde, made strenuous efforts to refute the arguments of the critics. Needless to say, these counterattacks were followed eagerly by the leaders of the Russian movement.[7] Probably the most important of the refutational works was Karl Kautsky's *Die Agrarfrage*. In it Kautsky conceded that Marx had perhaps given insufficient attention to the concrete details of agriculural development. He pointed out rather lamely that most of the complications had, after all, set in after Marx's death. From his own researches, however, Kautsky concluded that although Marx had probably been imprecise in predicting the simultaneous development of capitalism in industry and agriculture, he had certainly been correct as far as the general nature and direction of the process were concerned. In short, agriculture was merely lagging behind industry on the same path of capitalist development.[8]

Of crucial signicance for our purposes was Kautsky's treatment of the role of modern machinery in agriculture. Although admitting that the critics were partially correct on the problems of intensive utilization of expensive modern machinery in agriculture, he nevertheless upheld the superiority of modern methods over traditional methods of farming. Such advances as the deep-plowing techniques made possible by the new steam plows, he asserted, had introduced the prospect of truly revolutionary changes in the methods and potential output of agricultural production.[9] Capitalist experience had shown that the potential of mechanized farming could be realized only in large-scale operations. However, only the socialist state, the epitome of economic concentration and rationalization, would be able to apply these lessons consistently.

With this odd mixture of empirical and normative observations, Kautsky at once rehabilitated Marxism as a prediction of economic development and conceded its weaknesses as a prediction of revolutionary political development. On the one hand, he had demonstrated fairly cogently that Marxist theory with its stress on the "logic" of the machine was, despite appearances, being vindicated in agriculture as well as in industry. On the other hand, he had been forced to admit that the process of transformation in agriculture was much attenuated and was likely to remain so as long as the capitalist mode of ownership with its requirements of a standard high rate of return on investment continued to exist. The victorious proletariat would, in other words, have much work to do in completing the social and economic transformation of the village after the revolution.

While the arguments of Kautsky, Vandervelde, and others might have provided a good deal of solace to social-democratic politicians in the advanced Western countries, where the active revolutionary assistance of the peasants was important but not necessarily decisive, how much satisfaction could these arguments have afforded their counterparts in Russia, a country where the peasants formed 80 percent of the population?[10]

THE RUSSIAN MARXISTS AND THE AGRARIAN QUESTION

There is no need here to elaborate on how Marxism was able to gain so strong a foothold in backward peasant Russia. Adam Ulam and others have presented fairly convincing explanations of the peculiar attractions of Marxism in underdeveloped societies, where one would least expect to find it.[11] Russian agriculture was so primitive that the major agrarian questions of interest to the Western Marxists — the impact of modern machinery, the social and economic consequences of various forms of cooperation, the role of the state in agricultural development — had no real meaning. Yet the Russian Marxists for a number of reasons, not all of them valid, chose to express themselves in the terms and categories of the European debates. Because the objective conditions of Russia were so very unique, however, the Russian Marxists were eventually forced to develop programs and formulations of their own.

The primary symbol of Russian agricultural backwardness was the continued existence of the *obshchina,* the village commune, as the dominant system of land tenure in most of Imperial Russia at the end of the nineteenth century. The Emancipation of 1861 had actually strengthened the commune by attaching to it the land detached from the landlords' estates rather than giving the land to the individual peasant households. In theory the commune was the sole owner of the land, periodically redistributing individual parcels for cultivation among the member households. Nevertheless, there was a marked tendency toward the disintegration of the communes. Redistribution of the land became less and less regular, and the more enterprising of the peasants found many ways to circumvent the restrictions of joint ownership. As the century drew to a close, Russian land-ownership practices seemed unmistakably to be following the path of other European societies.[12]

The Russian revolutionary Marxists were ambivalent in their attitude toward the commune. Under the strong Populist influences that had held sway over many of their number before their conversion to Marxism, they had at first entertained the hope that Russia might be able to avoid the horrors of capitalism by a "great leap" from the commune, with its quasi-communist attitudinal patterns, to socialism.[13] It soon became obvious that this hope was illusory. The continuing rapid disintegration of the commune and the decidedly unrevolutionary response of the peasants to the famine of 1891–1892 evoked a decidedly antipeasant reaction among many of the Russian progressives and radicals.[14] Their attitude was perhaps best exemplified by Georgii V. Plekhanov, the "Father of Russian Marxism." By the turn of the century Plekhanov had severed all connections with his Populist past. In a review of Vandervelde's *La Propriété foncière en Belgique,* he explicitly set himself apart from "those Russians attempting to prove the possibility of the transformation of our rural commune 'into a higher form of community.' " [15]

As the century ended, therefore, the Russian Marxists found themselves in an uncomfortable position. The stronger and more radically oriented they became, the less promising appeared their opportunities for effective revolutionary action in Marxist terms. The proletariat was growing rapidly, but it could not hope to become a decisive political force for many years to come. This lack of a really promising, "objectively" revolutionary situation was to have an important influence on the character of the Russian Marxist movement, especially its radical Bolshevik wing. The frustrations of the latter over the underdeveloped state of the economic and social components of the revolutionary matrix led them to exalt the political component. The result was that theoretical economic issues which were genuinely relevant to the western European social and political situation were in Russia often merely polemical rallying points in the interminable factional struggles. This instrumental use of theoretical argument as a screen for political infighting was to become standard procedure in the politics of Bolshevism, and nowhere more frequently than in the agrarian sphere.

With Plekhanov at their head it is not surprising that the Russian social democrats should have been the least willing of all the radical groups to offer concessions in their political programs to the peasantry. Plekhanov was even more negative than his Western colleagues in his assessment of the possibilities of cooperatives as instruments of social transformation. He charitably conferred upon the leftwing supporters of the Russian cooperative movement the title of "socialist-reactionaries." [16] Driven by his own past disappointments in dealing with the backward Russian peasantry, Plekhanov had clearly taken refuge in an extremely rigid and dogmatic reading of Marxism. Russia's only course was to endure the purgatory of capitalism, and anything that promised to ease the plight of the peasant was to be vigorously condemned.

Plekhanov's sometime protégé, Vladimir Ilich Lenin, did not at this time differ essentially with his mentor on the peasant question, although he does seem to have displayed more interest in it than did many of his Russian colleagues. Before 1903 Lenin, too, placed almost exclusive emphasis for the revolutionary future on the small but rapidly growing urban proletariat. He saw in the peasantry a hodgepodge of interests basically antagonistic to the working class.[17] During this period Lenin hoped for the swiftest possible victory of capitalism in the village. He saw no sense in trying to prop up the disintegrating commune by material aid and cooperative organization, as some contemporary reformers were urging. In a review of Kautsky's *Die Agrarfrage* he warmly seconded the author's assertion that the victory of large-scale, mechanized capitalist farming was inevitable — and desirable.[18]

On the question of the role of the machine in agriculture, Lenin appeared to be strongly attracted by the prospect of its socializing power. He explicity stated his faith in mechanization as the key to the eventual socioeconomic transformation of the Russian peasant.[19] Unlike many others, however, Lenin sought some kind of empirical confirmation for the theory. Thus, on the basis of statistical data from Pskov Guberniia in 1899, he found it possible to predict that

the hiring of machines which accustom the householders to the common use of machinery, in all probability, is only a transitional stage toward a new form of organization of the machinery inventory of the farms, in which only a part of this inventory will be the personal property of each particular household, and the most expensive part of the inventory, consisting of machines able to serve a whole group of households (threshers, flaxbrakes), will be acquired by whole groups . . .[20]

Capitalism would bring the machines, and the machines would bring the social and psychological changes required for the victory of socialism in the countryside. The elimination of capitalism by the October Revolution did not weaken Lenin's faith in the transformational efficacy of the machine. The proletarian state would simply assume the functions of the private capitalists. Nicholas Berdyaev has, rightly or wrongly, characterized Lenin's tremendous fascination with this mechanistic aspect of Marxism as a peculiarly Russian phenomenon:

Lenin could not realize his plan of revolution and seizure of power without a change in the soul of the people. This change was so great that the people who had lived by irrational fate suddenly went almost mad about the rationalization of the whole of life without exception. They believe in a machine instead of in God. The Russian people having emerged from the period of being rooted in the soil and living under its mystic domination, entered upon a technical period in which it believed in the almighty power of the machine, and by the force of ancient instinct began to treat the machine like a totem. Such switchings over are possible in the soul of a people.[21]

After his break with Plekhanov and the majority of the Russian social democrats over the issue of his revolutionary elitism, Lenin became progressively more interested in the peasantry as a source of revolutionary social material. A major turning point in his attitude was the 1905 Revolution and the unexpectedly radical behavior of the peasants against the existing order. The wave of peasant uprisings in 1905 convinced Lenin that the muzhik was not merely a potential auxiliary of the proletariat but a central force in his own right in any readily conceivable revolution against the Autocracy. For a long time he would remain virtually alone among Russian revolutionary Marxists in his perception of this fact.[22]

The proclamation in 1907 of the Stolypin Reforms threw Lenin into a state of near panic. He feared that these reforms, the objective of which was to break up the village communes and create a stable farmer class as a bulwark of the Autocracy, would indeed remove the peasantry from the revolutionary camp. Consequently, he launched a vigorous attack against the reforms, employing a variety of dubious arguments to discredit them.[23] Despite the obvious opportunism of his objections and the pitifully small likelihood that they could have any effect on the progress of the Stolypin program, many of the ideas expounded by Lenin during this period are of considerable value for the insights they provide into his conceptions of agricultural development. Of particular interest are his numerous commentaries on the evolution of capitalism in American agriculture. One of his major analytical works on agriculture bore the title "Capitalism and Agriculture in the United States." Written in 1915 at a time when Lenin despaired of seeing a successful revolution in his homeland during his lifetime, this work was perhaps more seriously objective and analytical than a good many of his writings. In it he returned to the problem of concentration in the ownership patterns of farms in modern capitalist states. He addressed himself to the seeming paradox of increasing capital growth in small owner-operated farms in the United States and concluded that concentration could have a qualitative as well as a quantitative dimension. Thus, in the American context the basic mode of capitalist development was the progressive accretion of machinery and technology in the small farm, which thus became a large farm in terms of scale of production.[24] He added the observation, however, that the small size of the typical American farm did place finite limits on the effectiveness of capital utilization and that concentration of land was still the ultimate prerequisite for optimum agricultural production.

On the broader question of the lag of agricultural development behind industrial development and its significance for the socialist revolution, Lenin asserted that the level of development was not really an important obstacle. (This argument would be used later to justify the New Economic Policy [NEP].) Citing the American case, he noted that even in that relatively advanced capitalist country manual labor was still dominant in agriculture, but that this fact did not

in any way prove the impossibility of socializing agricultural production even at the present stage of its development. Those who control the banks *directly* control one-third of all the farms in America, and, consequently, indirectly dominate them all. The organization of production according to a simple general plan on a million farms supplying more than half the total agricultural output is absolutely feasible at the present level of development of all kinds of associations and the technique of communications and transportation.[25] [Emphasis in original.]

Because in 1915 the revolution in Russia seemed far off indeed, the American model evidently appeared to Lenin to possess a good deal of relevance, especially if the Stolypin Reforms continued. In Russia, too, it was reasonable to expect that capitalism would prepare the "commanding heights" of the economy for eventual seizure by the victorious proletariat, thus facilitating the effective socialization of agricultural production.

If this conception of socialization appears rather shallow and formalistic, it can hardly be called un-Marxian. The Western Marxists had long before conceded that the full transformation of the village would probably occur only after the revolution, necessitating conscious guidance by the proletarian state. In any case, from his vantage point in exile in 1915, Lenin saw the proletarian revolution as being decades away. In the meantime there was every reason to believe that the development of capitalism in the Russian village would have traveled far in the American direction.

THE REVOLUTION AND THE BOLSHEVIK AGRARIAN PROGRAM

This less than exciting (for a man of Lenin's activist temperament) long-range prospect was abruptly and radically altered by the February Revolution. Returning from exile in April 1917, Lenin was again far in advance of his colleagues in perceiving the new set of opportunities. Revolutionary politics, the preparation for a rapid seizure of power, took precedence over objective consideration of economic and social preconditions. Lenin saw as one of the most crucial tasks of the Bolsheviks the encouragement of chaos in the village and the prevention of any consolidation of property interests.[26] Unlike the Socialist Revolutionaries and the Mensheviks, who had quickly acquired a stake in the Provisional Government, he openly encouraged the seizure of land by the peasants.

There is no need here to recount the events of the Bolshevik seizure of power. While it would be something of an exaggeration to say that Lenin and his supporters rode to power on the backs of the peasants, they were quick to take maximum advantage of a situation no one could hope to control. One of Lenin's first acts on the morrow of the Bolshevik coup was to issue a Decree on Land, the first formal agrarian program by a ruling socialist government. Although much of the decree was merely a ratification of the inevitable — indeed, a large section was admittedly a Social Revolutionary (SR) program which that party had previously drawn up in response to peasant demands — it did place on record certain programmatic commitments which would eventually have significance for the socialization of the village. For example, private ownership of land was abolished. The estates of the landlords, the crown, and the church were to be confiscated without compensation. Efficient, modernized, large estates were to be preserved intact for use as demonstration points under state control.[27] For the moment the most forceful of these measures necessarily remained in the verbal realm because of pressing foreign and domestic political problems.

Nevertheless, the more serious aspects of the agricultural and peasant questions could not long be ignored. As they confronted the realities of the Russian countryside, Lenin and his colleagues soon became aware of how poorly prepared they were, both theoretically and materially, for the tremendous social and economic tasks ahead. The Western socialist agrarian theory from which they began was surely of dubious relevance and validity. Nevertheless, it did provide them with a vague model of a future socialist agricultural system. What is surprising is the extent to which they adhered to this model, despite the overwhelming difficulties encountered in trying to impose it on reality.

Essentially, the model was that of a nationwide system of large, factorylike farms, situated on state-owned land and utilizing the most modern machinery, artificial fertilizers, selected seed, and agronomic technique. The labor force was to consist of relatively small numbers of highly skilled, class-conscious proletarians, working under the direction of democratically elected managers with specialized agronomic training. Either state- or cooperatively owned, these "farm-factories" would be totally integrated into the national economy through general plans of investment, production, and product exchange, preferably not involving the use of money.

It was assumed that sufficient impetus for the achievement of the model could be obtained by setting up a number of seminal demonstration points on strategically located estates. These sparklingly efficient enterprises would, by their example, win the surrounding peasants over to the system. This was the rationale for the retention of the estates. However, as a practical matter, even such a limited pilot project would have required at least a basic fund of machinery and equipment, not to mention a corps of trained managers and specialists. Furthermore, a substantial length of time under ideal operating conditions would have been necessary before any material or psychological profit could be anticipated. Needless to say, none of these prerequisites were available. The onset of civil war and the rapid disintegration of the estates at the hands of the local peasants made even a beginning virtually impossible.

WAR COMMUNISM

As Lenin well knew, the food crisis had been a key factor in the collapse of both the Tsarist and the Provisional Governments. It was clear that the spread of anarchy in the countryside, which the Bolsheviks had previously encouraged, had to be checked. At first he had followed a scrupulously nonantagonistic policy toward the peasants,[28] and there is considerable evidence that he would have preferred to continue the gradualistic, permissive strategy consonant with the model.[29] By the middle of 1918, however, with the rapid spread of the Civil War, the provision of food supplies for the Red Army and for the hard-pressed urban population became paramount concerns.

Lenin therefore found it necessary to adopt a policy of forcible extraction of peasant grain supplies. Anticipating methods that would be used a decade later during the mass collectivization campaign, Lenin resorted to the active fomentation of class warfare in the village, utilizing the poorer elements to aid in uncovering and removing the "surpluses" of their more prosperous neighbors. In May he ordered the establishment of a Food Dictatorship with a state monopoly of the grain trade. The decree summoned "all toilers and needy peasants to immediate unification for a merciless struggle with the kulaks." [30] This appeal was subsequently institutionalized in a decree of June 11, "On the Organization and Supply of the Village Poor," which ordered the creation of special operational Committees of the Village Poor (abbreviated in the Russian as *kombedy*) at the township and village levels.[31] Acting under the direction of Party officials and in conjunction with the detachments of armed workers organized in the so-called Food Army, the *kombedy* carried on vigorous activities in the village during the six months of their existence. Besides assisting in the forcible confiscation of peasant grain supplies, they brought about a radical redistribution of land and farm implements previously seized by the peasants from the former landlords' estates.[32] At the time it seemed to many that this and other activities during War Communism represented true communism in action.* In recent Soviet historiography, however, there has been a tendency to reassess some of the early policies of the regime. It is now conceded by some that the formation of the *kombedy* may have been a mistake.[33] The violence and arbitrariness associated with the *kombedy,* commonly comprising the dregs of village society, tended to discredit Bolshevik rule in general.[34] At any rate, in a relatively short time the evidence of peasant alienation had become so overwhelming that the regime was compelled to liquidate the *kombedy* (except in the Ukraine), and in November of 1918 they were, by order, fused with the local soviets.

This move did not by any means imply a change in the basic policy of food requisitions. The apparent simplicity of requisitioning as a method of grain procurement appears to have attracted a number of high Party leaders who saw it as a short cut to the achievement of the ideological desideratum of direct exchange between city and country — not that the city was offering anything as its part of the bargain. Thus, A. G. Shlikhter, the Extraordinary Commissar of Food, who was in charge of the requisition campaigns, asserted in an interview that even under normal trade conditions the peasants would sell only enough of their crops to

---

* Victor Serge has given us an excellent description of the atmosphere of euphoria during War Communism in the following passage from his *Memoirs*:

"The social system in these years was later called 'War Communism.' At the time it was simply called 'Communism,' and anyone who, like myself, went so far as to consider it purely temporary was looked upon with disdain. Trotsky had just written that this system would last over several decades if the transition to a genuine, unfettered Socialism was to be assured. Bukharin was writing his work on *The Economy in the Period of Transition,* whose schematic Marxism aroused Lenin's ire. He considered the present mode of organization to be final. And yet, all the time it was becoming simply impossible to live within it: impossible, not of course for the administrators, but for the mass of the population. In fact, in order to eat it was necessary to resort, daily and without interruption, to the black market; the Communists did it like everyone else. Bank notes were no longer worth anything, and ingenious theoreticians spoke of the coming abolition of money. There was no paper or coloured ink to print stamps: 'a new step in the realization of Socialism'" (Victor Serge, *Memoirs of a Revolutionary, 1901–1941,* translated and edited by Peter Sedgwick [London: Oxford University Press, 1963], p. 155.

pay for essential manufactured goods. This would be far less than the total amount of their surplus produce and far less than state requirements for food and fiber. Consequently, he declared himself in favor of the use of extractive methods as a more or less permanent adjunct to normal commercial methods.[35]

Lenin, it should be pointed out, was not seduced by these supposed short cuts to socialism. He was aware that sooner or later the peasants would retaliate against the requisition policy by cutting back on their sown area. At the Eighth Party Congress in March 1919 he cautioned specifically against making virtues out of the necessities of War Communism. He warned that the existing policies of requisitions and ill-prepared collectivization were alienating the masses of middle peasants upon whom the country would have to rely indefinitely for its food supplies.[36] These jeremiads went unheeded, however, and the congress gave a vote of confidence to the existing policies and to the speediest possible introduction of socialist forms of agriculture as the only solution to the food problem.[37]

Among the various measures proposed for "telescoping" the revolution in the village during War Communism, the policies concerning farm machinery were of particular interest. Throughout the period the policy of treating modern machinery as a trump card for state controlled social transformation in the village was fairly consistently observed. A decree of November 30, 1917, established a state monopoly over the disposition of all agricultural machinery in the country.[38] In the same vein the Eighth Party Congress, although committing the Party to a policy of aiding the middle peasants in certain specified ways, explicitly excluded sales of machinery, offering only to set up state-owned rental points and repair stations to provide services under controlled conditions. Nowhere was the rationale behind this special handling of machinery more outspokenly stated than in Lenin's main address to the congress. His words were to become a standard reference in the Soviet literature on the MTS: "If tomorrow we could supply one hundred thousand first-class tractors, provide them with fuel, provide them with drivers — you know very well that this is at present sheer fantasy — the middle peasant would say: 'I am for the *kommunia*' (that is, for Communism) [*sic*] . . ."[39] In the context of the Civil War and the chaotic conditions of agriculture and industry in the country, such reflections were indeed "sheer fantasy." Meanwhile, the requisitions continued, and the peasants, as Lenin had predicted, responded by cutting back their sown area.[40] The time was obviously far from ripe for long-range programs of economic and social development.

In many respects War Communism was a dress rehearsal for the tragedies of mass collectivization and the system of agricultural administration that followed in its wake. During these early years Soviet agricultural officials began to display some of the traits of the so-called administrative style of leadership. Orders and commands were issued from the center with minimal concern for, or understanding of, local conditions and the operational capabilities of the local cadres. Furthermore, given the status configuration of the proletarian dictatorship, service in the agricultural administration was hardly considered an attractive assignment for the ambitious young bureaucrat. And the strongest, most dedicated local official was likely to become demoralized by the task of imposing central policies on a skeptical, often actively hostile local population. Even assuming that a meaningful, consistent nationwide agricultural policy could have been devised for a country the size of the Soviet Union, the network of administrators was not strong enough to carry it out.[41]

Accordingly, it was during War Communism that the practice began of dispatching contingents of urban Party officials and trusted workers to the villages to assist the local officials in enforcing central directives. The stories of the Party plenipotentiaries (*upolnomochennye*) and the Food Army and their disruptive effects on the local authority structure during the War Communism period would have their parallels throughout the history of the Soviet agricultural system.

THE NEW ECONOMIC POLICY

The Kronstadt uprising in March 1921 finally brought home to most of the Bolshevik leaders the realization that they were on a collision course with the major forces of Russian society. It was suddenly crystal clear that the apparent congruence of political, economic, and ideological requirement which had made War

Communism seem so close to the ultimate goals had been an illusion. The economy, particularly its agricultural sector, was a shambles. Lenin was now able to argue convincingly that the entire Bolshevik power edifice, despite its victory in the Civil War, would surely be brought down if drastic changes were not made immediately.

It was more than obvious that the agrarian question was the crucial variable in the Bolshevik power equation. Further discrimination against the peasantry would be politically, as well as economically, disastrous. Thus, at the Tenth Party Congress Lenin called for a fundamental shift in the orientation of agricultural policy from procurements to the stimulation of production, from primary reliance on political compulsion to economic incentives. Ignoring his own past arguments on the eve of the seizure of power, Lenin now told the leftwing opponents of new policies that Russia was not yet even a capitalist country. Before any meaningful transition to socialism could be effected, the material and socio-psychological preconditions would have to be carefully prepared. NEP was thus admittedly a retreat to a presocialist stage, especially in agriculture. Any program of rapid collectivization of the individual peasant farms would have to be postponed indefinitely.

The new policies were introduced under the slogan of "restoring the bond [smychka] between town and country," that is, the re-establishment of trade links between the producers of food and the producers of industrial goods. The food requisition policy was replaced by a tax in kind on peasant produce designed to leave the peasants with a substantial surplus to trade for consumer goods and other manufactured essentials. The tax was progressive, based on the size of the harvest of the individual peasant household with adjustments for the number of mouths to be fed.[42] Freedom to dispose of the after-tax surplus on the open market was guaranteed, but special incentives in the form of implements and consumer goods from state reserves were to be offered to those who agreed to sell their surplus directly to the state. The intention was to utilize commercial processes to attract a sufficient supply of grain to pay for the restoration and future development of Soviet industry.[43] The theory was that because Russian agriculture was so primitive, it would require only a minimal investment to restore its productive capacity. Also, because the types of industry which supplied the relatively simple range of products demanded by the peasant were among the least capital intensive, the "bond" could be effected at modest cost.

But if the economic arguments for NEP were fairly attractive, the political implications were far less comforting. As Marxists, the Bolsheviks were acutely sensitive to the political dangers that might arise from granting substantial economic freedom to the peasantry. Lenin fully acknowledged this problem. He admitted that "it would be ridiculous to shut our eyes to it." [44] But he assured his critics that since political power was to be retained securely in the hands of the proletariat, any dangerous situation could be safely contained. At the same time it was necessary to develop measures to direct the anticipated flow of urban-rural trade into safe, state-controlled channels.

Lenin's assurances on the manageability of the economic relaxation were not fully borne out in practice. The disastrous famine of 1921 necessitated a substantial expansion of the concessions to the private peasants to provide the initial impetus for recovery. Thus, a decree of the Ninth All-Russian Congress of Soviets in December 1921 gave the peasants a free choice of their system of land tenure in a given area, not excluding even the Stolypin type of individual farmsteads. [45] The new Land Tenure Law of May 22, 1922, permitted the rental of land and the hiring of labor. The law went so far as to give tacit enouragement to the liquidation of inefficient collective farms. [46] Even the previously sacrosanct policy toward farm machinery distribution was significantly relaxed, and the acquisition of complex machines and implements was made a simple commercial transaction. The surviving collective and state farms were even deprived of their special privileges in the acquisition of scarce farm machinery, being required to purchase machines in competition with others, rather than receive them gratis as in the past. [47]

The excellent harvest of 1922 seemed to justify the expanded concessions and to reinforce the arguments of those, like Nikolai Bukharin, who favored a very liberal peasant policy. Total grain procurements in 1922 were three times those of 1921, and production recovered from less than half of the 1913 level to approximately two-thirds.[48] Because of the tremendous backlog of demand in the village for manufactured goods resulting from the scarcities of the wartime and Civil War periods, the peasants were buying up virtually everything industry could produce, regardless of price. For a brief time it appeared that NEP was working at least as well as anticipated.

This favorable situation could not endure indefinitely, however, for it was implicitly grounded on the questionable expectation of continuing inelasticity of peasant demand. The inordinately high prices of domestic manufactures, protected by the state monopoly of foreign trade — an application of Evgenii Preobrazhenskii's theory of "primitive socialist accumulation" — began to depress peasant demand once immediate requirements had been satisfied. Furthermore, the initial increase in the quantity of grain brought to market was inevitably followed by a decrease in grain prices, making the peasants doubly reluctant to offer their surpluses. The result was that in the 1923–1924 agricultural year state procurements actually declined in the face of an increase in gross production.[49] These phenomena formed the essence of the famous "scissors crisis" described by Leon Trotsky at the Twelfth Party Congress in April 1923. By October 1923, when the "scissors" had reached their maximum point of divergence, the general level of industrial prices had risen 3.1 times those of agricultural prices.[50] The forced savings aspects of NEP were obviously being pushed beyond the point of diminishing returns.

At this point, with Lenin near death, the question of whether to continue the more permissive aspects of NEP in agriculture became a central issue in the rapidly developing succession struggle. In a good example of the tendency to blur lines between policies and high Party politics which has come to be a hallmark of the Soviet political system during succession crises, Trotsky now came under severe attack. He was accused of anti-Leninist adventurism and a general failure to understand the requirements of economic recovery, ostensibly because of his early reluctance to support the concessions to the peasants. In the polarization of forces on the issue, the Right, led by Bukharin and Rykov, had the advantage of apparent orthodoxy in the NEP context. Characteristically, they were not averse to having their economic arguments used as a basis for discrediting Trotsky politically. Stalin, for his own reasons, threw his support behind them.

It was against this background of political infighting that the policy of concessions to the peasants was driven to its logical conclusion. At the end of 1923 the tax in kind was replaced by an exclusively cash levy, and procurements were placed on a fully commercial basis.[51] In an effort to close the "scissors," industry was subjected to considerable pressure to lower costs and prices.[52] In May 1925 the policy of supporting the private peasant was pushed to the limit as virtually all restrictions were abolished, short of the sale of the land itself. The Third USSR Congress of Soviets decreed on May 20, 1925, that henceforth land could be rented for up to twelve years, and hired labor could be used on rented land. It was even suggested that weak sovkhozes in thickly settled areas be dissolved and their land divided among the surrounding peasants.[53] The congress, furthermore, committed the state to the replacement and expansion of supplies of farm machinery and implements, including tractors, at prices accessible to all.[54] This was truly the golden age for the peasant under Soviet rule, as many a *kolkhoznik* would sadly recall in later, leaner years. It was the time when Bukharin would utter the fateful (to himself) summons to the individual peasants: "enrich yourselves, accumulate, develop your economy." [55] Within a few months, however, Stalin would have disposed of the Left Opposition and begun his campaign against his erstwhile allies on the Right, using their extreme permissiveness toward the private peasant as a devastating weapon to destroy them.

THE POLITICAL SITUATION IN THE COUNTRYSIDE UNDER NEP

Certainly one of the most frustrating aspects of NEP for its more politically oriented critics was its failure to provide the requisite ideological and institutional leverage for the extension of political control over the countryside. For most of the period the Party was not strong enough in the village to impose its authority directly, and efforts to assert its will indirectly through such local institutions as the soviets and the cooperatives often failed in the face of the peasants' determined opposition.

NEP brought about important changes in the status hierarchy

of the village. More precisely, it opened the way for a return to pre-Soviet patterns. Of all groups in the village the poor peasants (*bedniaki*) probably felt these changes most acutely. Their previously favored position during War Communism was almost completely lost, and once again they found themselves at the mercy of their more prosperous neighbors. The peasants of the well-to-do and ambitious upper strata, despite sporadic efforts by the Party to hold them back, soon rose once again to the apex of village society and assumed *de facto* (and often *de jure*) leadership positions. The middle peasant (*seredniak*) majority, ostensibly the main beneficiaries of NEP, were disappointingly eager to support this "natural" elite whenever there were cases of conflict with Party and state officials.

In many respects the rigid class differences which Lenin and his colleagues of both Left and Right professed to see in the village and upon which they claimed to be basing their social and economic policies were without much practical meaning. There is some evidence that the peasants did not see themselves in such terms.[56] Iurii Larin, a prominent leftwing theorist, pointed out, in refutation of the orthodox interpretation, that the less prosperous peasants almost invariably aspired to pull themselves up to the level of the well-to-do and saw nothing immoral in attempting to do so.[57] This ambition served as a powerful attenuator of class differentiation and class consciousness. The peasants assiduously created and maintained their own institutional arrangements outside of the formal Soviet framework and sought, quite successfully for a while, to resist pressures exerted from the outside.

The internal cohesiveness of the village made the task of extending Party influence extremely difficult, especially in the essentially noncoercive atmosphere nurtured by the temporarily predominant rightwing leaders. Deprived of the military support they had enjoyed during War Communism and plagued by poor communications with their superior organs, the Party organizations in the villages and *volosti* simply withered on the vine. One *Pravda* reporter lamented in 1923: "Our village cells, distant from the *uezd* [centers], having no close connections with strong Party organizations, almost totally abandoned for the winter, gradually weaken and, in some places, fall apart."[58]

Perhaps the most obvious explanation for the inability of the Party to extend its authority in the village was its serious numerical weakness. In spite of the fact that the vast majority of the population of the country (over 80 percent) lived in the rural areas, only 14,982 out of a total of 32,281 Party cells in the Russian Socialist Federated Soviet Republic (RSFSR) in 1922 were located in the countryside.[59] The typical rural cell was also significantly smaller and weaker than its urban counterpart, containing on the average 11 members as compared with more than 40 for the urban cell.[60] If in 1922 there were 281 Communists for every 10,000 inhabitants in Leningrad, 271 in Moscow, and 59 in the industrial provinces of the RSFSR, there were only 22 in the agricultural provinces of the republic.[61] Fainsod shows a similar pattern of urban-rural Party distribution for the country as a whole.[62]

But the mere fact of Party weakness in the village explains very little. The relative inattention to the political situation in the countryside during the first half of the NEP period was apparently the result of a conscious policy. After the indiscriminate recruitment of members during the Civil War, the leaders of the Party were seeking a return to the Party's characteristically selective, proletarian image. In 1921 there was a purge of "unreliable elements," aimed particularly at the flood of peasant recruits who had joined during the latter stages of the Civil War. The Party was regrouping and purifying its forces for the difficult, long-range tasks of reconstruction. For the time being, therefore, it was decided to de-emphasize Party work in the village until a reliable corps of organizers could be formed. This policy was reflected in the new rule for Party recruitment laid down at the Twelfth Party Conference in August 1922 and subsequently reinforced in a directive of the Twelfth Party Congress the following April. Peasants were placed in a less favored entrance category than were workers and Red Army men; they were subject to more stringent recommendation procedures, and they were required to spend a longer period in the newly introduced candidate's stage.[63] In 1925 there was yet another purge of disaffected peasant Communists.[64] In the face of this obvious retrenchment, existing Party forces in the village were left more or less to fend for themselves, often with dire consequences.[65]

After the Thirteenth Party Congress in May 1924, however, a process of preparing the ground for a vigorous expansion and consolidation of Party control in the countryside began. The Central Committee sent out special organizers to penetrate and gain control over the local soviets and the cooperatives.[66] Although the actual gaining of influence in these institutions was certainly not an easy task, the outcome could hardly have been in doubt. This period would provide valuable experience in the development of techniques of direct and indirect Party control in the village, preparing the Party apparatus for the monumental task of mass collectivization.

THE LENIN COOPERATIVE PLAN

From its inception and at least through 1925, NEP in agriculture had been characterized by an increasing divergence from the accepted models and standards of a socialist agrarian program. To many, NEP seemed far more likely to nurture the growth of capitalism than to prepare the way for socialism in the village. Lenin was deeply aware of these facts and dangers, and he expended a good deal of his declining strength on working out a theoretical justification for NEP and a program for putting agriculture back on the proper socialist "rails." In one of his last important works, "Better Fewer but Better," he explained NEP in terms of the image of a large-scale industrialization program borne, at least initially, on the back of a "poor *muzhik* horse." Only after the completion of extensive electrification and a heavy capital goods industry would it be possible to proceed to the development of the rest of the economy.[67]

Thus, the spavined peasant nag of Russian agriculture was to be the bearer of socialist industry. But what of the muzhik horse itself? How was it to be transformed into a new socialist tractor? Two months earlier, in January 1923, Lenin had sketched out a general outline — it hardly deserved to be called a plan — for the long-term development of agriculture along socialist lines. Over the years the vague prescriptions contained in these two articles entitled "On Cooperation" have come to be enshrined in the treasure house of Marxism-Leninism as the Lenin Cooperative Plan. In it Soviet policy makers have professed to find a clear blueprint for virtually every major departure in agriculture since Lenin's death, including forced collectivization and the creation of the MTS system.[68]

One of the most notable aspects of Lenin's line of reasoning in the articles was his "rehabilitation" of cooperation as a vehicle of socialist construction. While acknowledging the basis for the traditional Marxian antipathy toward the cooperative movement under capitalism, he asserted that under the aegis of proletarian rule cooperation acquired new legitimacy and entirely new perspectives.[69] And one must admit that the Soviet collective farm system ostensibly based on Lenin's Plan was indeed unique in the annals of cooperation.

Lenin was not very specific as to the precise application of cooperation to the conditions of Russian peasant agriculture, but it is possible to extract certain vaguely programmatic inferences from "On Cooperation" and his other writings. He envisioned an organic network of cooperatives as the institutional expression of the *smychka* between town and country. The process of drawing the peasants into the cooperatives was to be gradual and entirely voluntary. Lenin foresaw a long period of education of the peasantry in the simplest forms of cooperative endeavor before the full socialist transformation of the village was achieved. The process would occupy, he said, "a whole historical epoch . . . at the very least, one or two decades." [70]

In the Lenin Plan, as elaborated by subsequent Soviet agrarian theorists, there were to be two main forms of cooperation: consumer cooperation and producer, or agricultural, cooperation, the latter encompassing a variety of producing and processing associations, along with credit unions. Because of the great fear of a resurgence of private control over commodity trade under NEP conditions, one of the primary goals of the cooperative plan was to provide a state-controlled channel of urban-rural exchange. The consumer cooperatives were thus intended to organize the individual peasants for effective competition with private traders for the acquisition of manufactured goods. By means of linkages between urban and rural consumer cooperatives, a closed circuit of commercial exchange would theoretically exist, effectively denying money or produce to the private traders and jobbers. The intention was ultimately to unite all primary cooperatives of workers and peasants in a hierarchical organization, at the apex of which would be *Tsentrosoiuz,* the Central Union of Consumer Cooperatives, through which the state would coordinate overall national commercial policies. This was to be the pattern for organizing the peasants as consumers and introducing them to the benefits of collective endeavor.[71]

The pattern for organizing the peasants as producers, the most important goal, was somewhat more complex. The basic idea of the agricultural and credit cooperative system was to win the peasants over to collective farming methods by furnishing them with a broad range of services and organizational arrangements for improving production. The system would make available the credits and equipment for modern, capital-intensive farming operations; the effect of the demonstration would do the rest. One of the most important functions of the local branches of the agricultural cooperative system was the encouragement of collective purchase and utilization of expensive farm machinery through the granting of joint loans and credits.[72] Local cooperative officials were given broad discretionary and supervisory powers over the disbursement of credits and were instructed to favor collective applicants over individuals.[73] Of particular importance was an order to the cooperatives to set up machinery rental points, seed-cleaning stations, and land-reclamation stations to be operated with state subsidies.[74] It was expected that the demonstration effect of such machinery complexes, which were too expensive for the individual peasants to purchase on their own, would induce them to band together to acquire and operate similar facilities on a collective basis. Last, and in fact least, the system of agricultural cooperatives was given the task of supporting and expanding the number of genuine collective farms.[75] For most of the NEP period this aspect of the cooperative program was decidedly of minor importance. The main emphasis of the policies was on economic viability and demonstration of effectiveness, rarely features of the existing collective and state farms. Even in the ideologically sensitive area of machinery supplies, the prevailing tendency was toward direct sales to the largest possible number of effective producers, be they groups or individuals.

Theoretically, there was to be a neat division of labor between the two main forms of cooperation. The consumer cooperative system was to supply the peasants with consumer goods and manufactured necessities in return for cash and limited amounts of produce. Agricultural cooperation, on the other hand, was to serve as the primary source of capital goods and capital investment funds for the peasants, essentially on a barter basis; that is, credits and equipment would be paid for in kind. The agricultural cooperative system was thus expected to be the main channel for state grain procurements.[76] In the intensely commercial atmosphere of NEP, however, this theoretical division of labor broke down. The demand for peasant grain was so great that the two systems of cooperation often engaged in bitter competition to sell the peasants what they needed. Frequently the consumer cooperatives became deeply involved in the sale of heavy machinery and equipment and the provision of credits; for a time it appeared that the local consumer cooperatives might even drive their agricultural cooperative rivals out of business.[77] Furthermore, central control over the cooperatives was weak. Many of them were indeed spontaneously organized or "wild" (dikii) and under the control of local elements that were not at all in tune with nationwide policies.

Meanwhile, private traders continued to exert an often dominant influence on the local grain trade.[78] The socialist transformation of the village was obviously not on the immediate agenda, and the Lenin Cooperative Plan, with its stress on gradualism and voluntary participation, served mainly to reinforce the sense of legitimacy of the leading rightwing officials in doing what they were naturally inclined to do in any case. However, the Lenin Plan did establish a set of directions and goals for the future. Subsequent practice under Stalin would show that it could be used to justify a much more forcible policy of change in the village.

POLICY CHANGES ON THE EVE OF MASS COLLECTIVIZATION

The smashing defeat of the Left Opposition in 1926 permitted Stalin to begin disassociating himself from the permissive policies of his allies on the Right. There is no need here to discuss the details of the subsequent political struggles. Suffice it to say that the tortuous course of Stalin's rise to power made it only natural that he attack the Right with precisely those arguments which had been marshalled against them by the defeated Left. Agriculture was to be a main battle ground in this remarkable dialectical struggle.

The atmosphere of confidence engendered by the generous concessions of NEP, particularly those of 1925, had encouraged the well-to-do peasants to expand the scale of their operations. This tendency was especially notable in the use of machinery and implements. With the encouragement of the state and its liberalized import and sales policies, the wealthier peasants became major purchasers of expensive mechanized equipment.[79] In the rapidly changing political atmosphere of 1926 these developments began to arouse concern. Once again machinery policy was an important indicator of official attitudes. A sharp crackdown on the sale of tractors to individuals was instituted. In July the Council of Labor and Defense advanced a proposal to favor collective users in the distribution of tractors.[80] Ia. A. Iakovlev, a prominent Party agricultural spokesman, wrote in *Pravda* in September: *"The distinguishing characteristic of the plan for 1926–1927 as compared to previous years is the complete exclusion of individuals from the group of tractor recipients . . ."* [emphasis in original].[81] The new line was made official in a decree of December 3, 1926, which directed the various supply agencies "to sell tractors only: (a) to state and cooperative institutions, (b) to peasant collectives (communes, agricultural artels, machine and reclamation associations)." [82]

Increasing emphasis was placed on collective forms of endeavor in the countryside. Machinery associations and cooperative machinery rental points, where farm equipment was collectively owned, if not always collectively used, underwent rapid expansion, although they were never to bulk very large in agricultural production in absolute terms. The following tabulation shows the expansion of the network of state and cooperative machinery associations and rental points in the RSFSR from 1925 to 1928 (as of October 1):[83]

	1925	1926	1927	1928
Machinery associations	2,268	6,356	10,268	15,942
Rental points	4,495	6,266	7,300	10,600

Thus, by the end of 1926 Soviet agricultural policy had clearly begun the shift to a more activistic interpretation of the Lenin Cooperative Plan. The change implied a more aggressive fostering of the producer cooperatives and strengthening them with scarce farm machinery. Anastas I. Mikoyan emphasized the new course with appropriate, conventional references to the role of the machine when he declared at the Second All-Russian Conference of Tractor Workers of Agricultural Cooperation in February 1927:

This year . . . we want to give all tractors to the cooperatives, the machinery associations, and the collectives . . . The tractor is not only a good means of mechanized cultivation of the land, but also the best cooperator. It creates the basis for cooperation in the sphere of production. This is the revolutionary significance of the tractor in agriculture . . . *It is the first and best builder of socialism,* and therefore we attribute great significance to the tractor. [Emphasis in original.] [84]

The actual results of the new machinery policy at the local level were far from revolutionary. While the machinery associations and rental points did enhance the accessibility of various types of machines for the poorer peasants, their impact on production was extremely limited. Their number was never very large relative to the number of potenial users. In mid-1927, for example, there were not more than 25 thousand machinery associations and rental points combined for the nearly 25 million peasant farms in the country.[85] Moreover, most of the associations and rental points were very small and poorly equipped. According to one survey, almost half of their machinery was in serious need of repair.[86] Nor were they very profitable economically. The cooperative rental points operated at considerable losses each year.[87]

Given the increasing atmosphere of impatience over the tempo of economic development being stimulated by Stalin and his supporters, it was obvious that these small-scale, voluntary associations were too limited in scope. By December 1927 Stalin had reached the decision to press forward with the socialization of the entire economy. In industry this meant the beginning of the Five Year Plans of forced draft industrialization. In agriculture it meant mass collectivization. The Fifteenth Party Congress was the forum at which many of the related decisions were announced.

In his report to the congress "On Work in the Village," Viacheslav M. Molotov declared that the measures taken in the past year to help the poorer peasants, such as the establishment of rental points and machinery cooperatives, had been only partially effective. The kulaks alone had reaped the full benefits of the concessions offered under NEP, he said, while the poorer strata were still refusing to accept the obvious superiority of collective farming.[88] Collectivization, he implied, would have to be imposed from above and on a scale commensurate with the grandiose plans being contemplated for the development of the economy as a whole.

The acceptance of the need for mass collectivization now stimulated, perhaps for the first time among the top leaders of the Party, a serious discussion of the practical organizational questions involved. The new emphasis on large-scale socialized production demanded a hard reassessment of the known techniques for the introduction and utilization of advanced farm machinery. At the congress there was a general consensus among the Party leaders that the cooperative framework was far from perfect. The piecemeal distribution of machinery, particularly tractors, to the small cooperative machinery associations and rental points was doing little to advance the cause of collectivization. On the contrary it was apparently helping the well-to-do peasants, who knew better how to use the machinery, to increase their economic advantages over their neighbors. Credit cooperation was having the same general effect.[89]

Thus, it was obviously not enough merely to ship machinery into the countryside to win the peasants over to socialism. Referring to Lenin's famous dictum on the 100,000 tractors, Molotov asked the congress in good Stalinist rhetorical style:

Didn't Lenin really understand what a difficult business it is to develop a collective economy in the village? Of course, he understood better than we do, he knew the village a hundred times better than we do, understood the muzhik a thousand times better. But with his example of a hundred thousand tractors Lenin *was focussing* attention on the *concrete means* of realizing communism, and we should remember this now and draw from it the necessary practical conclusions. [Emphasis in original.] [90]

What were these "practical conclusions"? Mechanization was one. But mechanization so organized and so concentrated as to effect the most rapid possible transformation of agriculture to a large-scale, industrial basis. For the time being the precise organizational forms were left unstated, but there were many schemes in circulation — all of them grandiose.

One of these schemes which had recently been tried with some success was mentioned by Stalin himself in his address to the congress. It involved the setting up of detachments of tractors — or "tractor columns" — for the cultivation of individual peasant farms surrounding the Shevchenko sovkhoz in the Odessa Okrug of the Ukraine. Stalin read to the delegates of the congress a letter allegedly written by the peasants involved in the experiment. The letter had been published previously in *Izvestiia* on November 22. Because it apparently played an important part in the origins of the MTS, the letter and Stalin's comments at the congress are worth reproducing here at length.

Here is one of the examples of how sovkhozes are helping the peasants shift to collectivization of the land, to the great benefits of the peasants. I have in mind the assistance of the Ukrainian Union of Sovkhozes with tractors to the peasants of the Odessa Okrug, and the letter from these peasants recently printed in *Izvestiia* in gratitude for the help given. Allow me to read the text of the letter (Voices: "Please do!") [*sic*]

"We, the immigrants of the *khutors* Shevchenko, Krasin, Kalinin, 'Chervona zirka,' and 'Voskhodiashchee solntse,' offer our deepest gratitude to the Soviet power for the great assistance that was given to us in the matter of restoring our economy. The majority of us are poor peasants, without horses, without implements; we were not able to work the land given to us and *were forced to rent it out to the local kulaks for a part of the harvest*. The harvest was miserable, since, as is well known, a renter will not cultivate someone else's land conscientiously. Those small credits which were received from the state were spent by us on food, and each year we became poorer. This year a representative of the Ukrainian Union of Sovkhozes came to us and proposed to work our land with tractors instead of giving monetary credits. All the immigrants, except for individual kulaks, gave their consent although they didn't have much faith that the work would be done well. To our great joy and to the consternation of the kulaks, the tractors plowed up all the virgin and idle land for fallow, they replowed and harrowed it five or six times to clean it of weeds and, finally, sowed the whole field with high quality wheat seed. Now already the kulaks are not laughing about the work of the tractor detachment. This year in our region, because of the lack of rain, the peasants have sown almost no winter crops, and on those lands where they were sown there are still no shoots. But on our *immigrant fields hundreds of desiatinas of excellent wheat are turning green on fallow land, the likes of which don't exist in the wealthiest German colony.* Besides the sowings of winter wheat the tractors turned over the whole area under spring crops. *Now we don't have even one desiatina of land out or uncultivated. We don't have even one poor peasant who does not have several desiatinas of winter wheat sown in fallow.* After the work of the tractors that we have seen we don't want to operate small poor farms, and *we have decided to organize a collectivized tractor economy on which there won't be any individual peasant patches of land.* The organization of a tractor economy for us has already been undertaken by the Taras Shevchenko sovkhoz, with which we have concluded a contract."

Stalin concluded his reading of the letter with the comment: "Would that we had more of such examples, comrades; then we could move this matter way ahead." [91] His favorable comments on the experiment were quickly picked up by other speakers at the congress. However, it would be several years before the tractor column idea and its offspring, the MTS, would evolve into a major nationwide institution.

In many respects the socialist transformation of the countryside was for Lenin and his colleagues a far more formidable challenge than the seizure of political power. The obvious diffidence with which Lenin approached the solution of the crucial agrarian question reflected his keen awareness of the frailty of the proletarian base of his revolution. In addition to the overwhelming demographic obstacles to the introduction of the changes they desired, the Bolshevik rulers were soon made to realize that the legacy of theoretical guidance they had brought with them for the solution of the agrarian question was of little practical use. The Bolsheviks were literally breaking new ground, and Lenin, if not all of his colleagues, fairly quickly prepared himself to think of the process in terms of decades.

The Civil War compelled a radical change of pace and forced Lenin to acquiesce in the premature imposition of a number of quasi-socialist measures. Inevitably these measures proved abortive, and the regime was driven to accept the necessity of a drastic retreat to a New Economic Policy of concessions to the peasant masses. However distorted their results, both War Communism and NEP did provide the Bolshevik leaders with a golden opportunity to test various theories and institutions for the eventual drive toward modernization. If nothing else, these experiences engendered a healthy respect for the magnitude of the problems that would ultimately have to be solved and a realization that drastic measures would probably have to be used if the original goals were to be achieved. In the meantime the Party was developing a set of political and economic techniques for maximizing the effectiveness of its scanty human and material resources in the village. Thus, when Stalin finally decided to push ahead with the wholesale social and economic transformation of the country, the regime had already accumulated a considerable backlog of experience with institutional arrangements for the organization and control of the peasantry.

It is important to note the special role attributed to the machine for the economic and social transformation of rural life in both European and Russian Marxist thought on the agrarian question. Lenin and other Bolshevik leaders quite genuinely believed in the socializing powers of the tractor and, indeed, were counting on it to do much of the necessary transformational work in the Russian peasant village. Thus, the officially expressed attitudes and policies toward the disposition and use of the tractor and other modern farm machines were a fairly sensitive indicator of the degree of commitment to the socialization of agriculture as an immediate goal at any given time during the first decade or so of Soviet rule. In the immediate aftermath of the Revolution and during the Civil War, conscious efforts were made to insure that the limited supplies of tractors and machines were carefully preserved under state control for the encouragement of collective forms of agriculture. During NEP, on the other hand, as collectivization was effectively removed from the agenda for the immediate future, controls over the disposition of farm machinery were almost totally relaxed, and private peasants were encouraged to mechanize their individual holdings. Similarly, once the decision had been made to reverse the permissive policies of NEP, one of the first acts of the regime was to restore controls over the distribution of tractors and to assign them exclusively to collective users. And as the momentum of the collectivization drive increased, there was a concerted search for institutional arrangements to maximize the effectiveness of the available stocks of modern farm machinery, not only as a spur to production, but as a means of providing impetus to the collectivization process itself. The experiment with the prototype of the MTS at the Shevchenko sovkhoz in the Ukraine was looked upon as a promising development in this search.

2 The Development of the MTS System

The evolution of the MTS from an isolated experiment into a central institutional bulwark of the Soviet collective farm system took place in a series of fairly well defined historical phases that were related to major events or stages in Soviet development. Consequently the pattern of growth of the MTS system exhibited many of the cyclical characteristics that are noticeable in other Soviet institutions.

THE MTS AND MASS COLLECTIVIZATION

Despite Stalin's verbal encouragement, there was no widespread construction of tractor columns or machine-tractor stations immediately following the Fifteenth Party Congress. For some time the tractor column remained merely one of a number of approved schemes for the transition to socialism in agriculture. Indeed, the project seemed to become lost in the welter of violence and confusion which accompanied the shift to mass collectivization. Whatever development there was remained confined to the place of origin of the tractor column, the Shevchenko sovkhoz.

The Shevchenko sovkhoz, named for the great Ukrainian national poet, Taras Shevchenko, had been selected for a number of experiments by the Ukrainian Sovkhoz Trust in 1927. One of these experiments concerned the organization of a fully mechanized pilot farming operation under an agreement with the Ukrainian Tractor Committee, the main coordinating agency for tractor procurement in the republic.[1] The sovkhoz allocated seventy-five hundred acres for the experiment and designated a contingent of ten imported Fordson tractors with twenty-four drivers.[2] The director of the project, A. M. Markevich, an energetic young Communist agronomist who was later to become the head of the MTS system, found that the machinery available was in excess of the requirements of the experiment. It was on his initiative that the tractor column was set up for servicing the surrounding
36

private peasant farms in the manner described in the letter read by Stalin at the congress.

The circumstances of the Shevchenko tractor column operation were not really typical of Russian peasant agriculture, however. The households involved consisted of peasants from overcrowded regions who had been resettled by the state in certain virgin and abandoned lands in the Odessa Okrug. The immigrants were not given sufficient capital to cultivate the new lands effectively, and many were compelled to rent out their land to local kulaks. Thus, they were especially receptive to the tractor column project. The atypicalness of the situation was apparently well enough known to cause considerable skepticism about its broader relevance. Professor F. R. Dunaevskii, a contemporary supporter of the idea, noted that

> Some skeptics are saying "It's all right for the Sovkhoz Trust to cultivate, on credit, the lands of resettled peasants who have nothing to work it with themselves. Of course, they would be happy, because they have nothing to lose anyway. Try to do the same thing with peasants who have a going operation . . ." [3]

Given these special circumstances, it is not surprising that the tractor column did not immediately receive wholehearted official endorsement. As the collectivization drive gained momentum, other more traditional methods of machinery utilization, such as the machinery association and the rental point, continued to attract an inordinate share of publicity despite their obvious limitations for large-scale operations. [4]

Thanks largely to Markevich's efforts, however, the tractor column project showed considerable vitality, and a modest program of expansion was budgeted by local officials in the Ukraine for 1928. The new columns were set up in sovkhozes following the Shevchenko pattern. By the end of the year there were operational tractor columns in seventy-three sovkhozes, totaling approximately seven hundred tractors. [5]

The year 1928 also witnessed the beginnings of an important cooperative tractor column movement, again initially in the Ukraine. The cooperative columns were usually linked to the so-called land associations — semi-official organizations of a political and economic character based on the old peasant communes. During the year fourteen cooperative tractor columns were established, serving sixty-six land associations with a total of 66,739 hectares of land. Late in 1928 all of these more or less spontaneously organized columns were formally taken over by the national grain cooperative system, *Khlebotsentr,* which, together with the Agricultural Cooperative Union, *Sel'skosoiuz,* subsequently managed the major part of cooperative tractor column construction.[6]

In practice the cooperative tractor columns were often not much more effective than the ordinary machinery associations and rental points. Ideally, they were supposed to include the full complex of machines required for the major cultivation operations, as well as the necessary repair and storage facilities. Actually, they were often poorly equipped, poorly staffed, and poorly situated to exert a major influence on local farming practices. As in other branches of the contemporary cooperative system, many of these shortcomings were due to a shortage of financial resources and poor planning and management at the local level.[7] But some of the blame probably rested with certain officials in the central cooperative leadership, whose ambivalence, if not outright hostility toward the MTS concept was a matter of public record. (See Chapter 3.)

An important landmark in the discussions on the course of Soviet farm organization and mechanization was the appearance in 1929 of a book by Markevich entitled *Inter-Village Machine-Tractor Stations.*[8] Generalizing from his two years of experience with tractor columns at the Shevchenko sovkhoz, Markevich enunciated a new concept of state-owned and state-operated energy centers to mechanize and organize the production activities of the surrounding peasants, effectively collectivizing them in the process. Unlike the tractor columns, which were attached to sovkhozes or existing cooperative associations, the MTS were to comprise an entirely new, self-contained type of production enterprise, combining peasant labor and auxiliary services with state machinery and state managerial and technical direction.

While the debates on the MTS and tractor column arrangements were still going on, a few tentative steps were taken towards the implementation of Markevich's ideas. In addition to the MTS formed from the tractor columns at the Shevchenko sovkhoz in November 1928, stations were set up in the "Khutorok" sovkhoz in the North Caucasus and the "Titusovka" sovkhoz in Berdichev Okrug in the Ukraine. These three remained the only operational full-scale state MTS in the entire USSR through 1929.[9] Meanwhile the agricultural cooperative system proceeded with its own construction program, converting some of its tractor columns into MTS. Until well into 1930 the cooperative line of development seemed to enjoy the greater official support.[10]

In the winter and spring of 1929 still another MTS-type organization appeared: the so-called group union (*kustovoe ob"edinenie*). The *kust* was a production and administrative federation of from ten to twenty-five small kolkhozes, constituting a type of secondary cooperative. Although the number of "group" MTS never reached large proportions, the *kusty* did play a significant role for a brief period in the acquisition and utilization of tractors and machines in the kolkhozes.[11] By the summer of 1930 there were some sixteen hundred such unions encompassing over twenty thousand kolkhozes, with just under sixteen tractors per *kust*.[12]

While these different experiments with farm machinery organization were proceeding, the kolkhozes themselves continued to receive a substantial share of the available machinery supplies. Table 2-1 shows the changing patterns of agricultural machinery distribution as collectivization gained momentum.

Table 2-1 suggests the absence of any clearcut decision concerning the future course of agricultural machinery policy other than the implementation of earlier prohibitions on sales to private individuals. Judging from the relative growth rates, it would appear that the orthodox conception of self-contained kolkhoz production units was winning out, since the kolkhoz share of machinery was evidently growing most rapidly.

This period of indecision would last until late in 1930. In the meantime, although the number of tractor columns and MTS grew steadily, the growth was hardly systematic. There was little standardization of equipment or of operational practices, nor was the pattern of service relationships with the surrounding peasants at all uniform. Managerial, technical, and operating personnel

Table 2-1. Changing percentages of different types of farming units in distribution of advanced farm machinery, 1927/28 to 1929/30.

Type of farming unit	Agricultural year		
	1927/28	1928/29	1929/30
Sovkhozes	5.5	5.0	12.3
MTS	—	—	2.7
Kolkhozes	6.0	12.5	39.2
Cooperative unions	17.9	19.0	15.4
Individual farms	70.6	63.5	30.4
	100.0	100.0	100.0

Source: M. Golendo, "Mashinizatsiia sel'skogo khoziaistva SSSR," *Na agrarnom fronte,* no. 1 (January 1930), p. 60.

were usually ill trained. Sites were poorly chosen. In short, virtually all of the sins of haste and premature expansion that Markevich had explicitly warned against were being committed.[13]

The first real indication that the new concept of centralized agricultural mechanization was being actively discussed in high Party circles came at the Sixteenth Party Conference in April 1929. Several speakers, including M. I. Kalinin, came out in favor of the MTS and the principle of a state monopoly of the main energy resources in the kolkhoz sector. However, there was considerable opposition to making the MTS arrangement universal.[14] Although many speakers had something favorable to say about the MTS in principle, there seemed to be little consensus on the magnitude of its future role in the Soviet agricultural system. In the end the conference did agree to establish a special commission to work out recommendations for the organization and methods of financing of an MTS network of as yet undetermined size.[15]

From the deliberations of this commission a decree emerged which marked the transition of the MTS from a pilot project to a limited, nationwide system. The Decree of the Council of Labor and Defense of June 5, 1929, set a target of one million hectares of cropland to be cultivated by machine-tractor stations in the 1929–1930 crop year.[16] As yet there was no decision to make the MTS the exclusive channel of mechanization, but it was now being viewed as a major element of the socialist agricultural system.

To head the program of MTS construction the Decree of June 5th created an All-Union Center of Machine-Tractor Stations (*Traktorotsentr*), to be organized as a joint stock association with most of the shares held by governmental and cooperative agencies.[17] Part of the financing was to be obtained through sales of Traktorotsentr shares to the peasants. (See Chapter 5.) Among the charter members of Traktorotsentr were the People's Commissariats of Agriculture of the union republics, the USSR Supreme Council of the National Economy (*Vesenkha*), and various other state and cooperative organs connected in one way or another with agriculture. The initial capitalization was fifty million rubles, and the distribution of shares was such as to preserve for the state a controlling voice in policy-making. Traktorotsentr was to be administered by a five-man bureau, headed by Markevich. Finally, all existing MTS in the sovkhoz system were to be transferred to Traktorotsentr.

It would be incorrect to suggest, as Soviet writers customarily do, that the June 5th Decree represented the final decision on the mechanization question. For at least one more year Soviet policy makers continued to vacillate over the extent of the state's commitment to the MTS. Meanwhile, the cooperative MTS and tractor columns and the kolkhozes, as well as the state MTS, continued to receive sizeable shares of the available tractor park. Table 2-2 shows the planned distribution of tractors for 1930 as of September 1929.

Table 2-2. Planned distribution of tractors for 1930.

Recipient	Number of tractors
MTS and tractor columns	8,100
Sovkhozes	5,100
Kolkhozes	6,800
Other unions	500

Source: A. I. Muralov, "Zadachi sel'skogo khoziaistva v 1929–1930 g.," *Sel'sko-khoziaistvennaia zhizn'*, no. 35 (September 2, 1929), p. 2.

Despite the apparently firm position of the MTS as at least one of the major components of the new nationwide socialist agricultural system, it was clear that no exclusive commitment had been made. In fact, toward the end of 1929 the relative importance of the MTS in official thinking may well have declined. Stalin's references to the stations in his famous speech to the Conference of Marxist Agrarians on December 27, 1929, indicated that their future long-term role was far from settled.[18] Moreover, in the beginning of 1930 the opponents of the MTS actually succeeded in convincing the Central Committee to allow the purchase of existing stations by the kolkhozes they served.

Once the decision had been made to press for total collectivization, however, the entire status of the MTS-kolkhoz relationship in official thinking began to change. By the beginning of 1930 Stalin had cast aside previous objections that the necessary "material and technical preconditions" for collectivization were lacking. A decree of January 5, 1930, called for a "resolute struggle" against any attempts to hold down the rate of collectivization on such grounds.[19] Under conditions where the majority of the newly created kolkhozes were desperately short of machinery and were likely to remain so indefinitely, the role of the MTS assumed new importance. From its previous status as merely an economically and ideologically attractive means of utilizing existing technology in special circumstances, it began to appear as a universal solution to the problem of machinery shortages in the kolkhoz. When it was proclaimed that the MTS had passed the test of the spring sowing campaign of 1930, they were assured of a central position in the future socialist agricultural system.

An immediate indication of the new importance attributed to the MTS at this time was the decision to remove existing cooperative stations and tractor columns from the jurisdiction of the less fully centralized cooperative system. A decree of September 10, 1930, placed the construction and management of all MTS in the hands of Traktorotsentr and transferred to it all cooperative and kolkhoz stations and repair facilities. Traktorotsentr was also given the responsibility for technical supervision of tractors held by individual kolkhozes.[20]

The next two years witnessed a steady expansion of the MTS

network and its gradual incorporation into the emerging structure of political control in the village. Although it retained for a while certain aspects of its partially cooperative parentage, the MTS system rapidly evolved into a full-fledged state institution. In a decree of December 29, 1930, the Central Committee announced its intention to rely exclusively on the MTS for the future mechanization and operational direction of the collective farm sector. The decree ordered a huge program of MTS construction for 1931, setting a target of 1400 stations (later reduced to 1040) to be completed by the end of the year and providing for the training of large numbers of technical personnel. Foreshadowing the future role of the stations as direct instruments of central control, the decree expressly prohibited local officials from interfering in the planned operations of the MTS in their territories.[21]

As the data in Table 2-3 indicate, the growth of the MTS system

Table 2-3. Growth of the MTS system during the period of mass collectivization.

MTS equipment and coverage	1930 (June 1st)	1931 (June 1st)	1932 (Dec. 31st)	1933 (Dec. 31st)
Number of MTS	158	1228	2446	2916
Tractors in MTS (1000)	7.1	50.1	74.8	123.2
Combines	—	—	2.2	10.4
Sown area of kolkhozes served by MTS as percent of total kolkhoz sown area	—	37.1	49.3	58.7

Source: I. S. Malyshev, ed., *MTS vo vtoroi piatiletke* (Moscow-Leningrad, 1939), p. 11.

in these initial years was extremely rapid. This expansion was not distributed uniformly throughout the country, however. In January 1930 the Central Committee had scheduled a three-phase program of collectivization. In phase one the major grain-growing areas were to be collectivized — the Lower Volga, the Middle Volga, and the North Caucasus. In these areas the process was to be "basically completed" by the end of 1930 or the spring of 1931. In the second phase the other major grain areas were to be collectivized, the target date being the fall of 1931 or the spring of 1932. In the third phase the remainder of the country was to be collectivized. The entire process was to be essentially completed by the end of the First Five Year Plan.[22]

The construction of new MTS generally followed this pattern. Of the 1040 MTS slated for construction in 1931, well over 50 percent were to be located in the main grain regions. An additional 130 were to be set up in the cotton-growing areas; 150, in sugar-beet areas; and 150, in the flax and hemp areas.[23] By the summer of 1932 half of the 2115 MTS in operation were grain-oriented.[24] The geographical patterns of MTS distribution can be seen in Table 2-4, which shows the percentages of MTS coverage in areas with well defined crop specialty characteristics for 1933.

From the beginning it was assumed that the MTS would play an important role in the process of collectivization itself. This had been one of Markevich's biggest selling points. A resolution of the November (1929) Plenum of the Central Committee devoted to collectivization had emphasized this role by ordering that "machine-tractor stations must become the center of complete collectivization of entire regions." [25] Accordingly, in the areas singled out for heavy concentration of MTS construction, the individual stations were selectively placed to aid collectivization.*

The criteria for the selection of an MTS site included the following: (a) the existence of considerable areas of virgin or abandoned land particularly suitable to tractor cultivation — in the early years the expansion of sown area was one of the most tangible achievements of the MTS; (b) proximity to railroad lines or other communications facilities; (c) evidence of effective prior

---

* The author was told by three scholars at the Timiriazev Agricultural Academy in Moscow that A. M. Markevich, whom they described as a particularly forceful and knowledgeable individual, personally conducted much of the work of selecting sites for future MTS, traveling about the country and making on-the-spot investigations. Many of the older scholars and high officials in Soviet agricultural institutions were personally involved in the collectivization drive, a fact which probably contributes to the manifest reluctance of the regime to contemplate profound changes in the agricultural system.

Table 2-4. Percentages of MTS coverage of kolkhoz sown area
for selected regions by crop specialty in 1933.

Region and crop specialty	Total number of MTS	Percentage of kolkhoz sown area served by MTS
RSFSR (total)	1857	54.8
Grain		
Altai Krai	88	62.9
[a]Krasnodar Krai	120	78.2
Volga German ASSR	38	89.8
[a]Rostov Oblast	101	85.9
[a]Saratov Oblast	96	58.8
[a]Stalingrad Oblast	69	64.9
Grain and sugar beet		
[a]Voronezh Oblast	95	76.2
Ukrainian SSR	657	77.1
Flax and mixed farming ("consuming" region)		
Moscow Oblast	14	19.9
Leningrad Oblast	37	—
Gor'kii Oblast	13	12.8
[a]Smolensk Oblast	27	25.4
Vologda Oblast	8	15.1
Belorussian SSR	63	40.1

Source: Compiled from data in I. S. Malyshev, ed., *MTS vo vtoroi piatiletke* (Moscow-Leningrad, 1939), pp. 12–13.

[a] Data refer to territories which assumed the names listed in the table during the thirties.

economic and political preparation for collectivization by the local authorities and/or the existence of some collective farms in the area; and (d) the presence of a large number of poor peasants lacking sufficient animal draft power in the area.[26]

These selection criteria help to explain why the percentage of collectivization in MTS zones was generally significantly higher (from one and one-half to two times as great) than in the surrounding areas. Table 2-5 shows the relative percentages of collectivization for selected major geographical regions at the height of the collectivization campaign.

Table 2-5. Percentages of peasant farms collectivized within and outside of MTS zones for selected regions on July 1, 1931.

Region	In MTS zones	Outside MTS zones
North Caucasus	89	59
Ukraine	65	40
Lower Volga	55	43
Middle Volga	47	28
Central Black Earth	85	36
Siberia	46	25
Kazakhstan	61	34

Source: Iu. V. Arutiunian and M. A. Vyltsan, *Istoricheskaia rol' MTS i ikh reorganizatsiia* (Moscow, 1958), p. 32.

Whether as cause or effect, the MTS did appear to be associated with a higher than average rate of collectivization. Moreover, as Soviet writers delight in pointing out, the rate of withdrawals from the collective farms during the mass exodus following the publication of Stalin's "Dizziness from Success" article in *Pravda* on March 2, 1930, was significantly lower in MTS zones than in surrounding areas. However, it should be noted that the stations were established precisely in those areas — near railroad lines and population centers — where preparations for collectivization had been most thorough and where there were relatively large numbers of Party and government officials who could apply pressure against withdrawal.

The rapid expansion of the kolkhoz sector in the latter part of 1930 created increasing pressure for the centralization of agricultural administration. One of the results was an enhancement of the administrative responsibilities of the MTS. Following the Sixteenth Party Congress in June–July 1930, where strong sentiments had been uttered in favor of tightening up the cooperative system, the Central Committee ordered the consolidation of many of the uncoordinated activities of the various cooperatives in the kolkhoz sector. All cooperative operations at the raion level and below were henceforth to be directed by new raion kolkhoz unions (*raikolkhozsoiuzy*).[27] If there was an MTS in a given raion, the organizational and production affairs of the kolkhozes were to be administered through the station. The director of the MTS was designated ex officio deputy chairman of the *raikolkhozsoiuz* in order to formalize the relationship.[28] Even during the initial period, then, the MTS system was being conceived as an integral part of the agricultural administrative structure.

The movement toward full state absorption of the MTS-kolkhoz system and the elimination of the remaining cooperative "anomalies" proceeded rapidly. The process was finally completed by the transfer of the responsibilities of *Kolkhoztsentr* to the USSR People's Commissariat of Agriculture (PCA) in October 1932. On October 10, 1932, Traktorotsentr itself was formally abolished, and the MTS system was subordinated directly to the PCA.[29]

In addition to using the machine-tractor stations as part of the state administrative hierarchy the regime soon attempted to use them as centers of local Party control. The urban-industrial origins of the MTS cadres and the nature of their work made the stations veritable proletarian islands in a hostile peasant sea, making them uniquely appropriate as centers of Party influence in the village. A significant number of the twenty-five thousand urban Communists sent out to organize collective farms in November 1929 eventually gravitated to the MTS. As the MTS system expanded, the stations more or less automatically became centers of Party concentration.[30] The rate of growth of Party cells in the MTS, thanks to the urban contingents serving as cadre nuclei, was substantially greater than that in the kolkhozes and the sovkhozes.

The tremendous increase in the size of the MTS network and in the scope of its responsibilities was not without its negative consequences. By the middle of 1932 there were signs of serious shortcomings, particularly in the very operational and organizational activities for which the system had originally been created. The rapidity of MTS expansion had led to severe shortages of machinery and skilled managerial and operating personnel. Moreover, following the initial enthusiasm of MTS construction, there had been a general letdown in performance standards and organizational discipline.[31]

Thus ended the first stage in the history of the MTS. During the years of the First Five Year Plan it had grown from an isolated experiment into a nationwide system. By 1932 there was mounting evidence, however, that this system was suffering from more than the usual growing pains and was performing virtually none of its assigned tasks satisfactorily. By this time, however, the commitment to the MTS — material, political, and ideological — was too great to make turning back a serious possibility.

THE MTS AND THE CONSOLIDATION OF COLLECTIVIZATION: 1933–1934

The decline in the performance of the MTS in 1932 was symptomatic of the general malaise which spread through the countryside in the wake of the haste and brutality of collectivization. The years 1933 and 1934 were in many ways a transitional period in Soviet agriculture. On the one hand, they were years of mopping up operations in which the last vestiges of overt peasant resistance were eliminated and the kolkhozes were whipped into operational shape. They were also years of severe famine in large areas of the country, primarily the result of official policy; controlled violence reminiscent of War Communism was once again an accepted method of administration. On the other hand, they also witnessed the first preliminary steps toward the normalization of production and procurement procedures in the new kolkhoz system.

The MTS were called upon to play an important role in many of these processes. The establishment of political departments (*politotdely*) in the MTS in January 1933 symbolized the determination to make the stations central command points in the mopping up operations in the kolkhozes. Patterned after the politotdels in the Red Army, the MTS politotdels carried out intensive purges of allegedly dissident "class-alien" elements which had penetrated the stations and the kolkhozes in the wake of collectivization, replacing them with reliable Party members and sympathizers. The politotdels were also expected to maintain close Party supervision of daily operations in the MTS and kolkhozes. Whatever their contributions to improving the efficiency of MTS-kolkhoz production relations, the politotdels did establish a precedent for strong Party involvement in and around the MTS. In the process they succeeded in giving the MTS a coercive coloration which lingered long after the politotdels themselves were liquidated.

In the more positive task of normalizing the system of agricultural production and procurements, the role assigned to the MTS was no less important. Through the device of the MTS-kolkhoz contract, an annual document signed by the station with each of its kolkhozes and obligating each party to perform specific operations in the crop cycle, the MTS was made a key instrument in the implementation of state production plans. The 1933 Model Contract reinstated Markevich's original principle of payments in kind (*naturoplata*) by the kolkhozes for MTS services. This provision insured that the MTS would become a major source of state grain procurements.

The initial part of the consolidation period witnessed the expansion of MTS responsibilities in other areas as well. MTS agronomists were placed in direct charge of kolkhoz production activities. The stations were also made responsible for the organization of all procurement activities in their zones. Taken together, these various economic and political duties added up to a concerted policy of making the MTS system, rather than the state agricultural bureaucracy, the primary channel of centralized control in agriculture.

When the Seventeenth Party Congress met early in 1934, it was becoming clear to many leading Party figures, including Stalin himself, that the MTS could not shoulder so large a burden. Consequently, even before the liquidation of the politotdel system the search began for more regular methods of Party and government leadership.

NORMALIZATION OF MTS-KOLKHOZ RELATIONS: 1934–1939

The period from the end of 1934 to the beginning of war mobilization in 1939 saw a continuing quest for procedural norms and organizational arrangements to stabilize MTS-kolkhoz relations and coordinate them with plans of economic development. For much of the period efforts were made to replace the previous system of direct Party involvement in agriculural management with less direct forms of Party supervision and guidance. Accordingly, a good deal of attention was devoted to strengthening the formal machinery of agricultural administration. Along with this policy went a continuing elaboration of financial and legal

mechanisms to define and regulate MTS relations with the kolkhozes. The Great Purge, to be sure, imposed serious obstacles to
this normalization policy, but the policy was never entirely
abandoned.

An important factor in this movement toward rationalization
was the rapid expansion of MTS coverage. During the period the
MTS system reached the point where it was really becoming a
dominant feature of the agricultural scene. Table 2-6 shows the

Table 2-6. Expansion of the MTS system, 1934–1940.

MTS equipment and coverage	Year (December 31)						
	1934	1935	1936	1937	1938	1939	1940
Number of MTS	3,533	4,375	5,000	5,818	6,358	6,501	7,069
Number of tractors in MTS (1000)	177.3	254.7	328.5	365.8	394.0	422.0	435.3
Tractors per MTS	50	58	66	63[a]	62[a]	65	62[a]
Number of kolkhozes served by MTS (1000)	106.7	129.7	162.9	190.8	198.0	—	200.0
Sown area of kolkhozes served by MTS as percent of all kolkhoz sown area	63.9	72.4	82.8	91.2	93.3	94.0	94.1

Source: Compiled from data in I. S. Malyshev, ed., *MTS vo vtoroi piatiletke* (Moscow-Leningrad, 1939), p. 11; and V. G. Venzher, *Osnovnye voprosy proizvodstvennoi deiatel'nosti MTS* (Moscow, 1949), pp. 16, 40.

[a] The decline in the number of tractors per MTS in 1937 and 1938 reflected (a) the introduction of new large diesel tractors to replace older models, (b) the diversion of some tractors to new stations being set up in the non-Black-Earth regions under the campaign to redress an imbalance in MTS coverage, and (c) the breaking up of especially large stations in Siberia in 1937, part of the nationwide campaign against "gigantomania" at this time. The decline in tractors per MTS in 1940 reflected the setting up of new stations in the western regions incorporated into the USSR after September 1939.

growth of the MTS network through 1940. To a certain extent
the impact of the MTS was less profound than the percentages
in Table 2-6 suggest, however. Coverage was only nominal in many
areas of the country. Even where the range of agricultural services

performed by the MTS in the kolkhozes was fairly complete, the quality of MTS work was often unsatisfactory. Shortages of fuel and spare parts and inadequate machinery, coupled with insistent demands by the state for operating economies, forced the MTS to operate under constraints that made effective service to the kolkhozes virtually impossible. Many of the organizational measures introduced during the period were aimed at overcoming these problems without altering the basically confiscatory orientation of agricultural policy. The objectives of these measures may be classified under three main headings: administrative rationalization, financial accountability, and legal responsibility.

The issue of administrative rationalization was the object of continuing debate and experimentation throughout the period. At times the issue became involved in the Great Purge, which hit the personnel of the agricultural bureaucracy particularly hard. The successive reorganization schemes broadly followed the changes in the conception of the role of the MTS system in the total pattern of agricultural administration. Thus, the first major change (actually decreed in 1934) closely reflected the decision of the Seventeenth Party Congress to downgrade the administrative and organizational functions of the MTS and to transfer many of these functions to the local administrative organs of the Commissariat of Agriculture, the raion land departments (*raizo*). The MTS were left with enough administrative responsibilities, however, to cause serious jurisdictional discord with the raizos. Other structural weaknesses in the 1934 arrangement led to problems of control over the MTS by the provincial agricultural organs. During 1936 and 1937 several remedial proposals were debated and some were actually tried out in selected areas, but no fundamental changes were made. When a major reorganization was finally effected, towards the end of 1939, it reflected a growing tendency to make the MTS once again the centers of local agricultural administration.

The issue of financial accountability in the MTS system was one of the most vexing problems in Soviet agriculture during the period. For three years massive efforts were made to place the individual stations on an economically self-sufficient basis. Through a planned decrease in state subsidies, combined with improvements in operating efficiency, it was hoped that the stations could be speedily weaned away from the state budget and made capable of supporting themselves from their *naturoplata* receipts from the kolkhozes. These hopes remained illusory, however, owing to structural weaknesses in the MTS and the inflexibility of the state agricultural pricing policies. (See Chapter 5.) Ultimately, it was found necessary to renounce the goal of self-financing itself, and in 1938 the MTS system was transferred entirely to the state budget. The implications of this measure went far beyond the realm of finances, for the resultant de-emphasis of *naturoplata* as a criterion of efficiency meant a subtle change in the entire character of the MTS-kolkhoz relationship. (See Chapter 3.)

Efforts in the legal sphere were more persistent than those in finances, if not notably more successful. Their main focus was on the structure of the annual MTS-kolkhoz contract. The contract performed the important function of translating the aggregate production targets of the individual stations into specific operational programs for each kolkhoz. Successive attempts were made to render the Model Contract (on which the actual contracts were based) more precise in terms of MTS and kolkhoz obligations and to make them enforceable in the law courts. Owing to the one-sided nature of the MTS-kolkhoz relationship, however, the contract could not be made to function as an effective legal instrument, particularly from the standpoint of the kolkhoz. Its main practical utility was as a statement of governmental claims on kolkhoz produce.

Throughout the period the local Party organs played an important role in the implementation and supervision of these new regulatory arrangements. During these years a standard pattern of raikom involvement in agricultural affairs developed. Notwithstanding the official line against direct, politotdel-style involvement, most raikom secretaries found it impossible to avoid direct interference in managerial and technical matters at least during the critical periods of the agricultural year. The penalties for overinvolvement were invariably less severe than those for underinvolvement and failure to meet the production goals of the raion. For all intents and purposes the raikom first secretary was the *de facto* agricultural decision maker in the raion. Nevertheless, during much of the year some effort was made to conform to the official norms of indirect Party leadership. (See Chapter 6.)

Despite the liquidation of the politotdels the MTS continued to enjoy a unique Party status among rural production institutions. To head the MTS Party organization and provide special political guidance and coordination of MTS production activities a special position was created in each station, the Deputy Director of the MTS for the Political Sector (sometimes called the *zampolit*). Although his jurisdiction did not extend beyond the personnel of the station, the nature of MTS activities and the zampolit's official designation as a member of MTS management meant that he was a far more powerful figure than the ordinary secretary of a Party organization.

The worsening international situation towards the end of the period was reflected in a general tightening up of Party and governmental controls throughout the country. Increasing demands for agricultural procurements heightened pressures for direct Party interference in agricultural management. As war approached, earlier concerns for the maintenance of a concrete division of labor between Party, governmental, and economic functionaries were forgotten.

THE MTS IN WORLD WAR II

The German invasion of the USSR in June 1941 was followed by a rapid expansion of political controls over all aspects of Soviet life. In November politotdels were established in the MTS and sovkhozes to combat the collapse of production efforts and labor discipline engendered by the German advance. In structure, functions, and shortcomings as well, the wartime politotdels were a faithful reproduction of their 1933–1934 predecessors. (See Chapter 10.)

The war wrought severe physical damage to Soviet agriculture. By the fall of 1942 the Germans were in control of the Ukraine, the Crimea, Belorussia, the Baltic states, the main agricultural regions of the Don and the Kuban', and large parts of the Central non-Black Earth regions. These areas, with 107,000 kolkhozes and 3,000 MTS, comprised 40 percent of the total kolkhoz sown area, 37 percent of the grain-growing area, and 49 percent of the technical crop area in the USSR.[32] The MTS lost heavily in machinery from enemy actions and requisitions by the Soviet armed forces. From the end of 1940 to the end of 1942 the number of tractors in agriculture declined from 435,253 to 259,207 (a loss of more than 40 percent); the number of combines dropped from 153,353 to 102,124 (a loss of more than one-third).[33] Because of the shift of farm machinery plants to war production, almost no new tractors or spare parts were being produced. Fuel shortages were particularly acute. As able-bodied males were drawn off into the armed forces, the supply of machinery operators declined rapidly, and the recruitment and training of women tractor drivers and combine operators became a major task of the local Party and MTS officials.

Under these conditions the MTS were not in a position to provide very effective production services to the kolkhozes. In some areas the entire pattern of formal MTS-kolkhoz relations virtually disintegrated. However, thanks to the efforts of the politotdels, the MTS did generally serve to keep the kolkhoz system together and to insure that something would be planted, harvested, and, most important of all, procured for the needs of the armed forces.

The victory at Stalingrad in early 1943 and the subsequent improvement of the military situation were soon reflected in the countryside. In May 1943 the MTS politotdels were abolished, and full responsibility for agricultural producton devolved upon the raikom. The result was a noticeable loosening of political control in the MTS zones, which the regular raikoms, totally immersed in production affairs, were apparently unable to counteract. Physical reconstruction began immediately, if often in a very haphazard fashion, in the areas liberated from the Germans. Emphasis was placed on rebuilding the MTS in each district as a focal point of agricultural rehabilitation. With this end in mind orders were issued during 1943 for the return to the individual MTS of machinery that had been evacuated to the East and for the procurement of spare parts and construction materials to restore the operational capabilities of the stations.[34]

In simple physical terms the recovery of the MTS system was quite impressive. During 1943, according to one report, 502 MTS were rebuilt in the Ukraine alone. By the end of 1944 all stations in operation in that republic at the end of 1940 had been re-stored.[35] For the country as a whole 1702 MTS were rebuilt by the beginning of 1944.[36] And at the end of 1945 there were 7500 MTS in the country, or 431 more than at the beginning of 1941.[37]

In operational terms, recovery was far less rapid. The stock of MTS machinery was in extremely poor condition. In the Ukraine, for example, at the end of 1945 only 55 percent of the prewar tractor force was in operating condition.[38] For the country as a whole there were only 327,271 tractors in the MTS system — roughly 25 percent below the 1940 total.[39] Many of them were in poor condition; breakdowns and stoppages due to lack of spare parts were universal. At a Plenum of the Rostov Obkom in the summer of 1945, for example, it was stated that fully one-half of the existing tractor pool in the 121 MTS of the oblast stood idle for mechanical reasons.[40] Other areas reported similar problems.[41]

Thus, it is not surprising that the recovery in MTS performance lagged considerably behind the officially stated rate of physical reconstruction. Table 2-7 shows the relative recovery rates of the MTS system during the wartime and early postwar years. In the light of the complaints at the February (1947) Plenum of the CC

Table 2-7. Recovery of the MTS system from wartime damage in terms of output relative to 1940 performance levels.

Year	Number of MTS (end of year)	Volume of tractor work (as percent of 1940 volume)	Output per standard 15 hp tractor (as percent of 1940 output)
1940	7,069	100	100
1943	5,229	28.5	48.0
1944	7,251	43.1	58.5
1945	7,470	51.9	72.7
1946	7,577	63.0	84.3
1947	7,700	81.2	101.9

Source: Compiled from data in the following sources: V. G. Venzher, *Osnovnye voprosy proizvodstvennoi deiatel'nosti MTS* (Moscow, 1949), p. 117; *Sel'skoe khoziaistvo SSSR* (statistical handbook) (Moscow, 1960), p. 74; *Ekonomicheskaia zhizn' SSSR* (Moscow, 1961), pp. 437, 465; G. Shrabshtein, "Mashinno-traktornye stantsii v poslevoennyi period," *MTS*, no. 11 (November 1947), p. 15.

AUCP (B), there is reason to question the claim of a steady rate of improvement in output per tractor in the postwar years indicated in the table. Even with the normal caveats on Soviet data, Table 2-7 barely suggests the full extent of the wartime damage to Soviet agriculture and the difficulties involved in restoration. Thus, it was not until well into 1950 that the total number of tractors in the MTS reached the 1940 level.[42] Until mid-1947 recovery was a piecemeal affair. The tractor pool of the average station contained so motley a collection of machines, most of them severely depreciated, that operational programming and maintenance were exceedingly difficult. The few spare parts being turned out by Soviet industry were notoriously defective. All of these factors, naturally, had their effects on MTS performance.[43]

The war also adversely affected the condition of morale and discipline of the MTS and the kolkhozes, particularly after the liquidation of the politotdels. Many of the formal devices for regulating MTS activities, such as the annual MTS-kolkhoz contract, were ignored. Large parcels of kolkhoz land were seized by industrial plants, government institutions, and even private persons. Finally, 1946 was a year of widespread drought, and famine once again haunted large areas of the country.

THE MTS AND POSTWAR AGRICULTURAL POLICY: 1947–1953

Despite these problems the campaign to restore production and normal discipline in the countryside did not begin in earnest until the summer of 1946. In September the Central Committee established a special Council on Kolkhoz Affairs under the chairmanship of A. A. Andreev, the Party's chief agricultural spokesman. The council was given extraordinary powers to reimpose firm discipline in the village and to eliminate the effects of the wartime "squandering" of kolkhoz land.

The campaign was intensified in early 1947, when a major reorganization of the agricultural bureaucracy was decreed, enhancing the position of the MTS system in the line of administrative authority. At the February Plenum of the Central Committee the MTS received further attention in a series of measures to improve production efficiency. Symbolic of the general tightening of controls was the decision to re-establish the position of Deputy

Director of the MTS for the Political Sector, which had not existed since the beginning of the war. The new *zampolity* were given greater rights of interference in kolkhoz Party affairs than their prewar counterparts.

In the period following the February Plenum the scope of MTS activities steadily expanded. The stations were looked to for leadership in many of the grandiose schemes encompassed by the "Stalinist Plan for Reshaping Nature." They played a major role in the forest shelter-belt program and the grassland crop rotation scheme of the late forties and early fifties. A number of Forest Shelter-Belt Stations (LZS), similar in organization to the MTS, were also set up to assist in these projects.[44] The MTS were brought into the campaign to improve kolkhoz livestock herds, an area in which they had had no substantial involvement previously. Under the "Three-Year Plan for the Development of Socialized Kolkhoz and Sovkhoz Productive Animal Husbandry (1949–1951)," the MTS were to have major responsibilities for fodder procurement and the electrification and mechanization of labor-intensive operations in kolkhoz dairies. As in the case of the LZS, a number of specialized Machine-Animal Husbandry Stations (MZhS), were set up, and many existing MTS were specially re-equipped for this work.[45] These new programs reflected the progressive adaptation of the MTS principle — the principle of centralized, state controlled direction of the means of agricultural production — to all areas of agricultural endeavor.

Probably the most important development during this period from the standpoint of the MTS system was the kolkhoz amalgamation campaign initiated by N. S. Khrushchev shortly after his return to Moscow in late 1949. The objective was to merge small, inefficient farms into larger, more viable economic units. The campaign proceeded very rapidly in most areas: in some regions the number of kolkhozes was reduced by as much as one-half or even two-thirds by the end of 1950.[46] In Moscow Oblast, for example, the number of kolkhozes declined from 6059 on the eve of the campaign of 1668 in late June 1950; in Voronezh Oblast the decline was from 3188 to 1119 by August 20, 1950.[47] In the Ukraine the number of kolkhozes declined from 33,653 on January 1, 1950, to 16,186 on January 1, 1952.[48] For the USSR as a whole the number was reduced from about 254,000 at the beginning of 1950 to 121,000 at the end of that year and to 97,000 on the eve of the Nineteenth Party Congress in October 1952.[49]

The size of the average kolkhoz in each region grew proportionately. And as Khrushchev had indicated in his speeches promoting the campaign, these physical changes would have important effects on MTS coverage of the kolkhozes. Table 2-8 illustrates some of these effects.

Table 2-8. Coverage of kolkhozes by MTS tractor brigades, USSR average for selected years.

MTS tractor brigades: equipment and coverage	Year				
	1940	1947	1949	1950	1952
Number of tractor brigades:					
per MTS	15.00	13.00	12.00	12.0	12.0
per kolkhoz	0.51	0.56	0.48	0.9	1.2
Number of tractors per MTS brigade	4.30	3.30	4.20	4.6	5.2

Source: Iu. V. Arutiunian, *Mekhanizatory sel'skogo khoziaistva SSSR* (Moscow, 1957), p. 130, table.

The most obvious result of the mergers was an improved MTS-kolkhoz ratio. The average number of kolkhozes served by each station declined from 32 in 1948 to 11 in late 1952. In the main agricultural regions, where kolkhozes were already quite large, the mergers resulted in a decline in the service ratio of from 12 to 14 kolkhozes per station to 5 or 6 per station.[50] In some cases individual kolkhozes in these areas were now being served by more than one tractor brigade. For the first time it was becoming possible to achieve the ideal of a stable relationship between tractor brigades and individual kolkhozes.

The merger campaign also had an impact on the extent of Party coverage in the countryside. The decrease in the number of kolkhozes meant a corresponding increase in the proportion of farms with primary Party organizations (PPO). For the future this improvement in Party coverage portended a relative decline in the special political status of the MTS as Party "support points" in the village.

For the time being, however, the position of the MTS remained virtually impregnable. Indeed, when two prominent Soviet economists suggested to Stalin in late 1951 that the MTS system might profitably be dismantled and their machinery sold to the kolkhozes, their proposal was contemptuously rejected as an attack on the fundamental principles of socialist agriculture.[51] (See Chapter 3.)

Despite these and other expressions of confidence in the MTS principle, the actual performance of the stations remained disappointing. The limits of feasible expansion of the system, at least as it was conceived by Stalin, had apparently been reached. By the fall of 1952 the number of stations was approaching its historical maximum of approximately nine thousand. Further construction was contemplated only for the Baltic republics, where collectivization was just being completed.[52] The lack of perspective for a real solution to agricultural problems was symbolized by the nature of the one innovation in agriculture proposed by Malenkov in his report to the Nineteenth Party Congress. This was a proposal to create a new system of Electro-Machine-Tractor Stations to be based on huge, unwieldy electrical tractors that were connected to their power supplies by tremendous spools of wire! The project was soon forgotten.

THE MTS UNDER KHRUSHCHEV

The aura of stagnation which had pervaded Soviet agriculture in Stalin's final years was quickly dissipated in the fall of 1953 when Khrushchev launched his broad new offensive on the agricultural front. The most important thrust of this offensive was a new pricing policy for kolkhoz produce. For the first time the kolkhozes were given substantial material incentives to increase their production. Economic methods were added to the traditional administrative and political devices in the arsenal of state controls over agriculture.

Once again a leading role was assigned to the MTS. Indeed, the period from September 1953 to the end of 1957 witnessed the most severe test the MTS system had ever had to undergo. For the first time the MTS were placed out in the open and given virtually complete responsibility for the economic and political leadership of the kolkhozes. The raizo was abolished, and the individual stations were left to bear the major part of the local administrative burden, as well as additional responsibilities for the technical supervision of kolkhoz field crop and livestock affairs. Later in the period the MTS were also placed in charge of agricultural procurements.

To carry on their new responsibilities and reinforce their general operating capabilities the MTS were given massive infusions of new personnel. Managerial and technical capabilities of MTS leadership were raised by the recruitment of thousands of industrial managers and engineers to serve as MTS directors, chief engineers, and repair shop managers. Tens of thousands of agricultural specialists from the kolkhozes and the various echelons of the agricultural bureaucracy were attached to the MTS to carry on continuous supervision of MTS-kolkhoz production operations. Finally, hundreds of thousands of tractor drivers and other farm machinery operators, who had formerly served as part-time MTS employees, were made permanent staff members of the stations. Thus, within six months of the September (1953) Plenum of the Central Committee, the MTS enjoyed a near monopoly of skilled agricultural personnel in the village (excepting, of course, those employed in the sovkhoz system).

The concentration of leadership in the MTS applied to the local Party organs as well. Khrushchev reorganized the rural raikoms essentially along politotdel lines by permanently assigning to each MTS a resident raikom secretary with a group of Party instructors to supervise political and economic activities in the kolkhozes of the MTS zone. The new format represented a return to the direct mode of Party control in agriculture, reflecting his general campaign to move Party influence closer to production in all areas of the national economy.

While perhaps gratifying to the partisans of the MTS, the massive accretion of responsibilities had its dangers. Khrushchev was interested above all in concrete results. Although the MTS seemed at first the ideal instrument for achieving these results, the unequivocal nature of its responsibilities made the real strengths and weaknesses of the MTS that much more visible. In short, the MTS had become much more vulnerable to attack on pragmatic grounds. Each aspect of MTS work could, and would, now be scrutinized and evaluated on its merits. Accordingly, the ultimate decision to abolish the MTS was the result of a piecemeal testing and curtailment of functions, rather than an abrupt change of heart.

By far the most crucial area in which the effectiveness of the MTS was put to the test was that of financial costs. The manner in which this sensitive issue was raised and pressed for solution was an indication of the pragmatic attitude with which Khrushchev was approaching the hoary problems of the agricultural system. Proposals to return the MTS to a self-supporting basis had been made from time to time ever since the 1938 decision to finance them directly from the state budget, but each time the idea had been rejected on ideological or economic grounds. By 1954, however, Khrushchev himself began to demand an answer to the difficult question of the actual costs to the state of the commodities procured as payments in kind for MTS services. At the Twentieth Party Congress he announced a campaign to transfer the MTS to a cost-accounting basis, beginning in certain selected regions. Before the campaign was far enough along to show results, however, the MTS system was abolished.

If the MTS were showing serious signs of weakness under Khrushchev's new policies, the kolkhozes were proving to be an unexpected source of strength. As a result of the mergers and the beneficial effects of the liberalized pricing policy, a significant number of kolkhozes were beginning to demonstrate genuine economic vigor. In response, Khrushchev gradually shifted the focus of his attention to the kolkhoz side of the MTS-kolkhoz relationship. In 1955 he launched a major campaign to recruit thousands of experienced managerial and professional personnel as kolkhoz chairmen. In all, more than thirty thousand of these persons were sent to the kolkhozes. Their presence tended, among other things, to help redress the old, one-sided relationship between the MTS and the kolkhozes. (See Chapter 13.)

By the middle of 1956 Khrushchev was ready to entertain pre-

viously unheard of suggestions for experiments with kolkhoz ownership of tractors and other machines. In 1957 newspaper accounts
of schemes for combined management of MTS and kolkhoz production units were quite common. By the end of the year large-
scale transfers and sales of MTS equipment to the kolkhozes were
being actively discussed. Although there was vigorous opposition
in leading Party circles to many of these experiments, by the end
of 1957 it was clear that Khrushchev had made up his mind: the
MTS must be abolished. They had played their role in the socialist
transformation of the village. Now "life itself" decreed that they
be relegated to the scrap heap of history.

3   The MTS and Soviet Ideology

The development of an official theory of the MTS and its subsequent influence on agricultural policy represents an interesting case study of the role of ideology in the Soviet decision-making process. Indeed, the transformation of the MTS from a simple production institution into a main pillar of socialist agricultural theory surely ranks among the most striking illustrations of the tortuous operations of the vaunted "dialectical interaction of theory and practice."

Students of Soviet affairs are invariably confronted with a dilemma in attempting to assess the real importance of ideology in the operation of the political system. It is impossible to ignore the apparent cynicism with which ideological symbols are so often invoked. One has only to compare the official theories and formulas on agricultural collectivization with the brutal facts of the collectivization process itself for ample evidence of this cynicism. At the same time, it is almost equally impossible to ignore the tremendous amount of energy that the Soviet leaders have always devoted to the development of consistent theoretical foundations for their policies. The presumption is inescapable that they do attribute a considerable degree of relevance to theoretical work at least at some stage of the policy process. What remains to be determined, then, is the manner in which ideology is, or is perceived to be, relevant and at what stages of the policy process it operates. In short, the question to be investigated is the following: Is the function of ideology mere ex post facto rationalization — a form of window dressing for policies determined on grounds of pure expediency, or is it more than this? This chapter will suggest answers to this question from the evidence of the history of MTS theory.

The prominent place formally assigned to ideology in the Soviet political system has long been a source of interest to Western students of Soviet affairs. Few systems in the history of politics have so self-consciously and purposefully sought to propagate and apply a formal political doctrine in their governmental processes. For historical parallels one would have to look back to John Calvin's sixteenth century Geneva, an avowedly theocratic state.

Zbigniew Brzezinski has characterized this self-conscious proclivity for ideological reinforcement and exegesis as a distinguishing feature of totalitarian systems. He notes in such systems "an *organizational compulsion* for ideologically focussed and compatible action" to legitimize and mobilize mass support for the regimes and their policies.[1] Attention has also been called to the special function of ideology in the Soviet system as a link between theory and practice, between basic doctrinal principles and specific policy actions.[2] In this sense ideology is applied theory, continually expanding and "enriching" itself in the confrontation with new situations. These observations would appear to suggest, then, that theory, or at least theorizing, is an integral part of the Soviet policy process.

Throughout Soviet history there has indeed been a continuing effort to explain, justify, and to a certain extent prescribe current policies in terms of the basic "laws" and categories of Marxism-Leninism. In so far as positive influence on the decision-making process is concerned, logic would lead one to expect that the theory-building phase would precede the actual making of decisions. This is undoubtedly the ideal sequence, but it obviously has not always been the actual sequence. For example, Stalin found it necessary to exhort a group of leading agrarian theorists on the eve of the mass collectivization drive: "it is essential that theoretical work not only keep pace with practical work but should keep ahead of it and equip our practical workers in their fight for the victory of socialism." [3]

It is precisely this frequent reversal of the ideal theory-practice sequence which perhaps more than anything else has tended to depreciate the significance of ideology as an operative factor in Soviet policy-making in the eyes of Western observers. And deservedly so. Nevertheless, there are grounds for arguing that ideology is more than mere cynical rationalization. Even when the ideological formulation of a given institution or relationship clearly follows its establishment in practice, Soviet policy-makers frequently treat that formulation as having genuine normative force. Indeed, sometimes they appear incapable of *not* treating it as having such force; an ex post facto formulation will often exert tangible influence on subsequent decisions involving the given institution or relationship. In general, the ideological mode of policy-making as practiced in the Soviet system, so highly valued as a scientific, progressive method of analysis and action, quite often has unintended consequences which are just the reverse of scientific and progressive. These effects are well illustrated by the history of the ideological formulations involving the MTS, which, although postdating the establishment of the MTS system itself, eventually came to exert a powerfully conservative influence on agricultural policy, effectively shielding the performance of the key agricultural institutions from scrutiny.

These general observations suggest that ideology performs a number of distinctive functions in the Soviet political system. With due regard for the difficulties and the artificiality of treating the individual functions in isolation, it is nevertheless analytically useful to do so. The three primary functions may be listed as (1) analysis, (2) legitimation, and (3) conservation.[4] In considering this classification scheme it may be useful to employ Robert K. Merton's concepts of "manifest" and "latent" functions. Merton defines manifest functions as "those objective consequences contributing to the adjustment or adaptation of the system which are intended and recognized by participants in the system"; he defines latent functions as "correlatively, . . . those which are neither intended nor recognized."[5]

Analysis relates most directly to the policy-formulation aspect of ideology. Ideology furnishes the lexicon and conceptual apparatus for describing and explaining a particular policy or institution in terms of accepted "laws" and general principles of Marxist-Leninist doctrine. No doubt as a result of their many years of training in and exposure to the doctrine, Soviet policy-makers appear to require the theoretical understanding and the sense of continuity which the process of analysis allegedly furnishes. The psychological dimensions of this felt need will be discussed more fully below with reference to the legitimation function. With respect to the policy process itself, however, the primary purpose of the analytical exercise is its supposed predictive result. That is, classification and analysis are expected to have deductive consequences. The formulation of a consistent ideological model of an institution or policy will, ideally, suggest a future course of action for the institution or policy. The analytical function is clearly "manifest" in the sense that it is fully intended and actively pursued by Soviet policy-makers. However, there is reason to question how important the analytical function, and particularly its predictive features, have consistently been in the making of actual decisions.

There is substantially less doubt about the salience of the *legitimation* function. The intensive socialization of Party members and, to a lesser extent, the population at large has conditioned them to expect theoretical consistency in the handling of policy issues. Thus, the overt formulation of policies in ideological terms reinforces the legitimacy of both the policies and the policy-makers. Policies are made authoritative by demonstrating that they conform to basic ideological principles. Similarly, the authority of the policy-makers is enhanced by their demonstrated concern for ideological consistency and the traditional verities of the founding fathers. Stalin's appropriation of the Lenin Cooperative Plan to legitimize the forced collectivization program is a good example of this process. Soviet rulers are obviously well aware of the utility of ideology as a source of political legitimacy. The result is presumably considered sufficiently worthwhile to warrant the risk of cheapening the entire stock of ideological currency by using it as ex post facto rationalization. Yet the careful, almost gingerly fashion in which even such rationalizations are undertaken suggests a great awareness of the risks. Indeed, in certain cases, it may well be questioned whether the Soviet rulers are aware that they are engaging in mere rationalization. In this sense the legitimation function may, perhaps, be relegated to the gray area between manifest and latent functions.[6]

The *conservative* function presents fewer problems of classification. There is a marked tendency for a given ideological formulation, even one whose origins were ex post facto, to become petrified and to inhibit empirical investigation and evaluation. This is obviously a latent function, an undesirable, or at least undesired, consequence of the ideological mode of policy-making. After Stalin's death the Soviet rulers appear to have become somewhat aware of the more stultifying effects of the ideological methodology. To some extent the successive post-Stalin leaders have been able to overcome these effects, although they continue to strive to avoid any "descent" to "mere empiricism". The noticeable differences in the style and content of Soviet policy-making in different periods suggest the potential flexibility of the method and the crucial importance of the personal style of the ruler or ruling group in the operation of the Soviet system.

THE ROLES OF THE MTS

One of the root problems of the use of ideology in the policy process is the confusion it often engenders in the distinction between empirical and ideological "truths" and the relative weights to be assigned to each in the formulation and evaluation of policy. In the case of the MTS much of this confusion can be traced to the complex interweaving of production and nonproduction responsibilities. The steady accretion of nonproduction functions, in particular, tended to obscure the conception of the primary nature of the institution and to encumber efforts to define criteria for evaluating its performance. Although the ideological model of the MTS-kolkhoz relationship was drawn to encompass both types of functions and, in fact, fostered the expansion of nonproduction functions, it provided at best only a vague kind of policy guidance as to their relative importance in the total scheme of MTS activities.

Soviet discussions of the MTS customarily referred to two closely related but distinguishable roles: a direct production role and a so-called organizational role. The former comprised the concrete agronomic and mechanical field operations which the MTS performed in the kolkhozes, usually in return for a portion of the crop. The latter, sometimes referred to as a political role of the MTS, comprised the administrative and political control functions exercised by the MTS over the kolkhozes of their zones.

The nature of the production role was fairly simple to express and explain in ideological terms. The MTS was perceived as the vehicle for the introduction and control of large-scale state-owned instruments of production and modern agronomic techniques in the collective farms. Given the extreme scarcity of modern farm machinery and the technical expertise to operate it, combined with the built-in ideological biases in favor of centralization and bigness, the idea of concentrating the available machines and technical cadres in a few thousand strategically located command points rather than scattering them among a hundred times as many backward kolkhozes had many obvious attractions.

Superficially, the political role should not have been much more difficult to predicate in ideological terms. The Marxian postulate of the relationship between economics and politics should have led Soviet policy-makers to expect that the MTS would become centers of political control in the countryside. In practice the evolution of the nonproduction functions was considerably more spontaneous and unplanned, although the ideological analysis did undoubtedly reinforce the predisposition of Soviet policy-makers to accept it and give it normative force once it appeared. The original enthusiasm for the MTS was based largely on optimistic forecasts that the initial investments would quickly be repaid out of payments in kind for MTS services. It was confidently expected that these payments would eventually cover the total basic grain requirements of the state: a perfect example of the principle of direct exchange between town and country.[7] The entire scheme was based on the assumption that the MTS would indeed serve the kolkhozes in an effective manner and the kolkhozes would, thus, be able and willing to pay for the services rendered. But under the Stalinist model of industrialization it was clear almost from the outset that the state would be keeping its investments in agriculture, including those in the MTS system, to a bare minimum. As a result the MTS were rarely equipped to provide effective service. And the kolkhozes were placed in double jeopardy. On the one hand, they had to pay very high prices for the work done by the MTS, prices which bore only the slightest relationship to the value of the services actually received. On the other hand, they received very low prices for the large portion of their crops surrendered to the state as obligatory deliveries. Thus, the regime had effectively renounced economic incentives to induce the peasants to grow what was required and found it necessary to resort extensively to non-economic methods to achieve the same result. Here the organizational or political role of the MTS was important. The theoretical justification of this role required a good deal of imagination and ingenuity, not to mention downright cynicism, but Soviet ideologists were quite equal to the task.

The adjective "political" may be somewhat misleading as a description of this complex area of MTS activities, for it encompassed a range of functions by no means all of which bore the coercive connotations usually associated with the term. In the Soviet use of the term with respect to the MTS, "political" took on some of the "policy" implications of the Russian word *politika*. That is, a significant aspect of the role involved the direction of policy in the kolkhozes. For a more precise understanding of the various aspects of the nonproduction role of the MTS, it will be useful to describe the main functions actually performed.

First, there was what might be called a *direct control function*, or a pure political function, where the individual machine-tractor stations served as the physical headquarters for Party and secret police operations in the surrounding countryside. In the history of the MTS this function was carried on only intermittently and did not usually involve the regular operating personnel of the stations. The activities of the MTS politotdels of 1933–1934 and 1941–1943 and, to a certain extent, those of the "zonal" raikom instructor groups of 1953–1957 were examples of this function. These political organs were not permanent. Indeed, as will be shown in Part III, each time the regime attempted to use the MTS as agencies of direct political control it found them unsuitable. Thus, while the direct control responsibilities of the MTS were quite important during certain stages of Soviet history, they did not constitute a principal long-term function.

Historically more important was the general *organizational function* of the stations. As the main, and in some periods the only, state agency at the local level concerned with the implementation and operation of national agricultural policies, the MTS were called upon to perform a wide range of administrative and regulatory functions. Through its involvement in the kolkhoz planning process and in the formulation of the annual MTS-kolkhoz contract the individual station played a large part in determining what and how much the kolkhozes planted. In the process of training and employing large numbers of kolkhozniks as tractor drivers, equipment operators, and auxiliary service personnel, not to mention their overall generalship of field operations, the stations disposed of a significant portion of the kolkhoz labor force. They were also responsible for the training and supervision of kolkhoz administrators, particularly bookkeepers. These tasks were of continuing importance, even if the MTS often performed them with something less than complete effectiveness.

Finally, related to the first two functions was the very important, if less formal, *supervisory* or *watchdog function*. Because of their direct physical presence in the kolkhozes during key phases of the agricultural year, MTS officials were in a position to serve as eyes of the Party and the state in the village, protecting the national interest against self-serving local interests. The politotdels were designed specifically to formalize and enhance the effectiveness of this function. But throughout the history of the MTS, station personnel were expected to keep their eyes open for violations of official policies and norms. Except when there was active collusion between MTS and kolkhoz personnel, the presence of such officials in the kolkhozes did undoubtedly make state control more effective.

From this brief discussion of the nonproduction role of the MTS, it is clear that the economic and political functions of the MTS were very closely intertwined. Both were directed to the same end: the maximizing of food and fiber procurements. The political role also involved the MTS in the task of political and social control in the village, but this was clearly secondary. The most important implication of the dual role and the great weight given to the political and organizational functions was the fact that the MTS system could not operate effectively as a purely production institution. It was largely to justify, if not conceal, the reliance on non-economic means of control that the elaborate ideological formulation of the MTS-kolkhoz relationship was developed.

THE DEVELOPMENT OF THE IDEOLOGICAL FORMULATION OF THE MTS

The original appearance of the MTS can hardly be said to have been a result of any ideological forecasting. The earliest champions of the tractor-column and MTS ideas tended to couch their arguments chiefly in terms of economic advantage. Nevertheless, by the late twenties the entire discussion of agricultural policy had become heavily charged with ideological considerations as the Stalinist and Bukharinite forces jockeyed for position. Most of these considerations were offered under the rubric of the Lenin Cooperative Plan, a banner of legitimacy under which any number of conflicting policies could seemingly be paraded.

Under the conventional interpretation of the Lenin Plan it had been taken more or less for granted that the individual collective farms would receive tractors and other modern implements. This was certainly the standard conception of a modern socialized agricultural system. Given the accepted myth of the socializing power of the tractor, moreover, it was only natural to assume that the best possible face would have to be put on the kolkhoz, as an integral farming unit, so as to maximize its attractive force for the peasants.

The idea of treating the energy base in agriculture as a separate entity did not arise until after 1926, except in the marginal cases of the rental points and machinery associations, mainly because there were too few tractors to attract anyone's attention to the problem.[8] Once tractors became available in substantial numbers, however, the question of organizing their use became more significant. The publicity given by Stalin to Markevich's experiment at the Shevchenko sovkhoz suddenly raised the issue of machinery organization to national prominence. There was a rapid crystallization of opposing forces. Not only were there arguments for and against the entire tractor-column concept, but there were also divisions on the question of ownership of the separate energy bases themselves. The leaders of the cooperative system, particularly of the two main centers of producers' cooperation, *Khlebotsentr* and

Sel'skosoiuz, manifested a strongly proprietary attitude toward the collective farm movement and the orthodox interpretation of the Lenin Cooperative Plan. On the whole they upheld the principles of voluntary membership and strong, integral kolkhozes. Thus, it was with something less than wild enthusiasm that they greeted Markevich's scheme of state-owned tractor columns. Once Stalin's position had been set forth, however, a number of the leading cooperators — probably a majority — settled for a plan of appropriating exclusive control over the development and management of tractor columns for the cooperative system.[9] And for the first few years the cooperative system actually did play a dominant role in tractor-column and MTS construction.

A few bold cooperators, however, continued to oppose the entire concept of energy-base separation as a matter of principle. The most outspoken and consistent of them was N. Gordienko, a high-ranking official of *Ukrkolkhoztsentr,* the coordinating center of cooperative-kolkhoz construction in the Ukraine. His article "Against Tractor Columns" in the November 1928 issue of the journal *Khoziaistvo Ukrainy* provoked a storm of controversy and was frequently cited as the extreme rightwing position on the MTS. Because of its prophetic insights and the fact that it apparently reflected the opinions of a fairly large number of conscientious agricultural officials at the time, the article is worthy of some comment.

Gordienko argued bluntly that the masses of peasants would never willingly subject themselves to the type of arrangements specified by Markevich.[10] In general, he said, the diversion of large farm machines from the kolkhozes would rob them of their economic independence and nullify their attractiveness for the peasants.[11] To Gordienko, the Shevchenko experiment was twice cursed. First of all, it was based on a state institution, which implied compulsion and subordination rather than voluntary cooperation. Second, the contractual basis of the organization of the peasants at the Shevchenko sovkhoz was bound to be unstable because it was not grounded on ownership of the means of production: that is, the peasants had no real stake in maintaining it. To the arguments of his fellow cooperators that cooperative ownership of the tractor columns would meet many of these objections,[12] Gordienko replied by insisting that in the end it did not matter who owned or operated them; the principle of separation of the energy base was fundamentally harmful, for it diverted attention from the construction of real, full-fledged collective farms:

the noise being stirred up around the organization of tractor columns and the desire of a certain segment of officials to substitute the organization of these columns for collectivization should be considered harmful, even if this organization of tractor columns is concealed behind some alleged wish to help collectivization. For, in our opinion, no matter who organizes the columns, they are a brake on the development of the collectivization of agriculture . . .[13]

Gordienko indicated that his use of the first person plural was not merely a bow to editorial custom. He implied a sharp division among the officials involved in collectivization between those, like himself, who wanted to proceed directly to the formation of fully equipped kolkhozes and those who favored the construction of tractor columns, leaving the final collectivization of the individual peasants to a later stage. He suggested that this split essentially followed the functional division between the cooperative system and the state agricultural organs. Gordienko may perhaps have been exaggerating the extent of support for his position among the cooperators. But the split was apparently fairly serious and was substantially along the lines he described. An article in the important journal of agrarian theory, *Na agrarnom fronte,* five months later declared,

The right deviation in the cooperative system, which expresses itself in the underrating of the large-scale socialized agriculture that tractor columns undoubtedly creates, is a threatening phenomenon, inasmuch as the point of view of Gordienko on tractor columns and stations is shared by many responsible directors of Centers of agricultural cooperation.[14]

The author of the article, A. Lozovyi, claimed that the negative attitude toward the tractor column and MTS was especially prominent in the Ukraine, where the experiment had had its origin and where the subsequent expansion program was most heavily concentrated. This fact would seem to suggest either that the MTS idea was so popular there that the leaders of the co-operative movement felt their position threatened or that it was so unsuccessful as to arouse genuine opposition on practical grounds. The latter explanation is probably closer to the truth.

Opposition was not confined to the cooperative system, however. M. Anisimov, writing in the Party's main theoretical journal, *Bol'shevik*, in January 1929 noted that Party, as well as Soviet and cooperative officials, were underestimating the value of tractor columns. Anisimov himself, incidentally, favored the tractor columns over the more formally structured MTS, arguing, like Gordienko, that the peasants would never accept the latter form and that it would not have the socializing effects intended by the original Lenin Plan.[15] Evidently the issues and possible solutions were being debated quite thoroughly.

Gordienko's opposition, as we know, proved to be of little consequence, even if the basic soundness of many of his prophecies was beyond question. His observation that the MTS was incompatible with a strong collective farm movement was particularly insightful, as events were to prove. But it was largely irrelevant, given the manifestly coercive direction that collectivization was to take. A strong, self-sufficient collective farm movement was the last thing Stalin wanted.

Against this background of opposing arguments the appearance of Markevich's book *Inter-Village Machine-Tractor Stations* in 1929 assumed special significance. The fact that it contained a warmly approving preface by V. V. Kuibyshev, then Chairman of the USSR Supreme Council of the National Economy and a staunch supporter of Stalin in the struggle against the Right Opposition, strongly suggests that the book was intended as an authoritative endorsement of the MTS against its rightwing critics.

The arguments of the book are mainly economic and technical. Markevich, as a professional agronomist, was understandably prone to stressing the technical aspects of the MTS. (This one-sidedness would eventually haunt him when the evaluation of MTS operations shifted from technical to political criteria.) Nevertheless, the book contains suggestions of some of the ideological formulations that would later be used to explain and justify the MTS. In general, the formal structure of MTS-kolkhoz relations which

Markevich outlined was followed remarkably closely in subsequent practice.

Markevich emphasized first of all the uniqueness of the MTS concept. All other contemporary schemes for mechanization and consolidation of peasant farms were based on the principle of self-contained, fully equipped agricultural units.[16] He pointed out that unfortunately neither the state nor the collectivized peasantry would be able to construct such independent units on a sufficiently large scale for a long time. Therein lay the dilemma. The peasants would not be attracted to collective farming until they could see for themselves the benefits of mechanization. Widespread mechanization within the kolkhoz framework was physically impossible at the present level of development. What was the answer?

The creation of new forms of production, the creation of large-scale inter-village energy stations, the prohibition of the procurement of draft power, not only by individual farms, but also by entire villages, the technical concentration of complex implements of production in one powerful productive fist outside of the boundaries of individual villages, the overcoming of the contemporary integral farming unit — the organization of Machine-Tractor Stations.[17]

The main innovation of the concept was that the energy component of modern agriculture could feasibly be separated from the land and labor components. The ideal of the agricultural factory, which Markevich shared with many other Bolshevik agrarian theorists, could be achieved in no other way, he said, given the resources available.[18]

In developing the details of the scheme Markevich seemed to address himself specifically to Gordienko's objections. As far as peasant attitudes were concerned, he asserted, material profitability would be the crucial factor, not patterns of ownership or organizational autonomy and self-sufficiency. If the peasant was convinced that the MTS was profitable for him, he would eagerly seek its services.

The only binding force, insurmountable and powerful, can and must be the material benefit of the new production [system] which is a result of the development of productive forces. If this is lacking, if the peasantry after the transition to collective, mechanized production does not see real benefit for himself, it is absurd, hopeless and harmful to try to hold him and bind him with other contractual articles. Thus, the attitude of the peasantry will be the best indicator of the viability of this production form.[19] (Emphasis in original.)

To the objection that the MTS concept was incompatible with the kolkhoz and a serious deviation from Lenin's Cooperative Plan, Markevich answered that, on the contrary, the MTS was the highest form of kolkhoz construction.[20] He rejected the notion that the MTS was a means of bringing agriculture under state control (*ogosudarstvlenie*). The peasant associations formed for work with the stations would retain their essentially cooperative character. They would not be transformed into sovkhozes, nor would the peasants be transformed into laborers. Nor, he continued, would MTS construction signify the postponement or cessation of ordinary collectivization. The ordinary kolkhozes should continue to be fostered as the best means of utilizing existing peasant technology and as a vital intermediate form of socialized agriculture.

Thus, the basic task of contemporary collective construction consists not in the opposition of some productive forms to others, not in the opposition of the Machine-Tractor Stations to the existing form of kolkhoz unions, not in the struggle of the forms, but in the correct combination of them in conformity with our organizational, technical, and material possibilities in each separate period of our economic development. But along with this combination, one must always keep in mind that the most rational, cheap, and lasting use of modern high-level technology in agriculture is possible only under the conditions of the MTS, through whose channels this technology should be introduced.[21]

In this connection he warned that one of the greatest dangers would be a premature expansion of the MTS system before the material and technical preconditions were prepared. He cautioned specifically against the fragmentation of MTS construction among a number of cooperative and state agencies and against relying too much on local initiative. The MTS was a highly complex enterprise, requiring the attention of experts, not amateurs. Accordingly, he urged the establishment of a single directing center under firm state control for coordinating and managing MTS construction and operations.[22]

As a concession to the argument that the peasants would need to have some stake in a collective venture if it was to exert a real socializing force, Markevich agreed that shares in the MTS should be sold among the population to be served; this would be good business. However, he was quite explicit in recommending that these shares not imply proprietary rights in a particular station, but rather in the MTS system as a whole.[23] The actual setup of *Traktorotsentr* would follow most of these prescriptions closely.

Markevich did not devote very much attention to the political implications of the MTS, but a few of his observations are worth mentioning here. He was enthusiastic about the collectivizing influence of MTS construction on the surrounding populace, but as he was not greatly concerned about the kolkhoz itself as a producing unit, he tended to favor the Association for Joint Cultivation of the Land (TOZ), the loosest form of collective association.[24] He was sensitive to the problem of kulak resistance to the MTS and urged MTS organizers to fight it vigorously and concentrate on winning over the poor and middle-peasant masses, allegedly most susceptible to the lure of the machine. "All these tasks," he said, "are no less important for the Station than planned organizational-technical work." [25]

From the arguments of the book, however, it is clear that Markevich saw the MTS as primarily a production institution. Its success or failure would, he thought, depend entirely on its economic viability. But he was so convinced of its success and, consequently, of its wholehearted acceptance by the peasants[26] that he never seriously considered the obverse possibility: namely, that the peasants might reject the MTS precisely on grounds of performance.

Despite the various endorsements of Markevich's general idea, the final status of the MTS in the overall scheme of agricultural development was still far from settled. The Sixteenth Party Conference, which met in April 1929, was virtually the last major opportunity for discussion of the MTS in fairly objective terms, unclouded by ideological rhetoric. Stalin had yet to appropriate the MTS idea as his own personal contribution to the Lenin Cooperative Plan, and it was still possible to talk of the future of the MTS in a pragmatic manner. Thus, in comparison with what would come later, it is almost refreshing to read a speech wherein M. I. Kalinin, the main agricultural speaker at the Conference, compared the *fortuitous* appearance of the MTS and its meaning to Newton's alleged discovery of the law of gravity via the falling apple: "Thus, thanks to a simple accident — the fall of an apple," said Kalinin, "a great discovery appeared, on the basis of which science made giant steps forward." [27]

Like Markevich, Kalinin appeared to be most interested in the technical and economic aspects of the MTS. Others, however, seemed to grasp some of the political implications. Among them, not surprisingly, was A. G. Shlikhter, former head and chief apologist of the food requisition program during the War Communism period and now Commissar of Agriculture in the Ukraine, who emphasized the theoretical and practical importance of state control over farm machinery for the implementation of the collectivization policy and the maintenance of control in the village. [28]

But there were others who were somewhat less enthusiastic about the MTS idea and its broad applicability. I. M. Vareikis, head of the Party Committee of the Central Black-Earth Oblast (CBO), for example, sought to limit MTS construction to overpopulated regions, such as existed in the Ukraine and the CBO, where kolkhozes tended to be small. In these areas the MTS would be used to form *kusty* or communes, composed of a number of small kolkhozes that were too weak individually to function on a modern technological level. [29] Contrary to Markevich's precepts, moreover, Vareikis envisioned the MTS merely as way-stations on the road to the formation of giant kolkhozes.

The most persistent, albeit tacit, resistance to making the MTS pattern universal — after the Gordienko affair it was already impossible openly to oppose the MTS per se — came, as was to be expected, from the representatives of the kolkhoz-cooperative movement. G. N. Kaminskii, the chairman of *Kolkhoztsentr*, carefully sidestepping political and ideological considerations, actually fought for the expansion of tractor columns in opposition to total reliance on the MTS. The tractor columns were a solidly cooperative enterprise, he argued, and would not swallow up the kolkhozes, as many kolkhoz officials feared the MTS would do. The best solution of all, according to Kaminskii, was to proceed simultaneously on all three fronts — MTS, tractor columns, and fully mechanized kolkhozes — using each form where local conditions seemed appropriate.[30]

The results of the Sixteenth Party Conference were inconclusive. The MTS, under both state and cooperative auspices, were accepted merely as "one of the methods for . . . collectivization." [31] At the sessions of a special commission appointed by the conference to work out details of an MTS building program, opposition voices continued to be heard. The representative of *Sel'skosoiuz* was reported to have demanded that "the stations must be kolkhoz-owned." [32] In the end, however, the commission opted for state ownership and control. The fiction of cooperative participation was preserved for the time being by the profitable expedient of continuing the solicitation of MTS share purchases from cooperatives and even private peasants.

As MTS construction gained momentum and the favorable attitude of the regime became clearer, there was a rush to climb aboard the MTS bandwagon. The MTS began to figure prominently in the voluminous theoretical literature on agricultural organization that accompanied the onset of mass collectivization. Stalin himself had given impetus to this outpouring of theoretical work when he chastised an audience of Marxist agrarian theorists for letting theory lag behind practice in a speech on December 27, 1929.[33]

The rash of radical new proposals involving the MTS was a good example of the analytical function of ideology and its limitations. As a result of the new analyses, Markevich soon found himself dangerously outflanked on the left. Some writers began accusing him of an insufficiently vigorous class approach to collectivization.[34] Others charged him with underestimating the political and organizational significance of the MTS and of treating the stations as mere rental points.[35] Contemptuously brushing aside Markevich's warnings on the need for careful planning and strict limitation of functions, the new converts to the MTS idea fashioned a series of grandiose projects for the MTS in the "industrialization" of agriculture. In one of the most widely publicized schemes the MTS were cast in the role of centers of huge

"Agro-Industrial" or "Industrial-Agricultural" Combines (often referred to as AIK or IAK) engaged in the large-scale production and processing of agricultural raw materials. The idea had originally been presented in 1927 by a Professor Batiushkov, who had subsequently been discredited for prescribing "capitalist methods" in the operations of the combines.[36] The Batiushkov plan had envisioned units of approximately 2500 hectares each. The new, far more grandiose schemes involving the MTS were by 1930 already being conceived in terms of units of 100,000 hectares or more.

The various projects, although differing in detail, all had one important principle in common which distinguished them from Markevich's model of the inter-village MTS. They all envisioned the merger of the MTS with the surrounding peasants in a single, all-encompassing enterprise that was, dialectically speaking, bigger than the sum of its parts. The machine-tractor station would serve as the center of administrative control and technical guidance for the mechanized farming establishment; and the collectivized peasant villages, if they were to be allowed to continue to exist at all, would serve simply as suppliers of labor.[37] In many respects the combines appear to have been little different in conception from the already existing, huge sovkhozes. Indeed, some theorists saw the combines as a means for transforming groups of small kolkhozes into sovkhozes. The majority of supporters of the AIK's and IAK's, however, presented them as something qualitatively new, as full-fledged, industrial-proletarian enterprises operating the year round and, thus, offering the first real opportunity for achieving that "holy grail" of Marxist agrarian theory, the elimination of the differences between city and country.

The popularity of these ambitious projects was to be extremely short-lived. After a flurry of activity in late 1929 and early 1930, during which some three hundred of the combines were actually reported to be under construction,[38] the entire idea was suddenly condemned as a "leftwing Trotskyite" distortion. This shift was part of the general reaction against "gigantomania" and the radical excesses of collectivization of early 1930, when, for example, the commune was discarded as the ideal form of the kolkhoz in favor of the artel. The supporters of the AIK's and IAK's were forced to recant and confess to their misunderstanding of the true social character of the MTS and their violation of the principles of voluntary association and cooperation! [39]

Under the circumstances these "woe-begotten" theorists might well be forgiven their sins, for despite the approval of Markevich's book and the promulgation of the decision to proceed with MTS construction on June 5, 1929, there was still no official theoretical line on the MTS. Stalin all but ignored the MTS in his pronouncements on agriculture during this period. Indeed, from his published speeches one would have been justified in assuming that the policy was still to deliver tractors directly to the kolkhozes. In his report to the Sixteenth Party Congress on June 27, 1930, for example, he declared: "[The Soviet State] can and must take only the line of organizing large farms of a *socialist* type, equipped with modern machines. Our *state farms* and *collective farms* are precisely farms of this type." [40]

There were many other examples of indecision on the extent of commitment to the MTS. L. I. Dembo, a pioneer in the legal aspects of the MTS, wrote in 1930 that it was perfectly legal for a kolkhoz to acquire full administrative and operational control over the MTS serving it — in effect, to buy it out — if the kolkhoz owned a sufficient number of shares of Traktorotsentr and if the Council of Labor and Defense signified its approval. In such cases the MTS would become part of the indivisible fund (fixed capital) of the kolkhoz.[41] As a rule, such approval was far from easy to obtain, but early in 1930 the Party Central Committee, bowing to the insistent demands of a group of kolkhoz "shock-workers," actually agreed to permit regular sales of existing MTS to the kolkhozes they served. Twenty-two years later Stalin asserted that this permission had been only provisional, but at the time it may have seemed otherwise. After a few months — in fact at the end of 1930 — it became evident that very few kolkhozes were able to bear the financial costs, however, and the experiment was terminated.[42] But the very fact that the Party leadership was willing to entertain such a proposal and give it so long a trial period strongly suggests that the MTS did not yet enjoy any special ideological status among socialist agricultural institutions.

A harbinger of change in the official attitude was the publication of an article in *Bol'shevik* in February 1930 stressing the unique appropriateness of the MTS as an agency of collectivization by virtue of its proletarian class character.* The article implied the beginning of the crystallization of a consistent ideological line on the MTS. The basic direction of that line could be seen in the following passage:

The building of machine-tractor stations differs from other forms of social reconstruction of the peasantry, first of all, in the peculiarity that it is a method of direct proletarian leadership of that reconstruction, it brings about the bond [smychka] of the working class with the toiling masses of the village in a concrete manner.[43]

As Stalin's statement in the June 27 report suggests, however, the decision to substitute the MTS pattern for the self-sufficient kolkhoz was still several months away. Meanwhile, the mass collectivization campaign was raising certain important theoretical questions on the nature of the kolkhoz itself. The standard conception of the kolkhoz had been linked to Lenin's rehabilitation of cooperation in his articles of January 1923. Under the dictatorship of the proletariat, Lenin had said, agricultural producers' cooperatives — kolkhozes — were for all practical purposes fully legitimate socialist enterprises. It will be remembered, however, that the producers' cooperative was seen by Lenin as a product of a lengthy process of social, economic, and psychological evolution extending through various stages of cooperative endeavor. That is, the peasants should have completed the prescribed sociopsychological transformation by the time they were ready to accept the kolkhoz.

By 1929, when mass collectivization "from above" had become official policy and the kolkhozes were showing signs of becoming hotbeds of antiregime sentiment, the old formula that the collective farm was already a fully socialist enterprise could hardly be maintained. Stalin himself signalled the change in evaluation when he told the audience of Marxist Agrarians in December 1929, "No, a great deal of work has still to be done to remould

---

* It is perhaps significant that the article appeared in Bol'shevik, rather than in one of the regular journals of agrarian theory, such as Na agrarnom fronte, where most of the radical proposals for the "combines" were published. Na agrarnom fronte was discontinued in 1935, and most of its erstwhile contributors were "cleaned out" during the purges.

the peasant collective farmer, to set right his individualistic mentality and to transform him into a real working member of a socialist society." [44]

Once the decision to collectivize had been made, it was clear that the proletarian state would not only have to push the peasants into the collectives, but it would also have to exercise a "guiding hand" over them for an indefinite period thereafter. The major problem now became the means by which the state would go about accomplishing these tasks. The mounting, if inconclusive, evidence of the viability of the MTS system, particularly the successful completion of its share of the spring sowing campaign in 1930, seemed to offer a solution. On December 29, 1930, the Central Committee announced a crash program of MTS construction for 1931. The preamble of the decree asserted:

The results of the first year of work of the machine-tractor stations have fully confirmed that in the person of the MTS there has been discovered and proven in a mass experiment that form of organization by the Soviet State of large-scale collective agriculture on a high-level technological base, in which the spontaneous activity of the kolkhoz masses in the construction of their collective farms and the organizational and technical assistance and direction of the proletarian state are most fully combined.[45]

The firm commitment to the MTS was thus proclaimed. In a graphic example of ex post facto rationalization, a theoretical explanation of the developing inequalities of the MTS-kolkhoz relationship soon followed. The formula, centered on the concept of the "consistently socialist enterprise," borrowed somewhat ingenuously from Lenin's second article "On Cooperation," where it had been employed to distinguish between private, cooperative, and socialist enterprises under the conditions of NEP.[46]

According to the new formulation, the standard artel type of kolkhoz was not a "consistently socialist enterprise," because it was technically the property of its members, who retained certain small instruments of production of their own. However, through the production services of the MTS, which *was* a "consistently socialist enterprise," the kolkhoz was effectively linked to the socialist economic system and thus obtained a legitimate right to exist as part of the socialist economy. To the extent that the relative weight of the MTS in kolkhoz production increased, the kolkhoz theoretically came that much closer to the consistently socialist condition. One writer in early 1932 actually proposed a method of measuring the progress of a given kolkhoz towards full socialism by calculating the specific weight of "state means of production in the form of the MTS in the sum total of all means of production" in the kolkhoz.[47] Mercifully, there were never any concerted efforts to pursue this absurd quantification aspect of the formula. But as a general qualitative statement it became the standard ideological expression of the MTS-kolkhoz relationship.

FURTHER EVOLUTION OF THE FORMULA

The practical implications of the "inconsistently socialist" label now firmly affixed to the kolkhozes were tremendous. By relegating the kolkhoz to an inferior, subordinate status among Soviet institutions, the formula provided a powerful justification for the continuation of warfare against the peasantry. It essentially legitimized, if not actually reinforced, the policy of exploiting the kolkhozes and the peasants as second-class citizens politically. The peasants, understandably, replied in kind and in their behavior often supplied "confirmation" of the theory. Thus, what had begun as rationalization eventually became description. As has often been noted in the case of foreign policy, an ideological analysis, rigorously acted upon, eventually acquired the characteristics of a self-fulfilling prophecy.

As far as MTS operations were concerned, the ideological model of the relationship probably contributed to the early relative de-emphasis of the direct production functions of the stations. The formula reinforced the attitude that merely by existing the MTS were performing a vital service to the kolkhozes, namely, giving them the right to exist in a socialist society. Production services came to be looked upon virtually as a gift from a social superior to an inferior. As a consequence the kolkhozes found themselves with little intrinsic *moral* recourse in attempting to secure improved performance by the MTS. This situation, in turn, could not help but impair the effectiveness of the limited *legal* recourse which the state made available to them.

The evolution of the Model Contract regulating MTS-kolkhoz relations illustrates this complex influence of ideology. Originally intended as a straightforward legal statement of mutual obligations, the contract became an embarrassing anomaly when the fundamental inequality of the partners was elevated to the status of an official principle. But instead of discarding the notion of contract altogether and relying solely on direct administrative controls, the regime decided merely to alter the conceptual basis of the contract to suit the asymmetrical nature of the relationship. As in the case of the Collective Contract (*koldogovor*) between Soviet trade unions and industrial plants, the alleged educational and agitational benefits of the contract-signing process were apparently considered worth preserving, even if the nature of the instrument had to be changed beyond recognition.

Thus, a prominent agrarian legal theorist, P. Piatnitskii, wrote proudly in 1938 that the MTS contract was quite unlike any contract known in "bourgeois" law. "Any attempts to draw an analogy between the MTS contract and other types of contracts . . . are foredoomed to failure," he asserted. Why? Because the interests of the parties (the MTS and the kolkhoz) "fuse with the general state interest, with the interests of the general public, which consist in an unswerving aspiration to strengthen socialist relations and the socialist system." [48] Under socialism, where there were by definition no longer antagonistic contradictions and no selfish interests such as exist in bourgeois society, there was allegedly no need for special protection of the particular interests of the contracting parties.

Subsequent elaborations of the theory of the Model Contract were considerably more sophisticated and forthright than Piatnitskii's (after all, he was writing at the height of the Great Purges), but the basic principle remained the same: the MTS-kolkhoz relationship was one of unequals. A. A. Ruskol, the dean of MTS legal experts, would write as late as 1956:*

---

* Incidentally, Ruskol pointedly condemned the fact that the MTS had never been granted a formal "Statute" (*Polozhenie*) setting forth its role and nature as a socialist enterprise, unlike most other Soviet enterprises. The Model Contract thus constituted the only document defining its role and its relationship to the kolkhoz. Ruskol questioned the efficacy of an ambiguous legal instrument like a contract to perform this important function (A. Ruskol and N. Salishcheva, *Pravovoe polozhenie mashinno-traktornoi stantsii i kharakter ee dogovornykh otnoshenii s kolkhozami* [Moscow, 1956], p. 150).

Thus, the contract of the MTS with the kolkhozes is not an ordinary agreement between two socialist organizations. In the contrast there is expressed the directing role of the machine-tractor stations in relation to the kolkhozes. The state uses the contractual method of regulating social relations for an active influence on the development of the kolkhoz, directing it along the path to communism.[49]

The MTS-kolkhoz contract in addition to its specific operational functions, was largely an annual symbolic reaffirmation of the ideological paradigm of kolkhoz subordination. To be sure, by 1933 the Model Contract contained a penalty clause, in itself a tacit recognition that MTS-kolkhoz relations might involve conflict, rather than identity of interests. But the history of legal actions involving the contract shows that the balance of power was clearly weighted in favor of the MTS.

Another area where the ideological model of the MTS had important practical effects was the rather mundane question of finances. Once again the model appears to have functioned initially as a rationale for basically expediential considerations. For almost seven years the regime had made a concerted effort to render the MTS financially self-supporting in accordance with Markevich's original criteria. There had been a succession of experiments with rewards, penalties, and partial subsidies — all to no avail, owing primarily to the extreme pressures for cost reductions and shortages in operating resources. (See Chapter 5.) The continual demands for operating economies were simply incompatible with the demands for plan fulfillment.

Finally, after a series of devastating purges of the agricultural bureaucracy, it was decided to tighten central controls over the MTS system. The old methods of modified profit-and-loss financing and partial subsidies were abandoned, and the financing of the MTS system was transferred directly to the national budget. Thus, in early 1938 the original economic goals of a self-supporting MTS system were willingly sacrificed on the altar of direct control.

The ideological justification for the new policy was set forth by Molotov at a conference of agricultural officials in February 1938. After reciting a rather slanted history of the changes in the nature and role of the MTS to date, he suggested that budgetary financing had actually been immanent in the MTS concept all along.

We did not at once approach the MTS as state organizations. As is well known, we began wide spread construction of MTS in the beginning of 1929. [sic] But at the time the state character of the MTS was not yet clear to us. In the beginning, as you know, a joint-stock association soliciting peasant funds was designated for the direction of MTS construction. But soon experience showed that the MTS play a decisive role in the kolkhoz cause. A joint-stock format was obviously unsuitable for such an organization. The MTS had to and did become the basic state organization in the village, which the Soviet power made its mighty lever in the cause of raising kolkhoz construction. And yet, until the latest decision of the Party and the government on the new system of financing the machine-tractor stations, the matter of organization of the MTS as state institutions for assistance to the kolkhozes was not finished. With the transfer of the MTS to the state budget an entire stage in the development of the MTS is being completed . . .[50]

Molotov's explanation of the decision was perhaps not quite so disingenuous as it at first appears. Although there were obviously powerful political and economic reasons for the shift in the method of financing, it is likely that ideological considerations concerning the nature of the MTS were already strong enough to have played some part in the decision. The chain of reasoning may have proceeded in approximately the following manner. The MTS is a unique form of socialist enterprise. Not only does it engage in material production, like other socialist economic enterprises, but it also performs for the state a number of vital leadership and control functions in the kolkhozes. Thus it acts also as a quasi-soviet organ.* Previous financial arrangements have been based on an incorrect understanding of the nature of the MTS. By over-emphasizing the economic side of MTS activities, these past policies had often diverted the efforts of local officials from the important tasks of organization and control and had led to certain distortions in their methods of work. Budgetary financing represents a recognition of the primary importance of the administrative and control activities which the MTS performs for the state and is a powerful means for ensuring that MTS workers will act in accordance with the norms of official conduct.

This hypothetical statement of the argument, if it has any

* Molotov, in the course of the same speech, actually referred to the MTS as a "soviet organization" under the new financial arrangements, but this view was later expressly repudiated, as will be shown in Chapter 5.

similarities to the actual process of reasoning, suggests the manner in which an ideological analysis of a given institution can influence (predict) policy. The crucial question may seem to be whether the decision came before or after the analysis. The argument offered in this chapter suggests, however, that such a question may be too simple. Even a definitely ex post facto analysis can have the effect of so reinforcing a decision as to foreclose all but a particular set of future policy options, a repeated occurrence in the case of the MTS.

A further illustration of this phenomenon was the effect of the evolution of the ideological model on the system of payments in kind for MTS services. Originally, these payments had been intended as a direct return for services rendered, with a slight surcharge for amortization and overhead expenses. The introduction in 1933 of an extremely arbitrary multiple price system for kolkhoz produce, however, made it very difficult to compare the payments-in-kind income of a given station with its costs in any meaningful way. Nevertheless, as long as the MTS were financed on a partially self-supporting basis, the effort to tie income to services rendered continued.

The newly expanded conception of the MTS as a state organ financed, like the soviets, from the state budget, significantly changed the ground rules. There was no longer any objective necessity of linking the payments-in-kind income of the individual station to the quality and quantity of services it rendered. At the same time, as in the case of the Model Contract, the moral and psychological value of the notion of payments for services, as opposed to an outright levy, was considered too important to be discarded altogether. Consequently, an elaborate theoretical explanation of the nature of payments in kind was developed. Some idea of its basic outlines can be seen in the following passage from a textbook on the economics of the MTS published in 1956:

Payment in kind, in its economic content, is nothing else but a transfer by the kolkhozes to the state of that part of agricultural production which is created by the living and dead labor of the machine-tractor stations, including the labor of MTS workers for society.[51]

That is, payments in kind were to be viewed as an aggregate. The payment by a kolkhoz to an MTS was thus explained not in terms of the production services performed in the particular case but as part of the aggregate compensation paid by all kolkhozes for the services provided to them by the MTS system as a whole. Such a formulation was obviously an important step in the process of de-materialization of the MTS-kolkhoz relationship, for it reinforced the tendency to ignore actual performance. It also afforded a useful justification for the collection of payments for the broad non-production functions of the MTS, while avoiding the embarrassing question of the concrete material value of these functions. And although repeated efforts continued to be made to relate the payments-in-kind incomes of the individual stations to their performance in *relative* terms, the acceptance of the ideological formulation tended to rob such efforts of any real sense of urgency.

Incidentally, the ideological analysis of the concept of payments in kind had special practical consequences of its own. The concept was linked closely to Marx's theory of Differential Rent in Volume III of *Capital*.[52] Every system the regime seemed able to devise for increasing kolkhoz production incentives through the weighting of the rates of payments in kind had the practical result of penalizing the wealthier, more advantageously situated kolkhozes. (See Chapter 5.) In a socialist society this problem of unearned income was considered particularly vexing. Eventually, it became common to view the MTS, through the collection of payments in kind, as the ideal instrument for absorbing this "differential rent" (primarily Differential Rent I). Indeed, ever since the abolition of the MTS, Soviet political economists have been wrestling with the problem of finding a successor "rent collector" to relieve the wealthier kolkhozes of some of their advantages.[53]

The preceding examples suggest the extent to which the MTS had become enshrined in the doctrinal foundations of Soviet agriculture. By the beginning of World War II it was already unthinkable to posit the existence of the collective farm system without the MTS.* In the postwar period the position of the MTS was, if any-

---

* This statement bears some qualification. The author was told by a prominent Soviet agricultural economist that a small group of economists were actually urging the end of the multiple pricing system for agricultural commodities in 1937. Part of their argument was that if the kolkhozes received an adequate return for their produce, they would be able to buy their own machines and save the state the costs

thing, even stronger as a result of the devastation of the kolkhozes and the virtual extinction of their supplies of draft animals in large areas of the country. The strength of the MTS was reflected in the greatly expanded role assigned to them in reconstruction and the various postwar agricultural development programs.

Paradoxically, it was one of these programs, the kolkhoz amalgamation campaign, which had been initiated largely to facilitate MTS operations, that served as the opening wedge for a renewed assault on the MTS. The attack was made purely in economic terms and was, therefore, bound to fail under Stalin's rule. But the episode was extremely important, both as an illustration of the strength of ideological considerations and as a preview of the arguments that would eventually prevail under the more pragmatic leadership of Khrushchev.

The amalgamation campaign had striking economic consequences. The simple physical merger of small, weak kolkhozes significantly increased the physical assets of the average Soviet kolkhoz. In the main agricultural regions particularly there were signs that the mergers were having a multiplier effect, as cash incomes and indivisible funds grew more than proportionately.[54] For the first time since collectivization the accumulation of capital in the kolkhozes themselves was becoming more than a mere academic question.

A prominent agricultural economist with a history of bold, pragmatic ideas, Professor V. G. Venzher, addressed himself to this question and its implications for future mechanization policy. In an article in the journal *Voprosy ekonomiki* in March 1951 he suggested that there were "various channels" for injecting modern technology into the kolkhoz sector. Through the MTS the state had been for a long time the most important of these channels. But now, he said, the kolkhozes themselves must play a larger role by the investment of their own accumulated capital. As examples

---

of the MTS. It is evident that at this time a thorough review of the agricultural system was being undertaken in connection with the decision to alter the method of financing the MTS. None of the discussions were published, to my knowledge, and it is not known how many of the group of economists fell victim to the purges. However, the fact that my informant, presumably a member of the group, escaped the purges and that the discussion was being held suggests that the MTS system was not yet entirely beyond the realm of discourse.

he suggested that they could install electric power generators, build enclosures and livestock barns, and establish auxiliary enterprises.[55] Venzher stopped short of encouraging the purchase of tractors and other farm machinery (although it soon turned out that this was his main point), but he did urge ending the policy of indiscriminate additions to the existing MTS machinery inventory. He suggested, instead, a more rational utilization of the machinery already on hand.

Venzher had long been concerned with the high costs of MTS operations. When in late 1951 Stalin issued an invitation to the country's leading economists to submit their pet projects for discussion in conjunction with the writing of a new standard textbook on political economy,* Venzher and his wife, Professor A. V. Sanina, also a prominent economist, accepted the challenge. They submitted a number of letters proposing the abolition of the MTS and the sale of MTS equipment to the kolkhozes. An integral part of the proposal was the replacement of the multiple pricing system with a single price, offering a more equitable return to the kolkhozes for their crops. This, they argued, would permit the kolkhozes to purchase and maintain the machinery at a net cost to the state that would be far lower than the cost of the MTS.[56]

Early in 1952 Stalin called a halt to the flow of proposals. Several months later, in October, he set forth his comments in book form under the title *Economic Problems of Socialism in the USSR.* Appended to it was his famous "Reply to Comrades A. V. Sanina and V. G. Venzher" in which he unconditionally rejected their suggestions, while accusing them of "breaking with Marxism and taking the stand of subjective idealism." [57] In seeking to abolish the MTS they were, he said, flouting the "objective laws of socialism."

First of all Stalin attacked their economic arguments. In a passage which might well have been applied with considerable force to the post-1958 situation he asked,

---

* Stalin had intended the textbook as a guide to standard practice and interpretation in the expanding Communist world. When the draft manuscript was presented for discussion at a conference in November 1951, Stalin found what were for him alarming divergences of views on fundamental questions. His *Economic Problems of Socialism in the USSR* thus represented an effort to set the doctrinal record straight. See the "Editor's Note" in Joseph Stalin, *Economic Problems of Socialism in the USSR* (New York: International Publishers, 1952), p. 4; also, Stalin's own comments, pp. 36–37.

Are our collective farms capable of bearing such an expense, even though their incomes may run into millions? No, they are not, since they are not in the position to undertake the expenditure of billions of rubles which may be recouped only after a period of six or eight years. Such expenditures can be borne only by the state, for it, and it alone, is in the position to bear the loss involved by the scrapping of old machines and replacing them by new; because it, and it alone, is in a position to bear such losses for six or eight years and only then recover the outlays.[58]

This was not really a valid objection to their argument. Sanina and Venzher were not talking about the ability of the kolkhozes to bear the costs under the *existing procurement arrangements*. But their argument was couched almost exclusively in economic terms. As such it was naive, virtually irrelevant, and, from an ideological standpoint, even dangerous. Stalin's main attack thus focussed on the ideological principles threatened by their proposals. The entire textbook episode had awakened him to the untidy state of theory in the economic area. And just as the Marr linguistics controversy a year earlier had stimulated him to "legislate" in the realm of epistemology, he now used the occasion of the Venzher-Sanina proposals, among others, to update the laws of political economy.

First he addressed himself to the specific ideological question of the nature of the kolkhoz. What would be the result of selling MTS machinery to the kolkhozes he asked?

The outcome would be, first, that the collective farms would become the owners of the basic instruments of production; that is, their status would be an exceptional one, such as is not shared by any other enterprise in our country, for, as we know, even the nationalized enterprises do not own their instruments of production. Now, by what considerations of progress and advancement, could this exceptional status of the collective farms be justified? Can it be said that such a status would facilitate the elevation of collective-farm property to the level of public property, that it would expedite the transition of our society from socialism to communism? Would it not be truer to say that such a status could only dig a deeper gulf between collective-farm property and public property, and would not bring us any nearer to communism, but, on the contrary, remove us farther from it?

Ominously, he introduced a broader issue, the problem of commodity circulation under conditions of the advance to Communism:

The outcome would be, secondly, an extension of the sphere of commodity circulation, because a gigantic quantity of instruments of agricultural production would come within its orbit. What do Comrades Sanina and Venzher think — is the extension of the sphere of commodity circulation calculated to promote our advance toward communism? Would it not be true to say that our advance toward communism would only be retarded by it? [59]

In the context of the Venzher-Sanina proposal the abstract question of commodity circulation, which had been an important part of the textbook discussion, took on new meaning. Stalin was now implying the future elimination of *all* monetary payments to the kolkhozes for their crops. Even the private plot was threatened.[60] Had the dictator's death not mercifully intervened, the kolkhozes might have had a lot more to worry about than the purchase of farm machinery. As it turned out, then, the challenge had merely strengthened the position of the MTS. Stalin's assignment to it of the role of the main vehicle for the elimination of commodity circulation from urban-rural exchange undoubtedly reinforced the ideological position of the MTS system.[61]

Venzher quickly recanted — even before Stalin's *magnum opus* had gone to press — praising the MTS as the "leading force in socialist agriculture." [62] Under Stalin, at least, it was clear that mere economic arguments would never be sufficient to challenge the sanctity of the MTS.

The first three years of the post-Stalin period illustrated the great carry-over strength of the official conception of the MTS. There was a growing realization that Soviet agriculture was in desperate shape. Yet, whether out of genuine conviction or simply the desire not to rock the boat in matters of basic principle during the critical succession period, no important figure questioned the leading role of the MTS in any possible configuration of agricultural institutions. Indeed, the very asperity with which Khrushchev himself acted to strengthen the political and economic influence of the MTS during these years strongly suggests a genuine acceptance of the existing basis of the MTS-kolkhoz relationship.

From the beginning of his reforms in September 1953, however, there was a clear, if subtle, shift in the emphasis of policy toward the MTS. Khrushchev began to stress once again the economic aspects of the role of the MTS. In fact, in his programs to improve the managerial and technological basis of MTS operations he seemed to be returning to the original production orientations of the initial Markevich model. It was only when he became convinced of the serious shortcomings of the MTS-kolkhoz relationship in terms of that model that he changed his attitude toward the MTS. Thus began the rapid dissipation of the ideological fog shrouding the MTS. The doctrinal support for the MTS system was not eliminated without a struggle, however. When it became clear in 1957 that Khrushchev's real intention was to do away with the MTS entirely, his conservative opponents frantically revived the old ideological arguments used by Stalin in 1952. These developments will be discussed in Chapter 13. Here it will suffice to note that, the ideology of the MTS aside, even for Khrushchev ideological considerations were not an entirely negligible factor in policy-making, although their influence would be significantly altered under the impact of his unique style of leadership.

Western students of Soviet politics have increasingly tended to write off ideology as an active influence in the Soviet decision-making process. At most they will concede that ideology may affect the climate in which decisions are made, perhaps modifying in some way the manner in which Soviet decision-makers perceive reality. But when the chips are down, they argue, Soviet leaders operate pretty much the way their Western counterparts do. That is, ideology merely furnishes the window dressing for what are really pragmatic decisions. The fact that ideology does not operate precisely as officially advertised lends a good deal of superficial validity to these arguments. The material presented in this chapter, however, suggests that ideology is not irrelevant to the Soviet decision-making process, but that its functions are much more complex than is commonly supposed.

In the beginning of the chapter three generic functions of ideology were identified: *analysis, legitimation,* and *conservation.*

These functions do not operate in isolation but are interwoven at various levels of consciousness and purposefulness. Analysis is probably the source of most of the credibility difficulties. It is the officially advertised function; its manifest purpose in the system is to provide a sufficiently thorough comprehension of a given issue or phenomenon and its underlying "laws" to enable the prediction of future developments. The crucial question to be asked concerning this function is the level of precision that the Soviet policy-makers expect in the prescriptive conclusions of their analyses. Official pronouncements would have us believe that the expected level is high indeed. However, actual practice suggests otherwise. In concrete matters, such as political or economic organization, ideological analysis clearly can provide only the most general type of guidance. Ideological analysis certainly did not predict the appearance of the MTS, Stalin's later assertions to the contrary notwithstanding. It is safe to assume that Soviet leaders have generally been aware of these methodological limitations. The history of the MTS suggests that their reliance on ideological analysis for policy prescriptions is limited to the level of general orientation: that they value it more for its utility in the posing of relevant questions than for the precise answers it can give.

The usefulness of this type of analysis for a teleological system like that of the USSR should not be completely discounted. Psychological benefits aside, the self-conscious attention to matters of principle it engenders helps to keep policy-makers and policies on the right track, so to speak — something the American problem-solving approach frequently fails to do. The distortions and downright failures of American efforts to deal with such problems as urban blight, public welfare, and mass transportation should give pause to any categorical criticism of the more formally structured Soviet methodology, although there is obviously plenty to criticize in the Soviets' use of that methodology.

Within the limitations indicated above, therefore, ideology undoubtedly does exert a prescriptive influence on policy. Once the MTS concept had been accepted and an appropriate ideological formulation of the MTS-kolkhoz relationship had been worked out to legitimize it, the analytical model did have a conditioning effect on subsequent agricultural policy. The 1938 decision on the transfer of MTS finances to the state budget was a case in point. A better illustration, perhaps, was Stalin's 1952 project for incorporating the MTS into a new set of policies for eliminating "commodity circulation" from urban-rural exchange transactions. Had the dictator lived a few years longer, these policies would doubtless have had far reaching effects on the entire pattern of agricultural development. Another even more striking illustration was Khrushchev's reversion to the original principles of the MTS-kolkhoz relationship in September 1953 in his attempt to recast the MTS as the central instrument of agricultural reform.

However, it should be pointed out that in none of these cases was the ideological model apparently capable of suggesting or generating new policies by itself. Each time, there were situational factors that forced the policy-makers to seek policy prescriptions in the accepted ideological formulations. Although ideology did exert an important formative influence on policy, its specific impetus in the making of any particular decision will probably remain impossible to determine, given the kind of documentation that is likely to be made available.

The nature and effects of the legitimation function are somewhat easier to comprehend. Since the beginnings of the Soviet regime foreign observers have marvelled at the intensity with which it has sought to imbue the populace at large with the principles and values of the official doctrine. The constituents of the Soviet policy-makers have, thus, been socialized to expect ideological explanations for policy. Although the effectiveness of the legitimation process has probably been attenuated in recent years and was probably never as great or widespread as some commentators have suggested, the appropriate manipulation of ideological formulas and symbols has traditionally been an accepted means of conferring legitimacy on policy and reinforcing the authority of the policy-makers. This manipulation is not necessarily cynical. There is a good deal of circumstantial evidence that the expectation of ideological consistency and elaborateness is to a large extent shared by the policy-makers themselves. It would be strange indeed if this were not so. High-ranking Party officials apparently accepted as authoritative the official ideological explanations for some of the most dubious policies of the Stalin era.[63] To be sure, Stalin helped to foster this climate of acceptance by the perverse expedient of liquidating all overt skeptics. But there is reason to believe that he, too, took the business of ideological analysis seriously at least some of the time. His vigorous intervention in the so-called linguistics controversy in 1950 and in the debates on political economy in 1951 and 1952 suggests a genuine concern for doctrinal purity and for his own historical responsibility as its high priest.

These phenomena further illustrate the extreme complexity of the mixture of manifest and latent functions performed by ideology. On the one hand, when the ideological analysis of an issue is genuinely undertaken for policy purposes, it has latent legitimizing consequences. On the other hand, even when such an analysis is employed entirely instrumentally — that is, as ex post facto rationalization — the pervasive reverence for "theoretical work" makes it very difficult to ignore the analysis in future policy-making. The author would argue, therefore, that the Soviet use of ideological analysis is rarely, if ever, entirely cynical.

The foregoing discussion points to the extreme importance of the latent conservative function of ideology in the Soviet system. The Soviet political culture takes pride in its dynamism and receptiveness to the imperatives of change. The analytical-prescriptive process supposedly provides the means for comprehending the dynamics of reality and shaping policy accordingly. As has been demonstrated, practice frequently diverges from this decision-making model. Once a given formulation has been accepted as authoritative, it tends to acquire a truth-value of its own in the making of policy. Particularly in Stalin's day there was a demonstrable reluctance to introduce new empirical evidence which might call into question the original theoretical and institutional basis of the formulation. Since Stalin's death there have been signs of a growing awareness of the conservative bias of the ideological method of policy-formation. One of the main reasons for the apparent "de-ideologization" of the policy process in the post-Stalin era, aside from the different styles of the latter-day leaders, is the absence of a universally acknowledged ideological legislator. It has become more difficult to obtain general acceptance of new ideological formulations. At the same time, de-Stalinization has tended to undermine many past formulations.

In this connection it might be pointed out that conservation may not have been an entirely negative function from the stand-point of the operation of the political system as a whole. Given the extremely weak development of traditional and institutional re-straints on the political leadership, the conservative bias of the methodology has occasionally had a salutary effect on policy. There were numerous occasions during Khrushchev's reign — the era of the "hare-brained scheme" as it is now quaintly called — when the dead weight of past ideological formulations might have exerted a beneficial attenuating influence. The frenetic pace of the liquidation of the MTS system in 1958 is an excellent example.

The substantive and theoretical discussions in this chapter sug-gest that the ideological method of policy-making is by no means entirely worthless. For a nation involved in massive programs of social and economic development, ideology can provide a power-ful integrative and orientational impetus to policy. At the same time, it can undoubtedly do a good deal of harm, particularly in engendering confusion between what is and what ought to be. Under Stalin the original ideological model of the MTS came to have a reality of its own, almost independent of the real opera-tional strengths and weaknesses of the institution itself. Marx had asserted that the purpose of theory is to change reality, not merely to describe it. He did not urge the total denial of reality, how-ever unpleasant. After all, one has to know something about what it is he is attempting to change.

Under Stalin, ideology served as a shield against real scrutiny of the MTS. To this extent it impeded genuine improvements. It contributed to the freezing of MTS-kolkhoz relations at a very primitive level, making substantial development virtually im-possible. Khrushchev at first accepted the original model as a given, but his more pragmatic approach to policy-making soon led him to see the obvious discrepancies between the model and reality. For a number of reasons, which will become apparent in subsequent chapters, his reaction, or over-reaction, was to discard the entire package of MTS-kolkhoz relations, ideological wrapper and all. The vehemence of the opposition to his abolition of the MTS indi-cates that more than mere cynicism had been involved in the persistence of the old formulas.

Part II   The MTS and the System of

Agricultural Administration

*the state has done all it possibly could to help the departments
of the People's Commissariat of Agriculture and of the People's
Commissariat of State Farms to direct the work of collective-farm
and state-farm development.*

Can it be said that the best use has been made of these possibilities?

Unfortunately, it cannot.

*To begin with, these People's Commissariats are more infected
than others with the disease of red tape. Decisions are made,
but not a thought is given to checking up on their fulfillment, to calling
to order those who disobey the instructions and orders of the
leading bodies, and to promoting honest and conscientious workers.*

Stalin

4 The Organization of the Individual

Machine-Tractor Station

In recent years Western students of Soviet politics have become increasingly aware that many of the problems of the Soviet bureaucracy are not really unique.[1] Such typical problems of public administration as staff-line tensions, conflicts between the norms of hierarchical structure and the need for local flexibility, differences in role expectations between generalists and specialists — all have their parallels or analogies in Soviet public administration. Thus, if only as a limiting case, the all-pervasive bureaucratization characteristic of the Soviet system can be instructive for the student of comparative public administration. The history of the administration of the MTS is particularly useful in this connection. It illustrates many of the common problems of bureaucracy, while, at the same time pointing up some of the unique aspects of the Soviet approach to public administration.

One of the most striking features of the Soviet approach is the fetishism of reorganization as a method for solving substantive problems. As Meyer has aptly expressed it, the operative motto of the Soviet rulers when faced with such problems seems to have been: " 'When in trouble, reorganize.' "[2] The history of Soviet agricultural administration richly confirms this observation. Part of the reason for the preoccupation with organization is ideological. Soviet theorists tend to view organizational arrangements as more or less deterministically defined by the state of socioeconomic development at any given point in time. The assumption is that there is a proper "mix" of structures and functions immanent in the set of productive relations at each stage.[3] This is not to say that practicing Soviet politicians have had any particular illusions as to the ease of discovering the proper "mix." But, unlike their

101

Western counterparts, who are prepared to accept a "satisficing" set of administrative arrangements,[4] Soviet leaders act under the ideological assumption that for every period there exists a perfect administrative pattern which can be comprehended through systematic analysis and which they are under an obligation to put into practice. This attitude may, perhaps, be viewed as the philosophical underpinning of the traditional Bolshevik faith in organization as a primary element in the solution of all human problems.

This ideological factor has had important operational consequences. It has reinforced the impetus for keeping the performance of the bureaucracy under perpetual scrutiny. And, as a result of frequent reorganizations, it has allowed the regime to develop a good deal of empirical experience in tailoring structure to perceived situational requirements. Over the years the range of structural options has tended to become narrower. Certain characteristic problems have tended to suggest particular structural responses. The effect has been to give the overall appearance of the sequence of reorganizations a roughly cyclical shape. In agriculture the pattern of alternations has been basically between centralization and decentralization of control over production operations. This pattern can be seen fairly clearly at the various levels of the MTS system.

Before proceeding, it should be pointed out that the Communist Party apparatus is intimately involved in the administrative system at all levels. Even in strictly economic matters there is really no precise separation between the activities of the Party and governmental bureaucracies, despite official claims to the contrary. For purposes of analysis, however, the two will be considered separately here: the administrative organs in Part II, and the Party organs in Part III.

THE INTERNAL ORGANIZATION OF THE MACHINE-TRACTOR STATION

Strictly speaking, it is somewhat misleading to speak of *the* internal structure of the MTS. Although there were certain major common features, the internal arrangements and the structures for dealing with the kolkhozes changed as new responsibilities and functions were assigned to the MTS. Most of the structural changes involved the roles of the MTS specialists, particularly the agronomists, in the conduct of operations in the kolkhozes.

Before discussing these changes and the administrative patterns they reflected it will be useful to list the most important positions in the MTS and describe their respective responsibilities. Soviet commentaries customarily distinguished among three categories of MTS personnel (albeit with some disagreement as to who belonged in each category):[5] (1) leading managerial personnel, (2) middle managerial personnel, and (3) production workers. The following list includes the most important positions in each category.*

Leading Managerial Personnel

Director
Chief Engineer
Chief Agronomist
Deputy Director of the MTS for the Political Sector (1935–1941, 1947–1953)
Secretary of the MTS Primary Party Organization (During the 1935–1941 period this position was held by the Deputy Director for the Political Sector.)
Chief Bookkeeper
Chief Zootechnician
Senior Veterinary Doctor
Engineer–Land Surveyor
Fuel Supply Manager

Middle Managerial Personnel

Specialized Agronomists
Sector Agronomists (after 1953 MTS agronomists in the kolkhozes)
Dispatcher
Repair Shop Manager
Specialized Mechanics
Engineer Mechanic
Sector Mechanics
Traveling Mechanics
Brigadiers of Tractor Brigades[6]

* The relationships among these various categories of personnel at different stages in MTS history are shown in Appendix A.

Bookkeepers
Economists
Cashier–Record Keeper

Production Workers

Assistant Brigadiers
Combine and Special Machinery Operators
Tractor Drivers, senior and junior (one each per tractor). (Tractor
    drivers were not on the permanent staff of the MTS until after
    September 1953.)
Truck Drivers
Timekeepers–Fuel Attendants (one per brigade)
Hitch men
Tractor Brigade Service Workers } Not on full-time staff of the MTS.

The operational high command of the station was comprised of
a small group of officials of the first category. It included the
director and his chief assistants: the chief engineer, the chief
agronomist, the chief zootechnician, the chief bookkeeper, the
deputy director for the political sector (when the position existed),
and, according to some commentators, the engineer-land surveyor,
the manager of the repair shop, and the manager of the seed
laboratory.[7] The nature of the authority of these and certain
other members of the MTS management was unique in Soviet
administrative theory, as the legal literature frequently pointed
out.[8] This special status was due to the fact that the work of these
officials was performed not only within the confines of the MTS
itself, but also in the autonomous kolkhozes of the MTS zone.
Theoretically, the peculiarities of the MTS-kolkhoz relationship
placed certain restrictions on the ability of the MTS management
to issue direct orders to the kolkhozes. In practice, however, these
formal restrictions were fairly easily overcome.

The director was the paramount figure in the MTS. He was
formally the *edinonachal'nik,* or manager-in-chief, of the station.
The principle of *edinonachalie* (literally, "one-man management")
in Soviet administrative theory is in many respects similar to the
concept of line authority in the Western literature on public
administration. The principle of *edinonachalie* asserts that one

man in each enterprise or administrative unit bears full responsibility for its performance once a policy has been set.[9] He represents the enterprise or institution in its dealings with higher organs and the latter, in turn, must deal with the institution only through him. This pattern is repeated within the enterprise or institution. Thus, the MTS director would have to work through the chief engineer, who would in turn work through the manager of the repair shop, in all matters concerning the repair shop of the given station. The reciprocal of *edinonachalie,* and in many ways its opposite, is the principle of *kollegial'nost'* (collegiality) under which every policy decision is to be arrived at through a process of collective discussion, involving the immediate subordinates of the manager-in-chief. Throughout the history of MTS administration there was a continuing search for the proper "dialectical" combination of the two principles, although, as one might perhaps expect, genuine concern for collegiality in decision-making was not always evident.

As has frequently been the case in Soviet practice with *edinonachalie,* the authority of the MTS director was not nearly as clear-cut as the principle suggests.[10] He did not have the right to hire or remove his chief assistants. In Party matters he was outranked by the Secretary of the MTS Primary Party Organization. On the other hand, the director was usually an important man in the rural district. He was very often a member of the raikom bureau, the main policy-making body in the district; consequently he was effectively removed from petty abuses of power by the MTS Party secretary.

Until 1953 the MTS director could be appointed or dismissed solely by the USSR Minister of Agriculture, acting on the recommendations of a special certification commission located within the ministry. After September 1953, in line with Khrushchev's successive decentralizations of the agricultural bureaucracy, the appointment and dismissal of directors was transferred: first, to the republican ministers of agriculture and then, in 1955, to the oblast or *krai* agricultural administrations, with the republican ministries retaining certain supervisory rights.[11] As will be shown later in the chapter, staffing the MTS with competent directors was a continuing problem, one that was frequently compounded by the interference of Party and higher administrative officials.

One of the main causes of the staffing problem was the incredibly broad range of responsibilities entrusted to the MTS director. Among the formal rights and responsibilities of the director listed in a major legal commentary on the MTS in 1956 were the following:

1. The organization of the operations of the MTS tractor and machinery park; the appointment of brigadiers and machinery operators for the tractor brigades; the confirmation of work plans of the tractor brigades; checking the general performance and conditions of tractor operations.

2. The maintenance of the tractor and machinery park, with the right to levy fines and penalties on his subordinates for damage to MTS equipment.

3. The compilation of short-term production plans.

4. The disposition of production funds, funds for wages, fuel, lubricants, parts — within limits set forth in the annual MTS plan.

5. The disposition of the so-called director's fund — for housing, improvements in living conditions, premiums for production workers and other personnel of the station.

6. The appointment of all subordinate personnel except the chief engineer, chief agronomist, chief zootechnician, engineer-land surveyor, and manager of the repair shop.

7. The right to issue obligatory instructions to all MTS personnel "without exception." [12]

In addition to these rights and responsibilities within the MTS the director was held generally responsible for the state of agricultural production in the kolkhozes of the MTS zone. He was charged with the timely conclusion and fulfillment of the contract between the MTS and each of the kolkhozes it served and for the fulfillment of the station's production plans based on the aggregate of these contractual obligations. Legally, the kolkhoz was not administratively subordinate to the MTS. Accordingly, the MTS director could not issue formally obligatory instructions to a kolkhoz chairman. But there were numerous ways in which the director could exert his influence on the kolkhoz. In addition to the ubiquitous Party channels, he could invoke the authority of the *raiispolkom* (district executive committee), which was legally superior to the kolkhoz in production matters. Also, there were formal regulations giving MTS agronomists and other specialists certain specific powers over kolkhoz production operations.[13]

Supposedly, one of the main channels of MTS influence over the kolkhozes was the MTS Council, which was first introduced in 1939. The council was made up of the MTS director (ex officio chairman of the council), his deputies and other MTS specialists, the chairmen of the kolkhozes served by the MTS, kolkhoz specialists, and leading brigadiers of the MTS tractor brigades. The council was supposed to meet not less than three times a year — before major phases of the agricultural year — and whenever a kolkhoz chairman or the MTS director requested.[14] Council meetings were devoted, as a rule, to discussions of future plans or the state of fulfillment of current plans. In addition they served as a general forum for propagandizing and explaining new policies and for the airing of local grievances. Besides his appearances at council meetings the MTS director was expected to deliver reports on the work of the station in each kolkhoz at general meetings of the kolkhoz membership at least twice each year.

The existence of the MTS Council, the regular meetings with the kolkhozniks, and similar institutionalized arrangements in Soviet industrial enterprises reflect a long-standing belief in the usefulness of management-labor discussions for obtaining policy consensus. (In recent years American specialists on business organization and public administration have found empirical confirmation of the utility of this kind of worker participation in decision making.)[15] However, the formal character of the MTS Council and its procedures and the routine nature of the semi-annual reporting sessions in the kolkhozes appear to have robbed these institutions of much of their potential significance for the actual operations of the MTS-kolkhoz system. There is little evidence that such consultative devices ever became important operative features of MTS-kolkhoz relations, except as safety valves for popular dissatisfaction.[16]

Nevertheless, the preparing of reports and the chairing of meetings appear to have occupied a good deal of the time of the

MTS director. A prominent Soviet specialist on MTS administration, S. V. Fraer, has presented a time-budget of an MTS director in the Arkhangel' Oblast for the month of May, 1950 (Table 4-1).[17]

Table 4-1. Time-budget (hours) of the director of the Khoz'minskaia MTS, Arkhangel' Oblast for the month of May, 1950.

1. In the kolkhozes and with the tractor brigades		214
2. In the MTS		97
Preparing for conferences with brigadiers and chairing the conferences	16	
Preparing for the meeting of the MTS Council and chairing the council	20	
Working out and confirming tractor work schedules	16	
Checking progress of construction	6	
Receiving MTS colleagues, tractor brigade workers, and kolkhozniks	9	
Analyzing operational accounts, reading mail, formulating orders, signing various documents, settling financial questions	17	
Work connected with the subsidiary economy	3	
Work on material and technical supplies for the MTS	10	
3. At sessions of the *raiispolkom* and other conferences in the raion center		26
Total		337

Source: S. V. Fraer, *Organizatsiia raboty MTS v kolkhozakh* (Moscow, 1952), p. 387.

The data, if not necessarily typical, are indicative of the kind and distribution of activities which the regime considered desirable. As the time-budget suggests, the MTS director was expected to spend the major portion of his time seeing for himself how his orders were being carried out. On the other hand, under the principle of *edinonachalie* the director was obliged to operate the station through his specialized deputies, issuing his orders through them.

The chief engineer of the MTS, also called the deputy director for the technical sector, was the director's first deputy. He bore responsibility, along with the director, for the general condition of the machinery pool and its effective and economical operation. He was also responsible for setting work norms for the various field operations. It was he who bore much of the brunt of the incessant campaigns organized in Moscow to introduce advanced techniques and practices in the use of farm machinery.[18] Working through the manager of the repair shop, who was responsible to him directly, the chief engineer guided the all-important repair operations of the station, both in the MTS shop and in the field. This was among the most onerous of his responsibilities because of the generally poor state of MTS repair facilities and the perennial shortages of spare parts.

The chief agronomist, deputy director for the production sector, was a particularly important figure as far as MTS relations with the kolkhozes were concerned. He was in charge of the corps of regular (sector) and specialized agronomists of the MTS who operated throughout the zone. The general organization of MTS production activity was his major responsibility. Like the chief engineer, he had a certain amount of leverage vis-à-vis the MTS director in that he was appointed and dismissed by the higher agricultural authorities (the oblast or krai agricultural administration) and not by the director himself. However, in day-to-day operations the chief agronomist was fully subordinate to the director in accordance with the principle of *edinonachalie*.[19] In the last years of the MTS the positions of the chief agronomist and other technical specialists of the MTS became increasingly important.

One of the most important functions of the chief agronomist was the formulation and coordination of MTS and kolkhoz production plans. In this connection he was jointly responsible with the director for the fulfillment of the obligatory delivery and payments-in-kind assessments levied on the MTS zone. In practice this required that the chief agronomist engage in a good deal of non-agronomic manipulation in the assignment of tasks to the kolkhozes. Indeed, the author was told by the chief agronomist of a kolkhoz, who had formerly served as an MTS agronomist, that before 1954 there was actually very little technical agronomic planning and control in MTS-kolkhoz production relations. Most of the "planning" amounted to the arbitrary apportionment of the station's aggregate output targets among the kolkhozes of the zone.

Communist Party activities in the MTS were usually an important feature of MTS-kolkhoz relations. For much of the history of the MTS, the top level staff of the station included a deputy director for the political sector. It was his duty to apply political pressure, usually in the form of continuous exhortation through lectures and individual appeals to the production workers of the station. In addition, the *zampolit*, as he was called, served as the ranking Party overseer in the station. Given his special status as both a Party representative and a member of the managerial staff, he had considerable power to influence MTS affairs.

The fundamental operating unit of the MTS was the tractor brigade, which carried out the production tasks of the station in the kolkhozes. The average size of the brigade remained relatively constant over the years, despite the steady increase in the number of tractors available and the mergers of kolkhozes during the fifties. Although there were slight regional variations, by 1932 the average brigade (then called a detachment) contained four or five tractors.[20] In the mid-fifties the average was from four to ten tractors. Special permission from the republic ministry of agriculture was required to form brigades that were either larger or smaller than this norm.[21] The typical staff of the tractor brigade included the brigadier, one or more assistant brigadiers (if there were more than five tractors), a senior driver and one or two "shift" drivers for each tractor, a timekeeper–fuel attendant (*uchetchik-zaprav-shchik*), several hitchmen, and a group of kolkhozniks for auxiliary services to the brigade while in the field.

Before 1934 all brigade members, including the brigadier, were kolkhozniks, usually members of the farm or farms served by the given brigade. They received their wages from their parent kolkhoz according to the number of "labor-days" they had accumulated during the year. In 1934 brigadiers were given the option of becoming full-time salaried workers of the MTS.[22] Apparently, not all brigadiers exercised this option, for a trade union decree of January 8, 1937, applied pressure upon them to do so by declaring those not receiving their full salaries from the MTS ineligible for social insurance coverage.[23] The combine operators, who frequently were also skilled mechanics, had been full-time staff members of the MTS since the earliest period. They were considered an elite group among the production workers. Rank-and-file tractor drivers, on the other hand, were treated primarily as kolkhozniks. Until late in 1953 they were rated as only seasonal employees of the station. As a result of the September (1953) Plenum, at which Khrushchev had mounted a campaign to combat the high rate of turnover and the lax production discipline of the tractor drivers, they, too, were made full-time personnel of the MTS.[24]

The brigadier was an important figure in MTS-kolkhoz relations. Soviet commentaries customarily assigned the position to one of the two categories of managerial personnel in the MTS. The brigadiers were the lowest level of line authority in the MTS organizational hierarchy (see Appendix A). For much of the agricultural year, during MTS field operations, it was usually the brigadier who represented the authority of the MTS in the kolkhoz. Most commonly the brigadiers were selected by the MTS director from among his senior tractor drivers. He was the *edinonachal'nik* of the brigade, responsible for its production performance in the kolkhozes and for the mechanical condition and efficiency of its tractors and other equipment. His word was law for all brigade members.[25]

PROBLEMS OF STAFFING THE MTS

If the MTS system was to carry out its far reaching production and organizational tasks, it needed a massive corps of skilled managerial, technical, and operating personnel. The perennial lack of such personnel was undoubtedly a crucial factor in the continuing failure of the MTS to accomplish what was expected of it. Yet without the MTS the problem would have been considerably worse. For not only did the stations serve to concentrate whatever talent was available, but they also played a major role in the propagation of mechanical skills among the vast, untaught peasant masses.

The official image of the MTS as proletarian "missions" among the "heathen" peasant masses was not far from reality, especially in the early years of collectivization. At the beginning of mass collectivization in late 1929, the Central Committee had had to dispatch twenty-five thousand industrial workers from the largest cities to the most important rural regions. Owing to their semi-industrial orientation, the MTS proved to be particularly attractive as centers of operations for these "twenty-five-thousanders." Two thousand of them eventually remained in the MTS as permanent employees, giving the stations an initial proletarian flavor. Trade union data for 1933 reveal that of these two thousand, 40 percent were already working as MTS directors, deputy directors, or chairmen of MTS trade union committees; 31 percent were at the middle management level — heads of production sections, repair shop managers, or mechanics; and 29 percent were production workers — for example, tractor drivers.[26]

The rapid expansion of the MTS network placed considerable strain on the supply of trained personnel. In early 1930 Traktorotsentr organized a series of courses for training directors and agronomists in Moscow; courses for senior mechanics were established in Odessa. A broad program for training tractor drivers was set up at the local (okrug) level.[27] Personnel data for the first year of MTS operations show interesting patterns of social differentiation among the various categories of employees. (Table 4-2.) Clearly, even in the MTS only the "commanding heights" were firmly in the hands of reliable Party and class forces. Still, by comparison with the collective farms, the MTS was a bastion of proletarian influence in the countryside.

The demands of industrialization precluded any further mass transfers of urban workers to the MTS after 1931. A special decree at this time ordered that in the future all production personnel in the MTS be recruited and trained from among the local peasantry,[28] although a provision for such training had already been included in the first Model Contract of the MTS (Article 13).[29] However, urban enterprises continued to supply a limited number of machinery operators and drivers.

For leading managerial and technical cadres the MTS had to continue to rely exclusively on outside sources. The novelty of the MTS and the rapidity with which its responsibilities expanded caused a certain amount of confusion as to the job qualifications for managerial positions. In October 1930 the Central Committee

Table 4-2. Selected data on MTS personnel as of mid-June, 1930.

Categories of personnel	Total number	Social origins (percent)				Party status (percent)			Education (percent)	
		Workers	Employees	Peasants	Party members	Komsomol	Non-Party	Primary	Secondary
Leading cadres (directors, deputy directors, organizers)	322	75.1	19	5.9	52	—	—	86.7	13.3
Middle and lower level cadres (mechanics, senior and "shift" tractor drivers, etc.)	21,386	1.5	0	97.5	5	19.3	75.7	—	—

Source: Iu. Gololobov, "Na pervom etape stroitel'stva MTS," *Na agrarnom fronte* no. 6 (June 1930), pp. 122–123. Tabulated by author.

complained of serious weaknesses in the staffing of MTS leadership posts and ordered local Party organizations to undertake a two-month check on the suitability of incumbent MTS leaders. Those found wanting were to be replaced with "cadres that were politically and economically sufficiently prepared." [30]

From the beginning the high rate of turnover was one of the most serious problems with MTS managerial personnel. Even before the creation of the politotdels and the associated purge of 1933, the annual turnover of directors and senior specialists was as high as 30 percent.[31] For example, in 613 MTS checked by a special commission of the Central Committee in 1932, 60 percent of the directors had held their posts for less than one year.[32] Much of the blame for this situation lay in the habit of local Party officials, acquired early in the history of agricultural administration, of indiscriminate removal of managerial cadres for their failure to achieve the goals of the moment, regardless of objective circumstances. This spirit pervaded all levels of the system, as may be seen in the title of an article in the main Ukrainian Party and government newspaper announcing the dismissal of several MTS directors in 1931: "Let Us Not Allow Opportunists and Loafers to Disrupt Grain Procurements." [33]

By early 1933, with nearly twenty-five hundred MTS in operation and rising disaffection in the countryside, the management problem was becoming especially acute. In addition to the normal turnover there began, in January, a major purge in the countryside under the direction of the newly created politotdels in the MTS and sovkhozes. The MTS staffs were particularly hard hit. In some areas — such as the Ukraine, the North Caucasus, the Lower Volga, and Azerbaidzhan — 50–70 percent of the MTS directors were dismissed during the first nine months of 1933.[34] Middle management was similarly devastated.[35] Along with the purge, the Central Committee undertook a major effort to stabilize the tenure of MTS management by restaffing the stations with politically reliable and technically competent cadres. It established a special selection commission of high-ranking Party officials, including representatives of the Agricultural Department of the Central Committee, and chaired by the People's Commissar of Agriculture, Ia. A. Iakovlev. Candidates for appointment to leading MTS work were nominated by local Party and government organs or by special recruiters of the PCA. Those passing a preliminary screening (about one out of three) were brought to Moscow for training and individual scrutiny by the commission. Only those found to have the requisite political and technical proficiency were finally sent out to the MTS. Generally, the commission found it necessary to resort to a team approach. Complete troikas, consisting of a director, a senior mechanic, and a senior agronomist, were assigned to the stations. If the director was politically and managerially acceptable but lacked the necessary agricultural experience, he was teamed with experienced deputies for mechanical and agronomic work who might have been less well trained in political and administrative skills.[36] The extraordinary degree of involvement of the Central Committee in the selection process and the thoroughness of the process indicate the extreme importance attributed to the MTS in the consolidation and management of the agricultural system at this time.

The period of intense involvement by high Party leaders in MTS and other agricultural matters appears to have ended in the latter half of 1934. Purge activities declined markedly, as the MTS politotdels were being prepared for liquidation. A major reorganization of the agricultural bureaucracy had been announced at the Seventeenth Party Congress in February and was in the process of being implemented. Selection procedures became relatively routine. On paper, selection remained tightly controlled by Moscow. Candidates for MTS directorships were nominated by the chief of the oblast agricultural administration and then sent for personal interviews with the chiefs of the respective production administrations of the PCA in Moscow. Those passing muster were then checked by the Cadres Sector of the PCA. Final confirmation of assignment (or dismissal) required the signature of the Commissar of Agriculture or his first deputy.[37] These procedures were retained in form, if not in practice, until Khrushchev's reorganization in 1953.

In practice these formal procedures were more often honored in the breach than in the observance. Local Party officials, for example, the heads of *obkom* agricultural departments but sometimes even raikom secretaries, commonly appointed and dismissed MTS directors and other senior personnel without higher level approval.[38] For all practical purposes, the MTS director was on the *obkom nomenklatura* (official job list), although formally the position remained on the Central Committee *nomenklatura*. Once again it was probably the high rate of turnover that was the principal reason for this devolution of appointive authority. The outbreak of the Great Purge following the S. M. Kirov assassination in December 1934 saw an astronomical multiplication of personnel problems throughout the economy. Increasing numbers of responsible economic officials were arrested each month. The central authorities simply could not keep up with the personnel needs of the thousands of MTS scattered throughout the country. Approximately 800 MTS directors (20 percent) were removed in 1935.[39] In 1936 the number "leaving" or dismissed was 810.[40] By 1937 it was reported that 80–100 directors were being removed by the PCA each month.[41] The average incumbent had held his job for less than two years. On January 1, 1939, the new Commissar of Agriculture, I. A. Benediktov, reported that during 1938 approximately 3000 new MTS directors had been appointed — a turnover of almost 50 percent.[42]

Thus, as a result of the purges and the continuing expansion of the MTS network the demand for new cadres and replacements remained extremely high. Qualitative standards, such as they were, were exceedingly difficult to maintain. Indeed, one of the main reasons for the failure of the MTS to live up to the original ideals of scientific leadership — aside from the lack of capital investment and the pressures for procurements — was the low level of professional competence of managerial and technical personnel. The glaring lack of attention to agronomic norms in the planning and conduct of MTS operations in the kolkhozes may have been at least as much a product of this lack of professional skills as of conscious policies and priorities.

Some idea of the comparative levels of professional training in the various agricultural institutions and indirectly of the criteria for selection of MTS cadres can be obtained from data published by the Central Statistical Administration in 1935. The data in Table 4-3 are from a survey of specialists and managerial personnel in the system of the People's Commissariat of Agriculture in late

Table 4-3. Selected data on officials and specialists employed in the system of the USSR People's Commissariat of Agriculture on November 1, 1933. (percent)

Position in PCA system	Number in survey	Members and candidates of AUCP(B)	Members and candidates of Komsomol	Workers by social position	Education		
					Higher	Specialized secondary	"Practical workers"
Central apparatus	494	50.6	6.5	14.8	60.5	19.8	19.7
Republic commissariats	1,285	30.5	6.1	10.1	56.6	16.0	27.4
Oblast (krai) agricultural administrations	1,836	34.2	6.4	8.1	48.2	29.4	22.4
Raion land departments	17,014	17.1	8.8	4.9	17.8	49.2	33.0
Raion administrations of kolkhoz stock farms	2,816	33.2	14.1	9.6	5.8	52.1	42.1
Sovkhozes	3,086	27.8	6.9	16.6	18.1	37.6	44.3
MTS	19,136	39.7	9.4	28.2	10.0	36.6	53.4
Higher educational institutions	3,487	20.7	4.0	4.8	75.4	13.5	11.1
Others (including trusts, offices, functional departments, research institutions)	13,542	—	—	—	—	—	—
Total	62,696	27.2	8.1	13.8	26.8	37.2	36.0

Source: A. E. Beilin, Kadry spetsialistov SSSR (Moscow: TsUNKhU Gosplana SSSR, 1935), p. 262, table.

1933. Several interesting observations can be made from the data in Table 4-3. The MTS employed the largest single contingent of managers and specialists in the PCA system. Next to the central apparatus of the Commissariat (a much smaller body) they had the highest percentages of combined Party and *Komsomol* membership. They had the largest working-class composition, but, significantly, the lowest educational level. Of the organs closest to production (raion level or lower), only the raion administrations for kolkhoz livestock had a smaller percentage with completed higher education, but even these institutions were superior to the MTS in educational level if specialized secondary education is included. The overall impression left by the data is that MTS leadership was selected more for political reliability than for technical competence. This observation is certainly reinforced by other data (presented in Part III) on the character of MTS operations under the influence of the politotdels.

The quality of MTS leadership does not appear to have improved materially during the decade. At the end of 1932 the Central Committee had established a network of Higher Communist Agricultural Schools to strengthen the technical competence of MTS cadres.[43] Given the intensity of the demand, however, these schools could not begin to cover total personnel requirements. A study early in 1937 showed that of the 5400 MTS directors then at work only 551 were graduates of the Higher Communist Agricultural Schools or other specialized educational institutions, while 3294 (61 percent) had only a primary education.[44] Among the MTS specialists at this time 16.5 percent had a higher education, 44 percent a secondary education, and 39.5 percent a primary education.[45]

Leadership cadres, therefore, continued to be selected on a catch-as-catch-can basis as far as specialized training was concerned. This may be inferred from the amazingly varied range of previous occupational backgrounds of the aforementioned fifty-four hundred MTS directors. Given the high rate of turnover of MTS directors, many of the persons represented in the aggregate data of Table 4-4 were merely passing through. A substantial percentage of the directors were apparently being promoted from the ranks of workers and lower level managerial personnel in the rural areas. During the purges managerial cadres were in very short supply

Table 4-4. Previous occupations of MTS directors at the beginning of 1937.

Positions	Number	Percent
Industrial and other nonagricultural worker	785	14.5
Manager of consumer cooperative or raion procurement organ	383	7.0
Agricultural worker, not connected with the MTS	582	10.8
MTS		
Manager of MTS fuel depot or repair shop	898	16.6
Agronomist	45	0.8
Mechanic	20	0.4
Party and government work		
Politotdel worker	260	4.8
Raikom secretary or *raiispolkom* chairman	327	6.1
Chief of raion land departments (raizos)	400	7.4
Chairman of kolkhoz and village soviet	443	8.2
Graduate of Higher Communist Agricultural Schools or other specialized schools	551	10.2
Other[a]	706[a]	13.2[a]
Total	5,400	100.0

Source: Tabulated from data presented by D. Krinitskii, "O tekh, kto vozglavliaet MTS," *Sotsialisticheskoe zemledelie*, March 28, 1937.
[a] A residual.

throughout the economy. Consequently, the Party found it necessary to recruit increasing numbers of leading MTS cadres in the village. At the end of 1935 Iakovlev, at the time head of the Agricultural Otdel of the Central Committee, told a conference of agricultural leaders that the old practice of assigning MTS directors from the cities could no longer be continued. In the future, he said, they should be promoted from the ranks:

if you take Voloshin, the brigadier of the tractor brigade [a renowned brigadier in the North Caucasus], and tens of such people as Voloshin and raise their political level, you'll get directors from them who in a year or two will enter the ranks of the best MTS leaders. (Cries from the hall: "Right!") [46]

Iakovlev was obviously trying to make a virtue of necessity. In any case, Benediktov's New Year's report, cited earlier, indicated that most of the three thousand MTS directors appointed in 1938 had indeed been promoted from lower ranking local personnel. Among those listed were former kolkhoz chairmen, mechanics, agronomists, tractor brigadiers, and combine operators — in that order.[47]

By experience and professional training such persons were not very likely to possess the requisite skills for managing the relatively substantial, multifaceted enterprises which the MTS had become. The need for specialists to support these inexperienced directors was equally serious. Qualitative standards apart, there were simply not enough mechanics and agronomists to supply the demand. A report prepared by the Institute of Economics of the USSR Academy of Sciences in 1936 estimated the personnel requirements of the average MTS as approximately 400 persons, including 8 mechanics, 8 agronomists, 40 repair workers, 50 general and specialized machinery operators, 32 combine operators, 40 tractor brigadiers, and 160 tractor drivers.[48] By my computations these standards were being met for agronomists in 1940 by only 61 percent (70 percent in 1937), and for mechanics by only 58 percent (86 percent in 1937).[49]

World War II further aggravated these staffing problems. In the middle of 1946 the number of mechanics was almost 30 percent less than in 1940, and the number of agronomists 45 percent less.[50] If the official claims that there were by this time more MTS in the country than before the war are true (see Table 2-7), the shortage of specialists was at least that much more acute. In qualitative terms the situation was certainly no better. According to the Central Committee's agricultural spokesman, A. A. Andreev, at the February Plenum in 1947, 82 percent of current MTS directors had no special agricultural training. Of the remainder, 13 percent were agronomists and 5 percent engineers. The MTS agronomists were slightly more impressive. Of the 21,100 then on the rolls 11 percent had higher education and another 43 percent, secondary education; but the remaining 46 percent were only "practical workers." [51]

In the course of this speech Andreev touched upon one of the major continuing problems of agricultural leadership then and since: how to get trained agricultural specialists to work in production. The reluctance of the trained specialist to subject himself to the frustrations and hardships of work in the MTS and the kolkhozes was a particular bête noire of Khrushchev. In 1947 his predecessor, Andreev, noted that of the forty-six thousand agronomists with higher and secondary education in the country five thousand were in the kolkhozes, slightly over eleven thousand were in the MTS, two thousand were in the raizos, and thirty-seven hundred were working in seed selection and experimental stations. That is, fewer than 50 percent were actively engaged in agricultural production.[52]

Following Andreev's recommendations, the February Plenum decreed a number of measures to cope with these personnel problems. The practice of frequent dismissals and careless appointments of MTS directors by local Party officials was strongly condemned. Selection standards were raised, and the formal procedures under which only the USSR Minister of Agriculture (in March 1946 the various People's Commissariats had been renamed Ministries) could hire or fire MTS directors were strictly reaffirmed. Agricultural institutes were ordered to train twelve hundred MTS directors and thirteen hundred mechanics each year in special one-year courses. Similarly, fifteen hundred MTS agronomists were to be given special "finishing" courses each year in certain of the main agricultural institutes.[53] These measures apparently had some effect, for during the two years following the February Plenum more than eleven thousand agronomists, zootechnicians, engineers, and other specialists were reported to have gone out to the countryside for work in production.[54]

The kolkhoz amalgamation campaign launched by Khrushchev soon after his return to Moscow in late 1949 significantly enhanced the ability of the existing corps of MTS specialists to influence kolkhoz production. The MTS section agronomists simply had fewer kolkhozes to service. The average number of kolkhozes served by one MTS declined from thirty-two on the eve of the campaign to slightly more than fourteen at the end of 1950 and to eleven on the eve of the Nineteenth Party Congress in October 1952.[55] Meanwhile, during this same period the number of agronomists in the MTS continued to increase. Benediktov reported, perhaps somewhat overoptimistically, that fifty thousand agronomists were on hand in the stations at the beginning of 1951.[56] The specialist problem seemed on the way to solution.

Like previous reforms, however, the staffing drive appears to have run out of momentum rather quickly. Khrushchev complained at the September Plenum in 1953 that there were still only fifty thousand trained specialists (agronomists and zootechnicians) in the MTS — only 14 percent of the total of 350 thousand specialists with higher and secondary education in the agricultural system.[57] He noted also the consistently low educational level of MTS directors and engineering cadres. Less than 25 percent of the former and less than 15 percent of the latter had higher education.[58]

Consequently, as a major part of his campaign to revitalize the MTS, Khrushchev inaugurated a crash program for raising the quality and increasing the number of managerial and specialized personnel. As in the early years, the focus of recruitment shifted to industry and other nonagricultural branches of the economy. Trained and experienced engineers were sought out for assignment to the MTS as directors, chief engineers, and repair shop managers. The agricultural bureaucracy was ordered to furnish agronomists, zootechnicians, and veterinarians. Immediately after the Plenum every oblast, krai, and republic set about combing its cities for engineers willing — and sometimes not so willing — to go to the MTS. The campaign lasted through most of 1954, during which time about twenty-three thousand engineers and technicians were recruited.[59] By February 1956 the number had risen to twenty-nine thousand. In a relatively short time this influx of industrial cadres resulted in a significant improvement in the educational level of MTS leadership, as Table 4-5 shows.

Table 4-5. Percentages of MTS officials with higher education.

Officials	Before September 1953	On January 1 1954	On January 1 1955
MTS directors	22.6	39.3	59.3
Chief engineers	14.8	78.5	80.0
Repair shop managers	1.3	28.5	29.0

Source: Iu. V. Arutiunian, *Mekhanizatory sel'skogo khoziaistva SSSR v 1929–1957 gg.* (Moscow, 1960), p. 189, table.

At the September Plenum Khrushchev had also announced a goal of not less than 100,000 agricultural specialists to be transferred from the various niches of the agricultural bureaucracy to the MTS by the spring of 1954.[60] Most of them were to be assigned for work in the kolkhozes as permanent MTS staff representatives; each kolkhoz received at least one MTS agronomist and/or zootechnician. Apparently this target was met with relative ease. Agricultural Minister Benediktov told a conference of MTS workers in January 1954 that 104,644 of these specialists had already been assigned to the MTS.[61] And Khrushchev reported one year later that there were 120,000 MTS specialists at work in the kolkhozes.[62]

Thus, at one blow, Khrushchev had seemingly achieved his goal of getting trained specialists more closely involved in production. But in many cases the reshuffling was merely formal. A large number of specialists had probably come from the raizos, which Khrushchev had liquidated in 1953. Many others (nearly twenty thousand) were merely kolkhoz specialists who were put on the MTS payroll and remained where they were. On the other hand, it is true that a significant number were sent down from desk jobs in the higher echelons of the bureaucracy, including the central office of the ministry.[63] At Khrushchev's insistence most of these MTS specialists were transferred in August 1955 to full membership in the kolkhozes in which they were working.[64] Although they remained formally subject to the orders of the chief agronomists and zootechnicians of the MTS, this was one of the earliest signs of the official reappraisal and downgrading of the MTS.

In any case, the significance of these mass personnel shifts was that for the first time in their history the MTS were being raised to that level of scientific management and agrotechnical leadership which Markevich had envisioned in his original model. Unfortunately for the MTS concept, the new cadres were not to be given a real opportunity to prove the viability of the model, for the new staffs had barely begun to function when the entire MTS system was abolished.

So far the discussion on personnel has focussed on the upper levels of the MTS staff. At least equally important were the problems involving the production workers, especially the corps of tractor drivers. Again, the basic sources of difficulty were the low levels of professional competence and the high rate of labor turnover, but there were significant differences as well. Whereas the principal reservoir of cadres for managerial posts were the urban industrial centers, the overwhelming majority of tractor drivers, after the first year or so of the MTS, came from the local populace, with all of the cultural and attitudinal problems this implied. From the beginning the MTS had been looked upon as centers of political socialization and professional training as well as production activities. The first Model Contract between the MTS and the kolkhozes in 1930 had included an obligation on the part of the station to "take upon itself the training and preparation of kolkhozniks for work as senior drivers, tractor drivers, field managers, combine operatiors." [65] Indeed, except for a brief period during 1930–1932, when a number of drivers were trained in Schools of Peasant Youth, the lion's share of training of the basic production workers was carried on right in the stations. After the war increasing numbers of the operators of the more complex machines were trained in special "schools of mechanization of agriculture";[66] but the MTS remained until about 1956 their own principal source of production trainees.

Unfortunately, the MTS were poorly equipped for such a role. Complaints about the poor training of machinery operators — both in the MTS and the special schools, but especially the former — were almost a tradition. Khrushchev described the level of training in his own inimitable way at the September (1953) Plenum.

The time has come to change the system of preparing tractor drivers, combine operators and workers of other mass professions. Up to the present time these cadres have been atrociously trained. A lad will be sent to the courses for two or three months, they lead him around a machine a few times, and then they put the wheel in his hands — a tractor driver is ready. In the spring this tractor driver will get out into the field somehow, and if the machine stops, well, he sits down beside the tractor and waits until a mechanic comes, because he doesn't know what to do . . .[67]

To remedy this situation the Plenum ordered the expansion of the network of agricultural mechanization schools. These schools were to turn out drivers and machinery operators with more than one specialty (literally, "mechanizers of broad profile") in order to increase their utility to the MTS.[68] By the end of 1956 these schools were graduating twice as many tractor drivers as the older short-term courses in the MTS.[69] Since the abolition of the MTS they have continued to be the primary source of skilled kolkhoz machinery operators.

The main reason for the continuing shortages of machinery operators in the MTS was the extremely high rate of turnover. Despite the officially cultivated image of the tractor driver as an elite member of the rural working class, the job was apparently not considered particularly attractive by the peasants themselves. For most of the history of the MTS the tractor driver found himself between two stools. As a kolkhoznik, living in one of the kolkhozes served by the MTS, he and his family were subjected to the usual social and economic pressures associated with this lowest stratum of Soviet society. Consequently, he was likely to be particularly sensitive to the resentment felt by his neighbors toward his seasonal employer, the MTS, the direct agent of their exploitation. As an MTS worker, he was virtually compelled, by the nature of the MTS-kolkhoz relationship, to earn this resentment. There were many ways in which his fellow kolkhozniks could make their displeasure felt.

One of the enduring sources of discontent among the tractor drivers was the system of wages. Until 1934 drivers received their entire wages directly from the kolkhoz on the same basis as rank-and-file kolkhozniks. In fact, the pay scales were such that the tractor driver often earned fewer "labor-days" for his work than did the ordinary kolkhoznik. One contemporary writer, comparing the earnings of twelve kolkhozniks and twelve drivers in the zones of two Ural MTS in 1932, found that the average annual earnings of the latter were 45 percent lower than those of the former. He noted the case of one senior tractor driver who earned twenty-eight to thirty labor-days a month, while his fifteen-year-old daughter was averaging forty labor-days for her less skilled work in a kolkhoz dairy.[70]

Despite the existence of clear contractual obligations, the kolkhozes were often delinquent in paying the tractor drivers the cash value of their accumulated labor-days.[71] It was not until 1934 that the MTS assumed even partial responsibility for settling with the drivers. Beginning in January of that year, the kolkhozes were required to pay the value of the labor-days accumulated by the drivers working on their fields directly to the MTS at a specified (guaranteed) minimum amount in cash and grain. The stations would then pay their drivers. In the unlikely case that the drivers' labor-days were worth more than the guaranteed minimum, the kolkhoz was required to make up the difference.[72] This system, too, proved to be less than fully satisfactory, and as late as the end of 1937 approximately one-half of the kolkhozes served by MTS were in arrears on their payments of tractor drivers' wages.[73] In January 1939 the total of arrears amounted to more than 200 million rubles,[74] roughly equal to one month's cash wages for each MTS tractor driver in the country.[75] Thus, on January 1, 1939, the state (i.e., the MTS) took upon itself the responsibility for paying the prevailing guaranteed cash minimum of two rubles and fifty kopecks per labor-day.[76]

Given these various social, psychological, and material disadvantages of working for the MTS, the high rate of turnover of tractor drivers is not surprising. The permanent tractor brigade established by decree in 1932 remained an impossible ideal. The complement of drivers in a given brigade often changed several times during a single agricultural season. Iakovlev gave an eloquent description of the problem in February 1933, when he told the First All-Union Congress of Kolkhoznik-Shock-Workers:

We have many fly-by-night tractor drivers — today he's here, tomorrow there; but where the "there" is — that nobody knows. We checked a number of MTS to find out where their tractor drivers were. The director would begin to count for me: Ivanov is here, Petrov is there; he lists 30–40 percent. But where are the rest? He doesn't know. And this is what the rest of them do: they study for a month and get a certificate, "I'm a tractor driver" — and they run away from the village . . . How many of your tractor drivers have left in recent years? Have half of them left or more? (Voices: "More have left!") Certainly more! In many MTS as many are studying to be tractor drivers now as were working all last year. This means that many MTS have turned into passageways; the tractor driver goes in one door and out the other. We've got to put an end to this once and for all.[77]

By 1934 the politotdels had indeed succeeded in putting some modicum of stability into the tractor brigades, but the turnover continued at a fairly high level in absolute terms. MTS machinery operators continued to leave the stations for the apparently more attractive working conditions of industry, the sovkhoz, and even the kolkhoz. Table 4-6 shows the relative and absolute turnover of tractor drivers during the thirties.

Table 4-6. Number (thousands) and turnover of MTS tractor drivers, 1931–1939.

Year	Number at beginning of year, A	Number trained during year, B	Number leaving during year, C	Turnover $C/(A + B)$ (percent)
1931	50	136	81[a]	44.4
1932	107[a]	227	163	48.8
1933	171[a]	261	197	45.6
1934	235	248	119.3	24.7
1935	363.7[a]	281	152.3	22.9
1936	492.5	367.9	271.7	31.5
1937	588.7[a]	343.4	247.1	26.5
1938	685.0	267.5[a]	262.5[a]	27.5
1939	690.0[a]	267.5[a]	262.5[a]	27.4

Source: Iu. V. Arutiunian, *Mekhanizatory sel'skogo khoziaistva SSSR v 1929–1957 gg.* (Moscow, 1960), pp. 28, 46, tables.

[a] Denotes approximate or derived figures. (See notes to table in Arutiunian, p. 46.)

Some caution should be used in interpreting the data in Table 4-6. Iu. V. Arutiunian notes that a significant proportion of the annual dropouts represented what he calls natural turnover — those drafted into the Red Army and those who left because of illness. In addition some tractor drivers were customarily sent away for more intensive training as combine operators, brigadiers, or skilled mechanics. On the basis of information from certain oblasts, he estimates that almost 50 percent of the turnover in 1938 and 1939 can be accounted for as natural.[78] In this connection the high rate of turnover bears considerable scrutiny. The great need for skilled and semiskilled workers in industry and construction during the thirties undoubtedly did exert considerable autonomous pressure on the MTS labor force. However, given the coercive instruments available to the Party and the Party's often demonstrated willingness to use them, there is little reason to believe that such large numbers of MTS "mechanizers" could have departed if the regime had seriously wished to keep them in the MTS. The Party was fully aware of the various facets of the turnover problem. It was deeply involved in the recruitment and training of tractor drivers. Each year the local Party and MTS officials combed the kolkhozes of the MTS zones for driver-training candidates,[79] sometimes over the vigorous, but powerless protests of kolkhoz management. (The previous reliance on voluntary nominations by the kolkhoz was discarded in 1932.)

What these facts suggest is that the MTS system was being used as part of the nationwide machinery for preparing the peasants for industry. Here, too, the immediate needs of agriculture were secondary. The MTS were, indeed, in Iakovlev's quaint phrase, "passageways" for ambitious peasants — a kind of pretraining establishment for peasant youths destined to enter the ranks of industrial labor or the Red Army. Consequently, the turnover of MTS production workers must be viewed at least partly in the context of the huge planned demographic shift towards an urban industrial society. But the effects on the efficiency of the MTS and agricultural production were no less deleterious.

During World War II the problem of machinery operators became critical. The MTS were quickly depopulated of trained drivers, most of whom found their way into the motorized units of the Soviet Army. As the men went off to war, a major effort was made to train women as replacements. There had always been a small, highly publicized corps (5–10 percent of the total) of women tractor drivers in the MTS. The feats of Pasha Angelina and her girl tractor brigade had been built up into a national legend before the war. But it was only after the outbreak of hostilities that the recruitment of women for the MTS reached massive proportions. By the middle of 1943, 10 percent of the tractor brigadiers, 54–57 percent of the tractor drivers, 54 percent of the combine operators and 75 percent of their assistants, 12 percent of the mechanics, and 16 percent of the repair shop workers in the MTS were women.[80] Large numbers of high school students and adolescents were also recruited as MTS "mechanizers" during the war.

With the return of peace, however, most of these women MTS workers departed or were crowded out by returning veterans. By 1949 the proportion of women was back to the prewar level. Meanwhile, many of the factors that had been responsible for the high prewar rate of labor turnover soon appeared once again. In addition there was the added factor of exposure to urban and even foreign cultures. Having seen something of the outside world, many returnees were not long content to remain down on the farm. Because official policy was to give industrial recovery first priority, the regime did not initially raise serious obstacles to the outflow.

By early 1947, however, in connection with the general review of agricultural policies, there was a new recognition of the need to improve MTS performance and tighten labor discipline. The February Plenum placed great emphasis on enhancing the material incentive features of the MTS wage structure and ordered wages to be much more closely tied to the fulfillment of tractor work plans.[81] Further improvements in wage incentives were made in subsequent years, and in September 1951 the Council of Ministers launched a concerted campaign against the turnover problem by establishing incremental labor-day payments for seniority and additional training.[82] The result of these changes was to narrow the gap between the wages of MTS workers and their urban counterparts.

Nevertheless the absolute lag in salaries of the MTS "mechanizers" continued.[83] Turnover rates remained high and in fact increased significantly after 1950, when a massive migration of peasants to the cities began. (Khrushchev mentions a figure of nine million persons leaving the village from 1950 through 1954.)[84] By 1950 the annual turnover of tractor drivers was approaching the prewar level of approximately one-fourth, where it remained fairly constant for the next three years.[85] According to Khrushchev, the rate was actually considerably higher than that — perhaps 30–35 percent.[86] Many former "mechanizers," not requiring additional training — and thus escaping the census — were returning and leaving in the course of a single year, joining the exodus of new trainees.

To stop this disastrous outflow and tighten labor discipline in the MTS, Khrushchev found it necessary to resort to the drastic step of making all tractor brigade members and machinery operators, except for hitchmen, full-time employees of the MTS. He explained the need for such a step in his speech at the September (1953) Plenum:

The rich and complex technology of the machine-tractor stations requires an able labor force. But this technology is now in the hands of seasonal workers whom the kolkhozes provide during field work periods. The tractor driver in essence is not subordinate to the director of the MTS. If he wants, he goes to work; and if he doesn't go, the director has a hard time influencing him. Today he works on a tractor, and tomorrow he has returned to the kolkhoz or gone away to industry. This explains to a significant extent the low labor discipline and the great turnover of personnel.[87]

The new approach was part of the campaign to treat agriculture as an important sector in its own right, not merely as a source of capital accumulation and personnel for industry. The new arrangements concerning the MTS labor force included an increase in the guaranteed minimum wage for tractor drivers and the extension to them of the full range of social insurance and retirement benefits customary for workers in state enterprises. In general, the effort was made to make MTS employment at least as attractive as urban industrial work. The costs to the state would be high — this was one of the main reasons for not taking the step earlier — but Khrushchev apparently realized that any real improvement in Soviet agriculture would require greatly increased investments, among them an investment in material incentives to labor.

In addition to transferring the existing corps of tractor drivers to permanent status on the MTS payroll, the regime resorted to large-scale recruitment of former "mechanizers" who had left to work in industry, an even clearer sign of the changing priorities. In extending his "invitation" to machinery operators to return to the MTS, Khrushchev pointedly warned factory managers not to stand in the way.[88]

By February 1954 about fifty thousand former MTS workers had been induced to return to the MTS. At this time the total number of the tractor drivers, brigadiers, combine operators, and other production workers permanently enrolled on the MTS payroll had reached one and a quarter million.[89] Almost overnight a huge number of kolkhozniks had become bona fide members of the working class, eligible for trade union membership and its various benefits, but also subject to the stringent rules of Soviet labor discipline. Most of them, however, did not sever their ties with their native kolkhozes.* Many continued to reside in their old villages, where the state guaranteed them the continued enjoyment of their houses and private plots. Those returning from industry or choosing to leave the kolkhoz were given housing and private plots on the MTS grounds, where possible.[90]

The problems of the MTS labor force were hardly solved by this massive increase in the permanent staffs of the stations. The new situation presented a number of problems of its own, the most serious of which was that of finding sufficient work for all of the tractor drivers during the slack winter months.

CHANGING STRUCTURAL PATTERNS
IN MTS CONTROL OVER THE KOLKHOZES

At the beginning of the chapter it was asserted that the inner structure of the MTS underwent a series of changes. Most visibly, these changes concerned the position and status of MTS specialists in the chain of command over field operations. At the risk of some oversimplification, the structure shifts may be viewed in terms of the traditional distinction between staff and line authority.

According to the definition of Blau and Scott in *Formal Organizations*,

line organization places emphasis on differences in rank, and its members have authority over production processes. Staff organization directs attention to specialization, and its members usually function in a research and advisory capacity. In short, line officials possess formal au-

* The author was told by a knowledgeable Soviet specialist that polls were taken among the tractor drivers to determine their attitudes toward continued membership in the kolkhozes. The overwhelming majority voted to retain kolkhoz membership — perhaps an indication of a lack of confidence in the ability of the MTS to keep their promises of steady employment.

thority, whereas staff members furnish specialized and technical advice to the appropriate line officials in the organizational hierarchy.[91]

Blau and Scott point out, however, that this clear cut distinction rarely applies in practice. There is always a strong tendency for staff officials to become involved in line activity. In a special sense this was true in the MTS. Despite the requirements of *edinonachalie*, which is as precise a formula for line authority as one might wish, official attitudes concerning the role of the specialist in the MTS frequently seemed to invite an overlapping of the two types of authority. Thus, in certain periods the MTS agronomists were thrust into line positions in the chain of command, while in others they were expected to operate in a more characteristically staff capacity. Broadly speaking, the former structural pattern was employed in periods when local control over production was being most heavily concentrated in the MTS; the latter, when local control was more diffuse.*

Using the position of the MTS agronomists in the chain of command as an indicator, it is possible to discern four basic organizational periods in the history of the internal reorganizations of the MTS. From mid-1929 to February 1932 the agronomists were in a staff position; from February 1932 to April 1934 they were in a line position; from April 1934 until September 1953 they were again in a staff position; and from September 1953 to 1958 and the abolition of the MTS system, they were essentially again in a line position. The substantive meaning of these shifts is of considerable interest in the story of the development of the MTS.

During the initial period, when the MTS system was being established and the stations were still largely under cooperative control, the provision of agronomic services was a haphazard affair. Al-

---

* Even under the line format, however, it should be remembered that really effective agronomic guidance of MTS operations did not exist until the very end of the MTS period, if then. The dominant tendency was to ignore agro-technical considerations in favor of maximizing short-run procurements. Even in the rare moments of concern for agronomic improvements, the qualitative and quantitative shortcomings of the MTS specialists made the attainment of such improvements highly problematical. The position of the conscientious MTS agronomist was hardly an enviable one. And the frustrations of service at the production level were a powerful reason for the preference of the trained specialists for positions in the upper levels of the agricultural bureaucracy or even for nonagricultural jobs in the cities.

though Markevich had strongly insisted that the MTS agronomist must be the dictator of all agricultural work in the zone,[92] actual practice was far different. Any formal responsibility for agronomic services that existed was shared by the raion kolkhoz union, the raizo, and the MTS.[93] Under the chaotic conditions of collectivization the result was that no one could be held fully responsible, and there was little sustained agronomic guidance.[94] The poorly staffed MTS tractor detachments were not permanently assigned to any particular groups of kolkhozes and were ordered about directly by the MTS director. The senior agronomist and his staff of subordinates in the so-called "agronomic section" carried on a broad range of instructional and supervisory functions among the personnel of the tractor detachments, but were hardly the dictators of production that Markevich had had in mind. The organization of the staff during this period is shown in Diagram I of Appendix A.

By the beginning of 1932, after the extreme dislocation of the initial collectivization drive had somewhat abated, some of the main weaknesses of the MTS could be identified. The MTS network was already reaching substantial proportions (about 1250 stations), and for the first time serious attention was focussed on qualitative aspects of MTS operations. In general, the period from early 1932 to the middle of 1934 was one of feverish activity for the MTS system. As the difficulties of controlling the operations of the hastily expanded kolkhoz system became evident and signs of peasant resistance appeared, there was a strong movement to centralize political and economic authority at the local level. In practical terms this meant concentrating virtually all of the local control mechanisms in the production organs themselves, that is, in the MTS. The onset of famine later in 1932 reinforced this tendency. The establishment of the politotdels was merely the most striking manifestation of the new approach to problems of control during this period.

In the sphere of production the process of centralization took the form of concentrating all local agrotechnical direction in the MTS. The extent to which Markevich, as head of Traktorotsentr, was directly responsible for these changes cannot be ascertained, but their effect was to achieve his ideal of placing production operations in the MTS zones under the direct control of MTS agronomists, who were now situated in the chain of line authority in the MTS. In the spring of 1932 an order was issued over Markevich's signature establishing production sections in the MTS as a formal link between the director and the tractor detachments (renamed "brigades" in September 1933).[95] Headed by an MTS agronomist who was formally the *edinonachal'nik*, the production section was designed to serve the kolkhozes (eight to twelve kolkhozes on the average) in an area of four to six thousand hectares. Each section was assigned one or two permanent tractor brigades, each with four to six tractors under the command of a senior tractor driver. (These arrangements are shown in Diagram II of Appendix A.) Given the level of professional competence of the corps of agronomists and the highly political atmosphere of the period, it seems likely that the primary emphasis of the role of the section agronomist in this setup was on supervisory and control functions, rather than on more purely scientific agrotechnical functions. By the end of 1932, with famine approaching massive proportions, the two sets of functions were probably in conflict.

In the beginning of 1934 the worst of the famine was over. At the Seventeenth Party Congress, Lazar Kaganovich declared the need for a thorough reorganization of the agricultural control system.[96] The reorganization plan presented the following April was part of a fundamental shift in the national administrative structure from the "functional" principle to the "production-branch" principle of Party and governmental organization. At the raion level and below, the change had a marked decentralizing effect. The previous concentration of economic and political controls in the dominant local production organs — the MTS — was explicitly discarded in favor of a return to reliance on the regular territorial organs — the raizo and the raikom. Within the MTS the line-type production sections were abolished and replaced by agronomic sections with predominantly staff, or advisory and supervisory, functions. Once again the tractor brigade, through the brigadier as *edinonachal'nik*, was made directly subordinate to the MTS director.[97] Although considerably elaborated in the postwar period, this setup remained essentially unchanged until September 1953. (See Diagram III in Appendix A.)

Each of the new agronomic sections was assigned a section agronomist and a section mechanic, who were concerned with MTS operations in the ten or twelve kolkhozes of the section. The section agronomist functioned in a general advisory capacity for the kolkhozes and the tractor brigades assigned to the section. Among other things, he assisted in the planning of operations and served as an inspector and consultant on agro-technical matters.[98] A perennial complaint during the nineteen years of existence of this arrangement was that the section agronomists were forced to spend too much of their time in the MTS doing paper work.[99] Given the size of the area under their jurisdiction and their lack of direct authority, the section agronomists were not in a position to exert much influence on production. On the whole, this setup reflected the extent of the divergence that had been allowed to develop from Markevich's original model of MTS-kolkhoz relations.

Thus, for many of the most crucial years of the MTS, its role in improving the qualitative aspects of agricultural production remained essentially passive. Khrushchev called special attention to this situation at the September Plenum in 1953, when he announced that "the chief and decisive role in the future upsurge of agriculture belongs to the machine-tractor stations." [100] He thereupon outlined a series of organizational and personnel measures to recentralize economic and political leadership in the countryside in the MTS. In the political realm this meant transferring the center of gravity of raion level Party work, as in 1933, to the MTS zones. In the economic realm it meant shifting the bulk of specialized supervision and control of kolkhoz production activities to the MTS. An important step in this direction was the liquidation of the raizo. (See Chapter 5.) Another important step was the mass transfer of agricultural specialists from various slots in the agricultural bureaucracy, including the raizo, to direct production work in the MTS zones. The aim was to place at least one MTS agronomist in each kolkhoz of the zone to direct the planning and scientific organization of agricultural operations.[101]

Organizationally, the new policies were expressed in the shift of the agronomists to a line position in the MTS chain of command. (See Diagram IV in Appendix A.) The MTS agronomist in the kolkhoz received the right to issue orders to the brigadier(s) of the tractor brigades assigned to the given kolkhoz — albeit in the name of the chief agronomist and the director of the MTS.[102] A sign of the great importance Khrushchev now attributed to the role of the specialist in MTS operations was the extraordinary authority conferred on the chief agronomist as State Inspector for Control of the Quality of MTS Operations. This new authority was in clear violation of the principle of *edinonachalie,* since in matters of agrotechnical practice the chief agronomist was now directly subordinate to the oblast (krai) agricultural administration. The MTS director had no formal right to countermand his instructions in such questions.[103]

In numerous respects the reforms introduced by Khrushchev during this final period in MTS history represented the most concerted effort to implement Markevich's ideal. Khrushchev went about as far as ideological, political, and economic conditions permitted to make the MTS real centers of scientific agricultural leadership. The much delayed shift in emphasis from short-term procurements to long-term agricultural development, although far from complete, at last gave the MTS concept a chance to prove itself.

By the late thirties an observer of the formal structure of the individual machine-tractor stations, with its elaborate staffs of managerial, technical, and production personnel, might well have concluded that the MTS was well suited for its tasks of large-scale, scientific farming. Although a number of stations, such as the renowned Millerovo MTS and Shevchenko MTS, were able to use these structural arrangements effectively, the fact remains that the majority of stations were not. The very elaborateness of the structure, patterned after the best stations, tended to conceal, if not actually engender, certain grave weaknesses. The prescribed structural arrangements implied a tightness of organization and a level of technology, material supply, and personnel training that was simply unattainable given the official schedule of priorities. The equipment of the average MTS was never fully adequate, either qualitatively or quantitatively, for the enormous production tasks assigned to it. Repair facilities, spare parts, and fuel supplies were usually inadequate. But the most serious weaknesses of all were undoubtedly in the area of personnel. The position of the MTS director was even more demanding than that of the factory manager. His responsibilities extended far beyond the physical boundaries of his own enterprise. However, he had considerably less control over the subunits of his domain, particularly the kolkhozes, than did the factory manager over his shops. Yet both the MTS director and his chief staff subordinates were likely to be less well trained than their counterparts in industry, and his labor force was certainly less well disciplined.

In the beginning of the chapter the propensity of Soviet leaders to resort to organizational measures in the solution of substantive problems was noted. The MTS, by its very nature a symbol of centralization, was usually given an increased role in the economic and political control of the village during those periods when the regime felt the need to recentralize. What is perhaps most surprising, given this propensity to reorganize, is how few changes there really were in the internal structure of the MTS over the thirty years of its history. Except for the very beginning and the very end of that history, the internal structure remained remarkably constant. The longevity of the 1934 structural configuration, therefore, may be viewed as a tacit recognition that the MTS simply could not be made to function "as advertised" without major alterations in agricultural policy. That is, there was little sense in structural tampering if the basic mission of the MTS was not to be changed. Although additional functions were occasionally assigned to the stations — for example, the tree shelter-belt program and the mechanization of kolkhoz dairy farms — there was little effort to increase the authority of the agricultural specialist in the actual conduct of operations. It was only when, under Khrushchev, a drastic reappraisal of the place of agriculture in the total scheme of economic development was made that the status of the MTS specialists was substantially elevated.

5   The MTS and the Administration

of Soviet Agriculture

The basic principles of the "leading role" of the MTS in kolkhoz production had been set forth in the orginal ideological formulas on the MTS-kolkhoz relationship and the early legislation establishing the MTS. However, there remained the more difficult problem of transforming these principles into procedures and structures to incorporate MTS activities into the national system of agricultural planning and administration. As the frequency of reorganizations involving the MTS system suggests, no solution to this problem was ever found wholly satisfactory.

To a certain extent the numerous agricultural reorganizations were simply a response to changing developmental goals and priorities. Particularly during the first two decades of Soviet rule the unprecedented magnitude and pace of economic development and social transformation placed tremendous strains on the administrative machinery. The effort to fashion an efficient, centrally directed economic system out of a technologically and culturally backward peasant society was inevitably attended by costly failures, in administration as well as policy. Thus, major administrative reorganizations were to be expected. At the same time, the nature and frequency of the reorganization process suggest that something more than mere growing pains was involved. Reorganization achieved the status of an administrative technique in its own right. The philosophical and ideological aspects of the Bolshevik faith in the powers of organization have already been mentioned. In addition, a cynical realization appears to have developed fairly early that the only way to get vigorous action out of the burgeoning administrative apparatus, especially in times of crisis, was to shake it up periodically. The specific reasons for this phenomenon will

138

become clearer in the course of the discussion of Party involvement in local administration.

The reorganizations of the MTS system followed a roughly cyclical pattern, alternating between centralization and decentralization, or intensification and relaxation, of controls over production at the local level. The structure of the national agricultural bureaucracy was also usually affected by these shifts. The MTS was always a symbol of centralization. During those phases of agricultural policy when tightening of controls was being emphasized, one characteristically found a strengthening of the organizational intergrity of the MTS system and an increase in the scope of its administrative role. Conversely, during relaxation phases, the administration of the MTS system was usually fragmented, and control over production was dispersed among a number of administrative agencies.

The early organizational history of the MTS system was greatly influenced by the debates over the functionalist versus the production-branch principle as the dominant organizational format of Party and government administration. This was a question which occupied the attention of Soviet administrative theorists beginning in the early thirties.[1] Under the functional principle (pejoratively entitled *"funktsionalka"* once it was officially rejected in 1934), authority within a given commissariat was fragmented among a number of line and staff departments, from operations to planning, finance, personnel management, and technical services. These departments exercised direct control over their respective areas of responsibility in all subdivisions and enterprises subject to the commissariat throughout the country.

The Seventeenth Party Congress in 1934 attempted to abolish functionalism and replace it with the production-branch principle. Under the production-branch principle the central commissariat operated through a number of main administrations (*glavki*), each of which exercised line authority over a particular branch or sector of production throughout the country. (Under the production-territorial variant, which appeared a few years later, this authority was divided up among two or more similar main administrations, each of which directed the operations of the branch or sector of production in a given territorial area.)

Superficially the changeover appeared rational and clear cut. Functionalism, while useful as a method for organizing and staffing large numbers of new economic sectors and production enterprises, proved to be unwieldy for routine administration. It involved too many different agencies in the managerial process. By establishing a single line of authority the production-branch format helped to eliminate much of this confusion. But, while structural reform made it possible to eliminate functionalism as a general principle of administration, it was found very difficult in practice to get rid of all vestiges of *funktsionalka* in the actual operations of the bureaucracy. Western studies of organizational behavior have shown that staff authority tends to encroach upon and become interwoven with line authority.[2] The history of MTS administration offers many illustrations of this tendency.

The period from June 1929 to October 1932 was in many respects prehistory, as far as MTS administration was concerned. Before September 1930 the ownership of the individual stations was scattered among a number of specialized cooperative organizations in addition to Traktorotsentr. Even after the decree of September 10, 1930, which transferred control over the MTS exclusively to Traktorotsentr,[3] the latter, by virtue of its hybrid status as a stock association owned by cooperative and private, as well as state, shareholders, was still not completely integrated into the PCA system. By the summer of 1930 the continued participation of cooperative organizations in collectivization was becoming a distinct embarrassment because of the growing state commitment to central control. Ostensibly to eliminate this confusion, the Central Committee, on July 30, 1930, placed the direction of all aspects of kolkhoz construction and management in regions of mass collectivization into the hands of district kolkhoz unions (*raikolkhozsoiuzy*).[4] These unions were linked through oblast-level kolkhoz unions to the system of *Kolkhoztsentr*, the governing center of the kolkhoz movement, which operated under the policy guidance of the PCA.

The position of Traktorotsentr under the new setup was defined in a decree of August 23, 1930, which formally subordinated it to *Kolkhoztsentr* as an autonomous center. All work on the mechanization of the kolkhozes was to be carried on by Traktorotsentr. In those areas where MTS existed, the organization of new kolkhozes and the direction of their production activities were to be carried on by the stations, acting as the agents of the district kolkhoz unions. In order to insure the coordination of MTS activities with those of the kolkhoz unions and carry out a uniform mechanization policy it was recommended that the director of the MTS be elected the deputy chairman of the raion kolkhoz union. In addition, the director was expected to supervise mechanization policies in those kolkhozes not yet served by the MTS. In all his activities the director was supposed to operate according to a single raion-wide plan formulated in conjunction with the *raikolkhozsoiuz*.[5]

The tentative, almost diffident, manner in which the regime went about consolidating its control over the kolkhozes was a good illustration of the influence of ideology. Although he had definitively set his course for rapid collectivization under state control, Stalin evidently found it difficult to break completely with the cooperative traditions of the Lenin Plan. Indeed, for a considerable period the participation of the cooperatives in the setting up and administration of the kolkhozes was far from a mere façade. Until October 1932, when the cooperative influence was finally extirpated, a very real division of labor existed between cooperative and state agencies: namely, the People's Commissariat of Agriculture, the cooperative system of *Kolkhoztsentr*, and the mixed system of Traktorotsentr. The local organs of the PCA — the *oblzu* and the raizo — provided general technical supervision and policy guidance over kolkhoz production. The kolkhoz unions of *Kolkhoztsentr* at the oblast and raion levels focussed on the organization and direction of new kolkhozes. And where MTS existed, Traktorotsentr provided operational control. Presumably, as MTS coverage expanded, the Traktorotsentr system would progressively take over operational control from the kolkhoz unions. In fact, in early 1932 the Ukrainian authorities attempted to transfer all *raikolkhozsoiuz* functions in the raion surrounding the Shevchenko MTS to the station, but the effort was apparently a failure.[6]

In practice the various jurisdictional lines were not very strictly maintained. According to one contemporary expert, the oblast kolkhoz unions had the authority to direct the overall production activities of the "local organs of Traktorotsentr" (presumably including the MTS).[7] Thus, the special position of the MTS director accruing from his direct links with Traktorotsentr would seem to have been considerably circumscribed. Indeed, by the end of 1931, when the number of MTS had increased to the point where it was becoming difficult to administer them directly from Moscow, the system of direct communications was itself abolished. Traktorotsentr departments were set up at the republic and oblast levels and given control over most of the activities of the MTS in their area, including the training of cadres and the distribution of credits, new machinery, and spare parts among their MTS.[8] Thus, the process of bureaucratic "layering" in the MTS system had begun. It is interesting to note, however, that no additional layers were ever introduced between the MTS and the oblast authorities. The fact that the individual station looked directly to the oblast for its administrative guidance was a continuing source of strength in MTS dealings with the kolkhozes and the raion agricultural officials.

In addition to the structural confusions of this early arrangement, there were serious practical difficulties which impaired the effectiveness of the MTS as an instrument of local control. Working relationships among the numerous agencies in the raions were often less than harmonious. Local authorities, including Party officials, either viewed the MTS as competitors, in which case they gave less than full support to MTS construction, or they underestimated the extent of official commitment to the MTS and shunted MTS cadres off into other local work. The practical links between the MTS and the raion kolkhoz unions were far less close than they appeared on paper. Although the MTS directors were formally deputy chairmen of the unions, they apparently paid little attention to this function and often failed to appear at meetings. The result was very poor coordination of local plans and operations.[9]

The failure of communications at the local level was symptomatic of the general malaise in the village in the latter half of

1932 after the initial thrust of collectivization. The regime ultimately responded with a major campaign to consolidate its control over the kolkhozes, including a radical reorganization of the system of agricultural administration in which the main vestiges of cooperative participation were eliminated. By a decree of the Central Executive Committee on October 1, 1932, *Kolkhoztsentr* and all of the secondary cooperative unions (the *kolkhozsoiuzy*) in the kolkhoz system were liquidated. The kolkhozes were placed under the operational control of the PCA and its local organs. Traktorotsentr was abolished, and the MTS system was totally integrated into the national PCA bureaucracy.[10]

The new structural arrangements were designed to make the MTS system the main operational arm of the PCA, even if the number of stations throughout the country was not yet sufficient to make this physically possible. In general, the period from the late fall of 1932 to the middle of 1934 was one of the high points of official expectations concerning the role of the MTS. These expectations may be seen in the decision to make the MTS into political control centers with the establishment of politotdels.

The administration of the MTS during this period essentially followed the functionalist rubric. Five main MTS administrations were established directly under the Commissar of Agriculture, one *glavk* for each of the major crop specialties: a grain MTS glavk, a cotton MTS glavk, a sugar beet MTS glavk, a flax and hemp MTS glavk, and a vegetable and potato MTS glavk. These main administrations operated through corresponding departments (*traktorotsentry*) in the republic ministries of agriculture (except the RSFSR) and in the oblast and krai land administrations.[11] The individual MTS, autonomous repair facilities, and other enterprises of the former Traktorotsentr system were apportioned among the five MTS glavks in accordance with their primary crop specialties.[12] A typically functionalist aspect of this plan arose from the fact that since MTS coverage was limited (during the period the extent of MTS coverage did not increase much beyond 50 percent of the kolkhozes of the country), there had to be a parallel hierarchy for the administration of production in those kolkhozes not covered by the MTS. Thus, within the PCA there were crop glavks with many of the same concerns as the MTS crop glavks.

This pattern was repeated at the republic and oblast levels. From the standpoint of overall production of a given commodity, such an arrangement obviously suffered from serious weaknesses of coordination, a problem compounded by the fact that the kolkhozes not served by MTS tended to be located far from the centers of administration and communications.

Whatever provisions there were for coordination and general supervision of local production activities centered on the raizo, the lowest level of the PCA hierarchy. The raizo was responsible for the distribution of plans and delivery quotas among the kolkhozes of the raion. It kept raion production records and was supposed to carry on a range of technical control and advisory functions designed to raise the level of agronomic practice. In addition it provided operational direction for those kolkhozes not yet served by machine-tractor stations. Some idea of the scope of activities of the raizo at this time can be gathered from a list of the positions specified in a 1933 staff chart (see Appendix B). It should be noted that the number of specialized personnel was reduced for those raizos which operated where there were MTS nearby.

During this period the first signs appeared of what would become a tradition of rivalry between the raizo and the MTS over the question of jurisdiction in the kolkhozes. This rivalry would persist until Khrushchev's final liquidation of the raizo in September 1953. Actually, the competition between the two agencies was rather one-sided. Effective influence over kolkhoz production activities seemed to gravitate automatically to the MTS, which had the great advantage of direct physical leverage in the kolkhozes during crucial periods of the year. The balance of local power, therefore, had to be restored from time to time by outside intervention. This was customarily done during the periodic relaxation phases.

It is tempting to present this rivalry in terms of the familiar staff-line problem. Some elements of this problem were indeed involved, but there are certain reasons why the staff-line analogy is not applicable. First of all, the raizo performed both staff and line functions — as did the MTS. In addition to operational responsibilities in kolkhoz livestock matters, the raizo always retained certain formal powers of supervision and control over the kolkhozes. By virtue of the principle of "dual subordination," the raizo had the authority of the raion executive committee — a governmental organ — as well as that of the *oblzu* — an economic organ — behind it, giving its recommendations an official status, which those of the MTS did not normally have.[13] Although there may be superficial parallels to Western bureaucratic practice, the MTS-raizo interaction was an example of the *sui generis* in Soviet administrative behavior. Specifically, it was an illustration of the use of overlapping jurisdictions as a technique of administration. As is usual in such cases, a certain amount of managerial efficiency is sacrificed for the multiplication of channels of supervision and control. The extreme pressures exerted on the MTS and the kolkhozes for maximum procurements were recognized at an early stage as an invitation to mutual concealment and other collusive practices. The parallel involvement of the raizo in planning, supervision, and control was thus seen to be useful as an independent check on local conditions.

Nevertheless, during intensification phases, such as the 1932–1934 period under discussion, the status of the raizo invariably declined, and its functions were formally or informally usurped by the MTS. There were apparently numerous agricultural officials for whom the inefficiency of the overlapping authority of the raizo was always a sore point. During intensification phases they found it possible to enunciate their feelings. But in doing so they were always vulnerable to attack once policy shifted back to a decentralization of controls over production. Indeed the beginnings of a shift away from intensified controls were often announced by attacks on the opponents of the raizo, as the following passage in a speech by Pavel Postyshev in Khar'kov illustrates:

Some comrades, including chiefs of politotdels, have interpreted the Party's insistence on making the MTS into organizational, economic, and political centers in the village as a transformation of the raion land organs into appendages of the MTS and, generally, as a signal for the liquidation of the raion land organs. We don't need any raizos, they say. Let them do the general planning, and we'll take the veterinarians and zootechnicians and agronomists. We'll direct all of the agrotechnical and animal husbandry affairs in the kolkhozes; we'll concentrate everything . . . in our own place. This is a completely erroneous and harmful attitude. On the contrary, we should strengthen the raizo with cadres and point up its rights and duties as a most important and significant organ of state power in the village.[14]

The Seventeenth Party Congress in late January 1934 was a significant event in the history of Soviet public administration. It was at this congress that functionalism was condemned and the production-branch principle hailed as the panacea for administrative problems throughout the country. Agricultural administration was high on the list of problems discussed at the congress. In the preceding months there had been an increasing uneasiness in high Party circles over the disruption of administrative processes by the politotdels. The purges, the wholesale personnel transfers, and the heavy-handed interference in economic affairs engaged in by the politotdels had rendered normal administration virtually impossible. There was a growing awareness that stable growth in the agricultural sector required a more positive, long-range solution to the problems of local administration. At the congress, Iakovlev, who, as Commissar of Agriculture, came under severe attack for the ineffectiveness of the agricultural bureaucracy, gave voice to this new attitude. His solution was a top-to-bottom reorganization of the PCA in line with the new production-branch principle.[15]

The main speaker on questions of organization and their application to agriculture was Lazar Kaganovich, who had been playing a dominant role in the Party's stern agricultural policies during this period. Kaganovich announced a major change in the Party's approach to agricultural administration. The Party would no longer encourage direct interference in production activities by local Party officials; instead, it would require much greater reliance on the regular administrative organs. At all levels the newly reorganized PCA would have increased responsibilities in the direction and supervision of agricultural operations.[16] Much of the burden of the new system would devolve on the raizo, which would assume a number of new responsibilities, including some theretofore performed by the MTS. As for the MTS, Kaganovich set forth the new official line in the most authoritative terms possible:

Comrade Stalin has expressed the thought that we ought not to fasten on the MTS a number of functions that are inappropriate for it. It is necessary to reinforce the raizos in every way and rebuff the attempts to liquidate them. It is necessary for the raizo, this state organ, to take upon itself the direction of a series of agricultural operations . . .[17]

Thus, in the realm of agricultural administration the main message of the congress was decentralization. The center of gravity of the local control machinery was to be shifted from the MTS to the regular territorial organs of the Party and government, the raikom and the raizo. This meant a substantial decline in the status of the MTS, which was reflected in the structural arrangements of the PCA under the new production-branch format. The former MTS glavks and their provincial *traktorotsentry* were liquidated, and the MTS were subordinated to four new main administrations for the major crop specialties: (1) a glavk for grain and oil-seed crops, (2) for sugar beets, (3) for cotton, and (4) for flax and hemp. Each of these new administrations had several departments and sectors, including a machine-technical department, which was in charge of technical affairs for the MTS under the glavk.[18] Accordingly, the MTS network lost much of its former cohesiveness as an integral operating system directly under the Commissar. This subordinate relationship was repeated at the republic and oblast levels. The responsibilities of the raizo under the new arrangements were expanded and its staff strengthened.[19] Given the degree of fragmentation of operational administration among the various crop departments of the higher levels of the PCA bureaucracy, it was obvious that the raizo would have to be relied upon to supply an integrative influence at the local production level. The aggregate planning responsibilities of the raizo may thus be viewed as a means of ensuring that the claims of the various crop glavks were somehow covered among the kolkhozes of the given raion.[20] How well the raizo was able to supply this integrative force was another question.

MTS FINANCING DURING THE THIRTIES

One of the major problems of MTS administration during the thirties was the financing of MTS construction and operations. Originally, each individual station had been expected to become an independent economic unit operating on a cost-accounting (*khozraschet*) basis, with profits covering expenses. The initial chartering of Traktorotsentr as a stock association reflected this intention to make the MTS system self-financing.

One way of insuring the rapid repayment of the initial state investment was to compel the peasants to contribute to the financing of the construction of the stations that were to serve them. The decree of the Council of People's Commissars of December 30, 1929, required that the peasants at a prospective MTS site must pay in advance 25 percent of the estimated costs of construction through the purchase of Traktorotsentr shares.[21] In fact, peasant contributions accounted for nearly half of the 555 million rubles invested in MTS construction and equipment in 1930 and 1931.[22] The regime exerted considerable pressure to make sure that the quotas of shares were met, but there was also a certain amount of genuine eagerness on the part of the local officials to have a station constructed in their locale. Indeed, the failure to meet the prescribed goals of share purchases in a given locale carried the explicit threat that the station would be transferred to another site.[23] The writer has found two cases in the Ukraine, involving ten stations, where this threat was actually carried out.[24]*

During the first years of rapid MTS construction there seems to have been little effort to enforce strict cost-accounting procedures. Time soon revealed, however, which operations were most costly and which practices resulted in poor "financial discipline." Repair work was found to be especially wasteful and difficult to control. As a result, in the spring of 1932 all capital repair shops in the MTS system was transferred to an independent cost-accounting basis. The decree of the Central Control Commission and the People's Commissariat of Workers' and Peasants' Inspection which ordered this transfer also indicated that the stations themselves would be placed on *khozraschet* in the near future.[25]

The pressures for economic self-sufficiency soon had negative effects on the conduct of MTS officials. In some cases MTS directors found it necessary to resort to the extortion of money from the

* Relocation under these circumstances was evidently considered a severe punishment, although it is not easy to determine just who was actually being punished: the peasants or the local Party and government officials, for whom the presence of an MTS was apparently considered at first a prestige symbol.

kolkhozes in order to "correct" the financial situation of their stations. The conservative writer and *apparatchik* S. P. Trapeznikov cites the example of the Anastas'evskaia MTS in the North Caucasus, which charged one kolkhoz 57,000 rubles for work actually worth only 18,000 rubles, making up the difference by charging for various fictitious services. This was not merely a local aberration. According to Trapeznikov, "Such arbitrary charges, which on a national scale amounted to huge sums, undermined the economic foundation of the kolkhozes and, naturally, evoked great dissatisfaction from the kolkhoz masses." [26]

The turn to more stable administrative procedures in the latter part of 1934 was accompanied by an increased concern with costs and a renewed effort to strengthen financial controls over the MTS. The following statement by the chief of the Azov–Black Sea Krai agricultural administration was typical of the contemporary attitude: "The evaluation of the work of each MTS in the future must be calculated not only according to quantitative indicators of production-plan fulfillment, but also by the quality of the work; above all, by the achievements of the MTS in the lowering of costs and the raising of profits." [27] Experience soon showed, however, that there could be little serious thought of immediate financial self-sufficiency for the MTS. It was necessary to continue to rely for the time being on a system of budgetary subsidies, which one Western economist has described as "quasi-khozraschet." [28] The system was highly complex and, apparently, almost as confusing to MTS officials at the time as it is to the Western student today. Under the arrangements which persisted until 1938, the individual station received its fixed and variable capital through at least six different channels. Large fixed capital expenses — such as those for the construction of repair facilities, the purchase of machinery, or for major overhauls of equipment — were covered directly by the state through planned allocations from the Agricultural Bank.[29] These allocations were nonreturnable and, except for the usual delays and shortages of materials, caused relatively few problems.

Current operating funds were another matter. They constituted the main source of financial difficulties for the MTS director during the thirties. These funds were allocated in the form of repayable credits from the State Bank (*Gosbank*) and were earmarked for specific operational purposes according to a rigid system of planned cost estimates. Repayments to the state were made out of the proceeds of the sale of payments in kind received by the stations from their kolkhozes. But since the volume of such sales — which, by the way, were not always simply a bookkeeping operation but sometimes involved actual commodity transfers by the MTS — was usually insufficient to repay the credits in full, state subsidies were required to make up the difference.* In 1935, for example, a relatively good year in Soviet agriculture, the realization of payments in kind covered only 31 percent of MTS costs.[30]

The planned state expenditures on operating funds were allocated for the following specific categories: (1) a fund of turnover resources — general working capital; (2) a fund of operating expenditures — operating capital designated for specific purposes, such as fuel and lubricants, current and "medium" repairs, spare parts, and so forth; and (3) an assimilation fund — a catchall production contingency fund ostensibly for the mastery of new machinery and new production techniques. In addition, Gosbank issued special credits for the stockpiling of fuel and spare parts. Finally, the stations received a certain amount of cash directly from the kolkhozes for services not subject to the payment-in-kind provisions.[31] In order to facilitate control over specific types of expenditures, the transfer of the various funds from one category to another was formally prohibited.

The administrative technique for strengthening financial discipline was characteristically primitive. The individual stations were progressively weaned away from state subsidies by the simple expedient of reducing arbitrarily the annual planned costs for each major item of expenditure. The pressure of state demands for procurements, however, made the attainment of any realistic

---

* The extent to which the MTS actually covered their expenses was, of course, largely dependent on the prices at which the value of payments in kind was calculated. Since the artificially low obligatory delivery prices were usually used, there was really no way of telling just how close the MTS actually came to covering their costs. Davies claims that in the post-1938 period at least the MTS more than paid for themselves, if one includes state earning from the turnover tax on payments in kind. This line of reasoning would appear to be somewhat tautological, however. See R. W. Davies, *The Development of the Soviet Budgetary System* (Cambridge, England: Cambridge University Press, 1958), p. 174.

degree of financial discipline extremely difficult. Violations of the system were numerous. According to M. A. Chernov, the ill-fated successor to Iakovlev as Commissar of Agriculture, "the majority of MTS directors have not only failed to master the financial side of their economy, but they look upon it literally with scorn." [32]

One of the most common forms of violation involved the illegal transfer of current operating funds to unplanned capital construction, particularly for the improvement of repair facilities. As late as the middle of January 1938, 2088 of the 5819 MTS in the country had no repair shops whatever, and only 1200 of the remainder were equipped to do complete overhauls.[33] To keep their equipment in some sort of working order the MTS directors often found it necessary to divert available funds for the construction of repair facilities. The result was serious shortages in current operating funds. Reports were common of tractors standing idle because the MTS could not afford to purchase fuel and essential spare parts, or because of the refusal of the tractor drivers to appear for work until the MTS made good on wages owed them. Even the great Pasha Angelina found it necessary to complain at the Second Congress of Kolkhoznik–Shock-Workers in 1935 that her tractors stood idle for long periods in the heat of the agricultural season because the MTS could not supply her with fuel. "This is why," she declared with characteristic modesty, "I could not take first place in the country." [34] The problem was national in scope. As of October 1, 1935, more than 25 percent of the total operating funds allocated to the MTS were unavailable for the designated purposes because of illegal transfers to capital construction or payments of arrears owed to other organizations.[35] By the fall of 1937, despite an intensive campaign to remedy the situation, the MTS in four large provinces alone — Azov–Black Sea, Dnepropetrovsk, Saratov, and Stalingrad — had more than 30 million rubles tied up in this manner and were indebted to the tune of 265 million rubles more.[36]

As Pasha Angelina's lament suggested, the shortages of operating funds affected MTS fuel supplies especially seriously. Fuel and lubricants accounted on the average for 55.6 percent of the annual operating expenses of a station.[37] In the budgets of some MTS these items accounted for as much as 80–85 percent.[38] There were serious fuel shortages in the country during the thirties. And as agriculture was the largest user of petroleum products in the economy, the effects were felt there with especial severity. Pressures for fuel economy were, in fact, almost as harsh as those for gross output. The two demands were, of course, mutually contradictory and made MTS services to the kolkhozes even less satisfactory than they might have been with all the other weaknesses of the system. E. I. Riabinin, the First Secretary of the Voronezh Obkom, noted a typical example of the effects of these conflicting demands in the spring of 1935:

The tractor driver knows that he receives a premium for fuel economies, but he is not asked about the quality of his work, and thus some . . . begin to "economize" — they plow shallowly, their harrows do not work and only jump over the soil. The norm of fuel expenditures is maintained, but the land is spoiled.
    They usually ask the tractor driver:
    "Do you have an overconsumption of fuel?"
    "No."
    " 'At a boy!"
But how he plowed — that no one is interested in.[39]

Nor were these sacrifices in quality compensated for by any notable progress toward making the stations financially self-sufficient. In 1935, a particularly good year for the MTS, only fifty-one stations in the country were able to operate completely without subsidies. Interestingly enough, they were all cotton-growing MTS located in Uzbekistan, benefitting from the relatively high state prices for cotton in the disposal of their payments-in-kind income. All told, only about three hundred MTS in the entire country in 1935 were able to manage wholly or partially without state subsidies. The overwhelming majority of them were engaged in cotton, sugar beet, flax, or potato and vegetable cultivation — all crops which enjoyed relatively high state prices.[40] Thus, fewer than 7 percent of the stations in the country were operating at all satisfactorily from the financial standpoint. Payments in kind covered only 31 percent of total MTS costs during the year. Subsequent years would witness little improvement in this situation. Indeed, toward the end of 1937 the PCA found itself so heavily encumbered financially that the new commissar, R. I. Eikhe, had to turn to Stalin for supplementary allocations.[41]

These operational and financial shortcomings could not help but affect grain procurements, the most vital consideration of all from the regime's point of view. Payments in kind for MTS services had become an increasingly important source of grain supplies. If in 1933 they accounted for 16 percent of total state grain procurements, as compared with 70 percent for obligatory deliveries, by the end of 1937 their share had already been raised to 50 percent, as against only 35 percent for obligatory deliveries.[42] The shift toward greater reliance on payments in kind made the speedy transfer of the commodities received a matter of the greatest importance. Yet the existing system, under which the MTS sold their *naturoplata* income to the state for repayment of Gosbank credits, often impeded orderly and speedy transfer. Some MTS directors were accused of treating this income from the kolkhozes as the property of their stations and of withholding grain for local bargaining purposes. By 1937, in the heat of the purges, this and other manifestations of "indiscipline" in the operations of the MTS-kolkhoz system had become intolerable to the regime.

THE REORGANIZATIONS OF 1938–1939: POLITICS AND ISSUES

As the Second Five Year Plan drew to a close, the problems of MTS administration had become a matter of serious concern. There was a general fear of loss of control over the activities of the individual stations. Barely a year after the 1934 reorganization, the apparatus of the PCA, particularly its middle levels, had begun to come under attack for laxity in the management of the MTS. Some critics had complained that the reorganization had not eliminated the functionalism of the previous arrangement; it was still necessary for an MTS director to apply to a number of different departments for the settlement of simple questions.[43] At a conference of agricultural officials in early January of 1936 the subject of administrative weaknesses in the MTS system was discussed by a number of speakers, including the Commissar of Agriculture, M. A. Chernov. Chernov called attention to the great burdens on MTS administrators in the provincial agricultural organs under the existing production-branch format. As an extreme example, he noted the case of the Cotton Administration of the Uzbek Commissariat of Agriculture, which had to manage the activities of 111 MTS. Accordingly, he urged the breaking up of these production-branch administrations, particularly in areas of heavy crop specialization, into a number of parallel production-territorial administrations in order to enhance control over the MTS.[44] For example, it was suggested that the aforementioned Cotton Administration be broken up into several territorial cotton administrations, each of which would have control over a certain number of MTS. The same solution would be applied to the Grain Administration of the Azov–Black Sea Kraizu, which was then burdened with 141 MTS.[45] At the conference Chernov's suggestions were seconded by Vlas Chubar' of the Ukrainian Party organization and N. K. Antipov, Chairman of the Soviet Control Commission, both of whom spoke of the need for some coordinating points for the MTS below the level of an entire province.[46]

The basic argument of these speakers was for further decentralization of administration, although there was apparently some debate as to how far this decentralization should be allowed to proceed. In their speeches at the conference, Chubar' and Iakovlev hinted at recent efforts in high agricultural circles to diminish still further the influence of the MTS in the kolkhozes by transferring all agronomists and other specialists to the raizo. This would have meant, for all practical purposes, the subordination of MTS operations to the control of the raizo. Iakovlev, the Head of the Agricultural Otdel of the Central Committee at this time, roundly condemned the idea and suggested instead a strengthening of the MTS. Chubar', on the other hand, merely rejected it as premature.[47]

From what had transpired earlier and what was to happen subsequently in the purges, the renewal of the arguments over the relative status of the MTS and the raizo probably reflected the existence of an old and deep rift within the agricultural leadership of the country. As in the 1934 debates over the future of the MTS politotdels, the divisions seemed to run between the central Party *apparatchiki* and the provincial Party and government leaders.

The former, represented first by Kaganovich and then by Iakovlev, were, as might be expected, for centralization; the latter were for decentralization and greater local autonomy. The Great Purge would soon witness a settling of scores in favor of the former, although the fate of some of the centralizers, such as Chernov and Iakovlev, indicates that other issues may have been involved also.

In any case, the final decision on the reorganization was left in abeyance for the time being. Outstanding problems had been aired; there seemed to be a general consensus that major financial and administrative changes had to be made, but nothing concrete was done for almost a year and a half. When the signal for the reorganization was at last given, the decisions were made in an extraordinarily circuitous way. In late May of 1937 Chernov announced at a meeting of the PCA *aktiv* that work was in progress on a draft project for the reorganization of MTS finances and administrative structure.[48] This PCA draft, entitled "On Measures for the Improvement of the Work of the MTS," was scheduled for debate at the June Plenum of the Central Committee. An item bearing this title was listed on the prepublished agenda of the Plenum. At the Plenum, however, a consensus was apparently impossible to reach, and it was decided not to allow the publication of either the draft or the issues discussed in connection with it.* The "Informational Report" on the results of the Plenum in *Pravda* noted merely that "the Plenum has transmitted the proposals of the PCA USSR on improvement of the work of the MTS as material for discussion to the local Party and soviet organizations." [49] This was subsequently done by the distribution of a circular of the Central Committee Secretariat over Stalin's signature as General Secretary. It contained the PCA draft, clearly identified as the work of Chernov, with explicit instructions against publication. The author has seen two copies of this document: one in the Smolensk Archive; the other, published as a pamphlet in slightly altered form in Ioshkar-Ola, the capital of the Mari Autonomous Soviet Socialist Republic (ASSR).[50] It is

* That the draft actually was discussed seems likely, especially in view of the designation it was given in the secret protocols of the Plenum. The copy of the draft in the Smolensk Archive bears the label of a note to Protocol No. 10 of the June 29th session of the Plenum (Smolensk Archive, Harvard University Library, WKP 238, pp. 253–256).

possible that the publication of the draft in this manner represented a breach of Party discipline and was one of the factors in the subsequent arrest and execution of Chernov, although such a conclusion is merely speculative.

Certain sections of the preamble of the draft are worth citing here as an authoritative statement of those problems of the MTS which were considered most serious.

the Plenum of the CC AUCP(B) considers incorrect the system under which the MTS sell the state grain and technical crops which do not belong to them, but are the property of the state as payment in kind by the kolkhozes for work done on the collective farms by the state tractors and machines.

Such improper relations of the machine-tractor stations to the state lead to an incorrect understanding by many MTS directors of their obligations with respect to the state. Many directors of machine-tractor stations and land organs do not understand the fact that the machine-tractor stations are *special kinds of state rental points* and that all grain and technical crops received by them from the kolkhozes are the property of the state.

The cost of operations done by the machine-tractor stations is exceedingly high because of the over-consumption of fuel, expensiveness and unsatisfactory quality of repairs of tractors and agricultural machines, and the high level of administrative and managerial expenses.

The current system of financing the MTS conceals the uneconomical and planless character of the work of the machine-tractor stations and impedes the organization of strict state control over their activity.[51] [Emphasis supplied.]

The body of the draft dealt with the specific changes to be made. On the key question of finances it ordered the transfer of the MTS system to full dependence on the national budget as of January 1, 1938. The assessment and collection of payments in kind were to be more strictly controlled, and commodities thus obtained were to be sent directly to state procurement points. Among the other provisions concerning the MTS were a directive breaking up the giant MTS in Siberia into smaller individual units and an order to change the system of wage payments to MTS workers to increase incentives for higher quality work.

Most of these changes would eventually be implemented within the space of a year, but for the moment the entire issue was cloaked in secrecy. The omnipresence of the Great Purge at this time offers tempting food for speculation as to the reasons for the secrecy and delay. But actually there are many possible explanations, all of which may be partially correct, even if not particularly sinister. For example, Stalin and his chief agricultural factotum of the period, Molotov, may have wished simply to avoid the disruption of MTS operations which an early announcement of the changes might have occasioned. Nineteen thirty-seven promised to be a good year for agriculture, and, judging from past experience, it was feared that many MTS directors would view such an announcement as an open invitation to relax whatever financial discipline and cost-consciousness they had been able to maintain under the existing system of financing. As it was, appeals for the achievement of profitability and financial self-sufficiency continued to be made right up to the end of 1937.[52]

Another strong possibility is that the Central Committee genuinely desired further discussion of the draft. As indicated in Chapter 3, there were important ideological issues involved in the projected shift to budgetary financing. Chernov's characterization of the MTS as "special kinds of state rental points" in the preamble must certainly have evoked strong objections, for during the initial stages of MTS construction the rental point concept had been explicitly rejected. The idea of total subsidization of the MTS was itself a radical departure from the original conceptions and may have been difficult to sell on economic grounds. Evidently there was a considerable range of opinion on agricultural finances during this period, despite the pressures for conformity exerted by the purges. As already noted, a group of economists was proposing the elimination of the multiple pricing system for state procurements, arguing that despite the low prices paid for obligatory deliveries and *naturoplata*, the costs of the MTS-kolkhoz system were actually very high. In short, the entire basis of the existing MTS-kolkhoz system was being called into question.[53]

Finally, there is considerable circumstantial evidence that the secrecy surrounding the PCA draft was indeed closely connected with the Great Purge. Chernov was removed from his post as commissar in the late fall of 1937 and was subsequently condemned to death and executed, along with Bukharin and Rykov, in the Trial of the Twenty-One in early 1938. His downfall may have been due to his espousal of some of the more radical proposals for diminishing or even abolishing the special status of the MTS. He may have been involved in the unauthorized publication of the draft in Ioshkar-Ola, as mentioned above. Or perhaps Stalin, having already marked Chernov for liquidation, did not wish to have the forthcoming reforms associated with his name. Molotov implied as much at a conference of agricultural officials in February 1938, when he stated that the recent "cleansing" of the PCA had opened the way for great new advances by the MTS.[54]

The long-awaited changes in the system of MTS financing finally came in February 1938 with the promulgation of a decree "On the System of Financing the Machine-Tractor Stations." [55] The MTS were to be financed directly from the national budget. Under the new system a series of expense accounts was opened in Gosbank for each station, covering such items as fuel, repairs, wages, and administrative and housekeeping expenditures. Funds were to be disbursed semiannually for each category of expenses in accordance with estimates prepared by the stations on the basis of performance norms and financial "limits" established for each station by its superiors in the oblast or krai agricultural administration. It is interesting to note that after a year of experience with this system it was found necessary to reintroduce some cost-effectiveness criteria. Thus, the unconditional semi-annual disbursements were replaced by quarterly advances, partially contingent on the fulfillment by the individual station of its production plans during the preceding quarter.[56] This system remained essentially intact until Khrushchev made his last-ditch effort to return the MTS to a cost-accounting basis in 1956. In any case, the new budgetary financing system meant an important change in the nature of the MTS — perhaps a logical conclusion of the ideological formulation of the MTS-kolkhoz relationship. The MTS had now become more explicitly an administrative, as well as a production arm of the state.

With the arrival of the MTS at what Molotov called this "new stage of its development," the movement toward administrative reform, which had been stalled for nearly two years, received new impetus. In October 1937, N. A. Paskutskii, a First Deputy Commissar of Agriculture and one of the few high-ranking officials in the Commissariat to survive the 1937 purges, announced that work was underway on the reorganization of the PCA along production-territorial lines.[57] Once again there were delays. The only visible steps taken were at the oblast level, and there the changes were clearly of an experimental nature. Some time in early 1938 an order went out to reorganize the oblast-level land organs along the new production-territorial lines. As had been suggested at the conference in January 1936, the goal was to improve control over MTS operations by reducing the number of stations under each administrative unit. In a rather surprising display of flexibility, considering the times, the precise structure and the number of stations per unit were left to local option. The regime apparently wished to find out more about the effectiveness of the territorial variant before introducing it on a national scale.

What resulted was a considerable variety of organizational arrangements, all bearing the formal production-territorial label. In Ivanovo Oblast, for example, in place of the numerous "branch" MTS departments (*otdely*) two production-territorial administrations (*upravleniia*) were established for the MTS: a grain and potato administration and a flax administration. All MTS in the oblast were divided between the two administrations.[58] In addition, a number of staff-type administrations were retained for such questions as planning, finance, and agrotechnical advice. (In practice these functional administrations settled most of the really important questions of MTS operations, to the dismay of many local production officials.[59])

The most extreme reorganization scheme apparently was the one that was introduced in Voronezh Oblast. There the five previous branch departments were replaced by eight territorial administrations, each of which was to have full operational control over the 20–30 MTS in a given geographical subdivision of the oblast.[60] In this oblast, too, real power apparently tended to gravitate to the remaining functional departments, each of which had specific responsibilities for all 170 MTS in the oblast.[61] Thus, *funktsionalka*, like its staff counterpart in Western administrative practice, proved difficult to eliminate.

Meanwhile, debates on the precise form of the anticipated re-organization of the PCA as a whole continued. In the summer of 1938 the leading agricultural newspaper, *Sotsialisticheskoe zemledelie,* ran a series of articles containing reform proposals "for purposes of discussion." [62] The common denominator of the various arguments was a condemnation of the functionalism of the existing setup, but beyond this there were important differences of emphasis. Some of the contributors demanded that the new territorial administrations be given control over all aspects of MTS work, including planning, finance, and cadres policy, as well as daily operations. Others urged greater centralization in terms of crop specialization.

Once again the regime took its time in formulating the decision. It was not until December 1939 that the long-awaited reorganization was finally announced.[63] The new format represented a decided shift away from the production-branch principle. The former branch glavks were replaced by ten production-territorial administrations, each of which was to exercise general operational control over agriculture in a major geographical region in the country. For example, the Main Production-Territorial Administration of the South had responsibility for all agricultural matters in the Ukraine, the Crimean ASSR, and Voronezh and Kursk Oblasts. Under the chief of this new glavk were a chief agronomist, a chief engineer for mechanization, a cadres department, a department of planning and finance, and a number of production-territorial sectors for the various subregions covered by the glavk. In addition to the ten production-territorial glavks there was a glavk of Agrotechnique and Mechanization, evidently intended as a technical staff agency.

The increased role of the MTS in the new organizational plan is seen most clearly in the structure of the oblast-level organs. Operational control in the oblast or krai agricultural administrations was divided among several production-territorial administrations, each of which, apparently following the Voronezh model, had 20–30 MTS. Equalization of the number of MTS appears to have been a primary consideration in the setting of administration boundaries. A few of the old functional departments — specifically, planning, finance, and cadres — were retained in the provincial agricultural administrations.[64] But the main thrust of the reorganization was to redirect attention to the MTS as the focus of operational activities.

For the raizo, which had seemed to be gaining the upper hand in its rivalry with the MTS after 1934, the years 1938 and 1939 witnessed a sharp decline. Once again there had been moves in high agricultural circles to abolish the raizo and transfer its functions to the MTS.[65] Now that MTS coverage was nearly complete, at least in quantitative terms, with two or three stations in many raions, the activities of the raizo had been reduced almost exclusively to supervisory and checking functions (except for animal husbandry, and even here some were suggesting a transfer of functions to the MTS). According to one high PCA official, the raizos did not have sufficient numbers of trained agronomists and zootechnicians to perform even these functions effectively. The raizos had little authority in the village and the oblast organs tended to ignore them, concentrating most of their attention on the MTS.[66] Once again the Party leaders decided to intervene to arrest the decline of the raizo. If they did not seem to know what precisely to do with the raizo, they had evidently concluded that they could not do without it. The raizo "liquidationists" in the PCA (presumably connected with the disgraced Commissar Eikhe) were themselves liquidated in another series of purges. And the reorganization decree of December 5, 1939, gave the raizo a new lease on life.[67] The raizo staff was expanded and given new responsibilities for organizational and accounting processes in the kolkhozes, as well as increased authority over animal husbandry and land management.[68] Thus, although the 1939 reorganization had somewhat strengthened the MTS system as the operational arm of the PCA, it did not represent a full return to centralization. Control over MTS operations was still scattered among various (territorial) subdivisions of the Commissariat, and the administrative authority of the raizo vis-à-vis the kolkhozes had been significantly bolstered.

ADMINISTRATIVE CHANGES IN THE POSTWAR PERIOD

The 1939 organizational plan remained intact throughout the war, although it was subject to occasional breakdowns under the stresses of wartime conditions. Immediately after the war, however, a radical, if temporary deconcentration of the organs of agricultural administration took place. The jurisdiction of the PCA was pruned back to grain and vegetable cultivation. On November 11, 1945, a separate People's Commissariat of Technical Crops was established, which was given control over all MTS involved in the production of cotton, sugar beets, oil seeds, flax, hemp, and other technical crops.[69] Subsequently, on March 26, 1946, animal husbandry was also separated from the PCA, with the creation of a Ministry of Animal Husbandry.[70] Whether this dismantling of the PCA was merely part of the general reaction against the tight, highly personalized controls of the wartime period or an effort to approach the problems of reconstruction in a more flexible manner is not easy to determine.

In any case, the three ministries were reunited less than a year later. On the eve of the important February (1947) Plenum of the Central Committee, at which Andreev would call for a major tightening of controls over agriculture, the formation of a new USSR Ministry of Agriculture was announced.* It was to be headed once again by Benediktov.[71] The internal structure of the new ministry was substantially different from that of its predecessor of 1939. It represented an amalgam of old and new structural patterns. Thus, reminiscent of the 1934 branch plan, the central line apparatus of the ministry was divided up among crop specialty glavks, although the nature of the divisions was somewhat altered. There was a glavk of grain and oil-seed crops; a glavk of technical crops; a glavk of animal husbandry; and a glavk of fruit, vine, and subtropical crops.[72] Most interesting of all was the creation of a new glavk of MTS, which was given the responsibility "to direct all questions of the economy of the MTS." [73] Management of the MTS was once again united, essentially along functional lines.

The various glavks were organized to carry out their work through subordinate territorial (zonal) administrations for the major agricultural regions of the country. For example, the glavk

* The title of the new ministry was *Ministerstvo sel'skogo khoziaistva*, a broader conception translated literally as the "Ministry of the Rural Economy," as contrasted with the former *Ministerstva zemledeliia*, or "Ministry of Agriculture" proper.

of MTS contained an Administration of the South-East, an Administration of the North, and so forth. As compared with the 1939 plan the new arrangements represented a movement toward centralization, reflected in the return of the central apparatus to a production-branch format. This format was apparently viewed as offering better leverage for the coordination of postwar reconstruction. At the provincial level, however, the production-territorial system, with its greater flexibility for detailed operational control, was retained.

The centralizing tendencies of the 1947 reorganization were nowhere more evident than in the administration of the MTS, where for the first time in many years a single national center was created to handle the problems of the MTS system as a whole. Andreev was particularly insistent on the need for such a center in his speech at the February Plenum. He complained that

the administration of the machine-tractor stations is, it seems, scattered among numerous glavks of the Ministry of Agriculture, which encumbers the direction of the MTS, the conduct of machinery repairs, and the selection and training of personnel.[74]

It should be pointed out, however, that this recentralization of the MTS system was not immediately followed by a shift toward total reliance on the MTS as an organ of administration at the local level.* In this connection one other organizational "remedy" resulting from Andreev's criticism of the MTS should be mentioned here. For the first time the raizo was given the responsibility of assuming "leadership and control" over the technical activities of the MTS agronomists. The Plenum also established the position of "State Inspectors for Control over the Quality of the Tractor Work of the Machine-Tractor Stations." Among those designated as Inspectors were the chief agronomists of the raizos and the chief and senior agronomists of the oblast, krai, and republic agricultural organs.[75] These inspectors were enjoined to check MTS

* Indeed, the centralization of the MTS system in the new MTS glavk was not notably successful in accomplishing even its limited goals. After the reorganization there were still complaints that it was impossible to cut across territorial and branch boundaries to get necessary spare parts and other materials ("Upravlenie novoe, metody rukovodstva — starye" (lead editorial), *Sotsialisticheskoe zemledelie,* April 13, 1947).

performance in the fields. They were given broad rights to compel the redoing of unsatisfactory work and to levy fines and reprimands (through the MTS directors).[76] This was one of the rare situations where the officials of the raizo had direct powers over the activities of the MTS.*

In the long run the champions of the raizo would have little to cheer about, for the period following the February Plenum witnessed a steady expansion of MTS influence. The "Three-Year Plan of Development of Socialized Kolkhoz and Sovkhoz Productive Animal Husbandry" announced in April 1949 gave the MTS important new responsibilties in kolkhoz livestock affairs, the last major area where the raizo had retained significant operational responsibilities.[77] In retrospect, it is clear that the encroachment of the MTS in this area effectively sounded the death knell of the raizo. Khrushchev, with his special interest in production efficiency, would not long countenance the existence of an agency with no direct production functions.

The question of MTS finances was raised again in the late forties in connection with this expansion of MTS services in the kolkhozes. The issue of cost accounting was opened for the first time since 1937 at a conference of agricultural economists and MTS financial specialists in July 1947. Some of the speakers demanded greater financial independence for MTS directors and at least a limited return to cost-accounting procedures. Others, including Venzher, objected that it would be pointless to introduce strict profit and loss calculations before the wartime damage and dislocation had been overcome.[78] It was accordingly decided not to make any changes at this juncture. However, in 1950, when the MTS began to receive considerable amounts of cash as payment for some of their new services in the kolkhozes — for example, for the mechanization and electrification of kolkhoz dairy operations, the planting of tree shelter-belts, and land reclamation — it was recognized that a new element had been introduced in the structure of MTS income. Some economists began to urge that

---

* Another involved the raion commissions for assigning the kolkhozes to various crop yield categories for assessment of payments in kind to the MTS. The manager of the raizo was formally an important member of these commissions, although in practice he was subject to the wishes of the raikom secretary and the local plenipotentiaries of the procurement organs.

these factors be taken into consideration as part of a general reassessment of the system of financing the MTS.[79]

At the same time, the kolkhoz amalgamation campaign was beginning to have important effects on the kolkhoz side of MTS-kolkhoz finances. The kolkhozes were beginning to accumulate considerable funds of their own as a result of the increased scale of operations and the expansion of fixed capital. As noted in Chapter 3, this was the setting for the presentation by Venzher and Sanina of their proposals for a radical change in the system of agricultural prices, permitting the kolkhozes eventually to buy out the MTS. The vehement rejection of these proposals by Stalin in his *Economic Problems of Socialism in the USSR* effectively ended any consideration of changes in the administrative and financial systems governing MTS-kolkhoz relations.

ADMINISTRATIVE AND FINANCIAL CHANGES UNDER KHRUSHCHEV

The art of government by reorganization reached its zenith under Nikita S. Khrushchev. It was characteristic of his style of administration that the most massive redirection of agricultural efforts since the 1930–1934 period was launched with a radical reorganization of the agricultural bureaucracy.* If any one principle can be said to have characterized the essence of Khrushchev's numerous organizational manipulations, it was to be found in one of his favorite slogans: "closer to production." In terms of personnel organization the principle signified the transfer of persons with specialized training from desk jobs at all levels of the bureaucracy to field work in the MTS and the kolkhozes. In structural terms it meant a general decentralization of administration at the apex of the agricultural bureaucracy with a corresponding tightening of controls at the intermediate and lower levels, as evidenced by the greatly increased responsibilities of the MTS and the Party raikom.

The liquidation of the raizo and the transfer of its functions and its specialized personnel to the MTS were a good example of the Khrushchevian style of administration. To Khrushchev the raizo

---

* It is perhaps no accident that the Party leader in charge of the radical organizational measures in agriculture during the earlier period was Lazar M. Kaganovich, Khrushchev's mentor and patron during the thirties.

had degenerated into a mere producer of paperwork; it epitomized what he called "leadership by telephone." Rather than trying to reform it, as his predecessors had done so often in the past, he saw it as an unnecessary bureaucratic layer and simply abolished it.

Another illustration of Khrushchev's irreverence toward the traditions and hallowed principles of Soviet public administration was his designation of the chief agronomist of the MTS as "State Inspector for Control over the Quality of the Tractor Work of the MTS." [80] In complete violation of the principle of *edinonachalie,* the chief agronomist was thus placed over the MTS director in a very important sector of MTS activities. In this as in many other Khrushchev reforms, however, the old patterns had a way of reasserting themselves. The chief agronomist usually found it difficult to stand up against his director. The result was to make the MTS the inspector of its own operations, because the raizo was no longer there to add even its weak supervision. These inspection arrangements proved to be a source of repeated complaints during the final years of the MTS.[81]

At the September (1953) Plenum Khrushchev began his program of far-reaching organizational and policy changes and set forth what he considered the ideal division of labor among the various levels of agricultural administration. The central office of the ministry was to handle general policy and technical matters such as planning of production, finance, material and technical supply, personnel selection, training and assignment, and technical and procedural innovation. The administration of operations would devolve upon the agricultural organs of the republics, oblasts, and krais.[82] Following these suggestions, the Plenum decreed the transfer of most operational responsibilities to the republic ministries of agriculture, including, for the first time, the RSFSR ministry.[83] This shift had important effects on the administration of the MTS system, which was now operationally subordinated to the republic ministries and financed out of the republic budgets.[84] The formal reorganization of the USSR Ministry of Agriculture followed on December 9, 1953. The central apparatus was essentially transformed into a staff agency for the administrative organs in charge of operations further down in the hierarchy. However, in the new structure the MTS system was represented by a "Glavk of MTS and Mechanization," which exercised general supervision over all aspects of MTS activities through production-territorial MTS administrations at the republic and oblast levels.[85] Thus, the MTS system remained, in effect, the only line organization in the ministry.

The MTS glavk was to coordinate its operations with the "branch inspectors" of a new "Glavk of Production-Territorial Inspection," through which links were maintained between the central ministry and the administrative units at the lower levels. This system of "inspectorates" was another of Khrushchev's innovations. It amounted to an institutionalization of the traditional, if never fully approved, practice of dispatching plenipotentiaries to problem areas. The new principle of administration by inspectors was extended to the oblast level in 1955, following a speech by Khrushchev at the January (1955) Plenum of the Central Committee, where he had complained, as in the past, of the desk-bound nature of the administrative work of the provincial land organs.[86] Under the new plan many of the administrations and departments of the oblast (krai) agricultural administrations were abolished and replaced by "inspectorates." For example, the Oblast Administration of Mechanization was replaced by an Oblast Inspectorate for Mechanization, which consisted of a staff of roving inspectors who were required to be in the field continually, checking on the state of repairs and methods of utilization of MTS machinery.[87]

At the raion level, although most of the responsibilities of the liquidated raizo were transferred to the MTS, a few residual supervisory and staff functions were given to the *raiispolkom* (RIK). The RIK had important responsibilities for aggregate planning and financial accounting in the kolkhozes. It also inherited certain auxiliary departments from the raizo, such as the departments of kolkhoz construction and land-surveying. And it continued, as in the past, to register the contracts between MTS and kolkhoz and the kolkhoz charters. However, the nature of these functions was not strictly managerial. In the great majority of questions coming before it, the RIK had to depend for its information and statistical data upon the MTS.[88] In fact, the RIK was instructed to exercise its leadership in raion agricultural affairs through the MTS.[89]

It would appear that along with certain responsibilities of the raizo the RIK inherited some of the old problems, as well. When the RIK attempted to take advantage of its formal legal authority, it often came into conflict with the MTS. The duplication or overlapping of functions — for example, the department of kolkhoz construction in the RIK was paralleled by construction brigades in the MTS — was bound to cause friction. But, as the MTS possessed most of the equipment and did the actual construction work, the MTS usually prevailed. The general consensus of the commentaries on this problem was that the competing supervisory agencies in the RIK should be liquidated in favor of the operational units in the MTS.[90]

What is perhaps most striking about Khrushchev's reorganization of the agricultural system, and the MTS system in particular, is the strong similarity to the old semi-autonomous structure of Traktorotsentr, with its republic and provincial branches. The administration of the MTS seemed to have come full circle. Having decided in 1953 to give the MTS the leading role first envisioned for it by Markevich, Khrushchev seemingly found himself forced to adopt many of the principles of Markevich's model of administration, as well.

This tendency to return to the original model could be seen, also, in the area of MTS finances. Beginning in 1954, for the first time since Stalin's rejection of the proposals of Venzher and Sanina, there were signs of renewed official interest in the improvement of the MTS financing system. P. S. Kuchumov, Deputy Minister of Agriculture and for several years the chief of the MTS glavk, suggested in an article in *Kommunist* that elements of cost accounting be introduced in the MTS tractor brigade.[91] Others made similar proposals — all directed toward increasing the financial accountability of the individual MTS.[92] But it was only after Khrushchev himself expressed an interest that the subject became a major focus of practical inquiry. The signal was apparently given in June 1954 in the final pages of an unpublished memorandum to the Party Presidium on his observations from a trip through Kazakhstan.

At the present time our MTS are on the state budget, and not on *khozraschet*. As is known, the situation has varied: in their time the MTS have been both on *khozraschet* and on the state budget. I do not propose to reject the form of maintenance of the MTS existing at the present time . . . but obviously we need to create some other kind of accounting system for MTS work and make the machine-tractor stations report their accounts so that the costs of payments in kind are visible. Now we don't know this: no matter whom you talk to, no one knows how much it costs the state for a *pud* [36 pounds] of grain received by the MTS as payment in kind . . . Perhaps, as a result of a careful study of this question, we might even come to the transfer of the MTS to *khozraschet*.[93]

The ensuing flurry of reports and proposals had one common theme: that the MTS sytem was, indeed, a costly operation and that the existing methods of financing and accounting were no protection against the habitual overexpenditures of funds.[94]

By November 1955 Khrushchev was already convinced of the need for change. He told a conference of high-ranking agricultural bureaucrats in that month that "since the maintenance of the MTS on the state budget is not justifying itself," it was time to begin shifting them back to a cost-accounting basis. This was the only way, he said, to force MTS directors to pay any attention to costs of production. The formal order for the transfer, beginning with a few of the best stations in certain selected areas, was given in February 1956 at the Twentieth Party Congress.[95] Although the changes contemplated involved at first only a shift in accounting methods, it was clear that the eventual aim was to transform the stations into financially self-sufficient enterprises according to Markevich's original plan.

THE MTS AND THE ADMINISTRATION OF THE KOLKHOZES

So far, relatively little has been said about the specifics of the role of the MTS in the administration of kolkhoz production. Two especially important procedural features of that role were the production plan and the MTS-kolkhoz contract. Both were symbolic of the wide gulf between theory and practice in the Soviet socialist agricultural system. Both illustrated at once the formal comprehensiveness and the practical inefficiency of the system.

Although there were some procedural precedents in the system of precultivation obligations used by the cooperative organizations in the late twenties, comprehensive production planning did not begin until the imposition of the system of obligatory deliveries in January 1933.[96] The procedures then introduced remained in effect virtually unchanged until the major planning reform of March 9, 1955. The actual plan received by the kolkhoz was extremely one-sided. It was more of a tax assessment than a guide to scientific production and long-term farm development. The kolkhozes merely produced what they were told, regardless of crop rotations or other agro-technical criteria. The participation of the kolkhozes in the formulation of their own plans was minimal.

The procedure for planning grain crops developed in the early thirties was as follows. Each year *Gosplan*, through the Council of People's Commissars, transmitted aggregate plans to the PCA for spring and winter crops. (In the thirties these were separate plans.) The plans were expressed in terms of total acreages (1) for all kolkhozes and (2) for kolkhozes served by MTS. They included breakdowns for individual crops of major importance, such as wheat, rye, oats, and so forth; and they also indicated acreage allotments for the respective crops for individual republics, oblasts, and krais.[97] Having received their plans, the agricultural organs at these levels then distributed among the raions their planned acreage allotments for the respective crops. The raizos thereupon worked out detailed production plans, comprising acreages to be sown to each crop and target dates for the completion of specific farming operations (plowing, sowing, harvesting) for each kolkhoz in the raion. The entire process was rather primitive, considering the complexities of agricultural production. The raizos, in particular, were often criticized for the mechanical way in which they distributed planned tasks among the kolkhozes with little consideration for local capabilities or physical conditions.[98] But given the state of the art of planning and the nature of the pressures from above, such procedures were probably inevitable.

The individual MTS also had their own production plans, and difficulties frequently arose over the coordination of the

MTS plans with those of the kolkhozes. Although the MTS plans were derived from the same national acreage plans mentioned above, the methods of derivation and, usually, the results in terms of acreages were different. For example, on the basis of the nation-wide plan for grain crops, the MTS planners in the PCA worked out an overall plan for the total volume of tractor work, expressed in terms of hectares of soft, or standard plowing. This plan was then broken down and distributed among the republics, oblasts, and krais in accordance with their respective sowing plans. The agricultural organs at this level then worked out plans for each individual MTS involved in grain production, prescribing in detail the total number of hectares of soft plowing with subtotals for each specific type of tractor operation to be performed.[99] *

The station was then supposed to reconcile and coordinate its tractor work plans with the production plans of the kolkhozes, using the contract and so-called supplementary agreements to define the specific sequence and amounts of work, along with completion dates, for each kolkhoz. By the time the tractor work plans, in terms of soft plowing quotas, had reached the MTS and were translated into specific operational plans, the discrepancies between the MTS production plans and those the kolkhozes had received from the raizo were often quite substantial. Under the Model Contract it was the duty of the MTS to assist the kolkhoz in the formulation of its production plans. This assistance commonly meant forcing the kolkhozes to accept plans that best satisfied the needs of the station. Naturally, this was a source of friction with the raizo. But since the MTS were judged on the fulfillment of their operational and financial plans almost as much as on the volume of payments in kind delivered to the state, MTS directors were under considerable pressure to give the kolkhozes plans

* The following are some of the conversion factors used in translating common farming operations into soft plowing units:

1 hectare of harrowing = 0.15 hectares of soft plowing
1 hectare of disking and cultivating = 0.30 hectares of soft plowing
1 hectare of harvesting = 0.30 hectares of soft plowing
1 hectare of stubble plowing = 0.50 hectares of soft plowing

(Decree of the PCA USSR of March 10, 1934, "O plane traktornykh rabot mashinnotraktornykh stantsii i o zakliuchenii dogovorov MTS s kolkhozami na 1934 g.", *Biulleten' finansovogo i khoziaistvennogo zakonodatel'stva*, no. 8 [1934], p. 14; *ibid.*, no. 19 [1934], p. 33.)

which made their stations look as good as possible. It should be pointed out, however, that in these manipulations the MTS were never at liberty to decrease state targets for obligatory deliveries and total procurements. In their conflicts with the raizos the MTS had the obvious advantage of direct involvement in the kolkhoz production processes. The MTS were in a position to impose very real sanctions on recalcitrant kolkhoz chairmen.

A typical example of the type of manipulation involved was the case involving the Veselokutsk MTS in Odessa Oblast. On August 10, 1933, the Veselokutsk Raizo sent the kolkhoz "The Way of Il'ich" a plan to sow 229 hectares of winter wheat and 24 hectares of winter rye by September 20. The MTS countered with a plan for 270 hectares of winter wheat, to be sown by September 28 — a plan that was more favorable to the station because of the delayed completion date and the higher prices paid for wheat. The MTS plan prevailed.[100] It was not unusual for a substitution of this type to be approved by the higher authorities, since wheat was generally readily accepted in place of rye. However, such approval was not automatic, especially when delays in target dates were involved.

One of the main shortcomings of the planning system was the tardiness with which the plans were formulated. In the above case the transmission of the winter sowing targets a mere forty-one days before the planned date of completion hardly satisfied the criteria of scientific forecasting. On this occasion the MTS officials complained that because the raizo plans were already in the hands of the kolkhozes before the MTS had even received its aggregate tractor work plans from the oblast, the MTS was put at a serious disadvantage. It had to begin its planning and some of its operational preparations on the basis of the raizo plans. Later it would have to make signifiant corrections and adjustments when its own plans arrived.[101] Referring to this problem at the conference of MTS officials in January 1936, Antipov complained,

it is completely clear that in essence the MTS has had no annual plan. For if for the entire Ukraine the PCA of the Union confirms the MTS plan for 1935 only on the 29th of June, and for the central oblasts even in August, this is no plan but essentially a summary of operations already performed.[102]

And Chernov, speaking to the same audience, characterized the existing system as "not planning but a parody on planning." [103]

Similar comments were made on the detailed production plans of the kolkhozes. Nothing in those plans, except the statement of obligatory crop acreages, was of any practical consequence. S. V. Kossior, the Ukrainian Party chief, said as much at a Plenum of the Ukrainian Central Committee in May 1936:

Up to now — in 1934–1935, not to speak of other years, we had essentially no real operative plan in the kolkhozes. They wrote down certain figures on paper, and that was as far as they went. They hid the notebook or booklet with the figures in their pocket or in a drawer, and the sowing proceeded by itself, independently of the so-called plan.[104]

Had Kossior survived the Great Purge, he might have made the same statement in 1954. Despite occasional efforts at reform — for example, the campaign to restore crop rotations immediately after World War II — the agricultural planning system continued to languish. Not only were the rigid, virtually meaningless procedures maintained, but over the years the number of centrally determined planned tasks steadily increased. By September 1953 the kolkhozes were receiving from 200 to 250 specific tasks each year. They included such petty details as the number of crossbred hogs to be taken off fattening-up rations and the number of acres of long-stemmed plants to be planted as windbreaks on fallow land.[105]

The system of planning had a particularly stultifying effect on the MTS. MTS operations were set forth from above in such detail that the director had little room for maneuvering in case of emergencies. As a contingency reserve he was permitted only 5 percent of the total annual planned volume of tractor work.[106] This rigidity sometimes had ludicrous consequences. Kuchumov, the chief of the MTS glavk, noted in 1954 the case of an MTS director in Kurgan Oblast, who was penalized for substituting a special weed-killing operation for ordinary cultivation because the unusually moist soil conditions made the latter useless. Despite the fact that crop yields were more than doubled by this initative, the tractor drivers involved were deprived of their premiums because they had not fulfilled the cultivation plan.[107]

Khrushchev strongly criticized the rigidity of the planning system and the proliferation of centrally planned tasks in his speech at the September (1953) Plenum.[108] And the Central Committee ordered the creation of a new system, based on a less centralized form of planning.[109] But it took fully eighteen months for the new system to be introduced. Under the new procedures of March 9, 1955, centrally assigned tasks were to be restricted to the basic procurement needs of the economy. The central plan prescribed only the desired volume of procurements, broken down according to source: obligatory deliveries, payments in kind for MTS services, contract purchases, and additional state purchases. The plan also included the total volume of MTS tractor work for the year in hectares of soft plowing. As before, these plans were to be distributed among the republics, oblasts, and krais, which would, in turn, apportion them among the raions and the MTS. The kolkhozes received their quotas for procurements and payments in kind from the RIK. These were to be considered only gross annual targets. The concrete operational plans were to be worked out for each kolkhoz by the MTS. The MTS director and his chief deputies for planning were to coordinate the operational plans of each farm so that, while insuring the fulfillment of its procurement obligations, the aggregate tractor-work plans of the station would be met. As before, the contract was the formal instrument for defining the specific operational responsibilities of the individual kolkhoz and the MTS. It was noteworthy that for the first time the director was given the right to make minor changes in the contract during the year, if conditions so warranted — provided the changes were acceptable to the management of the kolkhoz.[110] If nothing else, this was a step toward making the contract a more realistic operational device.

The MTS-kolkhoz contracts were to be registered with the RIK where they were collated and checked for consistency with the procurement plans of the raion. There was some controversy as to whether the RIK had the right to order specific operational changes in a contract, but the consensus of the experts was, apparently, that it did not: the RIK could only suggest changes; it could not compel them.[111]

To illustrate the sequence of steps in the MTS planning process, a flow chart, or "operogram," of the procedures followed by the Millerovo MTS in 1954 is given in Figure 5-1. Although the chart is for the year before the planning reform of March 9, 1955, it is useful for understanding the postreform procedures, since the station in question was used as a pilot for the new system. The final stage of the planning process was the conclusion of a contract between the MTS and each of its kolkhozes. These contracts were specific applications of a standard Model Contract which remained in force for a number of years, changing in response to important

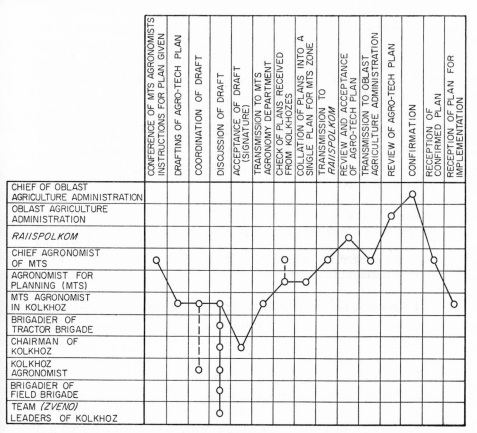

Figure 5.1. Operogram of the planning process for the 1954 agro-technical plan of the Millerovo MTS, Kamenskaia Oblast.

Source: B. A. Voronkov, "Organizatsiia upravleniia v mashinno-traktornoi stantsii" (Kandidat dissertation, Moscow, 1955), p. 35a.

shifts in agricultural or MTS policy. As pointed out in Chapter 3, the Model Contract served both as a legal instrument and as a symbol of the basic principles of the MTS-kolkhoz relationship, annually reasserted at the time of the conclusion of the contract. Here we are concerned with the contract as a legal instrument. Its functions were primarily the specification of the mutual obligations of the MTS and the kolkhoz for the timely performance of concrete agricultural operations according to plan. Even more importantly, in practical terms, it set forth the methods and rates for assessing payments in kind from the kolkhozes.

Although a Model Contract and formal contract signing procedures had existed ever since Markevich's original tractor-column experiment,[112] they had steadily lost importance in the confusion of the collectivization and MTS expansion campaigns. By the end of 1932, contract signing, where it was still practiced at all, had degenerated to an empty formality. Despite Markevich's arguments on the importance of payments in kind, the rule by 1932 was for the kolkhozes to pay for MTS services in cash. Little consideration was given to the size of the crop yields or the quality of MTS work. Describing the existing system in January 1933, Iakovlev had complained:

Instead of working as they should, the MTS have been tickling the soil on the surface, and this they call plowing. But the MTS got the money for every hectare. You plowed a hectare — eight rubles. Whether or not anything came up on the hectare, it was all the same to the MTS, it still got the eight rubles.[113]

To combat this situation, along with the radical centralization of planning and administration and the shift to obligatory deliveries in 1933, the regime promulgated a new Model Contract based on a strict system of payments in kind. In the new Model Contract payments in kind for MTS services were to be calculated as a fixed percentage of the harvest for each individual operation performed. For example, the kolkhoz was to pay 10 percent of the harvest of grain crops for spring sowing and fallow plowing, 9 percent for fall plowing, 3 percent for sowing, and 8 percent for threshing. If the MTS performed the entire complex of operations, the kolkhoz would pay a flat 20 percent of the harvest. A similar system existed for other crops.[114] This pegging of payments-in-kind income to kolkhoz crop yields was, of course, designed to increase MTS incentives in improving the quality of their work. However, the coercive activities of the politotdels and other organs in the village in 1933 at the height of the famine tended to nullify the incentive features of the contract, since the maximum amount of grain possible would be collected regardless of MTS performance.

The 1933 Model Contract had certain structural weaknesses, also. The main body of the contract consisted primarily of general statements of the kinds of assistance to be furnished by each party. For example, the MTS obliged itself to furnish agro-technical guidance and assistance in the planning and organization of kolkhoz labor. The kolkhoz promised to fulfill labor requirements promptly, to transport fuel and water to the tractor brigades, and to follow agronomic instructions. Concrete operational specifications and quality standards, such as the area and depth of plowing for each crop, completion dates, and so forth, were to be negotiated in Supplementary Agreements annexed to the contract. The Supplementary Agreement was, thus, the real substance of the contract under the 1933 procedures. In practice, however, many MTS neglected to conclude Supplementary Agreements. MTS officials realized that they were not equipped to carry out the jobs required by sound agronomic practice and, hence, preferred to avoid the inevitable embarrassments by refusing to commit themselves to the specific obligations and standards contained in the Supplementary Agreements.[115]

In order to combat this tendency the government substituted a new Model Contract in February 1934, which abolished the Supplementary Agreements and made the specific operational obligations a part of the main body of the contract.[116] This change at least solved the problem of getting specific commitments down on paper.

Another change in the 1934 Model Contract was the replacement of the harvest percentage method of assessing payments in kind owed to the MTS by a system of fixed payments related to categories of harvest yields. The new payment scales were progressive in the sense that the poorest farms paid relatively less per hectare, although the average rates were not materially different from those under the 1933 Model Contract. Under the new setup special raion commissions were created for assigning the kolkhozes to the respective yield categories for *naturoplata* assessments. They were to be presided over by the RIK chairman and/or the raion procurement agents (plenipotentiaries). The system operated in the following manner. After inspection the commission determined that a given kolkhoz would have, say, a yield of from seven to nine centners (quintals) of grain per hectare. The kolkhoz was assigned to the appropriate yield category in the 1934 Model Contract, which specified that it would pay ninety kilograms of grain for every hectare on which the MTS had done the full complex of operations; or eighty kilograms, if the MTS had done only the spring and fallow plowing.[117]

The 1934 Model Contract remained essentially unchanged until January 1939, when, in line with the general increase in demands on the economy as the international situation deteriorated, a more rigid and exploitative system of *naturoplata* assessments was introduced.[118] The raion assessment commissions were abolished and rates were set arbitarily for entire raions by the oblast agricultural administrations. Thus, at the same time that the MTS system was transferred to the state budget for its finances, payments in kind assumed the character of a direct tax on the kolkhozes.

Throughout the thirties there were many indications that MTS officials viewed the contract as little more than a bothersome formality. This was particularly true while financial solvency and economy of resource inputs were still primary criteria of MTS success. The signing of contracts was frequently delayed until well into the agricultural season, further diminishing their force as a guide to operations. Although such practices aroused concern, there were apparently some officials who considered the contracts of secondary importance. The Deputy Chief of the Grain Glavk of the PCA, Klimenko, for example, was quoted as having said, upon hearing that only 6 percent of the kolkhozes served by MTS had signed contracts by the end of February 1937: "I am interested in how many hectares will be sown to wheat; the contracts don't interest me." [119] Again, one of the main continuing problems was the reluctance of MTS officials to be tied down too closely to specific operations. An article in *Kommuna,* the Voronezh

Oblast Party and government newspaper, in March 1937 noted the tendency of the MTS to shirk those operations, such as cultivation, which were less profitable to the stations. Some stations even attempted to foist plans and contracts neglecting such operations upon their kolkhozes. Although the oblast agricultural authorities did not allow this practice, the MTS often managed to achieve their aims by simple omission.[120]

Nevertheless, under the active prodding of the politotdels and, subsequently, the Party raikoms, the signing of contracts gradually became the rule, even if the resulting documents were not very meaningful. Some idea of the general attitude of the MTS directors toward the annual contract-signing campaigns can be seen in the following passage from an editorial in *Sotsialisticheskoe zemledelie* in March 1937:

Many [MTS directors] act like typical bureaucrats, like narrow-minded functionaries. The MTS director rides about all the kolkhozes for two or three days and collects the signatures of the chairmen under the text of the contract, sometimes not even filled in; he returns to the MTS with a feeling of relief: at last he has gotten rid of such a "troublesome" job, such an unpleasant burden and can send in a report on the "completion of the current campaign." [121]

Nor was the contract particularly effective from the standpoint of legal force. As the kolkhozes quickly learned, it was a weak basis for court action. A contract in the common Western legal sense presupposes at least a certain degree of equality and independence in the parties. Each party must have the expectation of some benefit, and both must enjoy sufficient equality of rights and independence of action to enable them to perform their respective obligations. In Soviet law the interenterprise contract has had a somewhat different basis. It is an element of the planning process, tying the contracting parties into a broader system of planned relations of production and exchange. The question of benefits is, accordingly, subordinated to the interests of the state, although the interests of the parties are not completely excluded.[122] But even among Soviet contracts the MTS-kolkhoz contract was unique. As noted in Chapter 3, Soviet legal experts were careful to emphasize its special nature, arguing that because of the complementary character of MTS-kolkhoz relations the interests of the parties were supposedly indistinguishable and "fused with the total interests of the state."

In practice, the concrete interests of the MTS and the kolkhoz often diverged widely. The fact that lawsuits were actually brought to court under the penalty clause of the contract was solid evidence that the Hegelian "fusion of interests" described by Piatnitskii and others did not necessarily apply. However, the penalty clause was in fact quite difficult to invoke. For one thing, it was not always easy to assess the degree of loss attributable to a particular contractual violation by either party. For another, since guilt was likely to be mutual over any extended period, there arose what some authors called a "spirit of mutual amnesty." [123]* Very commonly the kolkhoz was simply afraid to offend its MTS by taking it to court, as the MTS was in a position to do the kolkhoz so much harm. Ruskol notes that a kolkhoz was likely to bring suit against a given MTS only in the rare instances when it had been transferred to the jurisdiction of another MTS. In a commentary on MTS-kolkhoz law cases involving the state arbitration system in the thirties he concluded that "kolkhozes evidently 'do not consider it convenient' to go to court with or, as they put it, 'to quarrel' with their own MTS." [124]

Throughout the history of the MTS the contract, despite official declarations that it had "the force of law," was never very effective in enforcing performance standards on the MTS, or for that matter, on the kolkhozes.[125] What the contract did provide was a means for registering and legitimizing state claims on kolkhoz produce. It helped to regulate and make predictable the flow of payments in kind as a major source of state grain procurements.

The tendency to minimize the contract and the distinct, if

---

* A good illustration of the type of collusion entered into by the MTS and the kolkhozes is given by Fedor Belov. He describes a common situation in which the kolkhoz was prevailed upon to buy spare parts for the MTS. The MTS was prohibited from making such purchases on the open market. If the kolkhoz wanted to avail itself of MTS services, it had to agree to supply the necessary parts. He also mentions cases where the kolkhoz had to repair MTS equipment in its own facilities, for which the MTS paid only a minimum compensation. Thus, the two enterprises often found themselves extremely dependent on each other (Fedor Belov, *The History of a Soviet Collective Farm* [New York: Praeger, 1955], pp. 119–120).

limited, role of payments in kind as a regulator of MTS performance were accentuated by the harsh conditions of World War II.
By the end of the war it had become common to assign payments
in kind as a fixed percentage of total raion procurements, thus
eliminating any incentive features.[126] At the February (1947)
Plenum Andreev noted with concern that some MTS had stopped
signing contracts altogether. Where contracts were still being
concluded, they were being violated almost as a matter of course.
He cited a survey of sixty-nine random MTS which revealed that
13 percent of the kolkhozes they served had no contracts and
that 71 percent had experienced delays of from two to nine
months in receiving their contracts.[127]

Accordingly, as part of its re-emphasis on the MTS as the key
to rural reconstruction, the Central Committee decreed a full re-
instatement of contractual procedures.[128] A year later a new Model
Contract appeared, which placed greater stress on quality control
and introduced greater penalties for tardy or incomplete work
by the MTS.[129] Payments in kind were made more directly dependent on the performance by the MTS of specific cultivation
operations, as opposed to the previous system of total volume of
soft plowing acreage.[130] Meanwhile, in May 1947 a new system
of figuring rates of payments in kind was introduced. The country
was divided up into three zones by climate and fertility in order
to adjust for natural advantages and disadvantages, or, in Marxian
economic terms, to siphon off a part of Differential Rent I. Within
the three zones the rate of *naturoplata* assessments was to increase
progressively in accordance with yields.[131] This system was incorporated into the 1948 Model Contract, which remained in
force until 1954.

As was the case with many of the agricultural reforms of the
late Stalin era, these attempts to use the Model Contract and payments in kind to improve the performance of the MTS were not
successful, largely because they did not go far enough. The 1947–
1948 modifications proved to contain many serious disincentive
features, which tended to reinforce the exploitative image of the
MTS. Wedded as he was to the old, rigid conception of the MTS-
kolkhoz relationship, Stalin could not countenance the radical

changes that were necessary to give real life to the contract and make the MTS and the kolkhozes sincerely interested in fulfilling it.

Khrushchev, on the other hand, was considerably more willing to accept the implications of interdependence in the MTS-kolkhoz relationship. At the September (1953) Plenum he called for a maximization of the incentive features of the payments-in-kind system so as to benefit both MTS and kolkhoz.[132] The new Model Contract of 1954 incorporated these suggestions. It also went far to specify in precise terms the various new responsibilities given to the MTS.[133] For example, it made specific provisions for the assignment of staff agronomists and zootechnicians of the MTS to the kolkhozes and set the conditions for their tenure and maintenance. It also made explicit the new responsibilities for the planning and accounting procedures employed in the kolkhozes.*

The major innovation in the new Model Contract was a new system of payments in kind, based on the principle of differential assessments exclusively by geographic zones, rather than by the size of the crop yield. The country was divided up into nine zones of varying fertility and climate — a much more flexible division than the previous three zones. The kolkhozes in the most favored zone (Zone I) were to pay from two to five times as many kilograms of grain per hectare for various operations as the kolkhozes in the least favored zone (Zone IX).[134] It was hoped that the dropping of the progressive payment-in-kind rates for increased yields would eliminate one of the most serious disincentive features of the previous systems and stimulate the best kolkhozes to increase their effort — even if this meant leaving more "surplus" commodities in the hands of the peasants. It was now realized that there were other ways, such as increased purchase prices, for channeling this surplus into the hands of the state. This new attitude toward procurements is perhaps the clearest reflection of the great changes that began to occur under Khrushchev's leadership.

* A new "Regulation on Instructor-Bookkeepers in the MTS" in September 1953 assigned a staff of auditors to the MTS for the organization and supervision of kolkhoz financial accounts. This regulation gave the MTS the means for exercising continual supervision over kolkhoz finances (I. F. Pokrovskii, *MTS — opornyi punkt gosudarstvennogo rukovodstva kolkhozami* [Moscow, 1957], p. 50).

The 1954 Model Contract remained in force until the liquidation of the MTS in 1958. Throughout the years there had been a notable tendency to increase the specificity of the contract (except during the war years). The prevailing attitude seems to have been that the greater the degree of concreteness in contractual obligations, the more MTS performance would improve. This notion was hardly valid. The contract could never be an effective guide to local practice as long as it was rigidly bound to centrally determined production tasks. Indeed, it was only with the changes in the planning process in 1955, giving the MTS and the kolkhozes greater leeway in planning their operations, that the contract had a chance of becoming more than a mere formality. This opportunity was to prove stillborn, however, for old habits died hard. The new planning procedures were never fully implemented before the abolition of the MTS.[135]

An effort has been made to explain as well as describe the numerous changes in the institutions and procedures of Soviet agricultural administration in the era of the MTS. Although the changes occurred according to certain broad patterns connected with shifts in agricultural policy, they cannot be explained solely in terms of agricultural requirements. Other important factors were also involved, such as undesirable practices within the agricultural bureaucracy, political infighting at the apex of the system, and the personal administrative styles of the dominant political leaders. Any critical analysis of Soviet agricultural administration must take into account the extreme complexity of the factors involved. In a country the size of the USSR, with tremendous variations in climate and soil fertility, the planning and management of agriculture are enormously difficult. If only from the standpoint of climate, precise planning on a nationwide scale is likely to be something of a fantasy. A late spring thaw or an unexpected snowfall at the beginning of the harvest season could, and often did, disrupt the operational plans of hundreds of MTS. When one considers that there were at one time as many as 240 thousand kolkhozes and 9 thousand MTS in the country, the dimensions of the administrative problem become truly staggering.

Yet there seems to have been no serious question on the part of the Soviet rulers that the goal of centralized planning and control in agriculture was realizable. The problem appeared to reduce itself in their eyes simply to devising the requisite set of administrative institutions and procedures. As the true complexities of the tasks became more evident, the tendency was to expand the bureaucracy accordingly in the familiar Parkinsonian manner. The data collection process alone became so formidable after a while that it began to occupy most of the energies of the bureaucracy, eventually crowding out the equally important functions of management and supervision. The inability of the raizo to exercise effective supervision over production activities was largely a result of this increasing information burden. The standing criticism that the intermediate levels of the PCA system were mere "paper mills" was inevitably justified.

At the same time pressures for performance steadily increased. The demands of the regime for commodities were insatiable, while the material returns to agriculture were kept to a minimum. Agricultural officials, from the People's Commissar of Agriculture to the lowliest kolkhoz chairman, found themselves, like the Children of Israel in Egypt, in the impossible position of having to make bricks without straw. The penalties for failure were severe, and service in agricultural administration, especially in the thirties, was fraught with personal danger. Commissars Iakovlev, Chernov, and Eikhe all paid with their lives for "wrecking" the national economy by failing to do the impossible in agriculture. Benediktov was saved, apparently, only by the outbreak of the war. The perils at the oblast level were, if anything, even worse. Appointment as head of the PCA or of a provincial agricultural administration was virtually tantamount to a death sentence. Under such conditions the morale and initiative of the agricultural bureaucrats could hardly have been high. Administrators sought security in routine and the avoidance of risk. A spirit of mutual amnesty and the "family circle" (*semeistvennost'*) pervaded the system from top to bottom. It was partly to break up these collusive arrangements and clear the channels of communications that the regime adopted the practice of frequent reorganizations and/or shifts of personnel.

But there were other, more substantive issues involved in the reorganizations. In the first part of the chapter the sequence of structural changes was seen to follow a roughly cyclical alternation between centralization and decentralization, or intensification and relaxation, of controls over agricultural production. The intensification pattern was usually introduced in periods of crisis; relaxation, during the periods which followed. Thus, the initial period of collectivization and rapid MTS expansion was characterized structurally by the concentration of many production and administrative responsibilities in the MTS system. This period was followed by a conscious drive to de-emphasize the MTS and to treat it primarily as a simple production agency. During the middle thirties this drive was accompanied by a parallel effort to develop formal economic and legal procedures and institutions to routinize MTS-kolkhoz production operations. Serious difficulties with the implemenation of these measures and the political upheavals of the latter half of the decade produced a general movement back toward intensification of controls. The transfer of MTS financing to the state budget was an important step in this process, as was the structural shift to the production-territorial format in the administration of the MTS at the provincial level. Although somewhat disrupted by the dislocations of the war, the tendency toward intensification of controls over production, applied increasingly through the MTS, received further impetus at the February Plenum of the Central Committee in 1947. The system of planning and administration became so heavily encumbered by organizational rigidity and red tape that further improvements in agricultural management and production were precluded until the death of Stalin. Upon assuming the mantle of agricultural leadership, Khrushchev made a major effort to cut this bureaucratic Gordian knot and revitalize the entire agricultural sector. He saw the period as one of crisis, and once again the response was an intensification of controls over production. As in the past, the role of the MTS in local administration was accordingly greatly enhanced. The pattern of controls which Khrushchev established was strongly similar to that initially formulated by Markevich in his original model of MTS-kolkhoz relations.

The differing approaches of Stalin and Khrushchev to the problems of agricultural administration were heavily influenced by their respective personal styles of leadership. Although both manifested a readiness to use reorganization as a technique of administration, Stalin was considerably more cautious and deliberate. His experiments with different models of the production-territorial principle at the oblast level in the thirties and the long delays before the shift to budgetary financing of the MTS and the reorganization of 1939 indicate this penchant for prolonged testing. Khrushchev was, as his critics have charged, much more precipitous. He was given to abrupt, radical reorganizations with a minimum of prior experimentation. The decentralization of planning and the wholesale shifts of personnel to the permanent staff of the MTS were good examples. The best was, of course, the liquidation of the MTS system itself in 1958. As far as the structural details of reorganization were concerned, Khrushchev showed himself much less bound by accepted principles of administration.

Of particular significance was Stalin's apparent commitment to the creation of a system of agricultural administration that would function without external intervention, except in times of crisis. The conflicting demands and pressures on the various levels of the agricultural system made this ideal unrealizable. As will be shown in Part III, repeated Party interference was found to be necessary even in relatively normal periods. But under Stalin it seems clear that such interference was looked upon as an aberration. Khrushchev had no such inhibitions when it came to administration. He realized that the agricultural bureaucracy was extremely weak and that it was unlikely to be an effective support for his grandiose schemes to improve the agricultural sector. Already committed to the revival of the Party as the prime mover of change in Soviet life, he eagerly built direct Party interference into his model of agricultural administration, ignoring past strictures against such interference. His slogan "closer to production" was made to apply to the Party *apparatchik* as well as the agricultural specialist and the administrator.

There is no simple explanation for the twists and turns of Soviet agricultural administration. To a certain extent there were important situational reasons for each of the reorganizations. But there were also reasons connected with the structure and practices of the agricultural bureaucracy itself. Finally, there were the intangible factors of political infighting and the personal styles of the leaders themselves. These last factors may indeed have been decisive. Had Stalin lived for another decade, it seems inconceivable that the MTS would have disappeared, regardless of substantive conditions.

Part III The MTS and the System

of Party Controls in the Village

*It is necessary . . . to explain that economic successes themselves,
their strength and duration completely and entirely depend
on the successes of Party-organizational and Party-political work,
that without this condition economic successes may turn out to
be built on sand.*

Stalin

*In many organizations Party-political work is carried on in
isolation from economic tasks. We have officials who talk a lot
about the fact that politics is indivisible from economics,
that it is necessary to combine it with the solution of economic
problems, but in practice divorce political activity from the
everyday, prosaic work of economic construction.*

Khrushchev

6 The Party and Agriculture

Thus far, little has been said of the role of the Communist Party in the workings of the agricultural system. This postponement by no means suggests that the role of the Party was minor or peripheral. The discussion has been postponed in order to present as comprehensive a picture as possible of the structural and operational elements of the agricultural system before discussing the nature and effects of Party involvement therein. The methods and style of Party activity in the village underwent significant changes during the lifetime of the MTS. As was true in the agricultural bureaucracy, these changes followed a discernible pattern which was intimately related to major developments in Soviet agricultural policy.

THE LOCAL PARTY ORGANS AND THE MANAGEMENT
OF THE RURAL ECONOMY

The role of the Party in economic affairs has been a continuing source of confusion and controversy in the Soviet system. The so-called leading role of the Party in the economy, as in all other spheres of Soviet life, has never been seriously questioned. However, what precisely constitutes the proper degree of involvement by the local Party officials in the details of economic management has traditionally been difficult to determine. In the words of Lazar Slepov, a noted Central Committee specialist on organizational questions, "The Party directs [*rukovodit*] the economic life of the country, but it does not administer [*upravliaet*] the economy directly." [1] No Soviet leader, from Lenin to Brezhnev, could possibly disagree with this formula. But where the precise dividing line between *rukovodstvo* (leadership) and *upravlenie* (administration) lies has never fully been determined. Slepov writes of a "precise division of functions between Party, Soviet, and economic organs" as a most important principle of Party leadership of the economy. [2] But the fact is that the functional lines between the

191

three types of organs have often shifted, sometimes quite radically. Indeed, in the case of the rural raikom the degree of Party involvement in local economic affairs was subject to wide fluctuations virtually on an annual basis.

The dilemma of the proper degree of involvement was particularly acute with respect to the local Party organs — the central committees of the union republics, the obkoms, kraikoms, gorkoms, and raikoms. By contrast, the economic functions of the highest and lowest echelons of the Party hierarchy have remained fairly constant. The Politburo and the Secretariat of the Central Committee have customarily performed the functions of economic policy formulation and the prescription of general measures for policy implementation and supervision. The lower Party organs — the primary Party organizations and Party groups in individual enterprises and farms — have traditionally carried on a range of ideological, educational, worker-mobilization, and general supervisory functions. However, the local Party organs, besides supervising the activities of the lower Party organs and serving as the agents of the higher Party bodies, have traditionally borne tremendous responsibilities for the performance of the economic enterprises in their territories. In a lecture at the Higher Party School of the Central Committee in 1954, Slepov spoke of these responsibilities in the following manner:

It must be noted that Party committees, as organs of political leadership, are called upon to unite and direct the activity of all state and economic organizations. They bear responsibility for the economy, *and by no means only symbolically:* the Party judges the work of this or that Party organization by the real results in the sphere of economics and the quality of the daily life of the toilers . . .[3] [Emphasis supplied.]

Thus, although the local Party organs have continually been enjoined against undue interference in the details of economic management and urged to follow a somewhat nebulous Party style of leadership in dealing with economic matters, they have been left in no doubt that concrete economic performance is the most important criterion of their personal success. The majority of local Party officials, it would seem, usually interpreted these conflicting instructions to mean that overinterference would be considered less of a sin than underinterference.

This discussion of Party involvement in economic matters is necessarily limited to the agricultural sector. To a certain extent the role of the Party in agriculture was unique. Owing to the blatantly exploitative orientation of Soviet agricultural policy and the inherent difficulties of centralized administration of agriculture, direct Party interference was more likely to be required there than in industry. The tendency toward interference was reinforced by a widespread attitude of Soviet leaders that agriculture did not require the same sort of scientific rigor and expertise as did other branches of production. The acceptance of the quackery of Trofim D. Lysenko is the best known illustration of this attitude, but there were many others. A good example is the following passage from a speech by the Ukrainian Party leader S. V. Kossior in 1936:

There is a widespread opinion that only an agronomist is capable of formulating a kolkhoz production plan. This is incorrect. Why only an agronomist, what is so special about it that the most ordinary person, without a specialized education — say, the Secretary of the raion Party Committee, the chairman of the *raiispolkom,* the head of a department of the *raiispolkom,* or the . . . MTS director or his deputy for political work, although they don't have specialized training — cannot help the management board of a kolkhoz formulate a production plan? Of course they can.[4]

Such an attitude made it all too easy for the local Party officials to ride roughshod over the advice of the agricultural specialists and administrators in the quest for short-term results.

The level of the Party apparatus most directly concerned with agricultural questions was the rural raikom. The obkom, to be sure, also had important responsibilities for agriculture. The MTS, it will be remembered, were directly under the oblast agricultural administrations for most operational matters and were accordingly subject to a good deal of scrutiny by the oblast Party officials. However, it was the raikom secretaries and their assistants in the raikom apparatus, the individuals literally and figuratively "on the spot," who were most directly involved in the business of agricultural production and procurements and who were held most directly responsible for the performance of the local farming enterprises.

Most of the ensuing discussion of Party leadership in the countryside, therefore, will focus on the raion link.

Despite official pronouncements on the importance of the division of labor between Party, governmental, and economic organs, the fact is that the raikom secretaries perennially found themselves compelled to intervene in the pettiest details of agricultural operations. Given the existence of the elaborate bureaucratic structure designed specifically to manage the nation's agriculture, why was this intensive Party interference necessary? Any satisfactory answer to this question must certainly include the serious shortcomings of the agricultural bureaucracy itself. Because of his tremendous personal responsibility for the success of the annual production and procurement campaigns, the raikom secretary found it extremely difficult merely to sit back and supervise the frequently inept managerial efforts of the local administrators and farm managers. At crucial times during the agricultural year the raikom secretary therefore rushed into the breach and undertook to dispose of the local forces of production in the most direct manner. At such times the line between *rukovodstvo* and *upravlenie* obviously disappeared.

In their intervention in agricultural affairs the raikom officials naturally concentrated much of their attention on the one or more MTS in the raion. As the main levers of production activities and as key centers of proletarian influence in the village the MTS were the focus of much of the Party activity in the rural areas. Whether this activity made the MTS centers of political control in the countryside is far from self-evident, however. Some Western writers have tended to accept Soviet clichés about the political role of the MTS too much at face value.[5] In many respects it would appear that the stations were at least as much the objects of Party control as they were the instruments of such control. Nevertheless, it is certainly true that the MTS were centers of substantial Party activity, especially in comparison with other institutions in the village.

PARTY FORCES IN THE VILLAGE IN THE "REORGANIZATION PERIOD"

One of the main reasons for the relatively high intensity of Party activity in and around the MTS was the general weakness of Party representation in the countryside. On the eve of the mass collectivization drive in early 1929, there were approximately 1,500,000 members and candidates in the Party.[6] Of these only about 310,000 members and candidates were enrolled in rural Party organizations;[7] that is, only slightly more than 20 percent in a country where more than three-fourths of the population still resided in the village. The socio-economic characteristics of the rural Party cells were a further cause of concern. The average rural cell had only fourteen members. Most of them were individual peasants who were preoccupied with the economic affairs of their own small farms. The level of literacy was usually minimal.[8] The cells were often very loosely run, with little concern for maintaining the purity of Party membership. Moshe Lewin cites instances where persons were admitted who had been village policemen under the old regime, as well as prostitutes and bandits.[9] According to a frequently cited survey by A. Gaister and A. Levin, twice as many peasant Communists as non-Party peasants employed hired labor on their farms, and they were ten times as likely to derive their principal means of support from white-collar work.[10] Obviously, the rural Party organization was an imperfect representative of the best toiling elements in the village from the official point of view. Not very surprisingly, therefore, the purges carried out in 1929 and 1930 struck particularly hard at the rural Party membership. Village cells lost 15.4 percent of their members, and in all, about 20 percent of Party members of peasant origin were excluded.[11]

The structural pattern of the typical rural cell was also considered unsatisfactory. The rural cells were organized predominantly along territorial lines. That is, they represented a gathering together of all Communists residing in a given geographical locale regardless of the nature or place of occupation. School teachers, cooperative officials, temporary plenipotentiaries of various higher agencies, and local peasant Communists were all lumped together in these cells. This made the coordination of efforts on particular economic or organizational programs very difficult, a problem that became more serious with the expansion of the kolkhoz system. In November 1929 the Central Committee called for vigorous measures to shift the organizational basis of the rural cells to the production principle by expanding the number of cells located in kolkhozes and sovkhozes and transforming existing cells. As Table 6-1 shows, these efforts had some effect, but the structural problem remained acute.

Table 6-1. Distribution (percent) of rural Party cells.

Date	Total number of cells	Type of Cells per 100 Party Cells[a] —		
		Territorial	Kolkhoz	Sovkhoz
July 1, 1928	20,930	94.1	2.9	3.0
July 1, 1929	23,458	89.7	4.7	5.6
April 1, 1930	24,750	63.4	6.0	30.6

Source: "Perestroika partiinoi raboty," Partiinoe stroitel'stvo, no. 11–12 (1930), p. 46.
[a] As yet the number of MTS cells was insignificant.

Party representation in the countryside was particularly weak in the Ukraine, which was to be a prime target for mass collectivization. With a peasant population of 25 million the republic had only 3000 village cells, linking some 25,000 Communists. By distribution, as of late 1929, only 222 cells with 2634 members were to be found in the 1250 sovkhozes of the republic and 174 cells with 1800 members in the 4037 kolkhozes of the republic.[12] Thus, the overwhelming majority of village cells were territorial.

Unable to rely very heavily on these few, poorly situated local Party forces for the collectivization drive, the regime had to resort to the assignment of large numbers of urban cadres to the village. In the period between the Fifteenth and Sixteenth Party Congresses a total of more than 250,000 industrial workers were sent into the countryside on temporary or permanent assignment. By 1929 almost 30 percent of the secretaries of rural Party cells were urban workers[13] Prominent among the hordes of urban workers were the so-called twenty-five-thousanders sent out to the main centers of collectivization by the Central Committee in November 1929. The resolution of the November Plenum announcing the transfer declared:

The Central Committee considers it necessary, in addition to the systematic reinforcement of the kolkhoz movement with leading Party forces, to dispatch to the countryside in the coming months for work in kolkhozes, machine-tractor stations, group unions, etc., no less than 25,000 workers with the requisite organizational and political experience.[14]

In all there were 27,519 of these twenty-five-thousanders, among whom 69.9 percent were Party members and 8.6 percent were Komsomol members.[15] A survey of 16,492 of them completed on March 15, 1930, revealed that 75.3 percent were employed directly in kolkhozes and large group unions (*kustovye ob"edineniia*). Another 3 percent were at work in the MTS.[16] The remainder appear to have been placed in rural administrative centers.

Toward the end of 1930 a series of efforts to strengthen Party influence in and around the MTS began. An increasing number of the twenty-five-thousanders gravitated to the stations. And gradually, the unique political leverage offered by the MTS, thanks to their commanding position vis-à-vis the kolkhozes and the proletarian character of many of the leading cadres of the stations, came to be recognized by the regime. In February 1931 the Central Committee established special Party support points in the MTS, the sovkhozes, and a few large kolkhozes in order to coordinate the activities of the scattered Party forces in the village. These support points were the direct forerunners of the MTS politotdels and will be discussed in more detail in Chapter 7.

Basically, the period from the end of 1929 to the middle of 1932 was a time of extensive and vigorous searching for effective methods of Party control over the new collectivized agricultural system. The entire network of agricultural organs set up in 1928 and 1929 — the agricultural *otdely* in the central and local Party committees and the raion Party link[17] — underwent a series of battlefield trials, as it were. Some of the lessons learned, such as the limited serviceability of the rural Party cells as regular instruments of raikom leadership, would have lasting influence on the long-term patterns of Party involvement in agriculture.

The major efforts of the Party officials in the countryside during the period were, of course, devoted to collectivization and related organizational problems. The setting up of new machine-tractor stations presented a number of particularly difficult problems — psychological as well as technological. In addition to the usual resistance of the peasants to collectivization (it will be remembered that the acceptance of MTS services entailed at least a limited degree of collectivization), the MTS organizers often encountered a genuine fear of modern machinery, especially the tractor. Many of the peasants were reluctant to stake their livelihood on these noisy, evil-smelling iron beasts. Rumors about the dire biological consequences of tractor cultivation were widely circulated. Lenin, it seemed, had been overoptimistic in his expectation that the peasants would rush to embrace Communism after exposure to the tractor. To a certain extent the regime recognized the delicacy and complexity of these problems. As early as September 1929 the Central Committee dispatched a number of special obkom instructors and other high level Party organizers into the raions to sell the MTS idea to the peasants.[18] Some of the twenty-five-thousanders also found themselves in this area of activity.

THE RAIKOM, THE MTS, AND THE PRIMARY PARTY ORGANIZATIONS

As the MTS network expanded and measures were taken to overcome the overt resistance of the peasants, Party activity in the raions gradually shifted its focus. From the purely organizational and punitive tasks associated with the collectivization drive the local Party officials began to turn increasingly to the difficult political and economic problems of operating the new kolkhoz and MTS systems. It was in the process of adjusting to these combined economic and political functions and learning to manipulate the institutions and personnel in the village during the first years of collectivization that there evolved what might be called a characteristic raikom mode of Party control in agriculture.

Before describing the structures and procedures involved in this raikom mode, it might be helpful to say a few words about the institutions of raion Party leadership. The raikom itself was not a real decision-making body. Given a membership of from thirty to sixty persons, depending on the period, comprising the leading activists of the raion Party organization — from Party professionals to outstanding kolkhoz brigade leaders — the raikom was simply too heterogeneous and unwieldy to serve as a day-to-day governing body.[19] For most of these people membership in the raion Party Committee was largely honorific, a recognition of their high economic or administrative positions or their distinguished work in local economic, political, or social agencies. Real decision-making power resided in the seven to eleven members of the raikom bureau, nominally elected by the raikom from among its leading Party and government professionals.[20] The raikom bureau included the two or three raikom secretaries (the first secretary was the chairman of the bureau) and the chairman of the raion executive committee. It also customarily included one or more "responsible workers" of the raikom apparatus — heads of the *otdely* of the raikom, the local representative of the secret police (OGPU-NKVD), the editor of the raion newspaper, the raion Procurator, and perhaps the director of the leading MTS or sovkhoz and the chairman of an outstanding kolkhoz.[21] A good 50 percent of the membership of the bureau was thus made up of full-time Party *apparatchiki*. The bureau met once a week to decide current local business, but the conduct of day-to-day operations was securely in the hands of the Party secretaries and their assistants in the raikom apparatus. In the following discussion I shall follow the Soviet practice of referring to the raikom, rather than its bureau, as the directing body in the raion.

In addition to the episodic campaigns it was called upon to direct during the agricultural year, the raikom performed a number of continuing functions that were only indirectly related to agricultural production. Probably the most important of these had to do with the management of personnel affairs. The raikom secretary had important responsibilities for the selection and disposition of leadership cadres among a large number of Party, administrative, and economic institutions in the raion.[22] Although the MTS director and his chief deputies were not officially on the *nomenklatura* of the raikom, it was quite common, as we have seen in Chapter 4, for the raikom to intervene actively in the appointment and dismissal of these officials. But even where the formalities of *nomenklatura* were strictly observed, the performance of MTS management was sure to come under the close scrutiny of the raikom because of the vital role of the MTS in the main concerns of the raion.

Another continuing function of the raikom was the direction of the activities of the primary Party organizations (PPO's) in the raion.[23] For much of the lifetime of the MTS the apparatus of the rural raikom contained three *otdely,* or departments: an organizational *otdel,* an agricultural *otdel,* and an agitation and propaganda *otdel.* Each *otdel* maintained a staff of instructors who were expected to spend most of their time in the field visiting the PPO's of the various agencies and enterprises in the raion. The instructors of the organizational *otdel* were responsible for the conduct of general Party affairs in the PPO's, but the representatives of the two more specialized *otdely* were also expected to operate primarily through the PPO's and to supervise their activities.[24] The aim of the work of the instructors, especially those of the organizational *otdel,* was to maintain certain standards in the selection and ideological and political training of Party members at the grass roots and, at the same time, to mold the PPO's into effective instruments of the raikom for the prosecution of its many faceted economic and political tasks.

The role of the raikom first secretary under the raikom mode of Party control was, in practice, a very ambivalent one. On the one hand, he was supposed to exercise his leadership through the various administrative and production officials in the raion, relying on his capacity to influence their activities, largely through the PPO's in the respective institutions. Nominally, therefore, his role in the economy of the raion was that of a general territorial co-ordinator and overseer, assisting and influencing the operational agencies to do their work efficiently and in strict conformity with national requirements. On the other hand, when pressures from above mounted, as they invariably did during the major annual agricultural campaigns, the first secretary was forced (indeed, expected) to involve himself directly in the most crucial economic sectors, even if it meant brushing aside the formal economic and administrative institutions. Thus, during the critical periods of the year his role became that of a manager of a huge raion-wide production enterprise, directly disposing of whatever material and personnel resources were available. Despite the fact that this second role and the practices associated with it were repeatedly condemned by the Party, it was, after all, the one in which the real leadership talents of the first secretary were ultimately assessed by his superiors. The ability to produce results in the form of crop deliveries was the primary criterion of success. How these results were achieved was usually considered far less important.

Ultimately, the tension between the two roles had to be resolved by the raikom first secretary on his own terms. The problem was basically one of leadership style. The ideal first secretary under the raikom mode was the one who managed to achieve the results associated with the second role while observing as many of the properties, or appearances thereof, of the first role as local circumstances permitted. Martynov, the hero of Valentin Ovechkin's *Raionnye budni* sketches, is a good example of this ideal type. His predecessor, Borzov, is a good example of what appears to have been the much more common type of raikom first secretary: the leader who is so deeply involved in the second role that he becomes a local tyrant, zealously devoted to the Party and its goals, but in the long run destructive of the model of Party leadership which the regime has attempted to create.[25]

When looked upon in ideal terms, what I have called the raikom mode of Party control in the countryside consisted not so much of two different roles as two phases of a single role. Although the production responsibilities of the raikom were paramount, they certainly did not exhaust its range of functions. During much of the year, when production questions were less urgent, the raikom secretaries were content to employ the indirect methods of economic leadership seemingly favored by the Party, while turning their attention to other tasks, such as the building up of the village PPO's and strengthening the staffs and capabilities of the local administrative organs. Once the pressures began to mount at campaign times, however, the raikom had to shift gears, so to speak, and move to the second phase of its duties, the more or less direct management of agricultural affairs. The smoothness of the transition to the second phase was largely a function of the effectiveness of the raikom secretaries' activities during the first phase. Indeed, there is a fair degree of plausibility in the official theory that the more successful the raikom was in the selection, training, disposition, and supervision of personnel and the strengthening of the PPO's in the production and administrative organs during the relatively quiescent periods of the year, the less need there would be for frantic interference by the raikom secretaries during the periods of stress. Unfortunately for the theory, the pressures for performance were so great at such times and the quality and quantity of the personnel resources available were so rarely adequate that the methods of the Borzovs were more likely to prove necessary than those of the Martynovs.

The existence of an effective network of primary Party organizations was perennially emphasized by the regime as the *conditio sine qua non* of proper raikom leadership. For example, in 1948 Khrushchev called the PPO's in the kolkhozes, sovkhozes, and MTS

the decisive force in the business of solidifying and mobilizing the kolkhozniks, the workers of the MTS and the sovkhozes in the struggle for the harvest, for the raising of animal husbandry, for the dawn of a cultured life in the village. Where the raikoms of the Party fully understand the role of the PPO's, guide their work on a daily basis, rely upon them, lead through them — there great and stable economic successes in the kolkhozes are achieved.[26]

Some idea of the importance attributed to the strengthening of the PPO's can be seen from the list of functions prescribed for them in the Party Rules.[27] The PPO was seen, first of all, as an agency for the recruitment and molding of a reliable corps of persons at the basic production level upon whom the local Party leaders could depend for the execution of their orders. It was considered very important to have Party members in all the crucial sectors of production. One of the most frequently cited achievements of the MTS politotdels in 1933 was their success in transferring Party members from administrative and office jobs to the kolkhoz field brigades and stock farms.

Through its secretary, the PPO also served as a watchdog over the activities of the management of the production enterprise. Because in many cases the kolkhozes and MTS were located at considerable distances from the raion center—sometimes fifty or more kilometers away—it was extremely useful to have a Party presence to guarantee the honesty and discipline of the managers. Given the primitive state of communications in the Soviet village, the need for such supervision was doubly urgent. Actually, it was not until 1939 at the Eighteenth Party Congress that the PPO's of production enterprises were given the formal "right of control" (*pravo kontrolia*) over the management of the enterprises, although less formal supervision was encouraged earlier.[28] This right, which conferred on the PPO the authority to demand access to records of business transactions and to hear regular reports from management, added considerably to the usefulness of the PPO to the raikom, at least in theory, as a check on economic activity.

Armed with these rights and functions, the PPO's were supposed to be the front-line troops of the raion Party organization in its day-to-day conduct of affairs. In practice, as has been indicated, the PPO's fell short of these expectations. For one thing, Party coverage in the village was woefully incomplete. Merle Fainsod asserts that as late as 1949 approximately 85 percent of the kolkhozes in the USSR were without PPO's.[29] (However, L. Mel'nikov, Khrushchev's successor as Party boss in the Ukraine, claimed that 52 percent of the kolkhozes in his republic contained PPO's at about this time.)[30] Another problem was the social composition of the kolkhoz PPO's. Most kolkhoz Party members were of the rural intelligentsia and tended to avoid assignment to "the front lines of production."

The situation of the MTS PPO's was traditionally somewhat better. Virtually every MTS had its own PPO by 1934, thanks largely to the efforts of the politotdels. Nevertheless, for a number of reasons the MTS PPO's could not fully make up for the lack of Party organizations in the kolkhozes. The MTS PPO's were composed primarily of the managerial, technical, and repair-shop personnel of the stations. The small absolute number of tractor drivers who were enrolled in the Party or Komsomol—and they were considerably more likely to be members than were other kolkhozniks—were almost always assigned to the PPO's of their respective kolkhozes, rather than to the MTS PPO's.[31] Thus, the MTS Party organizations were basically inner-directed as far as the focus of their activities was concerned. In order to overcome this inward orientation and to give some additional impetus to the special leadership role of the MTS, the Party created a special position, the Deputy Director of the MTS for the Political Sector (*zampolit*). In certain periods he had substantial authority over Party activities in the kolkhozes of the MTS zone. Undoubtedly, the presence of the *zampolit* in the various transactions between the MTS and the kolkhozes helped to give the MTS a political coloration. The functions of the *zampolit* and his place in the internal structure of the MTS will be discussed in detail in the following chapters. For the present it will suffice to point out that despite the relatively high level of Party representation in the MTS, the ideal type of raikom-PPO relationship was rarely attained even there. Throughout most of the history of the MTS the role of the PPO was decidedly a secondary one.

The weaknesses of the PPO's forced the raikom leadership to resort to other instruments of control during the periods of stress. One of the most common of these was the use of so-called plenipotentiaries *(upolnomochennye)*, a practice dating from the earliest days of the Revolution and Civil War and continued with special vigor during the collectivization and MTS construction campaigns. The plenipotentiaries were relatively high-ranking members of the *aktiv* of a given Party organization, sent out to various sectors of the economy to supervise and control a particular campaign. In this context they were usually members of the raion Party *aktiv*, say, officials of the *raiispolkom,* the chief of the raizo, or officials of the raion cooperative union. Usually they were attached to individual kolkhozes or MTS for the duration of a particular campaign, such as the spring sowing or the harvest. Armed with the authority of the raikom, they were expected to manipulate and exert pressure on the management of the enterprise for the attainment of the current objective. To a great extent the plenipotentiary was the hallmark of the second, direct phase of raikom involvement in the economy, just as the PPO was in a sense the symbol of the first, or indirect, phase. The two institutions were not necessarily mutually exclusive, but for the most part resorting to plenipotientiaries meant the short circuiting of the regular raikom-PPO channels and a qualitatively different form of Party control.

The use of plenipotentiaries in this fashion was always recognized as being basically destructive of the type of orderly Party and governmental procedures in agriculture. Yet it was tacitly accepted as essential for the attainment of immediate goals. Some sense of the ambivalence of the attitude toward the plenipotentiary can be detected in the following passage from an article by V. Suslov, the First Secretary of the Krasnodar Kraikom in March 1953:

Kolkhoz Party organizations are growing stronger, gathering strength, and this introduces important changes in the practice of leadership of the kolkhozes by many raikoms. Raikoms are ever more frequently refraining from sending so-called plenipotentiaries to the kolkhozes for current economic and political campaigns. When the raion Party *aktiv* goes to a kolkhoz, it acts through the primary organization. Under the constant attention of the raikom the primary Party organizations exert more influence on the course of all business than do various kinds of plenipotentiaries.[32]

Suslov is engaged here in the familiar practice of using the present tense to describe a practice that the Party would like to see employed in the future. Nevertheless, rather than condemning the use of plenipotentiaries outright, as most such articles were wont to do, he seems to have been taking the realistic position that it would be necessary to continue to use plenipotentiaries for some time to come. However, he suggests, the strengthening of the PPO's would allow the practice to be tempered by the more orderly procedures of the indirect form of raikom leadership.

The dilemma of the proper degree of Party involvement in economic and administrative affairs continues to be a major issue of Soviet political life to the present day. One of the most eloquent statements of the nature of the problem was contained in a lead editorial in *Kommunist* in November 1966:

The direct interference of Party committees in production and managerial activity is sometimes explained in approximately the following manner: "When a fire breaks out, you have to put it out, never mind who is supposed to do it and who is not." Of course, no one is going to object to this. But in all cases one thing ought not to be forgotten: putting out fires is still first of all the responsibility of the firemen. If someone else always does it for them, they will ultimately decide that this is the only correct procedure and that nothing really remains for them to do but criticize the others for their sluggishness in putting out fires.[33]

The tensions and ambiguities of the raikom mode of Party control were a capsule reflection of the general problems of Soviet agricultural administration. As has been noted in Part II, the regime exerted considerable effort over the years to fashion an efficient, smoothly working bureaucracy for the administration of the MTS-kolkhoz system. However, because of the unceasing demands for high rates of procurements and related pressures, Party officials at the various levels were frequently compelled to interfere in agricultural administration. In the process the regular bureaucratic apparatus was often circumvented, severely impeding its normal development. As we have seen, there were analogous problems within the Party itself at the raion level.

The ideal model of Party leadership envisioned a division of labor between Party, administrative, and production organs. What I have referred to as the first, or indirect, phase of the raikom mode was a good example of this model. It was based on the standard formula of Party guidance of production by means of influence on the personnel in charge of the various administrative organs and production enterprises. The primary Party organizations in these agencies were expected to offer special leverage to the local Party organs in exercising Party leadership. Thus, the first secretary of the rural raikom was supposed to exert his leading role in agricultural production through the chief of the raizo and the managers of the various MTS, kolkhozes, and sovkhozes in the raion, relying particularly on the PPO's in the respective institutions.

As will be shown in the following chapters, this model was rarely achieved in practice. Instead, the first secretary of the raikom and his assistants usually found it necessary to resort to direct interference in administrative and production affairs, both personally and through the use of emissaries to the various production institutions, during the annual agricultural campaigns. There were numerous objective reasons for this violation of the ideal setup. Foremost among them were the inefficiencies of the agricultural bureaucracy and glaring weaknesses of the rural PPO network.

In addition to the more or less regular oscillations between indirect and direct involvement of the raikom, which some Soviet commentators have likened to the jagged fluctuations of a fever chart (*likhoradka*), there were long-term trends during which one or the other type of raikom control was emphasized. These trends commonly reflected major shifts in agricultural policy, as we shall see in the following chapters. Thus, the period following the structural reforms of 1934 witnessed a concerted effort to enforce indirect methods of raikom leadership, while the general tightening of controls on the eve of World War II was accompanied by demands for direct raikom controls. Nevertheless, even during these periods the regular annual shifts at campaign times usually continued.

Under conditions of extreme crisis, such as the famine and peasant unrest of 1932 and the German invasion of 1941, the raikom mode itself was totally scrapped. At these times a radically different mode of Party control was introduced, the politotdel mode. Unlike the raikom mode, which was based on the territorial principle of Party structure, where the supreme local Party organ was responsible for all affairs — culture, general ideological training, and so forth — the politotdel mode was based on a so-called production principle.[34] In concrete terms this shift meant that the focus of local Party leadership concerns was narrowed to more or less purely economic matters. Physically it meant that the center of operations of the dominant local Party body moved from the raion administrative center to the production enterprises themselves. Until 1958 this meant a shift of the center of gravity of local Party leadership to the MTS and their zones. Although the raikom continued to exist during the pre-1958 politotdel periods, actual Party leadership in agriculture passed to the politotdels. The leadership style of the politotdel was totally oriented toward production. In a sense the politotdel mode was a caricature of the second phase of the raikom mode, a throwback to the old style of War Communism and the *prodrazverstka*. This was apparently the style of Party leadership with which the regime felt most comfortable in times of crisis.

Given this tendency of the Party to resort to direct involvement in periods of stress, the question may arise as to whether the ideal model of indirect leadership had any operational relevance at all. The answer is definitely affirmative. Each experience with direct

Party involvement, particularly under the politotdel format, witnessed such a rapid accumulation of pressures and systemic disruption that a cooling-off period was sooner or later felt to be necessary. Particularly after the technology of Soviet agriculture had risen above the most primitive levels, it became less and less feasible to substitute brute political pressure for rational management. Although it was imposible to do without an occasional period of direct Party interference, as V. Suslov seems to have implied in the passage quoted above, the model of indirect Party leadership appeared to become more and more relevant as the days of the MTS drew to a close. Khrushchev's failure to realize this fact may have been one of the most crucial errors of his rule.

7 The Party and MTS Construction, 1929–1932

MTS construction posed a number of special problems for the Party organizers sent to the countryside during the collectivization campaign. The MTS, it will be remembered, had originally been looked upon as an alternative form of collectivization — a special form of producers' association based on a higher level of technology and functional specificity than was envisioned for the ordinary collective farm. In addition to the usual peasant resistance to collectivization, the MTS organizers had to deal with the problem of imposing a relatively advanced pattern of technological culture on an extremely backward peasant culture, a culture in which the horse and the ox were seen as part of an unchanging, natural agricultural cycle. As was shown in Chapter 1, Socialist agrarian theory had relegated this extremely complex problem of modernization to the status of a non-issue. Lenin, it is true, demonstrated some awareness of the problem from time to time, notably in his articles on cooperation and his writings on the Tax in Kind, but his thoughts on the subject were probably just as well represented by his hyperbolic paeans to the socializing magic of "one hundred thousand first-class tractors."

On the whole, the Party organizers in the countryside were not really prepared for the kind of resistance they encountered in attempting to sell the MTS idea to the peasants. Until quite recently the standard Soviet interpretation of this resistance was to attribute it primarily to malicious kulak influence.[1] While there is considerable evidence that kulak agitation and violence were important factors in the opposition to the MTS, this interpretation by no means tells the whole story. For one thing, one must always distinguish between genuine kulaks, who opposed the MTS in order to protect their monopolistic economic position, and nominal

209

"kulaks," who were classified as such by the regime precisely for their opposition, regardless of their actual socioeconomic characteristics.[2] Indeed, the MTS organizers themselves often directly contributed to the creation of such "kulak" groups by their practice of resettling those peasants who refused, on whatever grounds, to accept MTS services. Whole groups of villagers were thereby physically thrown together in opposition.[3]

Furthermore, there were wide variations in the kind and intensity of resistance to the MTS. It is obviously important to differentiate between opposition to the tractor itself and opposition to the MTS as an organizational form. The receptiveness of large numbers of peasants to the widespread rumors of the harmful biological effects of tractor cultivation suggests that something more than kulak agitation was involved. True kulak opposition was probably more likely to have been focussed on the MTS as an organizational form. And even here it is difficult to distinguish between opposition that was based on simple peasant skepticism and opposition that was the result of politically motivated kulak agitation.

In recent years there has been a notable, if sometimes grudging, reappraisal of peasant attitudes toward the various aspects of collectivization in Soviet literary and historical writings. Peasant resistance may apparently now be discussed in less rigid class terms, with allowances for the possibility that opposition could exist on other than political grounds.[4] During the initial period of systematic MTS construction — that is, before the decision was made to impose the MTS as a universal component of the kolkhoz system — there appears to have been a genuine effort by the local organizers to rely as much as possible on persuasion. This was especially true of the representatives of the cooperative system. From contemporary accounts by these early organizers it is possible to derive some idea at least of the range of attitudes in the village with which the Party had to contend. The poor peasants, who, as Markevich's critics had pointed out, had nothing to lose, reacted rather favorably to the MTS. The kulaks resisted, often violently — although if the charges accompanying the rural politotdel purges of 1933–1934 were true, they soon accommodated to the new institutional framework. The middle peasants were reluctant to commit themselves.[5] For this large, uncommitted mass the viability of the MTS arrangement was strictly an empirical question. They did not wish to be rushed into buying a pig in a poke. There were cases where villagers actually expressed a preference for collectivization without the MTS when offered an opportunity to have both.[6]

A good example of peasant skepticism of the tractor and, incidentally, of the general confusion concerning the meaning of the MTS principle was given in a report by a cooperative tractor-column organizer in the Ukraine. Having called a meeting in a village to win acceptance of a cooperative tractor column, he was rather surprised to learn that they preferred a state-owned column. He wrote:

When I tried to discover the explanation for this, they told me: "The state column will work for a year or two, and then it will be clear what to do: maybe we won't need it already by the third year. But when the tractors are ours and they take the money for them from us, then there's already nothing you can do with them." [7]

Indeed, Shiriaev mentions a case where a group of peasants in the CBO (predictably, he dismisses them as "kulaks") actually petitioned Moscow for the removal of an existing MTS.[8]

The Party officials sent out to establish MTS and tractor columns as a rule employed a differentiated response to the various kinds and gradations of opposition. However, even where resistance was clearly nonpolitical, thus calling for persuasion rather than repression, the methods used were likely to be of an extremely "hard sell" nature. One writer, for example, describes the efforts of a group of Party organizers to establish a tractor column in a village in the CBO. The middle peasants resisted their blandishments doggedly with refrain: " 'Let others plow [with the tractors], and we'll see what happens.' " It was only after the Party organizers had held one hundred "meetings" in the space of three weeks that the village was finally pressured into accepting the tractor column.[9]

The anti-MTS forces were often quite resourceful. It was the practice of many MTS organizers in the Ukraine to lead excursions of prospective peasant "clients" to the Shevchenko MTS to demonstrate the benefits of scientific farming. Not to be outdone, a group of alleged kulaks in the Zaporozhe Okrug organized their own excursions to the MTS — to point out its shortcomings. These must have been fairly substantial, for, in the words of one commentator, the "kulak criticism . . . impeded the progress of the contract campaign more than just a little." [10]

MTS organizers had to contend with a continual barrage of hostile rumors. One of the most common themes was the allegedly harmful effects of tractor exhaust gases on the soil and on plant growth. There was a classic case in which a group of peasants, after long hesitation because of such a rumor, finally agreed to sign an MTS contract, but only on condition that International and not Fordson tractors be used. The International tractor, it seems, had its exhaust pipe directed skyward, while the Fordson had its pointed toward the ground.[11]

Where peasant resistance was of a more violent character, the local Party officials responded in kind. A group of "kulaks" in the Lower Volga region formed an underground organization under the slogan "For Bukharin," dedicated to the fight against the MTS and to the restoration of the permissive policies of the midtwenties. (How Bukharin must have relished such support at this stage!) The group was uncovered and smashed before it had a chance to engage in any real opposition.[12] In the North Caucasus, Party officials had to request rifles as standard equipment for tractor-column personnel.[13] Shiriaev notes that in the CBO militiamen were part of the regular staffs of the tractor columns.[14] A contemporary observer of the MTS scene was prompted to declare: "The history of each station . . . is repeating in detail the entire, still unfinished epoch of the struggle with the kulaks, an epoch no less heroic than many shining episodes of the Civil War." [15]

Overt violence was in many respects the easiest form of resistance for the regime to overcome. Far more difficult were the continuing skepticism, unfortunately not much alleviated by the actual performance of the MTS, and the natural hostility of the peasants toward outsiders. Like the Narodniks of the 1870's, the MTS organizers and the managerial and technical personnel who followed in their wake were the objects of a good deal of animosity and distrust. In addition to social ostracism, they were often subjected to more tangible forms of discrimination, such as exorbitant charges for their food and lodgings.[16] This more or less passive resistance posed continuing problems long after the MTS organizers had succeeded in gaining acceptance of MTS services in many a village. Even where formal contracts had been signed the peasants sometimes refused to honor their obligations, such as hauling water and fuel to the tractors working in their own fields, unless they were paid extra to do so.[17]

How well prepared were the rural Party organs to cope with these problems? In Chapter 6 it was pointed out that the permanent complement of Party members in the village was extremely weak, both quantitatively and qualitatively at the time of the collectivization drive. Much of the early work of setting up the MTS was carried out by relatively high-ranking Party emissaries on temporary assignment from the largest urban Party organizations. This arrangement could not, however, satisfy the manifest need for an authoritative Party presence to guide and supervise the operations of the MTS-kolkhoz system on a continuing basis.

Before very long the unique advantages of the MTS as vantage points for Party activity in the village became apparent. Among the original criteria for the selection of MTS sites, it will be recalled, was proximity to population centers and/or railroad lines. In addition, the sites were usually in areas targeted for intensive collectivization. As a result, the stations were potentially in a good position to further the effectiveness of the limited available Party strength in the expanding collectivized sector. It should be pointed out, however, that despite rapid growth after mid-1930 the MTS system was for a long time far from universal in its coverage. As late as the beginning of 1933 the MTS served less than 50 percent of the collectivized sown area in the USSR, and even there the degree of coverage was usually far from comprehensive. Recent Soviet critics have pointed out that the actual political role of the MTS in this initial period was also less significant than has often been assumed in Soviet historical writings.[18]

Nevertheless, it is true that the political potential of the MTS was recognized fairly early. In the latter half of 1930, when the future of the MTS was virtually guaranteed, Moscow began to focus on building up Party influence in and around the individual stations. The Central Committee Decree of December 29, 1930, announcing the crash program of MTS construction declared:

the construction and reinforcement of the MTS must be put at the center of attention of all Party and Soviet organizations. The Central Committee cautions all Party organs against any underrating of the role of the MTS, which, along with the sovkhozes, are the main support points of full collectivization and the liquidation of the kulaks as a class.[19]

Shortly afterwards, on February 11, 1931, the Central Committee promulgated a "Regulation on the Cell of the AUCP(B) in the Kolkhozes," which gave independent status to the MTS Party cell for the first time.

4. Communists working in a machine-tractor station are united in a special cell, which:
    (a) enters into the composition of a general kolkhoz cell with the rights of a shop [Party organization], if the MTS serves only one kolkhoz;
    (b) is a specially chartered cell and lies under the direct leadership of the raikom, if the MTS serves several kolkhozes having independent cells.[20]

Since the MTS customarily served more than one kolkhoz, the MTS cell usually followed the pattern under paragraph "b." Soviet writers have often seized upon this "Regulation" as placing the MTS in a particularly powerful position to lead the political and economic activities of the kolkhozes they served.[21] Such an interpretation is not really warranted, at least for 1931. Yet the new formulation did represent an important step in the developing official perception of the MTS as a separate politico-economic entity in the countryside rather than merely a subordinate component of the kolkhoz system.

The number of MTS party cells grew rapidly during 1931, increasing from 274 to 1847.[22] Table 7-1 shows the relative increases in the number of Party cells and candidates' groups in the MTS and other rural institutions during this first period of mass collectivization.

From the table it can be seen that the number of MTS cells and

Table 7-1. Growth and distribution of Party organizations in the countryside, July 1, 1929, to January 1, 1932, by location.

Date	Total number of cells and candidates' groups	Percentage in —			
		Sovkhozes	MTS	Kolkhozes	Villages
July 1, 1929	27,039	4.7	—	5.6	89.7
April 1, 1930	29,204	5.6	0.2	31.7	62.5
October 1, 1930	31,874	6.9	0.7	41.2	51.2
January 1, 1931	33,325	7.4	0.9	44.9	46.8
July 1, 1931	42,113	9.3	2.7	60.7	27.3
January 1, 1932	45,165	11.5	4.2	66.4	17.9

Source: V. V., "Rost partii v derevne," Partiinoe stroitel'stvo, no. 11–12 (June 1932), p. 46.

candidates' groups increased almost six and one-half times during 1931. This was more than three times the rate of increase in the number of kolkhoz and sovkhoz Party and candidates' organizations (2.0 and 2.1 times respectively).

By 1931 the MTS were accounting for a rapidly increasing percentage of the total number of Party organizations in the countryside. It might be pointed out that the rate of growth of the MTS system itself was more than twice that of the kolkhozes and sovkhozes at this time, a fact that would seem to detract somewhat from the significance of the higher rate of Party growth in the MTS.[23] However, when one examines the various rural production enterprises from the standpoint of intensity of Party coverage, the special character of the MTS, at least in comparison with the kolkhozes, is striking. In mid-1932 almost 90 percent of the existing stations contained Party cells, as compared with approximately 16 percent of the kolkhozes. The sovkhoz percentage was nearly equal to that of the MTS.[24]

In the meantime the Organizational Bureau (Orgburo) of the Central Committee had been addressing itself to structural problems of long-term Party control in the village. On February 21, 1931, the Central Committee promulgated an Orgburo Plan calling for the establishment of Party "support points" in machine-tractor stations, sovkhozes, and certain especially large kolkhozes to focus the energies of the weak, poorly distributed Party forces in the village. Among the instructions in the Introduction to the Orgburo Plan it was stated:

organizationally, this transformation should be established in the form of the unification of a number of village cells in surrounding settlements by the cells of the MTS, acting under the right of Party committees. The Party committees are charged with instructional duties in relation to the scattered village cells . . .[25]

That is, the support-points' Party committees (Partkoms) were to serve as operational command centers for the various local Party members and groups.

The support-point idea was interesting as an early expression of what would come to be a periodically recurring quest by the regime for an authoritative Party organ, below the raikom, to coordinate and direct production-oriented political activity in the village. The raikom was, at such times, considered to be too far removed physically from the production scene to be able to perform these functions directly. The politotdel, of which the support point was obviously a forerunner, was the ultimate expression of this quest.

During 1931 and 1932 the support-point arrangement was introduced on a fairly broad scale. In the Central Black-Earth Oblast in 1932, for example, there were support points in sixty-seven MTS, or almost half the total number of stations in the oblast. Each point directed, on the average, four or five kolkhozes and/or cells in the villages surrounding the MTS, the Party cell of the station setting up a Party committee to manage the affairs of the entire complex.[26] A typical MTS Partkom described by Shiriaev consisted of five persons, two of whom — the secretary and a propagandist — were full-time Party officials.[27]

In practice the support points were of limited operational effectiveness. The parent cells were often very weak themselves, and the MTS, the sovkhozes, and the large kolkhozes in which the Partkoms were located were frequently too poorly organized to serve as stable bases of operations. As a result the Partkoms were not always capable of exercising the kind of detailed Party control for which they had been created. Typical of complaints about their activities was a letter to the editors of *Partiinoe stroitel'stvo* in the summer of 1932 charging that Partkoms in Western Siberia were doing nothing more constructive than conducting sporadic forays into the surrounding kolkhozes to remove or reprimand kolkhoz officials. The author cited the case of the Partkom of the Kamginskaia MTS, which fired six kolkhoz chairmen in the MTS zone during one of these sorties.[28]

A major problem for the MTS support points was the nature of their relationship to the hard-pressed raikoms. The latter were so heavily burdened by collectivization and its related tasks that they attempted to avoid as many operational duties as possible. As a result the Partkoms found themselves transformed into virtual sub-raikoms without the requisite personnel and physical resources to carry out their responsibilities. The average MTS Party cell in 1932 contained approximately ten persons, half of whom were merely candidates. Numerically, it was not much larger than the average kolkhoz cell.[29] But the size of the MTS cells was deceptive. The typical MTS cell was likely to contain several relatively high-level officials sent down from the raikom and attached (*prikreplen*) to the MTS for limited periods. Consequently, in terms of the rank of its personnel, the MTS cell could be considered a fairly high-powered political body at any given moment. At the same time, however, the attachment practice often resulted in a sacrifice of stability and continuity of membership in the MTS cell. This was bound to affect the quality of Partkom leadership.

A good example of this instability was the Party cell of the Trebchevskaia MTS (Western Oblast). Of its seven Party members and two candidates only two were full-time MTS employees, the MTS director and his deputy. The rest were attached officials from various departments of the raion apparatus. During a single year this cell had four different secretaries — usually designated from among the attached officials.[30] A similar situation prevailed in the Party cell of the Briukhovetskaia MTS (North Caucasus Krai). Of its eighteen members eight were attached officials from the raion *aktiv* — including the chief of the raizo and the manager of the raion supply office. Six cell members were on temporary assignment from the *stanitsa* Party organization and only four were full-time MTS personnel: the Party secretary, the MTS director, the repair-shop manager and the manager of the construction materials procurement office.[31] Describing the general character of MTS Party cells, one contemporary writer was prompted to conclude that in many cases "Party cells exist only formally; in essence they are soviet [village] cells thrown together from the workers of the raion apparatus.[32]

Because of these internal weaknesses, the MTS support points were frequently unable to offer much support, despite the tremendous burdens imposed upon them by the raikoms. A particularly glaring illustration of the impossible magnitude of the problems they faced was the case of the Partkom of the Andreevskaia MTS (Western Siberia Krai). This Partkom had twelve village soviets, filthy kolkhozes, and twelve Party cells under its purview. The raikom made it responsible not only for the general activities of the Party cells and the soviets but also for the conduct of such detailed production matters as storing silage, haying, grain procurements, and plowing fallow land. During the various agricultural campaigns the raikom ordered it to assign staff members as plenipotentiaries to the kolkhozes. Finally, the raikom gave it exclusive responsibility for increasing the amount of peasant financial contributions to MTS construction. Not surprisingly, the Partkom was unable to handle this staggering range of assignments, and it settled into a passive routine of collecting statistics and writing reports for the raikom.[33]

By the latter half of 1932 there were increasing indications of disorder in the countryside. Overt opposition had been largely eliminated in most regions, but there were growing problems of labor discipline and morale in the kolkhozes and MTS as the peasants turned to passive forms of resistance. Ominous signs of famine were appearing in the main grain-growing areas of the country, especially the Ukraine.[34]

Evidence of retrogression was particularly strong in the operations of the MTS. The spring and fall sowing campaign of 1932 were carried out with serious delays, and harvesting losses due to poor use of machinery were reaching alarming proportions.[35] Formal contract signing procedures and the collection of payments in kind for MTS services were almost universally being ignored. In the Ukraine it was reported that only 69 of the 574 MTS in the republic had managed to fulfill their work plans as of December 1, 1932.[36]

The Presidium of the Central Control Commission and the Collegium of the People's Commissariat of Workers' and Peasants' Inspection were ordered to conduct a special investigation of the MTS. Among the most serious shortcomings uncovered were the following: (1) many MTS directors and local land organs were still treating the stations as rental points with no responsibility for the organization and direction of work in the kolkhozes; (2) there was a general lack of leadership in the MTS themselves, leading to a high rate of labor turnover, low quality of work, and poor labor discipline; (3) the physical condition of MTS machinery was very poor, resulting in a high percentage of idle time from breakdowns and a low level of utilization of available machinery resources; (4) fuel consumption was inordinately high; and (5) MTS directors were shirking their responsibilities for crop procurements.[37]

In practice the MTS were thus showing themselves to be but pale copies of Markevich's original model. However, by late 1932 the commitment to the MTS was far too deep to permit fundamental reappraisals. Given the political mood then developing in the country, the only solution to the problems of the MTS-kolkhoz system, seemed, to Stalin and his supporters, to lie in the direction of greater political pressures. S. V. Kossior, the Ukrainian Party First Secretary, had warned his colleagues in July 1932: "If you and I — the whole Party organization — do not help the MTS organize its apparatus, raise the productivity of the work of the tractor brigades, sectors, etc., we shall be risking serious harm to the course of socialist reconstruction of agriculture." [38] The help Kossior demanded was soon to be provided — by the politotdels.

8 The Politotdels, 1933–1934

The formal announcement of the setting up of political departments (*politotdels*) in machine-tractor stations and sovkhozes was
made at the January (1933) Joint Plenum of the Central Committee and the Central Control Commission.[1] Kaganovich and several
others at the Plenum made it quite clear that the new organs were
designed to maximize political pressure on the operations of the
production institutions in the village.

The politotdel itself was not a new device. It had long been used
in the Red Army at the division level and above as part of the
system of Party controls in the military. Indeed War Commissar
Voroshilov proudly announced to the members of the Moscow
military garrison in January 1933 that the Party "has decided to
utilize the experience of the army politotdels in the sovkhozes and
MTS." [2] Nevertheless, the adaptation of the politotdel form to the
civilian agricultural sector did represent a significant organizational innovation that was highly suggestive of the Stalinist approach to the problem of crisis management.*

At the January Joint Plenum Stalin himself had urged a radical
reinforcement of agricultural controls. In his report "On Work in
the Countryside" he called attention to the marked decline in
effectiveness of the regular Party organs in the village, complaining
that Party officials in the raions had completely lost touch with
the kolkhozes.[3] And he concluded ominously that "enemy" ele-

Note: This chapter is a modified and expanded version of an article which appeared in *The Slavic Review*, entitled "The Politotdel: A Lesson from the Past,"
XXV, no. 3 (September 1966), pp. 475–496.

* The discussion here will focus mainly on the MTS politotdels. For a number of
reasons largely connected with the nature of their links to the kolkhozes, the MTS
politotdels were probably more important in their overall impact, especially since
the jurisdiction of the sovkhoz politotdels was restricted to the territory of the
sovkhozes themselves. (See, for example, Iu. S. Borisov, "Dokumenty o politicheskoi i
organizatsionno-khoziaistvennoi deiatel'nosti politotdelov sovkhozov v 1933–1935 gg.,"
in D. A. Chugaev et al., eds., *Materialy po istorii SSSR* [Moscow: Institute of History, Academy of Sciences, USSR, 1959], VII, 355.)

ments had succeeded in penetrating the kolkhozes and MTS under the very noses of the local Party leaders, turning the enterprises into "nests of counterrevolutionary activity." [4]

But it was Kaganovich, then head of the Agricultural Department of the Central Committee and the main spokesman on agricultural matters, who furnished the details of the politotdel system and the basic philosophy that was to guide its operations. He declared,

The politotdels must approach all economic work from a political point of view, they must educate Communists in such a way that they will be vigilant in every sector of work, so that they will not believe in words alone, so that they will learn both to unmask spurious figures in a bookkeeper's books and find and punish persons who have consciously broken the teeth of a threshing machine, and [to] prevent sowing with gaps, and [to] guarantee the norms of sowing, and so forth and so on.[5]

In the words of the Resolution of the Plenum the politotdels were to serve as a "Party eye" in the countryside, exercising Party control "in all areas of work and life, both in the MTS and the sovkhozes themselves and the kolkhozes served by the MTS as well." [6]

THE FUNCTIONS AND ORGANIZATION OF THE POLITOTDEL SYSTEM

In accordance with the "production principle" the politotdels were given a broad range of economic and political tasks that were closely oriented toward production. One of the main complaints against the MTS at the Plenum had been their failure to exercise political influence on the kolkhoz masses. "The MTS frequently do not have a political aspect," it was stated in the Resolution of the Plenum.[7] The politotdels were explicitly designed to remedy this shortcoming. One of their most important continuing functions was to expand and direct Party forces in the MTS and the kolkhozes so as to enhance Party influence on production. In practice this meant placing special emphasis on the task of shifting from the territorial to the production cell as the basic unit of rural Party organization.

What really distinguished the politotdel approach to Party organizational activities, apart from greater concentration of effort, was the explicit use of coercive methods. The politotdels were ordered to unmask and weed out the so-called alien elements who had allegedly infiltrated the kolkhozes and MTS and had even succeeded in penetrating the PPO's. They were expected to participate in police operations, such as the apprehension of law violators and saboteurs in the MTS zones, and for this purpose they were given special links with the secret police and the Procuracy.[8]

The list of economic responsibilities of the politotdels was most comprehensive. It included such diverse concerns as the maintenance of labor discipline in the kolkhozes, quality control of seeds to be sown by the MTS and kolkhozes, supervision of tractor repairs and efficient utilization of machinery in production, and care and feeding of kolkhoz livestock. That is, they were expected to be involved in virtually every economic activity in the MTS zone. To be sure, as under the raikom mode, the politotdels were formally instructed to exercise their authority by indirect means — that is, by relying on the responsible managerial and technical personnel. Nevertheless, given the crisis atmosphere of the period, the nature of the cadres assigned to the politotdels, the structure of the politotdel system, and the strong pressures for direct interference, the standard formulas for indirect leadership were even less practically relevant than they were under the normal raikom mode. The nearly total control enjoyed by the politotdels over the Party members in the MTS zones gave them the power to act as directly and forcefully as they deemed necessary. And, as a rule, they took full advantage of their power.

The unique structural and functional characteristics of the politotdel system frequently led to confusion and friction at the local level. Particularly serious were the jurisdictional conflicts between the politotdel chiefs and the regular raikom secretaries who had retained certain poorly defined residual powers. In establishing the politotdels the Party had expressly sought to create a fresh, independent hierarchy of political organs attached to the administrative and operational organs of the People's Commissariat of Agriculture. The goal was to combine the presumed benefits of close Party involvement with sufficient structural separateness for the maintenance of "Party perspective" — the Holy Grail of Soviet organizational efforts even to the present day.

The structural arrangements were as follows. At the apex of the MTS politotdel system was a Chief of the Political Administration of the MTS, located in the All-Union Commissariat of Agriculture. He was formally designated Deputy Commissar for Political Work and was under dual subordination to the Commissar and the Party Central Committee. Significantly, the position was held by A. I. Krinitskii, a high-ranking member of the Central Committee apparatus.* Krinitskii's staff included two deputies for general Party work, an assistant for Komsomol work, and a corps of "responsible instructors," who supervised the work of the respective republic and provincial politotdel organs.[9]

This pattern was repeated at the republic, oblast, and krai levels. For example, in the oblast agricultural administration (*oblzu*) there was a political sector (*politsektor*) for the MTS. It was headed by a chief who was appointed by the Central Committee. The chief of the *politsektor* also bore the title of Deputy Chief of the *oblzu* for Political Work and was an ex officio member of the obkom (or, analogously, the republican central committee). The practical independence of the chief of the *politsektor* from regular local Party authority is suggested by the wording of the original decree, which required merely that he "coordinate" his activities with those of the obkom. Thus, unlike most other high officials in the oblast, he was not fully subordinate to the obkom leadership. The staff of the *politsektor* of the *oblzu* was structurally identical to that of the central Political Administration of the MTS.

The structure of the politotdels themselves closely followed the above pattern. The MTS politotdel was headed by a chief who also bore the title of "deputy director of the MTS for the political sector." He was directly subordinate to the chief of the oblast *politsektor* and was an ex officio member of the raikom. The politotdel chief, too, was largely independent of local Party authority, being required only to "coordinate" his activities with the

* The chief of the sovkhoz politotdel system, K. P. Soms, occupied an analogous position in the People's Commissariat of Sovkhozes.

raikom and give the latter "periodic information" on the work of the politotdel.[10] In addition to the chief, the typical politotdel contained two deputies for general Party work and an assistant for Komsomol work. Somewhat later, pursuant to a Central Committee decree of June 15, 1933, two more staff positions were added: a women's organizer and an editor of the politotdel newspaper.[11]

With regard to the two deputies for general work, it is clear from materials now available that the second deputy was in fact an OGPU agent. Merle Fainsod has noted an OGPU order of January 25, 1933, in the Smolensk Archive setting up the position of "deputy chief for OGPU work." (Iu. S. Borisov mentions a similar position in the sovkhoz politotdels.)[12] A separate clarifying circular of February 3 made the OGPU deputy independent of the politotdel chief in secret matters, for which he was responsible directly to the provincial OGPU organs. In all other matters he was to be at the complete disposal of the politotdel chief.[13] As might be expected, this arrangement turned out to be highly unsatisfactory, as the chief had little leverage against the OGPU. The presence of the OGPU deputy definitely tended to reinforce the punitive, coercive aspects of politotdel activities according to recent Soviet historical accounts.[14]

The dual Party-state status of the politotdel officials at the various levels was an interesting innovation in Soviet administrative practice. Ordinarily, as we have seen, there is a strict formal separation between Party and state administrative hierarchies. That is, Party officials are not given formal points of entry into the administrative chains of command.[15] In borrowing the politotdel format from the military, the Party took with it the "hybrid" Party-military authority of the Red Army political commissar. The designation of the politotdel chiefs as deputies of the administrative and managerial officials at the various levels gave them the legal right to participate directly in the decision-making process and also to issue orders backed by governmental, as well as Party, authority. Recent Soviet commentaries have called attention to this unique dual status. For example, Borisov has noted that "although they were, first of all, Party organs, the politotdels were simultaneously administrative organs . . . They were thus very specific, extraordinary organs of the Party."[16]

This special status gave the politotdel chief, as deputy director of the MTS, a position that was uniquely appropriate for the production principle, since it gave the local Party leadership formal status in the MTS-kolkhoz production relationship. However, the duality also had its negative features, as it sometimes obscured the real nature of the politotdel and reinforced tendencies toward jurisdictional conflict with the raikom. Before the establishment of the politotdels, the rural raikom secretaries had enjoyed a monopoly of the disposition of Party forces in the countryside. By 1933 they were naturally reluctant to share, much less give up, this power. At the same time there were substantial reasons for not abolishing the raikom, as Khrushchev was to do when faced with an analogous situation in November 1962. Yet this arrangement made jurisdictional conflict inevitable.

The original January resolution on the politotdels had been characteristically ambiguous in defining their relationship to the raikoms:

In fulfilling their tasks, the political departments of the MTS . . . must not supplant the local raion Party committees but carry out their work in full contact with them. At the same time, the raion Party committees must learn that with the creation of the political departments of the MTS . . . they are in no way relieved of the tasks and responsibilities laid upon them by the Party.[17]

Given the broad mandate of the politotdels for Party affairs in the MTS zones, it is difficult to see what was left for the raikoms to do. It must be pointed out, however, that MTS coverage was by no means yet complete. Only 41 percent of the kolkhozes in the USSR were served by MTS in 1933 (45.8 percent in 1934).[18] Although the kolkhozes served tended to be the most important ones in a given region and the regions of greatest MTS coverage were the most important agricultural areas of the country, there remained many areas where raikom control continued to be paramount. On the other hand, the great majority of MTS were located in administrative centers and/or on the main lines of rail and road communications. These points were also where the raikoms had their headquarters. The result was that the raikoms were usually given total responsibility for those kolkhozes which were physically most distant and economically least viable, a situation hardly likely to reduce their resentment of the politotdels.

In the beginning the raikoms attempted to contest the powers of the politotdel, claiming that they in fact retained ultimate authority throughout the raions, including the MTS zones. Some raikom secretaries, perhaps honestly confused by the dual subordination of the politotdels, refused at first to acknowledge the latters' status as independent Party organs and treated them as subordinate bodies, like the former support points, ordering their cadres about at will.

The classic example of this attitude, frequently cited as a horrible example by the contemporary Party press, involved a comrade Nal'chikov, first secretary of a raikom in the Kabardino-Balkar Autonomous Oblast in the important North Caucasus Krai. Nal'chikov, refused to recognize the politotdel of a local MTS as a Party organ, treating it instead merely as an economic organ subject to raikom control. He continued to claim authority over MTS and kolkhozes alike, refusing to permit the politotdel chief to remove "even a timekeeper in a kolkhoz without the consent of the raikom." On one occasion he was quoted as having warned, "If it becomes necessary, why, we'll arrest the chief of the politotdel, too." [19] Nal'chikov was ultimately removed from his post and expelled from the Party, but his attitude was not unique. One raikom secretary from Odessa Oblast was reported to have told a plenary session of the raikom, "The politotdel is in no case a Party *otdel;* it is the same sort of *otdel* as the finance *otdel,* the agricultural *otdel,* and other soviet *otdels.* We will be the ones to assign tasks to the politotdel." [20] These examples of opposition were, perhaps, rather extreme. However, it was apparently quite common for local officials to engage in petty harassments of the new politotdel cadres. The contemporary press carried numerous accounts of the refusal of the local authorities to provide housing and food rations to politotdel personnel and their families.[21]

The problems of friction and jurisdictional squabbling were eventually deemed sufficiently serious to warrant direct action by the Central Committee. On June 15, 1933, a decree was promulgated defining a more precise division of labor between politotdel and raikom. The decree confirmed politotdel jurisdiction over Party cells and associated groups in all kolkhozes served by MTS, but exclusive jurisdiction was to be confined to matters involving MTS production activities:

For all remaining questions of village life (soviet construction, finances, education, propaganda, etc.) the raikoms direct the cells of these kolkhozes, just as the raikoms direct territorial cells and production cells of kolkhozes not served by MTS, but [in the latter case] for all questions without exception.[22]

Moreover, in the future the politotdels would have to inform the raikoms of certain actions taken in the kolkhozes' Party organizations, notably on personnel transfers. The raikoms were also given the right to confirm all admissions to and expulsions from the Party by the politotdels and to examine all membership and dues records. Finally, the decree set up grievance procedures for settling future jurisdictional problems, placing final disposition with the first secretary of the obkom, acting in conjunction with the chief of the oblast *politsektor*.

Thus, the June 15th decree reserved considerable formal authority for the raikom on Party affairs in the MTS zones, although it retained primary operational control in the hands of the politotdels. Nevertheless, while the decree and the actual experience of working with the new organs appear to have brought some measure of alleviation, it cannot be said that the jurisdictional question was ever fully settled. In the words of a Soviet historian of the period, "The presence of two centers in the raion . . . made itself felt during the entire period of operations of the politotdels." [23]

STAFFING THE POLITOTDELS

One of the main problems in improving the performance of the new socialist agricultural system was the recruitment of sufficient numbers of skilled managerial and technical personnel. This problem involved the assignment of local Party leadership cadres as well. The staffing of the politotdels represented an interesting example of Party personnel policies at this time.

Having placed so much reliance on the politotdel as the solution to the agricultural crisis, the Central Committee paid particular attention to the selection of politotdel workers. At the January Plenum Kaganovich had said, obviously referring to recent unpleasant experiences with collectivization, that this time the Party wanted no "surprises" from the people it was sending out to the village. He announced that a special commission had been formed by the Central Committee at the end of 1932 to organize the recruitment and careful selection of politotdel cadres. The membership of the commission was impressive. Its chairman was P. P. Postyshev, second secretary of the Ukrainian Party organization, a rapidly rising star in the Party apparatus. Other members included Ia. B. Gamarnik, head of the Main Political Administration of the Red Army; Ia. A. Iakovlev, People's Commissar of Agriculture; N. I. Ezhov, future head of the NKVD; and A. M. Markevich, the originator and first director of the MTS system.

The commission processed applicants who had been nominated by counterpart commissions at the provincial level, headed by the first secretary of the obkom or kraikom. In the case of the deputies for OGPU work, nominations were made by the central OGPU authorities. Assistants for Komsomol work were selected personally by the first secretary of the Central Committee of the Komsomol, A. B. Kosarev. Final confirmation and assignment of politotdel chiefs rested with the Secretariat and the *Orgburo* of the Central Committee after each candidate had been personally interviewed by members of the special commission.[24] Commissar of Agriculture Iakovlev subsequently revealed that only one out of three of those nominated by the provincial commissions were accepted for further processing by Central Committee.[25]

Most of the applicants selected had been full-time workers in the Party apparatus. According to one frequently cited survey, 81 percent of the chiefs and 72.2 percent of their deputies had been *apparatchiki*, including, among the chiefs, 19 percent previously occupied in full-time military-political work.[26] Concerning this latter group, Kaganovich told the Seventeenth Party Congress that the first three hundred politotdel chiefs had come from the army.[27]

As of June 15, 1933, there were already some eight thousand

persons working in the MTS politotdels and two thousand in the sovkhoz politotdels. The aforementioned survey, which covered seven thousand who had been checked by the Auditing Department of the Central Committee, largely confirms the impression that the politotdels constituted a relatively high-powered group. The survey found that 53.6 percent had had more than three years of "leading Party work" experience. Among the chiefs almost 40 percent had had more than five years of such experience, the average for all chiefs being four years and seven months.[28] Data on length of Party membership are also impressive. As of the end of 1933, 38.9 percent of all politotdel workers and 87.6 percent of the chiefs had been Party members for more than ten years.[29] Table 8-1 shows the occupational backgrounds of some of the 3412 chiefs and deputy chiefs covered by the Auditing Department survey.

Table 8-1. Previous Party and governmental experience of politotdel chiefs and their deputies.

Position	Number
Secretary of Party committee, raikom level or higher (including 38 former okruzhkom and gubkom secretaries)[a]	285
Head of *otdel* of Party committee (including 50 former heads of organizational *otdel* of okruzhkoms and gubkoms)[a]	166
Komsomol secretary, raikom level or higher	172
Chairman of executive Committee of Soviet, *raiispolkom* level or higher	43
Chairman of okrug or guberniia trade union organization[a]	46
Political commissar of the Red Army (including 50 former commissars of brigades and divisions and chiefs of division politotdels)	103
Okrug or guberniia Procurator	23
Director of industrial enterprise or chairman of trust	37
Director of MTS or sovkhoz	13

Source: V. Markovich, "Derevnia poluchila moguchii otriad Bol'shevikov," *Partiinoe stroitel'stvo*, no. 13–14 (July 1933), pp. 62–63.

[a] Note the relatively large numbers of former okrug and guberniia officials. These two administrative levels had been formally liquidated in 1930 and 1929, respectively, although they continued to function in some locations for several years. Hence, there was a "windfall" reserve of high-ranking cadres available for assignment to the politotdels at this time.

On the whole, the educational level of politotdel workers was also comparatively high for the period. Thirty-five percent of the chiefs and 57 percent of their deputies for general Party work had a higher Party or higher specialized education.[30] Most of the politotdel workers were of urban background, at least in their adult lives; almost half of them came from Moscow and Leningrad alone. More than 60 percent claimed working-class social origins.[31]

From the statistical data and a number of contemporary biographical sketches it is possible to put together a composite picture of the politotdel chief which may be helpful for understanding some of the stylistic elements of politotdel rule in the village.[32] The typical politotdel chief was a vigorous, relatively well educated urban male in his middle thirties with considerable experience in middle-level Party work. He was likely at some point in his career to have had some military experience as a political officer in a Red Army unit. This factor added an element of military bearing to the usual Party leadership style in dealings with colleagues and subordinates. Quite probably, although the available data here are far from conclusive, his education and practical experience placed him a cut above the average raikom secretary, adding to the tendency toward friction with the raikom. Another significant characteristic of the typical politotdel chief was a lack of experience in agricultural production. Obviously, his authority was not expected to accrue from any special agrotechnical expertise.*

From this composite picture of the politotdel chief and from

* It is interesting to note in this connection that a significant proportion of politotdel chiefs appear to have been of Jewish ethnic stock, reinforcing the impression of nonagricultural background. A list of 110 MTS politotdel chiefs receiving honors, published in *Pravda* on May 10, 1934, contains 13–15 persons with Jewish names. This may be assumed to reflect the percentage of Jews (12–14 percent) among all politotdel chiefs. If so, the percentage of Jewish politotdel chiefs was significantly higher than the overall percentage of Jews in the Party (Fainsod, *How Russia Is Ruled*, p. 256). Incidentally, Leonard Schapiro, using a similar methodology, has found a similarly disproportionate representation of Jews in the NKVD organs during the Great Purges (Leonard Schapiro, "The Role of the Jews in the Russian Revolutionary Movement," *The Slavonic and East European Review*, vol. XL, no. 94 [December 1961], p. 165). The prominence of Jews in the lower-middle levels of the Party apparatus, especially in punitive-type organs, may perhaps be seen as a portent of Stalin's future policy of using them as scapegoats for the excesses of his regime.

various substantive details, such as the formal links with the OGPU and the Procuracy, the uniquely political nature of the politotdel stands out. Despite its close ties to economic and production organs at the various levels, the politotdel system was clearly oriented toward the disciplinary and organizational, rather than the technical, side of the production process. Victor Kravchenko, the author of *I Chose Freedom,* was an obkom plenipotentiary assigned to an MTS politotdel in early 1933. He quotes from a speech by M. M. Khataevich in Kharkov to a group of plenipotentiaries leaving for politotdel work in the village: "Your loyalty to the Party and to Comrade Stalin will be tested and measured by your work in the villages . . . There is no room for weakness. This is no job for the squeamish. You'll need strong stomachs and an iron will. The Party will accept no excuses for failure." [33]

THE POLITOTDELS IN ACTION

The politotdels began work almost immediately after the January Joint Plenum.[34] By the end of March more than half of the 2486 MTS in the country contained operational politotdels. As of January 1, 1934, politotdel coverage was total.[35]

The creation of the politotdels had been accompanied by the announcement of the purge of 1933. Consequently, at the outset purge work occupied a large share of their attention. The purge was to be far-reaching, especially in rural areas. The only persons not subject to investigation were members and candidates of the Central Committee and the Central Control Commission and the chiefs of MTS and sovkhoz politotdels, the latter having been "already checked in the process of their appointment." [36] The first purge campaign of the politotdels was directed against the personnel of the MTS themselves in order to guarantee a reliable base for further politotdel operations. Following a suggestion by Kaganovich, the purge struck particularly hard at the middle and lower levels of MTS personnel. Krinitskii reported to the Seventeenth Party Congress in January 1934 that in 1028 MTS surveyed the politotdels had removed 37 percent of the agronomists, 27 percent of the tractor brigadiers, 20 percent of the repair shop workers, and 13 percent of the tractor drivers.[37]

Some regions such as the North Caucasus, where opposition to collectivization had been extensive, were particularly thoroughly "cleansed." V. F. Larin, chairman of the Azov–Black Sea Kraiispolkom, reported (with evident displeasure) that in 200 MTS 148 directors were replaced during 1933. In 70 stations there had been one change of directors; in 50 stations the director was replaced twice; in 5, three times. He noted that there were MTS which had had four or five different directors in the course of the year.[38] *

Occasionally MTS directors attempted to resist these politotdel raids on their personnel. It will be remembered that the putting together of staffs of technical and operating personnel was no easy matter during the early days of the MTS. The purges threatened to disrupt MTS operational capabilities quite seriously. However, as the statistics of turnover indicate, the director had little leverage in a showdown with the politotdel.[39]

Soon the politotdels extended their purge activities to the surrounding kolkhozes. The primary targets were the upper and middle levels of kolkhoz leadership. In twenty-four krais, oblasts, and republics of the USSR, 36 percent of the kolkhoz chairmen, 40 percent of the business managers (zavkhozy), 31.3 percent of the dairy farm managers, and 25.6 percent of the field brigadiers were removed during 1933.[40] Some leaders in the North Caucasus, alarmed at what seemed to be developing into an indiscriminate destruction of kolkhoz cadres, ultimately began to complain of this excessive purging.[41]

As might be expected, the OGPU deputies played a leading role in the purge activities of the politotdels. Frequently they would operate as independent agents, concerning themselves solely with the purges, to the detriment of other assignments given to them by their nominal party superiors, the politotdel chiefs. According to Zelenin,

---

* The middle and lower levels of MTS personnel were also hard hit in the North Caucasus. In 191 MTS covered by a contemporary survey almost 25 percent of these categories were purged for various political reasons, ranging from "alien" social origin to sabotage of tractors, as part of a rather transparent campaign to attribute the failures of the past to "class enemies" who had infiltrated the local socialized enterprises. See A. Shteingart, "Politotdely Severnogo Kavkaza za rabotoi," Pravda, May 9, 1933.

In practice the work of these deputies in the majority of cases amounted to purging the kolkhozes and the MTS; already in these years a tendency was observed on the part of the OGPU workers to escape from the control of the Party. Everywhere politotdel chiefs confronted a situation in which the OGPU deputies refused to carry out their orders, declined the usual politotdel work.[42]

This attribution of all the excesses of the politotdels to the OGPU may be less than fully candid, since Zelenin was undoubtedly reflecting the de-Stalinization line of the Khrushchev era. But undoubtedly the *de facto* independence of the OGPU deputies was a serious problem. Kravchenko records the following dialogue between himself and the OGPU deputy, Skopin, concerning Kravchenko's conduct as an obkom plenipotentiary to the politotdel:

Skopin: "You see, we've received several statements and official declarations about your conduct here . . . They all amount to this: that you're breaking the law, ignoring Party orders and riding roughshod over local authorities."

Kravchenko: "Whom do you mean when you say 'we' have received? Are you referring to the Chief of the Political Department? Are you here at his request?"

Skopin: "That's beside the point."

Kravchenko: "No, it's the main point. Have you been authorized to examine me?"

Skopin: "I'm just here for a private friendly talk. It isn't an examination." [43]

Fortunately, Kravchenko received support against the subsequent OGPU charges from the politotdel chief, an unusually vigorous and influential ex-artillery colonel. Others in similar situations were probably less fortunate.

In their task of "cleaning out" hostile elements the politotdels had the assistance of the regular organs of justice, as well as the OGPU. Both the republican Commissariats of Justice and the Procuracy were directed to give special assistance to the politotdels. A resolution of the Collegium of the RSFSR Commissariat of Justice in April 1933, stated:

In view of the massive leading role of the MTS in the kolkhoz move-ment and the very poor work of the Procuracy in serving the MTS, it is proposed to the organs of the Procuracy that they reconstruct their activity in such a way that work on the reforming of the kolkhoz be coordinated with the management of the MTS and the politotdels of the MTS and sovkhozes . . .[44]

Shortly thereafter, special assistants to the raion, oblast, and krai Procurators were assigned to permanent work with the po-litotdels.[45]

The relationship between the politotdels and the Procuracy was apparently a complementary one, each giving the other re-ports on shortcomings or illegalities uncovered by their respective agents. For example, the raion Procurator of the Pushkin Raion in Leningrad Oblast found serious grain losses during threshing operations in a kolkhoz where he had been investigating property thefts. He informed the politotdel chief, who promptly ordered a second threshing.[46]

One of the implicit purposes of the campaign to identify and punish alleged "wreckers" and saboteurs in the village was un-doubtedly to divert peasant hostility away from collectivization and the regime that had imposed it. The politotdels thus per-formed an important safety-valve function. A good illustration of the image intended by the regime was contained in a "Letter to Comrade Stalin" allegedly sent by a group of kolkhoznik-shock workers of the Bezenchukskaia MTS zone (Middle Volga Krai) and published on the front page of *Pravda* on May 17, 1933. After thanking the politotdel for cleansing the zone of "hostile ele-ments" and for the many other things it had done for them, they declared:

There is no side of the life of the kolkhoz that the politotdel would not penetrate, and everywhere it lends its influence. This was felt immediately. Now initiative arising in the kolkhozes is speedily carried out through the politotdel. People now go to the politotdel for all kinds of business. Only yesterday some women came to the politotdel from the kolkhoz "Shliakh do kommunizma" and reported on the poor work of the chairman. The chief of the politotdel went back with them, checked everything, and it really was necessary to remove the chairman and expel him from the Party.

Such procedures would obviously not always be approved. During 1933, at least, they were being actively encouraged.

So far the discussion has focussed mainly on the more negative side of politotdel activities. Indeed, it must be admitted, the purges and investigations of 1933 did constitute perhaps the most visible aspect of politotdel operations from the standpoint of the peasantry. However, there was a more constructive side, as well. It was in the latter area that the production principle of Party involvement had real significance.

One of the most important (at least nominally) of the areas of positive activity was the recruitment, training, and disposition of Party members and sympathizers in the MTS zones. A continuing goal of the politotdels was to increase the quantitative and qualitative weight of Party influence in the key sectors of the agricultural production process. This goal was to a great extent directly antithetical to the purges, since the supply of village Communists was decidedly limited, but the politotdels were expected to achieve both.[47]

The problem was not merely one of numbers. The majority of Party and Komsomol members in the village were not to be found "in the front lines of production." Indeed, Fainsod quotes one politotdel chief as complaining that some young persons were joining the Komsomol specifically to avoid work in the fields.[48] Even structurally, as we have seen, the rural Party network was not production oriented. Despite the efforts of 1931–1932 the majority of the rural Party cells were still territorial. Consequently, much of the politotdels' organizational activity was devoted to a structural and functional reorientation of village Party forces toward production. A main provision of the June 15, 1933, Central Committee decree cited above was a call for a drastic shift to the production principle of Party organization.[49] Accordingly, the politotdels made it a special point to shift Party members from administrative duties to the kolkhoz field brigades and dairy farms.

Typical of contemporary reports of this phase of politotdel work was a description of the activities of the politotdel of the Ostrogozhskaia MTS (CBO). Before reorganization there had been ten territorial cells and three candidates' groups among the 30 kolkhozes of the MTS zone. The reorganization created 16 kolkhoz production cells, 2 candidates' groups, and 2 so-called Party-Komsomol nuclei — all supposedly intimately involved in production. The politotdel also directed 72 individual Party organizers into the 126 kolkhoz field brigades of the zone. Of 153 Communists in the Party cells of the zone, 48 percent were reported as working directly in production after politotdel reorganizational activities, twice the previous percentage.[50]

Data from the Lower Volga Krai show the same general pattern. In the Stalingrad zone of the krai, 2257 out of the 2917 Communists were transferred to work in kolkhoz brigades. In the Khoper zone, 1640 of the 1887 Party members in territorial cells were shifted to production cells and/or work in the kolkhoz brigades. In this zone, which had previously contained 146 territorial cells, the politotdels created 197 new kolkhoz production cells, and 3523 Communists and Komsomel members out of the 4284 on the rolls were transferred to kolkhoz production work.[51]

While aggregate figures for the USSR as a whole are not available, politotdel activities in this area appear to have been quite substantial. Zelenin claims that they succeeded in placing 70 to 80 percent of kolkhoz Party members in "decisive sectors of production." [52] On the other hand, he points out that the net effect of the purge, together with the general recruitment freeze which began in 1933, was a marked decline in the number of rural Party cells. Between the end of 1933 and the end of 1934 the number of kolkhoz cells declined from 30,000 to 18,300, and the total number of rural Party cells (territorial and production) dropped from 80,000 to 61,700.[53] Whether qualitative improvements could compensate for these serious quantitative losses may well be questioned.

The politotdels were given great power over the use and disposition of Party cadres in the MTS zones, although, as indicated earlier in this section, this power was not uncontested. In order to clear up some early confusion on this score the Ukrainian Central Committee on April 29, 1933, issued a decree, later adopted by the All-Union CC, of placing high-ranking plenipotentiaries assigned to the village at the complete disposal of the politotdel chiefs for extended periods of time. The decree was aimed particularly at an apparently growing practice — a variant of what I have called the second phase of the raikom mode — of city and oblast organizations to send their representatives to the village on short-term assignments. Rarely bothering to coordinate their activities with the local Party leadership, these representatives tended to become a law unto themselves, undermining the authority of the village Party organs. Under the April 29th decree plenipotentiaries could be sent only in special cases, and only high-ranking persons, such as members of obkom or raikom bureaus, could be so assigned. The best and most experienced of them were to be sent to the politotdel chiefs for designation as secretaries of weak kolkhoz Party cells for the duration of an entire agricultural campaign. In no case were they to be sent for less than two to four months. All other plenipotentiaries were to be placed in kolkhoz Party cells as rank-and-file members for the length of their stay in order to preserve local Party discipline.[54] From our general knowledge of Party status relationships and individual accounts, such as Kravchenko's, it may well be supposed that this arrangement was not without its difficulties.[55]

These Party organization and mobilization activities constituted a large part of the "economic" work of the politotdels. By traveling about the MTS zones themselves and stationing loyal Party members in key locations to follow up their instructions, the politotdel workers attempted to insure close supervision of and political support for the production and technical measures of the regular MTS and kolkhoz officials. One area of activity considered particularly important was the tightening up of the formal procedures of contract signing and fulfillment. The politotdels were given special responsibility for seeing that the new 1933 Model MTS-kolkhoz Contract was fully implemented and that the previous laxity and reluctance of the contracting parties to assume contractual obligations were overcome.[56]

The usual practice was for the politotdels to operate as teams of roving troubleshooters, investigating the causes of production failures and taking remedial measures on the spot. The politotdel of Veselokutskaia MTS in Odessa Oblast, which achieved a good deal of publicity in the contemporary press, offers numerous illustrations of what were apparently the desired modes of politotdel organizational and operational activities.

The chief of the politotdel, A. I. Nider, a former Red Army military and political officer, ran his organization on an egalitarian basis. He, his two deputies for general Party work, and his Komsomol assistant all performed the same tasks. The four of them would disperse among the kolkhozes of the zone during the major agricultural campaigns (spring plowing, sowing, harvesting, and so forth). Each one would spend five or six days in the group of farms served by a single MTS production section, remaining in each kolkhoz for one or two days. They were not permanently assigned to any one group of farms but each visited a different group during successive campaigns in order to maintain "perspective." [57]

The politotdel workers did most of their business in spot conferences in the kolkhozes. For example, Nider's first deputy Fomenko, arriving in one kolkhoz early in the morning to find a mere handful of peasants at work in the fields, initiated an inquiry. He saw that labor discipline was weak. The kolkhoz chairman, Udov, allegedly the son of a kulak, rarely appeared in the fields, and the kolkhozniks were extremely dissatisfied with him. Fomenko called a general meeting to hear grievances and discuss a solution. He learned that the former chairman, a Party candidate named Chernomaz, who was very popular, had been called into the army. After demobilization he had been assigned to a post in the raion center. Fomenko promised to arrange for his return to the kolkhoz. The politotdel put pressure on the raikom, and in a few days Chernomaz was once again chairman of the kolkhoz. From that time the kolkhoz improved steadily and was soon one of the best in the zone.[58]

Politotdel chief Nider found a somewhat more difficult situation in the "Kassel" kolkhoz, which had been formed in an old German colonists' settlement. The farm was reportedly under strong kulak influence, and during a short period twenty horses had suddenly died under suspicious circumstances. Nider ordered an autopsy, which revealed that the horses' stomachs were filled with metallic objects. After having summoned the kolkhozniks to view this evidence of "kulak sabotage," he turned the case over to the Procuracy. In all, there were more than two hundred trials in the zone involving the destruction of kolkhoz draft horses.[59]

These activities, as well as the still more dramatic purge work, were characteristic of the early "shakedown" period of politotdel operations. Long-term, continuing activities tended to be more prosaic. An important example of the latter was the training of kolkhoz personnel in leadership techniques. Collectivization and "dekulakization" had put many ordinary peasants into positions of authority for the first time, especially at the brigade level. One brigadier was quoted as saying, "If it weren't for the politotdel, I'd still be swimming in work. The politotdel taught me . . . how to organize people. Before, I had to go from house to house to call them to work. Now the people come by themselves, and even more than enough of them." [60]

Officially, the production role of the politotdels was to consist mainly in providing political impetus and authoritative Party backing for the technical measures of the regular managers and specialists. In practice, however, it was often very difficult to avoid direct involvement in technical details. Moscow furnished few guidelines, sometimes encouraging interference, at other times condemning it. In general, the extent to which politotdel officials themselves directly intervened in technical and managerial affairs seems to have been governed by the vigor and competence of MTS and kolkhoz management. For example, the politotdel chief of the Yelnya MTS is quoted by Fainsod as complaining to his superiors that the MTS director, Ustinov, was " 'too soft . . . He rarely visits the fields, has no idea of what is going on in the kolkhozes, and is constitutionally incapable of effective supervision.' " He concluded that if the director were not replaced, " 'it will thus force the politotdel to assume not only political but also the economic guidance of the MTS . . .' " [61]

CRITICISM OF THE POLITOTDELS

By the end of 1933 there were already strong sentiments that the coercive practices of the politotdels had passed the point of diminishing returns. Both at the grass roots and in certain high Party circles there were increasing pressures for a shift to more positive work on the part of the politotdels. Indeed, some were even prepared to call for the outright liquidation of the politotdels. These issues were of major concern to Party leaders assembled at the Seventeenth Party Congress in late January 1934 to discuss, among other things, the problems of agriculture.

The politotdels were far from the main topic of discussion at the Congress, but they did receive considerable attention. In his remarks on agriculture Stalin paid them a warm, if brief, tribute. But he devoted much more of his time to a scathing criticism of the various components of the regular agricultural system, particularly the MTS. As mentioned in Chapter 5, he hinted at the need for a major reorganization of the agricultural bureaucracy. Nothing was said of the role of the politotdels under the new arrangement.[62]

However, it was clear that there was as yet no consensus on the matter. As if missing the drift of Stalin's remarks, Krinitskii, who delivered the main report on the politotdels, warmly praised their record during the preceding year and declared that their role had just begun. He urged that both their political and economic operations be continued and even expanded.[63] From the ensuing commentaries and debates it was clear that many others did not share Krinitskii's assessment. Several speakers indicated their dissatisfaction with the politotdels, if only by damning them with faint praise. R. Eikhe, the First Secretary of the Western Siberian Kraikom, even interrupted Krinitskii with a sarcastic reference to the "assistance" that the politotdels had been giving the raikoms.[64]

The fate of the politotdels and of the politotdel mode of Party control was evidently a matter of serious controversy among the leaders of the Party. Much more than the economic and political effectiveness of the politotdels themselves appears to have been at issue. The list of opponents of the politotdels at the Congress, in view of their subsequent fate in the Great Purges, suggests that the entire philosophy of Party control in agriculture may well have been involved. Such important provincial and republican leaders as Postyshev, Eikhe, I. Vareikis, and B. P. Sheboldaev were among those who in one way or another had been opposing the politotdels and their extreme "political" methods. Zelenin implies that there was a continuing struggle between those who supported this "political" approach, headed by Stalin, Kaganovich, and Molotov — and those who consistently opposed it — he names Postyshev specifically.[65] The lineup of opposing forces suggests the probability that it was essentially a conflict between the center and the provinces; that is, between those trying to maintain the politotdels as a separate chain of command, independent of the regular territorial party organizations and those (the provincial Party leaders) attempting to regain control over all Party affairs in their respective regions. Whether this was primarily a conflict of personalities or of basic policy orientation — for example, a "hard" *versus* a "soft" line toward the peasantry in the post-collectivization period — is difficult to determine, although the latter hypothesis would help to explain the extent to which the Great Purges hit the provincial Party leaders.

Once again it was Kaganovich who set forth the official Stalinist line on the politotdels. In his long report "On Organizational Questions" toward the end of the Congress he made a number of interesting comments on the problems of Party control in agriculture. He admitted that with collectivization and the establishment of the politotdels the entire central Party apparatus had become preoccupied with agricultural matters. This situation, he suggested, could no longer be tolerated. As has been noted above the solution was seen in terms of strengthening the state agricultural administrative system, particularly at the local (raizo) level. A downgrading of the MTS (and their politotdels) as political and administrative control centers was clearly in the offing. Kaganovich told the Congress:

Comrade Stalin has expressed the thought that we ought not to fasten upon the MTS a number of functions inappropriate to it. We must reinforce the raizos in every way and rebuff any attempts to liquidate them. It is necessary that the raizo, a state organ, take upon itself the direction of a series of agricultural operations . . .[66]

The immediate fate of the politotdels was uncertain. Some speakers at the Congress, in particular Sheboldaev, the first secretary of the Azov–Black Sea Kraikom, came out directly for converting them to regular Party organs, preferably subordinate to the raikoms.[67]* Indeed, Kaganovich himself had entertained such a possibility for the future in his published pre-Congress "Theses." [68]

Now, however, Kaganovich hesitated, ostensibly taking a middle ground between Krinitskii and the outright opponents of the politotdels. He chided Sheboldaev for premature "liquidationism" and tried to put a damper on sentiments for immediate abolition. The authority of the politotdels, he said, was a priceless treasure, won on the field of battle, so to speak, and not lightly to be cast away. Besides, the tractor repair and spring sowing campaigns lay ahead. Liquidation of the politotdels might result in a slackening of effort.[69]

The resolutions of the Congress, not surprisingly, followed the middle course suggested by Kaganovich. The conversion of politotdels to regular raikoms and sub-raikoms was to be permitted on a piecemeal basis where conditions were ripe.[70] ** The Congress also outlined concrete steps to reorganize the raikoms in tacit anticipation of the eventual liquidation. The new structure, as outlined at the Congress (but substantially modified a few months later), borrowed liberally from the politotdel pattern. Thus, all raikom departments (*otdely*) were to be abolished in favor of a staff of traveling instructors, each of whom was to be attached to a group of kolkhoz Party organizations and made responsible for the entire range of their Party activities. Henceforth, the raikoms would be doing the same sort of work in the kolkhozes as the politotdels had been doing. It was expressly ordered that the two rival Party organs function jointly.[71]

This arrangement was obviously intended to be temporary. For the politotdels the period after the Congress was largely anticlimactic. Despite Kaganovich's warnings to the contrary, an "atmosphere of liquidationism" seems, indeed, to have pervaded

---

* Sheboldaev had been urging these changes in his home territory before the Congress had even met (*Molot* [Rostov-on-Don], January 23, 1934).

** The author has found no evidence that such piecemeal conversion ever took place. When the liquidation of the politotdels eventually did occur, it was under the terms of a new resolution (see below), ordering the wholesale abolition or conversion of all MTS politotdels.

the activities of the politotdels. They were effectively forbidden to engage in further mass purges and personnel transfers. On the very eve of the Seventeenth Congress the North Caucasus Krai leadership, perhaps sensing the change, had prohibited the removal of kolkhoz chairmen without the consent of the *Kraizu;* even field brigadiers were not to be discharged without raizo approval.[72]

In another sense the new situation offered a more thorough test of the production principle as a continuous mode of Party control. Cut off from the more direct forms of "political" activity, the politotdels found themselves thrust more deeply into concrete economic affairs. Postyshev, for example, returned from the Congress to tell the *aktiv* of the Kharkov Party organization that the politotdels must shift their emphasis to production questions. They had already proven their political efficacy. Their next task, he said, was to create a new type of authority for themselves based on technical competence. But at the same time, he warned that they must not attempt to supersede or undermine the raizos![73] This was a comedown indeed.

For the most part, politotdel officials now found themselves much less favored as an elite corps of the Central Committee and more closely supervised by the provincial Party committees. This tendency was especially noticeable in areas where their political and organizational activities had been particularly forceful — and disruptive — in 1933. In the North Caucasus, for example, they were now pointedly being directed into fairly technical economic matters. The provincial press carried many articles approving the initiative of politotdel chiefs in solving local problems, ranging from the establishment of permanent field camps (*tabory*)[74] to the care of pregnant mares.[75] In some regions they took a prominent part in the early forest shelter-belt campaigns.[76]

At the height of the agricultural campaigns of 1934 the politotdels were pressed into service as troubleshooters once again, but here, too, procedures differed from the 1933 patterns. Whereas before, the politotdel staffs had been firmly attached to given MTS zones, occasionally supplemented if necessary by temporary plenipotentiaries subordinated to the politotdel chiefs, now, politotdel chiefs themselves were being shunted about by provincial Party secretaries (or the Central Committee) and assigned as plenipotentiaries to lagging raions or MTS zones.[77] The traditional style of Party control was fast reasserting itself.

While the general tendency after the Seventeenth Congress was to encourage the politotdels to involve themselves in production activities, some Party spokesmen soon began to complain that they were losing themselves in managerial and technical details. In a complaint that sounds very familiar today one writer in *Partiinoe stroitel'stvo* lamented the fact that the politotdels seemed to have lost their "taste for the Party style of work":

The problem is that . . . many politotdel workers have been trying to solve problems by administrative means, forgetting about the development of such very important sectors of work as socialist competition and shock work, work with the kolkhoz *aktiv*, production conferences with tractor and field brigades, mass-cultural work, Party education, etc.[78]

A related charge was that the politotdels were interfering with and often countermanding the efforts of the local technical and administrative specialists. Having become accustomed to a command relationship, politotdel officials now balked at following the instructions of lowly specialists in the MTS and raizo. A *Pravda* editorial in May 1934 on the problems of agricultural specialists complained, for example, that MTS directors and politotdel chiefs commonly overruled the recommendations of agronomists and zootechnicians without even informing them of the changes.[79]

Perhaps the most serious complaint of all, however, was that of *mestnichestvo*, or localist tendencies. Politotdel chiefs began to be accused of losing their Party perspective and taking the side of their own kolkhozes and MTS against the higher Party and state authorities. Zelenin notes several cases where politotdel chiefs rejected arbitrary *ad hoc* increases in local procurement quotas by higher Party and grain procurement organs. Some officials saw in this behavior a very serious "anti-state" manifestation and considered it an important reason for hastening the abolition of the politotdels.[80]

Finally, the reorganization of the raikom, which gave the new corps of instructors parallel responsibilities with the politotdels in the kolkhozes of the MTS zones reawakened the old rivalry between politotdel and raikom. Now it was the politotdels who were refusing to give the raikoms access to "their" kolkhozes.[81]

THE LIQUIDATION OF THE POLITOTDELS

These problems would not be allowed to fester for very long, however. Work proceeded very rapidly on the reconstruction of the raikom and the raizo. By the end of the summer of 1934, the dissolution of the politotdels appeared imminent. On September 3 Kaganovich advised a conference of heads of Leading Party Organs Departments that they should quickly become acquainted with politotdel personnel in their respective regions, as the latter would soon be available as a major fund of cadres.[82]*

The formal act of liquidation did not take place until late November. A special Central Committee Plenum passed a resolution entitled "On the Politotdel in Agriculture" which stated:

The politotdel, as an extraordinary form of organization, relying on the strength and authority of the entire Party and on the economic might of the MTS, has achieved important successes in the cause of turning a backward sector of socialist construction — agriculture — into a leading one.

However, experience has shown that in view of the growth of the problems of village leadership the politotdels in themselves are already inadequate, that what is needed for the direction of all work in the kolkhoz village — political, economic, cultural . . . is the reinforcement of the normal Party and soviet organs, encompassing all work: administrative, economic, cultural, financial, and so forth.[83]**

The MTS politotdels, the resolution continued, had completely justified their creation, but now their work was finished. They were to be converted to "ordinary Party organs." This meant transferring their functions to the raikoms, which would now assume complete control over all primary Party organizations in the raions, including those in the MTS themselves. Where

---

* It is interesting to note the long delay in the publication of Kaganovich's address. (It was not published until November 24.) This suggests a continuing concern not to be stampeded into a premature liquidation of the politotdels. Or, perhaps, it was uncertain whether the politotdels would ultimately be destroyed.

** The sovkhoz politotdels continued in operation until 1939.

existing raions were particularly large, they were to be split up, with the politotdels serving as the nuclei of new raikoms. In order to handle their increased responsibilities the raikoms were to be further restructured. In large agricultural raions the raikom would add a Second Secretary and an agricultural *otdel,* to be headed by one of the secretaries.[84]

In the MTS the politotdel chief was to be replaced by a Party official who was also designated, like the former politotdel chief, as deputy director for the political sector. He was charged with providing "a political guarantee of the successful implementation of all measures and initiatives of the director of the MTS." He was also to serve as secretary of the MTS primary Party organization. Unlike the politotdel chief, however, he was explicitly subordinate to both the MTS director and the raikom. That Party work in the MTS was still considered more than ordinarily important may be seen from the fact that the deputy director for the political sector, along with the raikom secretary, remained on the *nomenklatura* of the Central Committee and could not be removed without its consent. Thus, he was a good deal more important than the ordinary rural primary Party organization secretary, enjoying a Party status higher than that of even the raikom instructor.[85] This was undoubtedly a concession to the special position of the MTS as an instrument of control in the countryside.

The November Plenum placed considerable stress on the retention of former politotdel workers in their respective raions. As a rule, politotdel chiefs were to be designated first or second secretaries of the new or existing raikoms. Their deputies and assistants would assume lesser posts in the raikom apparatus, or they might be assigned to MTS as deputy directors for the political sector.[86] In any case, they were to remain in the raions in which they had been working. In January 1935 Kaganovich found it necessary to issue a warning to obkoms and kraikoms against a growing practice of recruiting former politotdel cadres for their own organizations.[87]

Although this first experiment with the politotdel mode of Party control in agriculture was thus brought decisively to an end, it cannot be considered a total failure. Indeed, the Seventeenth

Party Congress had signified its approval of the politotdel concept for nonmilitary purposes by granting the Central Committee "the right to create political departments . . . in [other] lagging sectors of socialist construction acquiring special importance for the economy and the country as a whole." [88]* Moreover the retention of a special Party position in the MTS — the *zampolit* — indicated a continuing perception of the MTS as a focal point of Party activity in the village, albeit with a reduced scope of influence.

The MTS politotdels of 1933–1934 did unquestionably prove to be powerful instruments of directed change. Unfettered by local allegiances and possessed of the compelling authority of high Party status, the politotdel chiefs and their staffs were able to eliminate much of the deadwood and opposition in the MTS and the kolkhozes. They brought a fresh, if often merciless, approach to the struggle against the stagnation and hostility which had spread through the countryside in the wake of forced collectivization. In the process they effected significant improvements in the organization and operational capabilities of the hard-pressed, understaffed forces of the Party in the village.

These were tasks the politotdels were well equipped to handle by virtue of their structure and the special characteristics of their personnel. In other areas they were far less successful, and in the end even their achievements had some questionable implications. In carrying out their political tasks they tended to disrupt the processes of local administration, precisely the level of the bureaucracy that required strengthening if the long-term development of the kolkhoz system was to be achieved. The clashes of the politotdels with the raikoms, the MTS directors, and the raizo specialists, together with their growing tendencies toward interference in technical details, had a profoundly unsettling influence on the local administrators and specialists, resulting in a loss of initiative and responsibility. This loss was something for which the politotdel workers could not hope to compensate because of

---

* This resolution may possibly be viewed as a victory for Kaganovich and the centrist position. In any event, the Central Committee soon took advantage of the new provision by establishing politotdels in the transport system. It is interesting to note that Kaganovich became People's Commissar of Transportation at precisely this time.

their own lack of technical background and training. The decision to liquidate the politotdels at this time reflected, to a large extent, an empirical judgement on the severe limitations of the production principle as a long-term mode of Party control.

9   The MTS and the Normalization

of Party Controls, 1935–1939

The half decade following the liquidation of the MTS politotdels saw a prolonged effort to regularize procedures for the operation of the MTS-kolkhoz system. As has been shown in Part II, various financial, legal, and organizational means were devised for the regulation of the new production relationship. All of these measures were directed, in one way or another, toward the replacement of the previous *ad hoc* system of direct political controls with a more stable long-term system of smoothly operating procedures and institutions.

THE CHANGING NATURE OF RAIKOM LEADERSHIP

Naturally, the various normalization measures had important effects on the nature of Party leadership in the village. It was during this period that the raikom mode of Party involvement in the rural economy assumed its basic form. The organizational and political roles of the MTS were also significantly affected. With the liquidation of the politotdels the stations lost much of their former special status as centers of Party control. In general, the shifts from the production principle to the territorial-production principle signified a more comprehensive, but less intensively production-oriented type of Party leadership.

In the beginning of the period it was clearly expected that the raikom would exercise its guidance of production questions in line with the indirect methods described in Chapter 6. In practice, however, it soon turned out that the mere ordering of regular procedures and initiative and self-reliance on the part of the responsible officials was insufficient. Throughout the 1935–1939 period the various levels of the agricultural bureaucracy, from the central organs to the raizo, remained extremely weak. Experienced

249

cadres were always in short supply, and the intensity of the pressures on the bureaucracy for performance were such as to make a career in agricultural administration unattractive, to say the very least. Central to these personnel problems were, of course, the purges which were raging throughout the country during most of the period. The Great Purge hit the agricultural bureaucracy with particular severity. The parade of Party leaders who found themselves designated as People's Commissars of Agriculture only to be condemned as "wreckers" and "enemies of the people" had its counterpart in the lower levels of the system as well. Party secretaries, such as M. M. Malinov, the Second Secretary of the Azov–Black Sea Kraikom, began to consider an appointment as chief of a provincial agricultural administration as a prelude to arrest and, very likely execution.[1] The resultant atmosphere of terror and mutual recriminations had a disastrous effect on morale. The incumbents of leadership posts in the various agricultural organs became increasingly reluctant to exercise individual initiative and assume responsibility for decisions. Commenting on this tendency, the editors of the journal *Socialist Reconstruction of Agriculture* lamented in 1937:

> Leading agricultural officials have developed a habit of not deciding a single problem, not even the simplest one, on their own. There has evolved a system of endless agreements and coordinations in the sea of which all initiative and operational effectiveness have drowned.[2]

Thus, despite serious efforts, real improvement of the agricultural administration was not forthcoming. *De facto* operational control quickly reverted to the more vigorous hands of the local Party secretaries, particularly at the raikom level. To be sure, the raikom had never really been relieved of its responsibilities for general oversight of agricultural operations. What was at issue was the *extent* to which it was to be encouraged to occupy itself with concrete managerial details.

Very early in the period there were frequent admonitions from high Party quarters against undue interference. Detailed economic questions were to be left to the formal Soviet and economic agencies, while the raikoms were to concentrate primarily on such Party work as political agitation, the training of Party cadres, and work with sympathizers. A. Berezin, the head of the Otdel of Leading Party Organs of the Azov–Black Sea Kraikom, warned the raikoms specifically in 1935 to stop concerning themselves with the technical aspects of production. "Studying the decisions of many of our raikoms," he complained, "one becomes convinced that more than half of the questions they handle should be decided by Soviet and economic organs." He went on to say that although such matters had properly been of concern to the politotdels, they should not be undertaken by the raikoms.[3]

Although complaints of this type may appear rather trite to the modern student of Party affairs, at the time the problem was relatively new. A survey of the contemporary provincial press makes it clear that the issue of suitable forms of raikom involvement in agricultural questions was indeed highly salient. It also appears that the degree of raikom involvement considered proper varied from region to region. In Voronezh Oblast, for example, judging by the tone of newspaper commentaries, there was greater encouragement for active involvement than in the Azov–Black Sea Krai.[4]

In Moscow, meanwhile, the central Party leadership appeared to be struggling to enforce a middle course between the two extremes of neglect and overinvolvement. After two years of politotdel-style Party operations the definition of this middle course was no easy task. Some raikoms seemingly overreacted to the repudiation of the politotdels by completely washing their hands of economic problems. Others, apparently unable to break the habit of total involvement, continued to apply politotdel methods of Party control. In mid-1935, after the postpolitotdel setup had begun to crystallize, the authoritative Party journal *Partiinoe stroitel'stvo* published an article summarizing current practice. It characterized the two extreme forms of aberration in the following terms:

One of them consists *in the fact that some raikoms are completely refraining from the leadership of economic work,* frequently transferring it to the weak officials of the Soviet organs, who permit great lapses in their work . . . *The other extreme in the work of the raikoms is expressed in the fact that they rush to the other side and begin to supplant the raiispolkoms, the directorates of the MTS, the trade-*

unions, and many other organizations. This happens particularly in the heated times of the major agricultural campaigns.[5] [Emphasis in original.]

For a year or so, while enthusiasm for the normalization program was still high, the campaign against direct involvement was more or less effectively prosecuted.[6] But as time passed there was a notable tendency to drift back to the more intensive forms of Party interference. Meanwhile, at the beginning of 1937, with the Great Purge rapidly approaching its zenith and the campaign against economic "wrecking" and sabotage reaching fever pitch, Party officials throughout the country were being summoned to tighten their political watchfulness. At the end of February a special Central Committee Plenum was called to elucidate a new line on Party controls in the economy. The standard interpretations of the resulting decisions are somewhat misleading.[7] In his keynote speech at the Plenum Stalin had subjected local Party leaders to severe criticism for becoming so bogged down in petty managerial details that they were neglecting their proper political and ideological work, especially the selection and training of cadres.[8] In the context of the purges Stalin's instructions had a dual meaning. On the one hand, Party officials were being asked to increase their political supervision of the work of the economic institutions. On the other hand, they were not to interfere in the operational activities of the new class of industrial managers which Stalin was striving to develop under the aegis of the purges.[9] What is generally overlooked in connection with the Plenum is that agriculture was singled out for special treatment. There Party involvement was actually to increase. A lead editorial in *Pravda* devoted to an analysis of Stalin's speech made this exception quite clear:

This problem, the problem of the selection of cadres, remains especially acute in the sphere of agricultural leadership. In industry the situation is somewhat better. There cadres have already basically been developed; they have passed through a great school in the struggle for the realization of the Stalinist Five-Year Plans. But in agriculture cadres are weaker, less well prepared, and Party organizations must — and will still have to do so in the future — occupy themselves even with the petty details of economic construction until the land organs shall be really strengthened.[10]*

Still, there were the familiar warnings against "supplanting the land organs" and engaging in "petty tutelage" over the work of the agricultural officials.[11] Thus, although there were occasional but important shifts in emphasis, Moscow continued its efforts to steer a course between the Scylla and Charybdis of under- and overinvolvement in the rural economy.

It was not until well into 1939, when Andrei Zhdanov launched his campaign to recentralize the Party apparatus along essentially functionalist lines, that most of the remaining inhibitions against full raikom immersion in agricultural production questions were removed. Probably significant in this connection was the decision of the Eighteenth Party Congress to retain the Agricultural Otdel alone of all the former production-branch departments of the Central Committee apparatus. This was done "in view of the special importance of the tasks of control and supervision of the activities of the Soviet and Party organizations in the field of agriculture." [12] A good illustration of the new line concerning Party controls in agriculture was the following appeal by the editors of *Partiinoe stroitel'stvo* in June 1939: "The Party, if it wishes to direct the kolkhoz movement, must enter into all details of kolkhoz life and kolkhoz management. From this it follows that the Party must not decrease but multiply its links with the kolkhozes." [13] With war on the horizon, the Party leadership had decided once again to strengthen its controls over the hostile rural masses.

In assessing the difficulties of applying the norms of indirect raikom control on a long-term basis, it is useful to have some idea of the state of the Party in the village during the period. One of the most crucial reasons for the inapplicability of the ideal model of the Party-state division of labor was the continuing sparseness of Party representation in the countryside. As a result of the successive purges of the thirties, total Party membership was to decline from a high of 3,555,338 (members and candidates) in

---

* The last phrase about strengthening the land organs probably referred to the basic reorganization of the PCA system and the MTS, which continued to be a major topic of discussion throughout most of 1937.

1933 to a low of 1,920,000 in 1938.[14] The number of rural Communists was only a small fraction of even these declining totals. In 1939, when membership rolls were again increasing — reaching a total of 3,399,975 by the end of 1939, there were only 153,000 members and candidates in the kolkhozes. Among the 243,000 kolkhozes in the country at this time there were only some 12,000 kolkhoz PPO's.[15] Assuming an average of ten members in each of the PPO's of the 6400-odd MTS in 1939, there were only about 220,000 Communists in the dominant production enterprises.* For most of the period the situation was undoubtedly much worse than in 1939. Thus, in the important institutions of agricultural production, the raikom could count on little support from existing Party forces.

Under these circumstances it is perhaps not surprising that the raikoms, in exercising their leadership in production matters, tended to take little account of the few MTS and kolkhoz PPO's that did exist. The contemporary press carried numerous complaints of the lack of attention to the PPO's by the raikoms. Whatever dealings occurred were likely to be limited to the dispatching of circulars and the collection of completed forms.[16] The problem of communications was in large part physical. Personal contacts between the raikom and PPO's were supposed to be handled by the staff of raikom instructors, each of whom was assigned to a group of kolkhoz PPO's. However, the great distances and primitive communications facilities made close, systematic instruction of kolkhoz Party affairs extremely difficult. A contemporary study of the problem in Rostov Oblast showed that although the average instructor of a rural raikom had only half as many PPO's to cover as his urban counterpart (thirty to thirty-five, compared with seventy), the great dispersion of the PPO's made his job considerably more difficult than that of the latter.[17]

Given the great importance of economic performance as the

---

* It will be remembered that tractor drivers were counted as members of the PPO's of their home kolkhozes. The figure of ten members per MTS PPO is a rough average derived by the author from various accounts of individual MTS PPO's in the central and local press. Some MTS had much higher membership, but others were probably considerably smaller. If anything, the figure of ten members per MTS PPO is overly generous.

ultimate criterion of personal success and the difficulties of working through the PPO's, the raikom secretaries usually found it expedient to work directly with the managers of the local production enterprises. Often these contacts would involve the most detailed managerial questions, and although they did not have the legal authority to issue orders on such questions, the secretaries did not scruple to pull Party rank if the situation demanded. The following account of a case in Sverdlov Oblast illustrates the sort of problem that might occasion such behavior:

By a decision of the Chernov Raikom AUCP(B) . . . the secretary of the raikom, Comrade Saraev, removed the MTS agronomist, Comrade Pisarev, from his job and appointed him as agronomist of the raizo. In answer to the protest of the MTS director to the raikom they announced to him: "You're a Communist. Carry out the decision of the raikom and then complain."

All these facts are witness that many raikom secretaries and *raiispolkom* chairmen have not only been supplanting the MTS directors and rudely "administering," but they have also been occupying themselves with petty tutelage, fettering the initiative of the land organs, and teaching them to "coordinate" and "agree upon" every minor question.[18]

The power of the raikom over local agricultural affairs and personnel was considerable, even when compared with that of the higher administrative organs. There were occasions when raikom secretaries effectively challenged the authority of the provincial agricultural organs — a commentary on the relatively low prestige of the latter. The following complaint on a conflict situation of this type is from Krasnodar Krai in 1938:

The authority of the krai land department is not great. Its instructions are far from always considered obligatory at the local level.

In the middle of October, by agreement with the Secretary of the Kraikom AUCP(B), Comrade Gusev, several MTS directors were called into the krai land department. But some directors did not come. They sent telegrams such as the following: "The raikom has forbidden the trip." [19]

This was hardly indirect leadership. Before the "normalization period" was very far advanced, there were signs that the *de facto* standard pattern of raikom leadership in agriculture under the raikom mode had become firmly established. That is, at campaign times the raion took on the aspect of an integral agricultural enterprise, presided over by the raikom first secretary. Even during the more quiescent periods, when the indirect phase was in operation, the outlines of this pattern could still be observed, as the case in Krasnodar Krai suggests.

THE MTS IN THE PATTERN OF RAIKOM CONTROLS

Within this integral, raionwide framework the role of the MTS was extremely important. By the end of the Second Five-Year Plan MTS coverage was nearly complete, in physical terms, if not in terms of the intensity of service rendered to the kolkhozes. Raions with three or even four stations were not uncommon.[20] The MTS were thus in a position to function in most areas as the main operational and organizational instruments of raikom production management. The MTS directors became, in essence, the chief operational lieutenants of the raikom secretaries. In addition, with the increasing importance of payments in kind for MTS work as a source of crop procurements, the stations served as a primary lever of the raikom for the fulfillment of the crucial raion procurement targets.

It is important to note that the content of the evolving relationship between the raikom and the MTS was predominantly economic. The raikom secretary confronted the MTS director essentially as an administrative superior to his subordinate. As we have seen, there was no legal foundation for such a relationship. The authority structure lay entirely within the Party framework. However, the content of the communications between them was primarily economic. In sharp contrast with the politotdel arrangements, therefore, the MTS functioned during the 1935–1939 period chiefly as an economic agency, rather than as a center of political control over the kolkhozes.

A good indication of the changed role of the MTS in the local structure of Party authority was the position of the Deputy Director of the MTS for the Political Sector, or *zampolit*. Under the system decreed by the November (1934) Plenum the *zampolit* was expressly directed to limit his activities to the MTS. He was to have no jurisdiction over the kolkhozes or the kolkhoz PPO's of the MTS zone.* The position of the *zampolit* was a rather peculiar one in the hierarchy of Party and government officials. Like his predecessor the politotdel chief, he carried the dual authority of Party and governmental status. As a formal deputy of the MTS director, he stood in the regular chain of command of the MTS, which enabled him to issue orders to MTS personnel on a legal basis. At the same time, he was an ex officio secretary of the MTS PPO, subject to the authority of the raikom. His official function, in addition to directing the work of the PPO, was to provide political backing for the orders and instructions of the MTS director.[21] But beyond this vague prescription there were few guidelines as to his concrete responsibilities and the methods he was to use in carrying them out.

As has often been true in Soviet administrative practice, a more detailed job description would have to await practical experience with the new position after a good deal of haphazard experimentation. In the beginning neither the MTS directors nor the raikoms seemed to know just what to do with the *zampolity,* and they themselves did not know what was expected of them. Many *zampolity* who had formerly been members of MTS politotdels, found it difficult to break away from the now condemned "politotdel style of work." They continued to intervene in technical and administrative decision-making in the MTS, creating a good deal of friction with the directors, while neglecting the ill-defined "Party-mass work" which was their main official *raison d'etre.* Meanwhile, the raikoms often utilized the *zampolity* as ordinary plenipotentiaries on various assignments in the raions, disregarding their designated missions in the MTS.

After a few months the question of the proper employment of the *zampolity* became an important topic of discussion in leading Party circles. A number of shortcomings were beginning to cause serious concern. In June 1935 the Kiev Obkom, for example, passed a resolution:

> To consider completely incorrect the practice in a number of raions where the raion Party committees use the deputy directors of the MTS

---

* The *zampolit* did, of course, have jurisdiction over the kolkhoznik tractor drivers during their seasonal occupation in the MTS.

for the political sector as plenipotentiaries of the raikom, and also when the deputy directors of the MTS take upon themselves the functions of politotdels in the direction of the kolkhozes . . .[22]

The Kiev Obkom went on to list a number of activities thenceforth to be considered the proper province of the *zampolity*: (1) the political education of Communists working in the MTS; (2) mass-political work in the MTS — for example, socialist competition, the introduction of so-called rationalization proposals from the masses of MTS workers, the improvement of the technical qualifications of MTS personnel; (3) careful selection, training, and support of tractor drivers and other operating personnel of the MTS.[23]

The Voronezh Obkom issued similar instructions at this time. After listening to reports on their activities by three MTS *zampolity* at a Plenary Session, the Obkom criticized the *zampolity* of the oblast in general for unduly interfering in the economic work of the MTS and the kolkhozes while neglecting their Party-political responsibilities. It also castigated the raikoms for not employing their *zampolity* properly and specifically prohibited the practice of assigning them as plenipotentiaries for extended campaign periods.[24]

An authoritative clarification of the nature and functions of the new position finally appeared in August 1935 in an article in *Partiinoe stroitel'stvo*. The author, Ia. Osipov, after praising the efforts of those *zampolity* who had been limiting their work to political activities generally within the MTS and obtaining good results in terms of production efficiency, gave a catalogue of the most serious shortcomings observed in those raions where the decisions of the November 1934) Plenum had been "interpreted incorrectly." First of all, he pointed to the problem of friction between the *zampolity* and the MTS directors:

many directors either ignore them or use them improperly; they misunderstand the fact that although the deputy director is directly subordinate to the director, this in no way means that he can be put on any job at all, to the detriment of Party-mass work. The deputy director . . . is a Party organizer, a Party worker confirmed by the Central Committee, and his task is first of all to *secure by mass-political*

work all of the measures and initiatives of the MTS director.[25]
[Emphasis in original.]

The second major problem noted by Osipov was neglect of the *zampolity* by the raikoms. "In some cases," he said, *"the raikoms have impermissibly avoided the direction of the work of the deputy directors of the MTS* for the political sector, and from the very first days of their operations have completely forgotten about them." [Emphasis in original.] Conversely — the third major problem — some raikoms had been relying too heavily on the *zampolity* for control over the political affairs of the kolkhozes. "In such cases," complained Osipov, "the raikoms are completely incorrect in preserving for the deputy directors . . . the full role and responsibilities of the politotdel chiefs." To be sure, the *zampolity* must take an active interest in the life of the kolkhoz village, but no more than any other Communists in the raion Party organization. He concluded by saying that the *zampolity* "cannot bear full responsibility for the work of the kolkhozes, and no one has given them such duties." [26] The *zampolit* was not a politotdel chief; he should confine his activities to the Party and Komsomol affairs of the MTS itself.

It is doubtful that Moscow really intended so limited a conception of the role of the *zampolit* as Osipov's remarks seemed to indicate. The very nature of MTS operations — the intimate involvement of the stations in kolkhoz production and their utilization of kolkhoz workers for the bulk of their labor force — gave the *zampolity* a sphere of at least potential influence that far transcended the boundaries of the MTS *usad'ba* itself. This point was strongly emphasized a few months later in another article in *Partiinoe stroitel'stvo*. The author, N. Baryshev, complained that:

Some deputy directors of MTS lose sight of the fact that *the machine-tractor stations are very vital links* of Party and Soviet construction in the village. The machine-tractor stations perform their most important work not only through technical and economic means, but also with the aid of the cultural and political education of the kolkhozniks, combine operators, tractor drivers, and all others working on MTS machines. The organization of these persons for the better utilization of the machines, for the achievement of high records, for high quality and profitable work are the most important tasks of political work in the village, the primary responsibility of the deputy directors for the political sector.[27] [Emphasis in original.]

The procedures for defining a role for the *zampolit* offer some interesting insights into Soviet organizational practices. Having created the new position with only the most general notions of its scope and functions, the Party leadership undertook a fairly lengthy process of "zeroing in" on an appropriate role on the basis of the experience that was accumulating. The original conception of the post was undoubtedly colored to a great extent, as was the case with the post-1934 raikom, by negative memories of the politotdels. Thus, the initial impulse was to stress the limitations of the *zampolit*'s functions. Experience soon showed, however, that a more positive role was necessary and possible.

In theory the post of *zampolit* would appear to have been admirably suited for the ideal model of indirect raikom control. With his strategic position in the MTS command structure and his leadership of the MTS organization, the *zampolit* represented a potentially powerful instrument of the raikom for close contact and coordination of his activities with the raion leadership. Yet in practice the position did not turn out to be very effective. Raikom secretaries tended to pay relatively little attention to the *zampolity* in their dealings with the MTS. Many secretaries apparently preferred to work directly through or with the MTS directors. Indeed, in some cases the raikom secretaries ignored even the MTS directors and changed the disposition of tractors, altered work schedules, and shunted MTS personnel about without even bothering to inform the directors. Such brazen meddling in the operations of the stations was, naturally, not officially encouraged, but it seems to have been fairly common during campaign periods.[28]

In the meantime the *zampolity* gradually settled into their own narrow routines in the MTS. Baryshev claimed that their isolation from raikom business tended to be a mutual arrangement: the raikoms ignored the *zampolity,* and the latter, in turn, made no effort to maintain contact with the raikoms.[29] He noted the case of one Zhil'tsov, the deputy director of an MTS in Saratov Krai, who failed to attend sessions of the raikom bureau of which he was a member, for the simple reason that the raikom did not see fit to invite him.[30]

A somewhat different view of the same problem was presented by the Second Secretary of the Voronezh Obkom, I. Iarygin:

Many raikoms of the Party have been keeping themselves apart from leadership of Party work in the MTS, completely transferring the matter to the deputy directors. These raikoms assume that since there is a special worker in the MTS—the deputy director for the political sector, confirmed by the Central Committee, no less, why, probably he will take care of all the work by himself; probably he doesn't need the assistance of the raikom.[31]

By the end of 1935 the problem of over-bearing, politotdel-style operations by the *zampolity* throughout the MTS zones seems to have all but disappeared. Thereafter the tendency was for them to gravitate to the other extreme, as they became progressively more immersed in the technical details of MTS management. One writer voiced the complaint that they were beginning to look more and more like "deputy directors for the economic sector." [32] The situation in Saratov Krai in 1936, for example, was characterized in the following terms: "Many deputy directors for the political sector busy themselves with petty, day-to-day economic and administrative work, to the detriment of their Party and mass-political work, as a result of which they turn essentially into influence peddlers [*tolkachi*] for economic problems." [33]

It is a significant commentary on the waning of interest in the *zampolity* as important members of the local power structure that coverage of their activities in the central and local press declined noticeably after the middle of 1936. Thereafter, mention of the office virtually disappears from the press.

In assessing the relative importance of the deputy director for the political sector it is interesting to note that many MTS were without such an official for extended periods. As late as November 1936 the Voronezh Obkom, for example, was still demanding the completion of the process of staffing its MTS with *zampolity*.[34] Evidently, finding sufficient numbers of suitable candidates for the position was not easy. One raikom in the city of Voronezh reported being hard pressed to find even four of the seven candidates required of it.[35] A rural raikom in the same oblast found fault with all of the *zampolity* assigned to it and ordered an immediate review of their qualifications with the express intention of requesting their removal.[36] *

The process of selection was apparently not nearly so rigorous as for the politotdels in 1933. In spite of the provision that deputy directors for political work were to be confirmed individually by the Central Committee, the persons chosen were not particularly impressive from the standpoint of Party background and experience. Many were rank-and-file Party members drawn from the permanent staffs of the MTS, frequently at the level of brigadiers of tractor brigades.[37] A significant number appear to have been promoted from positions as Party organizers in the kolkhozes.[38] Others, probably a fairly large group, were holdovers from lesser positions in the politotdels. Although the evidence is far from conclusive, it seems safe to say that the *zampolity* were rarely comparable in status to the politotdel chiefs and their main deputies.

On the other hand, experience as a *zampolit* was often considered good preparation for assignment to leading raion-level Party work. The Azov–Black Sea Kraikom, for example, promoted twelve *zampolity* and raikom instructors to the position of raikom secretaries in December 1935, citing their special suitability for "leading raion Party work." [39] There were also a few cases where *zampolity* were promoted to the directorship of their MTS after the former directors had been fired or purged. Such instances appear to have been rare, however, and the appointments were likely to be only temporary.[40]

In the *de facto* Party status hierarchy the position of the deputy director of the MTS for the political sector was not much higher than that of the ordinary raikom instructor, even though his *nomenklatura* status was uniquely higher. The two types of Party officials were often mentioned in the same manner in Party documents and discussions, and they were generally treated as if they

---

* The raikom had to inform the agricultural department of the obkom in such cases. The latter would then petition the Central Committee to have the *zampolity* in question removed. Apparently, Central Committee confirmation of such actions was not very difficult to obtain. Thus, the *nomenklatura* status of the *zampolity* was largely a formality.

were in the same category. Indeed, in some respects the *zampolit* might be thought of as a raikom instructor permanently assigned to the MTS. On the other hand, his formal status as a state official (deputy director of the MTS) and as the full-time secretary of the MTS PPO gave him considerably more leverage for continuous involvement in operational matters than was the case with the ordinary raikom instructor.

Moreover, the *zampolit* was responsible for a special set of functions that were at least nominally considered quite important by the regime. In the modern-day jargon of developmental theory these functions would probably be classified as the mobilization and socialization of the backward peasant masses. More specifically, the *zampolit* was in charge of the process of inculcating the desired ideological attitudes and work habits in those peasants selected for training in the use of the relatively modern technology of the MTS. He also played a major role in the selection process itself. Thus, the *zampolit* was expected to be a key figure in the "mechanizer"-training program which was carried on by the MTS system. This important role required a fairly sophisticated combination of morale-building and psychological talents if the responsibilities were to be carried out effectively. From the available evidence it would appear that such talents were not in overly generous supply among the *zampolity*. This assessment would certainly apply in the case of the *zampolit* Surkov of the Prochnookopskaia MTS in the Azov–Black Sea Krai, as related in the following conversation between G. E. Evdokimov, the First Secretary of the Kraikom and a kolkhoznik who was employed as a combine operator in the MTS:

"Who is Surkov, do you know?"
"Surkov is the deputy director for the political sector."
"Well, what does this political sector consist of?"
"What do you mean?" asked the kolkhoznik. "He has political views."
"Well, what kind of political views are they? Does he talk with you? What does he do when he comes to your brigade?"
"What does he do?" The kolkhoznik thinks for a while. "Sometimes he curses out the combine operators." [41]

Just how typical Surkov's methods were and how they reflected the general level of *zampolit* activities is difficult to say. From the evidence available, however, it is fairly clear that the *zampolit* was hardly the imposing political overlord of the MTS and the surrounding peasant fields that has sometimes been assumed in Western accounts.[42] His position was significantly different from that of the politotdel chief whom he replaced and with whom he is often confused. The relative decline in influence of the chief political figure in the MTS symbolized the decline in the role of the MTS itself as a center of political and social control in the countryside during the 1935–1939 period. Not even the tightening up of Party control in the raions in 1939 seems to have altered this situation appreciably.

10 The Wartime Politotdels

The tightening of Party controls in agriculture in 1939 undoubtedly reflected the dramatic increase in world tensions on the eve of World War II. The respite afforded by the Russo-German non-Aggression Pact of August 1939 appears to have interrupted any tendency toward the wholesale monopolization of economic decision-making by the local Party organs. However, the German invasion in June 1941 and the subsequent early collapse of Soviet resistance in large areas in the west suddenly confronted Party leaders with the sort of extreme crisis situation which has characteristically evoked profound organizational as well as substantive changes in the nature of Party controls. Throughout the country and in all areas of endeavor individual Party leaders began to assume direct leadership. Regular procedures and institutional divisions of labor were laid aside under the slogan "Everything for the Front, Everything for Victory!" Describing the flavor of Party work under these conditions a Soviet historian has written:

The slightest manifestations of disorganization, of slackness, of complacency were considered a state crime. The violation of economic plans was looked upon as sabotage, undermining the military capability of the country. The war laid upon every Communist, at whatever post he found himself, a special responsibility . . .

Each Party member, in the words of Central Committee Secretary A. S. Shcherbakov, had to do the work of two or three persons.[1] At the apex of the political system the intensification of Party involvement was symbolized by the concentration of Party and governmental offices in the hands of individual members of the inner circle of Party leaders. Most notable was the assumption by Stalin himself of the posts of Chairman of the Council of People's Commissars, Chairman of the State Council of Defense, and People's Commissar of Defense, in addition to his duties as General Secretary of the Party. In agriculture this tendency was reflected in the appointment in late 1943 of A. A. Andreev, the Central Committee's chief agricultural spokesman, as People's Commissar of Agriculture. The former Commissar, I. A. Benediktov, was demoted to Deputy Commissar.[2]

In the first months of the war the Party resorted to a greatly increased use of the old system of plenipotentiaries within the framework of the regular raikom mode. During the various campaigns of the 1941 agricultural year a veritable army of plenipotentiaries of the raikom descended on the MTS, kolkhozes, and sovkhozes to apply pressure for the attainment of the immediate tasks and to uncover local shortcomings. One of the secretaries of the Altai Kraikom characterized the work of the plenipotentiaries thus:

What does it mean to send a plenipotentiary into a kolkhoz? It means that before the arrival of the plenipotentiary three plows were operating in the kolkhoz, while on the day after the appearance of our comrade six plows bit into the furrow. Still better: let's say they sent the comrade to organize the haying, and he . . . , seeing that the kolkhoz fields were overgrown with weeds, went to work and, not waiting for higher instructions, organized 30–40 persons for weeding the crops.[3]

It soon appeared that the normal framework of Party controls was insufficient. A more prolonged Party presence in the countryside was required, although the system of plenipotentiaries was to be continued as an auxiliary measure. Meanwhile the expansion of Party controls was being given special institutional expression in certain key sectors. On July 16, 1941, the system of political commissars in the Red Army, which had been abolished a year earlier following the initial debacle of the Russo-Finnish War, was reinstated.[4] And on November 17 politotdels were once again established in the MTS and sovkhozes.[5]

In addition to the general problem of the breakdown of authority in the village during the early stages of the war, there were specific reasons why the revival of the politotdel mode in agriculture seemed appropriate. First of all, the food needs of the armed forces and the urban industrial population made the extremely production-oriented type of Party work associated with the politotdels especially relevant. Second, military mobilization was siphoning off a large proportion of the rural male population, depriving the MTS-kolkhoz system of many of its most vigorous managerial and technical specialists and skilled workers. The politotdels were expected to compensate for the loss of leadership talent to a certain extent and to organize the selection and training of replacements. Third, and related to the latter problem, were the losses of a significant part of the Party complement in the village. In some areas the number of Party members was reduced by as much as three-fourths, seriously depleting an important potential force for cohesion and discipline at the basic production level.[6] As we have noted in previous chapters, the small number of Communists in production Party organizations, especially in the kolkhozes, had been a continuing problem from the standpoint of Party effectiveness. The early wartime losses further added to the diffusion and disarray of Party forces in production. One of the more important functions of the wartime politotdels was, therefore, to organize and consolidate the efforts of Party members in the village.

In reestablishing the politotdels the regime followed the organizational and functional patterns of the 1933–1934 period fairly closely. Once again a Political Administration for the MTS was set up in the People's Commissariat of Agriculture, and *politsektory* were attached to the oblast and krai agricultural administrations.[7] A politotdel was installed in each MTS, and once again it was given control over political activities in the kolkhozes of the MTS zone. The politotdel chief was expected to participate actively in the economic affairs of the station and its zone. If anything, the injunction to become involved was possibly even stronger than in the 1933–1934 version, for the chiefs were now designated as "deputy directors for the fulfillment of economic plans" as well as "for the political sector." [8]

Each politotdel contained a basic staff of three persons: a chief, a deputy chief, and an assistant for Komsomol work. Thus, the politotdels were significantly smaller than before.* The politotdel chiefs were confirmed by the All-Union Central Com-

---

* There was apparently no special deputy for NKVD work, as in the 1933–1934 politotdels. However, the author was told by persons with experience in the MTS during the war that the politotdels operated in close association with the raion NKVD authorities.

mittee, while their deputies and assistants were confirmed by the obkoms, kraikoms, and republic central committees.[9] In general, however, the selection process appears to have been considerably less rigorous than in the earlier period. The persons selected were less impressive from the standpoint of educational background and previous leadership experience. In all, approximately 13,000 persons were sent out to the MTS politotdels. Of 4703 chiefs covered in a study by V. Ashanin, more than 78 percent had been Party members since 1934 or earlier, and more than 74 percent had been engaged in some kind of leading Party work at the outbreak of war.[10] Working from data on a slightly smaller sample as of February 1942, Arutiunian found that by far the largest proportion of the chiefs (over 40 percent) had previous experience in raion-level Party work — as secretaries, heads of *otdely*, or instructors of raion Party committees.[11] He notes that the proportion of chiefs with oblast-level leadership experience was substantially lower than for the 1933–1934 group. The educational backgrounds of the wartime chiefs were also significantly less impressive: 12.3 percent had higher education, as compared with 45 percent of the 1933–1934 chiefs. The percentages with secondary education were 32.1 and 46 percent, respectively. In comparing the two groups, Arutiunian states, quite frankly: "It should be noted that the politotdels of the agricultural organs in the war years were weaker than their predecessors of the collectivization period." [12] Among the deputy chiefs and assistants for Komsomol work the same general picture could be seen. The chiefs and their deputies were relatively older persons. More than 50 percent were 36 years of age or older. The number of women was significant among both the deputies and Komsomol assistants: in the case of the latter, 58 percent.[13] Only 33 percent of the Komsomol assistants had had experience in leading Komsomol work.[14]

Nevertheless, judging from both contemporary and recent Soviet accounts, the wartime politotdels did represent an important leadership force in the countryside. Unfortunately, because of the nature of the Soviet press during the war, the coverage of the activities of the politotdels is rather scanty. One has a difficult task in attempting to reconstruct a picture of their day-to-day operations. During 1942 and 1943 there were a few scattered references to the politotdels in *Partiinoe stroitel'stvo*, the Party's main organizational journal. These articles all stressed the importance of organizational work and morale-building activities, such as conduct of socialist competition and mass-political work among the tractor brigades and kolkhoz field brigades. In the words of one writer in February 1942. "The chief weapon of politotdel work is lively organizational activity, continuous relations with the broad masses of kolkhozniks and MTS and sovkhoz workers." [15] Apparently, the politotdel workers were expected to spend the bulk of their time in the field, exhorting the kolkhozniks and machinery operators to maximize their production efforts. But, needless to say, this was far from the limit of their responsibilities.

Much of the so-called organizational activity of the politotdels was concerned with the rebuilding of the local Party and Komsomol organizations, depleted by wartime mobilization. They were evidently fairly successful in recruiting new members, at least in some areas of the country, although the data available are extremely fragmentary.[16] Another important sphere of activities was the selection and training of new machinery operators for the MTS and lower and middle level managerial cadres for the MTS and the kolkhozes.[17]

The training of women tractor drivers was especially stressed. Early in the war the Council of People's Commissars and the CC AUCP(B) ordered the mobilization of pre-draft-age youth for training as machinery operators. The politotdels, along with the raikom secretaries, were placed in charge of this recruitment program. The selection commissions were headed by the first secretary of the raikom and specialized in the supply of students to the mechanizer courses conducted in the MTS. The selection of candidates for the special mechanization schools was apparently assigned specifically to the *raiispolkom*.[18] Despite these efforts, military mobilization and other wartime needs prevented the supply of trained operators from catching up with demand. As of July 1, 1943, the MTS were short some 127,500 tractor drivers.[19] The general level of training, moreover, was a constant source of concern.

Not surprisingly, a central theme of the accounts of politotdel activities was the need "to reconstruct the work of the MTS . . . on a war footing." [20] This and similar phrases indicate an emphasis on disciplinary work in the official conception of the role of the wartime politotdels. In this respect there were, of course, many similarities to the earlier politotdels. Even the rhetoric of the earlier period was repeated from time to time. For example, one writer summoned the politotdels to become the "Party eye" in the village[21] — precisely the metaphor that had been used in the decree creating the politotdels in 1933. It is no surprise to find that one of the more important activities of the politotdels during 1942 was the carrying out of extensive purges of kolkhoz chairmen.[22]

The author was fortunate to have the opportunity to discuss the operations of a wartime politotdel at some length with a former Soviet citizen who had worked as an MTS tractor driver in Stalingrad Oblast during 1942 and 1943. Her initial replies to questions about the general functions of the politotdel were rather vague — "To lead along political lines" — strikingly similar, in fact, to the replies given to Evdokimov about the work of the *zampolit* Surkov, cited above. When pressed to be more specific, however, she commented that in addition to organizing socialist competition and holding political discussions the politotdel chief spent a good deal of his time traveling about the fields and farmyards to uncover cases of malingering and pilferage. The latter was apparently an especially serious problem. The politotdel chief operated more or less independently of the MTS director. There was little evidence of close coordination of their efforts. The director had his job; the politotdel chief had his; and the two went their separate ways.

This relationship was not necessarily the usual one, or even the most desirable one from the standpoint of the regime, however. The decree of November 17, 1941, which had created the politotdels, had explicitly given the politotdel chief collateral economic responsibilities with the director. Contemporary articles stressed the importance of cooperation with the directors in the conduct of economic affairs. Indeed, one author stated quite frankly, after paying the customary lip-service to the principle of one-man management, that there could be no valid separation between the economic and political tasks of the politotdels.[23] But this apparent discrepancy between the officially prescribed norms of conduct and actual practice, as described by an on-the-spot observer, merely confirms what must be one of the fundamental principles of Soviet organizational behavior: that each set of officials work out their own mutual relationships and their own methods of attaining the prescribed goals of the regime. There were no firm guidelines as to what constituted undue economic interference by the politotdel. As usual, this blurring of the line between proper economic involvement and supplanting MTS management caused considerable friction. Commenting on this problem in retrospect, Arutiunian notes that

there also appeared several negative features in their [the politotdels'] activities. In occupying themselves with economic and administrative matters along with the directors of the MTS and the sovkhozes, the chiefs of the politotdels to a certain extent undermined the initiative of the economic officials, supplanted them. Preoccupied with economic matters, the politotdel workers did not always sufficiently take care of political questions, explanatory work among the kolkhozniks and agricultural workers . . .[24]

Plus ça change, plus c'est la même chose.

Also, just as in the earlier period, the politotdels found themselves enmeshed in jurisdictional disputes with the raikoms. The November 17 decree had ordered the politotdels to work in close contact with the raikoms. The raikoms, meanwhile, were given certain parallel responsibilities for the MTS zones. Indeed, the position of the raikoms appears to have been considerably stronger vis-à-vis the politotdels than in the earlier period. They continued to send their plenipotentiaries to help the politotdels during campaign times, and, as we have seen, they had considerable responsibilities for the recruitment of candidates for "mechanizer" training. Nevertheless, the politotdels were supposed to reign supreme in the MTS zones, at least as far as production-oriented political questions were concerned. Once again, however, there were complaints that some raikoms were refusing to respect the special status of the politotdels and were interpreting their residual responsibilities as an invitation to order politotdel personnel about on raikom business.[25]

Thus, it would appear that virtually all of the problems that had been encountered with the 1933–1934 politotdels returned to plague the wartime politotdels. In the short run the regime evidently felt that the fogging of jurisdictional lines and the undermining of the authority of the economic officials were prices worth paying for the vigorous organizational and disciplinary services which the politotdels allegedly performed so well. But in the long run, after the original "freshness" of the new politotdel cadres had worn off and they had settled into a routine of their own, the negative characteristics of the politotdel mode were seen to outweigh the benefits. Presumably, also, the politotdels had managed to achieve a fair amount of success in working out a system of wartime controls to insure that the basic food and fiber needs of the economy were being met.

In any case, the politotdels were abolished for the second time in May 1943.[26] Soviet writers have customarily attributed this decision to the turn of the tide of the war and the strengthening of Party forces in the countryside. In short, they say, the politotdels had done their job and were no longer necessary.[27] As we have seen, this explanation was only part of the truth. The failure of the politotdel mode itself was certainly one of the most powerful reasons for the decision. In addition, it was suggested to the author by a knowledgeable Soviet scholar that experienced Party cadres, such as those tied up in politotdel work, were urgently needed at the front and in other critical economic sectors at this time.

An interesting aspect of the decision to eliminate the politotdels — one which, incidentally, lends some support to this last explanation — is the fact that no special Party position, such as a deputy director for the political sector, was created in the MTS to replace the politotdel as had been the case in November 1934. The MTS would have only a regular primary Party organization, fully subordinate to the raikom. The raikom thus assumed total control over the political, economic, and social affairs of the MTS and the surrounding kolkhozes. An editorial in *Partiinoe stroitel'stvo* shortly after the liquidation of the politotdels dealt with this radically changed situation in characteristically misleading terms:

It is impossible to tolerate the fact that many raikoms have recently been drawing apart from the MTS, they do not know what is going on in them. The raion committees must, in the most concrete manner, take upon themselves all problems of MTS operations: production, cadres, political work in the brigades . . .[28]

With the elimination of the wartime politotdels the MTS lost virtually all vestiges of their formerly unique position as centers of political, as well as economic control in the village. They would not regain a semblance of their previous status until February 1947, when the position of deputy director for the political sector was reintroduced, and a special campaign was launched to use the MTS as the keystone of postwar rehabilitation and reconstruction in the countryside.*

* In 1950 the Central Committee ordered the establishment of politotdels in the MTS of the western lands added to the USSR since September 1939 — the Western Oblasts of the Ukraine and Belorussia, Moldavia, and the three Baltic republics. The occasion was the consolidation of collectivization in these regions, including its most repressive features. The politotdels continued to operate there until the September (1953) Plenum, when the reorganization of the raikom by MTS zones was introduced. (See, for example, "Tak li dolzhen rabotat' politotdel MTS?", *Sovietskaia Moldaviia*, July 11, 1953.)

11 The Party and the MTS in the Postwar Period

In addition to tremendous physical damage the war brought many serious political, organizational, and moral problems to the MTS-kolkhoz system. Many of the formal peacetime controls over MTS performance, developed so laboriously during the thirties, were allowed to lapse. Payments in kind for MTS services became even more overtly a tax on the kolkhozes, and financial controls ceased to operate.[1]

Probably the most widely publicized cases of wartime disintegration involved the "squandering" of kolkhoz land and related violations of the kolkhoz Charter. Industrial enterprises and even private individuals preempted large chunks of kolkhoz land to provide themselves with food during the war years, apparently without the slightest resistance of local authorities. It was not until September 1946 that the regime finally addressed itself to this problem with the passage of a decree "On Measures for the Liquidation of Violations of the Charter of the Agricultural Artel' in the Kolkhozes." To head the new crackdown the Central Committee established a special "Council on Kolkhoz Affairs" with broad powers to impose order and punish violators.[2]

The MTS, supposedly the models of class-consciousness and discipline in the village, frequently turned out to be major abettors of the wartime disintegration of the system. Taking advantage of the loosening of Party supervision after the liquidation of the politotdels, the MTS directors would often use their key production situation to extort illegal gain from the kolkhozes.[3] The raikoms were often too heavily preoccupied with basic production questions to concern themselves with these relatively petty violations, but the effects on local morale were undoubtedly considerable.

274

In general, the period from the middle of 1943 to the beginning of 1947 was one of continuous experience with the direct form of raikom control. It offered many illustrations of the problems of rule by plenipotentiaries as a long-term institution. The pattern which evolved manifested many of the shortcomings of the politotdel mode, but without the compensating feature of a constant leading Party presence at the centers of production. Arutiunian, commenting on the extensive use of plenipotentiaries during the war, notes that in many cases their sporadic, campaign-oriented type of leadership was more of a hindrance than a help to the local production officials. He cites a report from a Plenum of the Kazakh Party Central Committee in July 1945 in which the plenipotentiaries were called *upal-namochennye* — a play on words which may be loosely translated as "mini-potentiaries." [4] He also quotes a description of such a figure from the archives of the Altai Krai:

he walks behind the chairman or a brigadier like a shadow, with an expression of hopeless sadness in his gaze, and he buzzes like a mosquito in the ears of the local officials with all kinds of instructions. Such plenipotentiaries we don't need. They stifle initiative, destroy all traces of discipline in the local cadres . . . [5]

During the war and in the immediate postwar period as well, direct raikom involvement in production matters was largely justified because of the lack of trained managerial and technical personnel. The system continued for at least a full year after the end of the war in Europe, while the regime undertook as its first order of business the rehabilitation of industry. [6]

THE RETURN TO NORMAL PARTY LEADERSHIP IN AGRICULTURE

As the nation settled down to the tasks of reconstruction and the re-establishment of Soviet rule in the liberated territories, the seriousness of the problems of agriculture came to be realized. By mid-1946 there were already signs of famine. The press began to express extreme dissatisfaction with the system of rural administration, particularly the arbitrary, meddlesome character of raikom leadership. Once again the old warnings appeared on the need to concentrate on personnel questions and on the loss of the proper Party style of leadership. In August *Pravda* carried a speech by Khrushchev at a Plenum of the Ukrainian Central Committee devoted precisely to these problems. He condemned the current tendency toward total preoccupation with immediate economic goals and claimed that it was resulting in an excessively high rate of turnover of scarce leadership personnel. During the preceding eighteen months, he reported, 38 percent of the raikom secretaries, 64 percent of the *raiispolkom* chairmen, and two-thirds of the MTS directors in the Ukraine had been replaced.[7]

Three days later *Pravda* again addressed itself to the problem of local Party leadership in agriculture with an important editorial on the work of the Sal'sk Raikom in Rostov Oblast. The raikom was singled out as a horrible example of current shortcomings, particularly "of forgetting the fact that the Party raikom is an organ of political leadership." The editorial condemned the practice of ignoring the *raiispolkom* and the agricultural organs and forcing the officials of the MTS, the kolkhozes, and the sovkhozes to come to the raikom for the solution of all economic questions — all this while completely neglecting the PPO's.[8] The signal was being given once again to return to the indirect pattern of raikom controls.

The renewal of emphasis on the MTS as the key to the recovery and future development of agriculture was bound to call attention to the absence of a strong Party presence in the stations. By the end of 1946 the press began to take special notice of the shortcomings of Party work in the MTS and to attribute to them many of the failures of MTS operations.[9]

As has been noted in previous chapters, the main impetus for the campaign to restore the agricultural system was provided by the February Plenum in 1947. The brief, but important, section of the Resolutions of the Plenum on Party work in the village ordered the local Party organs to turn toward agriculture and to find out what was really going on in the kolkhozes. Provincial Party committees were ordered to make sure that the raikoms concentrated on strengthening the kolkhozes. The last paragraph of the section resolved "To consider it essential to introduce in the MTS the position of deputy director for the political sector." [10] In addition to "securing the improvement of the work of the MTS," the new deputy directors were given responsibility for achieving "correct mutual relations between the MTS and the kolkhozes" and for "standing guard" over the strict observance of contractual relationships. They were also to expose mutual concealment of shortcomings by the stations and their kolkhozes. Finally, they were supposed to strengthen the work of the MTS Party organizations and "develop political, educational work among the tractor drivers, combine operators, and other workers of the MTS." [11]

The campaign launched at the February Plenum apparently did help to remedy some of the more egregious physical and moral aftereffects of the war. Discipline in the village was certainly tightened, but the underlying patterns of economic and political relationships and their shortcomings do not appear to have been appreciably affected. The perennial complaints of shoddy work by the MTS, insufficient guidance of the PPO's, and undue interference by the raikoms in daily operations continued to be voiced. Party leaders were well aware of these problems, as the contemporary press attests, but they were evidently reluctant to tackle the main issues head on. Khrushchev in the Ukraine, for example, was very sensitive to the problems involved, but he was unable to offer a real solution. On the one hand, he vigorously supported the principle of the removal of the raikom from direct interference in economic management.[12] On the other hand, when it came to the handling of specific situations and agricultural campaigns, he was second to none in demanding the most active raikom intervention.[13]

In January 1951 Lazar Slepov made what was perhaps the most concentrated effort to set forth general principles for proper Party leadership of the economy in an article in *Bol'shevik*. Essentially following the lines he was to lay down several years later in the longer works cited in Chapter 6, Slepov asserted that the issue was one of style. The local Party organs were certainly responsible for the conduct of economic work in their territories "and by no means only symbolically," [14] but overinvolvement in the concrete details of production tended to weaken, rather than strengthen, long-term economic success. The astute Party official must strive to find the middle course, to lead by "exerting the necessary influence" without disrupting the proper division of labor between Party, governmental, and economic leadership.[15]

Slepov's pontifications were hardly a solution to the grave problems facing the raikom secretaries. The hard pressed secretary, subject to the incessant demands of his superiors, could little afford to rely on indirect influence to bestir the mediocre personnel of the local administrative and production agencies. The Party forces at his disposal were still so weak and poorly distributed that it would have taken more time and effort than he had, given his limited tenure of office, to fashion them into a useful instrument of indirect control. Consequently, the style of leadership in the village remained essentially as before. The raikoms continued to intervene directly, relying on "massive assignments of plenipotentiaries" at campaign time, and more or less ignoring the PPO's.[16]

THE DEPUTY DIRECTOR OF THE MTS FOR THE POLITICAL SECTOR

In comparison with the situation obtaining in the raions as a whole, the state of Party activities in the MTS was in many respects much closer to the official ideal. Coverage of the MTS by primary Party organizations was virtually complete. And thanks to the presence of the *zampolity,* the MTS PPO's were assured, at least in theory, of continuing supervision by a higher Party official. Furthermore, given his explicit responsibilities for the production activities of the MTS in its zone, the *zampolit* was in a good position to perform a kind of integrative function, relating Party activities in the MTS and the kolkhozes to the common production goals of the raion. Thus, the *zampolit* was in an admirable situation to assist the raikom in carrying out its prescribed tasks of indirect leadership of production. Needless to say, not all *zampolity* were able to carry out these tremendous responsibilities effectively.

A comparison of the wording of the resolution setting up the position of deputy director of the MTS for the political sector in February 1947 with that in November 1934 reveals several important differences. For one thing, the 1947 *zampolit* was not designated as the secretary of the MTS PPO.* He was, in this way,

---

* In some areas, however, the *zampolity* did in fact serve as MTS Party secretaries — another example of the prevalence of more or less spontaneous local differences in Soviet administrative practices. An article in *Bol'shevik* in 1951, for example, noted

spared of much of the formal, day-to-day business of Party administrative work, ostensibly allowing him to concentrate more heavily on the operational problems of the MTS. This provision probably meant that the *zampolit* was formally a member of the primary Party organization of the raikom apparatus, and not of the MTS. (Otherwise, he would have been outranked in terms of Party status by the MTS Party secretary.) In this way he would be able to direct MTS Party affairs from above, so to speak, in the manner of a raikom instructor.

For another thing, the 1947 *zampolit* was much less confined to the jurisdictional limits of the MTS in the conduct of his activities. He was explicitly commanded to focus his attention on both sides of the MTS-kolkhoz production relationship, overseeing the total performance of the MTS zone. This broader jurisdiction was to include contacts with the kolkhoz PPO's.

From the standpoint of *nomenklatura* status, although the evidence is not conclusive, the postwar *zampolit* was apparently confirmed by the provincial Party committees.[17] This would indicate a substantially lower formal status than that of the prewar *zampolit,* although in practice his position in the raion power structure appears to have been at least equally prominent — or lacking in prominence, as the case may be.

The broader scope afforded to the 1947 deputy directors was in keeping with the new general line on local Party leadership set forth at the February Plenum. If in 1935 there had been a definite determination to curb local Party interference in economic affairs, in 1947 the Party committees were being encouraged to continue their leadership, albeit in a less direct manner than during the wartime period. The wartime experiences with total Party control had evidently not been considered entirely negative by the top Party leaders. After urging the local Party secretaries to strengthen their contacts with the rural Party members and rank-and-file kolkhozniks and improve their Party-political work, the Resolutions of the February Plenum had strongly reminded them

---

that the majority of *zampolity* in Voronezh Oblast were doubling as secretaries of the PPO's in their MTS. But the author of the article condemned the practice, saying that the *zampolit* should not be encumbered by routine Party business (K. Zhukov, "O partiino-politicheskoi rabote v MTS," *Bol'shevik,* No. 5 [March 1951], p. 60).

of their continuing responsibilities for the economic efforts of the kolkhozes.[18]

Unfortunately, aggregate data on the kind of personnel selected as *zampolity*, such as the statistics on the 1933–1934 and wartime politotdels, are not available. Most of the information is extremely fragmentary and must be pieced together from scattered sources and the records of a few regions. Of the 6780 *zampolity* appointed during the first half of 1947, 55.3 percent had been Party members for seven or more years and 24.4 percent, for seventeen or more years.[19] In Kursk Oblast, of the 120 deputy directors confirmed by the Obkom as of the middle of May 1947, 6 had formerly been obkom instructors and 28 had been members of wartime politotdels. Of the remainder many had served in minor Party or Soviet posts, and a few had been professional engineers and agronomists. Seventy-four of the 120 were Party members of ten years' standing or more. Surprisingly, 107 of them had a higher or secondary education — a strikingly higher percentage than for the wartime politotdel chiefs.[20]

In Kalinin Oblast the process of assigning *zampolity* was completed for all ninety MTS by the beginning of May 1947. According to Obkom Secretary P. Vorontsov, all of them had had previous experience in Party-political work: the majority, in the armed forces during the war.[21] But he gives no breakdown of the level or type of Party experience of the new appointees. In Voronezh Oblast all of the 165 deputy directors were reported to have had experience in "leading Party work," although only half of them had higher or secondary education.[22]

If there is any one outstanding common characteristic in the backgrounds of the postwar *zampolity* it is probably the experience of military-political work during the recent war. Many of the descriptions of individual *zampolity* in the contemporary press emphasized this feature. Undoubtedly this experience influenced their style of leadership. It was not necessarily the coercive, commanding style of the 1933 politotdel chiefs, but rather a vigorous, mass-mobilization style, which was probably just what the regime was looking for when it created the position.

In the weeks that followed the February Plenum the press devoted a good deal of attention to the *zampolity*. The regime apparently placed considerable reliance on the new position to aid in the rehabilitation of the MTS-kolkhoz system. At first the articles seemed to play down the more specifically economic aspects of the job, stressing the need to work indirectly through the PPO's and individual Communists and, especially, through the non-Party rank-and-file workers and kolkhozniks. In the words of an editorial in *Sotsialisticheskoe zemledelie,* "He is a political leader, a militant organizer of people, a man who knows how to support a worthwhile initiative in a timely manner, ably to direct the energy of the MTS workers toward the overcoming of the difficulties they encounter in their work." [23] Much emphasis was placed on liaison with the kolkhozes. The deputy directors was expected to be abreast of events in all the kolkhozes of the MTS zone. He was to work with the kolkhoz PPO's, where they existed, and help to establish a reliable non-Party *aktiv* in the kolkhozes to strengthen cooperation with the MTS.[24]

This early emphasis on the practices of indirect Party leadership did not last very long, however. As soon as reports on the progress of the spring sowing campaign came in, it was clear that the mere appointment of the new deputy directors would not suffice to eliminate the serious problems of the MTS. The quality of MTS tractor work continued to cause concern, and there were again frequent reports of violations of contractual obligations.[25] These were areas where the *zampolit* had been expected to be particularly effective. The reaction of the regime to the early failures was, predictably, to demand that the *zampolity* interfere in the most direct manner in the economic affairs of the kolkhozes, as well as of the MTS. An editorial in *Pravda* in May demanded

The deputy director of the MTS for the political sector can and must interest himself in the state of affairs in the kolkhozes. If things are going badly in a kolkhoz, if the kolkhoz is not fulfilling its contractual obligations, he must call the kolkhoz chairman to order. If a backward segment of the kolkhozniks are violating labor discipline and harming general kolkhoz affairs, he must not pass over these facts, but struggle to uproot them.[26]

It was clear from the outset that the postwar deputy directors were to have far greater responsibilities in the kolkhozes than did their prewar counterparts.

As with the case with the raikom, however, there were few concrete guidelines as to the methods the *zampolity* were expected to use. Following the usual custom in such situations, the Party press singled out individual *zampolity* for praise or blame as examples to the rest, once a certain amount of experience with the new position had been accumulated. For example, in May 1947 there appeared a number of articles devoted to the work of one Andreev, the deputy director of the Bezenchukskaia MTS, a bellwether station in Kuibyshev Oblast. The relatively large Party organization in this MTS (twenty-three Party members and twenty-seven Komsomol members) had been in a moribund condition for several years. Party meetings were invariably dull and irregularly held. Very few of the Communists were involved in Party or economic activities. Andreev allegedly managed to change all this. He reoriented Party activities to concrete production work. In the nineteen kolkhozes of the MTS zone he created a reserve of non-Party activists and fashioned close links with such Party organizations as existed. He paid special attention to the MTS tractor brigades, where many of the kolkhozniks were employed. Thus, he was able to make maximum use of the various points of contact offered by the MTS-kolkhoz relationship to enhance Party leverage on production.[27]

Other individual *zampolity* were similarly praised. The catalogue of useful activities carried on by the deputy directors of Kursk Oblast included the mobilization of kolkhozniks to improve their servicing of the MTS tractor brigades; the organization of socialist competition in backward farms; assistance to kolkhoz chairmen in planning and organizing campaigns; the setting up of training programs in the MTS for new tractor drivers; the organization of night-shift operations during the spring sowing campaign; the supervision of the quality of tractor work; and the organization of the contract-signing campaign.[28]

S. V. Fraer, whose work was cited in Chapter 4, has provided a time budget of an exemplary *zampolit* for the month of May 1950. The subject was a Comrade Konev, the deputy director of the Khoz'minskaia MTS in Arkhangel Oblast. Of the 322 hours Konev worked during the month, he spent 181 hours in the kolkhoz fields, checking MTS operations, the state of contract ful-

fillment, the progress of socialist competition, and so forth. He
also took part in sessions of the village soviets in two of the
villages of the zone. Ninety-one hours were spent in the MTS
itself, where Konev worked on the preparation and conduct of
Party meetings and helped to manage the sessions of the MTS
Council. He also spent 13 hours on the drafting and delivery of a
speech on the international situation for the personnel of the
MTS.[29]

It seems that the deputy director for the political sector was
intended to be a jack-of-all-trades, a super-coordinator and organizer, working for the smoothest possible performance of mutual
tasks by the MTS and the kolkhozes of its zone. He was supposed
to uncover shortcomings and to apply Party pressure and his
personal influence to eradicate them. Judging from his responsibilities and his relatively high Party status, it might be assumed that
the *zampolit* was a major figure in the village. This was not
universally the case, however. As in all levels of the Soviet political system, despite its apparent structural elaborateness and
formal specificity, the influence of individual personality and style
is crucial. Those *zampolity* who had an understanding of local
requirements and who had sufficient vigor and imagination to use
their broad powers to the full enjoyed considerable authority.
Those who did not were of little consequence in the local power
structure. In the Ukrainian kolkhoz led by Fedor Belov, for example, the deputy director of the MTS apparently played no
appreciable role. Belov mentions the existence of such an individual on the staff of the MTS, but he never refers to his activities
in the operations of the MTS or the life of the raion.[30] Another
example of a totally ineffective MTS political organization under
the *zampolit* arrangement was that of the Meshkovskaia MTS in
Rostov Oblast. This MTS was apparently twice cursed: the secretary of its PPO was completely lacking in Party experience and
made no effort to exercise the PPO's "right of control" over the
management of the station; the *zampolit* did nothing to assist the
hapless secretary and spent a major share of his time on his private
garden plot. The account of the activities of the *zampolit* concluded with the lament: "His role in the MTS is not felt." [31]

If the state of Party affairs in the Meshkovskaia MTS was, perhaps, considerably worse than the average, the general tone of published commentaries on the work of the *zampolity* was one of disappointment, especially in the later years of the period. After an initial flurry of activity the deputy directors, like the politotdel chiefs before them, tended to settle down into routine economic affairs. This was, of course, highly useful work, but it was not what had been intended in the original conception of the position. The case of the *zampolit* in Moscow Oblast who "could not find a place for himself and turned into a supply officer for the procurement of spare parts" [32] was apparently not uncommon. As in the 1935–1939 period, there were complaints that the deputy directors for the political sector were acting more like ordinary economic assistants of the MTS directors.[33]

At the same time, it may well have been that many of these complaints were not fully relevant. It was impossible for the center to give a complete prescription for the varied contingencies encountered by the *zampolity*. The very nature of the position demanded that they tailor their activities to the specific requirements of the local situations. Their influence and effectiveness was composed of many different elements, even the procurement of spare parts for MTS machinery if that was a major local problem. After all, economic performance was still the overriding concern of Party work. A Soviet acquaintance who had spent his adolescent years in a rural area of the Urals, in commenting to the author on the status of the MTS *zampolit* in his locale, characterized him as a person of great influence and authority. When asked to be more specific as to the nature of this authority, he emphasized the *zampolit*'s patronage of "cultural" affairs. As an example, he said that if the members of a kolkhoz wished to build a bathhouse or a club, the *zampolit* was the man to see for technical guidance and, more important, for the release of the necessary materials. He was often the source of initiative for such projects and was generally a central figure in community welfare matters.

Thus, the substance of the authority of the deputy director was as varied as his responsibilities were numerous. The objective conditions of the MTS zone and the personality and style of leadership of the individual were among the controlling factors. In addition, there was the question of the particular uses to which the *zampolity* of a given raion were put by the raikom leaders. Although the *zampolity* were formally on the *nomenklatura* of the provincial Party committee, they were largely the creatures of the raikom, which was responsible for the nomination of candidates.[34] Raikom domination of the appointment process was particularly prevalent in the later years, when the problem of replacements became crucial. In operational matters the *zampolity* were, of course, completely subordinate to the raikoms.[35]

However, in keeping with the practice of dealing with the MTS through the director in straight business terms, the general tendency was for the raikom to leave the *zampolity* more or less on their own. There were cases where the raikoms discussed matters of vital importance to the MTS without even bothering to invite the participation of the *zampolit*.[36] On several occasions the provincial Party committees were ordered to see to it that their raikoms attend more closely to the activities of the deputy directors and give them more positive guidance.[37] But such orders were apparently not consistently heeded, and the raikoms gave the *zampolity* little practical support. K. Zhukov, the First Secretary of the Voronezh Obkom, noted the case of a *zampolit* who had not been upheld by the bureau of his raikom in uncovering improper activities on the part of the MTS director. Zhukov concluded, "Not being assured that they will receive Party support from the raikom of the Party, some deputy directors of the MTS for the political sector become reconciled to shortcomings and are afraid of spoiling their relations with the directors." [38]

Left to their own devices, often without the attention or support of the raikoms, many *zampolity* found it easier to choose the path of acquiescence in the manipulations of the MTS directors, on whose good will they depended for their daily welfare and tranquility. Instead of Party overseers protecting the interests of the state in the MTS zones, they became in such cases mere accessories to the MTS directors, assisting them in making the stations "look good" in the eyes of the higher Party and state officials.[39] In a sense this, too, was an important (latent) function for the maintenance of the system of raikom control, but it was hardly the sort of activity for which the position had been created.

THE KOLKHOZ AMALGAMATION CAMPAIGN AND PARTY COVERAGE IN THE VILLAGE

One of the most important agricultural developments in the postwar period — one which would seriously affect the future status of the MTS — was the kolkhoz amalgamation campaign. This campaign had important political consequences in addition to the economic and organizational consequences discussed in previous chapters.

The campaign was a personal project of N. S. Khrushchev. Almost immediately after his return to Moscow to become First Secretary of the Moscow Obkom in December 1949, Khrushchev began maneuvering to replace A. A. Andreev as the chief agricultural spokesman of the Central Committee and to introduce his own ideas for the improvement of Soviet agriculture. The details of his manipulation of the controvesy between the "link" (zveno) and the brigade as the basic unit of organization of the kolkhoz labor force need not be told here. Undoubtedly there were purely political motives behind his singling out this issue to discredit Andreev, but the selection of issues was not entirely fortuitous. Khrushchev's main explicit objection to the link was that it tended to fragment the kolkhoz labor force and thus impede the rational utilization of complex MTS machinery.[40] Andreev was cleverly trapped into maintaining a position which was clearly untenable except as a short-run expedient, as he was certainly aware. In any case, the elimination of the link and the amalgamation of the kolkhozes may be viewed as part and parcel of the general scheme of concentration by which Khrushchev planned to solve the problems of Soviet agriculture.

On March 7, 1950, exactly one week after the appearance of Andreev's supine letter of capitulation on the back page of *Pravda,* Khrushchev announced the beginning of the amalgamation campaign.[41] Although the emphasis was on the economic and operational benefits of the mergers, there were important political dividends as well. The simple physical unification of adjacent kolkhozes meant that the percentage of farms with PPO's was bound to increase. The result was a more effective distribution of the still modest army of Party members in the village. M. A. Kraev, the Soviet economic historian, noted in *Bol'shevik* in June 1950 that

The amalgamation facilitates the creation of Party and Komsomol organizations in the kolkhozes, the conduct of systematic ideological and educational work, which has primary significance for the organizational and economic strengthening of the kolkhozes and the improvement of the organization of labor.[42]

The actual increase in Party coverage was substantial. L. Mel'nikov, Khrushchev's successor as First Secretary of the Ukrainian Central Committee, reported in February 1951 that the percentage of kolkhozes in the republic with PPO's had risen from 52 to 80 since the beginning of the mergers in 1950. The size of the average kolkhoz PPO had risen also. Before 1950, 46 percent of the kolkhoz Party organizations in the Ukraine had contained five Communists or less, while by February 1951 only 25 percent were this small, and 25 percent now contained ten to fifteen Party members.[43] Similar gains were registered elsewhere, although the total number of Communists in the village remained relatively small. Khrushchev would announce in September 1953 that there were over a million Party members in the countryside, but this was still less than 20 percent of the seven-million-odd members and candidates in the Party as a whole at that time.[44] Nevertheless, mainly as a result of the mergers, over 80 percent of the kolkhozes in the USSR would have primary Party organizations by the time of the September (1953) Plenum of the Central Committee.[45] Quantitatively, at least, the distribution of Party forces in the village was at last approaching the level where the indirect leadership ideal of raikom control was a physical possibility.

IN LIEU OF A CONCLUSION

In the meantime, the traditional methods of direct control at campaign time continued in effect. As an illustration of the atmosphere in the raikom end of the raikom-MTS-kolkhoz triad, the following extended passage from Valentin Ovechkin's *Raion-nye budni* is of particular value and relevance. The dialogue is between Viktor Semionych Borzov, the hard-driving First Secretary of the raikom, and Piotr Illarionych Martynov, the Second Secretary and hero of the story.

Borzov has unexpectedly returned from a vacation at a health resort, where he has been undergoing treatment for an ulcer. He learns from Martynov that grain deliveries in the raion are lagging. Borzov is furious.

Martynov: "Other kolkhozes have delivered more than the daily assignment. And 'Power of the Soviets', 'October', and 'Dawn' have paid up."

Borzov: "What do you mean, 'paid up'?"

Martynov: "Just that . . . in full. And with payments in kind for all services."

Borzov: "Is that what you tell the chairmen: 'You've paid up'? Ech, Piotr Illarionych! I've got to teach you over and over again! Where's the table with the breakdown of the kolkhozes?"

He sat down in the secretary's chair and pushed aside everything in his way — the lamp, the ashtray, the unfinished glass of tea. Under the thick glass lay a large cross-sectioned sheet of paper dotted with figures: sown area of the kolkhozy, head of livestock, delivery plans. Martynov smiled involuntarily, remembering the words of Opionkin: "He'll rest for a couple of hours and then start poking around."*

Borzov: "Yes, I see. I did the right thing coming back."

He took a sheet of paper and a pencil and ran his finger along the glass.

"In 'Power of the Soviets' how much did they have? So . . . State deliveries and payments in kind . . . So. That's for the seventh group. The Commission** placed them in the seventh group by crop yield. And if we give them the ninth group?"

Martynov: "The highest?"

Borzov: "Yes, the highest. What do we get? Let's figure it out . . . In the ninth group from Dem'ian the Wealthy*** — another one and a half thousand centners. And from 'Dawn' — about 800 centners. And from 'October' the same. There! Sonny boy! Don't you know how to get the grain out of them?"

---

* Chairman of the kolkhoz "Power of the Soviets."

** The raion Commission for rating the kolkhozes by yield categories for assessing *naturoplata* rates for MTS services. See Chapter 5, above.

*** The nickname of Opionkin — a play on the name "Dem'ian Bednii" (Dem'ian the Poor), the sobriquet of a popular author of rural stories during the thirties.

Martynov, the smile still on his face, went up to the table.

Martynov: "I'm not a little boy, Viktor Semionych. I know all about these little tricks. But it's time to put an end to all this, really! On what basis do you propose to refigure their payments in kind at the higher group level?"

Borzov: "On the basis that the country needs grain!" [46]

12 "Closer to Production": The MTS

and the Raikom in the Final Period

By the last years of Stalin's reign the sporadic, campaign-centered system of raikom leadership had won more or less grudging acceptance as the normal mode of Party control in agriculture. As we have seen, the extended periods of this raikom mode were interrupted in times of extreme crisis and replaced by a politotdel mode, which represented the movement of local Party leadership of production from the raion centers directly into the MTS.

THE DECENTRALIZATION OF THE RAIKOM

If the dominant raikom mode was generally acceptable to most of the Party chieftains of the Stalin era, it was decidedly not acceptable to Nikita Sergeevich Khrushchev. Motivated by the dual purpose of fundamental improvement of the country's critically lagging agricultural sector and the restoration of the Party's role as the prime leadership force in all areas of Soviet life, he sought to make the role of the Party in the village more directly relevant to the long-term growth of the rural economy. To Khrushchev this meant the institutionalization of maximal Party involvement at the basic production level. In his search for ways to achieve this goal, it is not surprising that he adopted many features of the politotdel mode as the best means of moving raikom control "closer to production." Specifically, he proposed to concentrate most of the forces of the raikom directly in the MTS for maximum leverage and control in production matters.

Khrushchev presented his arguments for reorganization at the September (1953) Plenum of the Central Committee, where he subjected the entire system of agricultural administration to searching criticism. In his attacks he singled out what he called the depersonalization of Party leadership in the village as the
290

main shortcoming of the traditional raikom mode. The existing system, he said, had tended to undermine the responsibility of any single Party leader for the concrete state of affairs in agricultural production. He concluded that

It has become necessary to bring Party leadership closer to the decisive sectors of production. At the present stage it is essential to reconstruct the work of the Party apparatus so that a given official carries on the work in a given kolkhoz and answers for it, so that there is someone to hold responsible for the proper selection of cadres, the correct distribution of people, for political work among the kolkhozniks, for the solution of the problems lying before the given kolkhoz . . .[1]

Following Khrushchev's recommendations the Plenum adopted a resolution essentially decentralizing the raikom. Each MTS was to be assigned a raikom secretary in residence, who would be in charge of a group of instructors serving the kolkhozes of the MTS zone. The first secretary of the raikom was to remain in the raion center to coordinate and provide general leadership of the work of the so-called zonal raikom secretaries and their subordinate instructor groups (IG's). Finally, the position of deputy director of the MTS for the political sector was abolished.[2]*

Thus, in the political as well as the economic sphere the role of the MTS in Khrushchev's new departure in agriculture was to be greatly enhanced. Nevertheless, from the very beginning there was a discernible note of hesitation concerning the form and methods of the new raion Party organization. In his own address to the September Plenum Khrushchev had professed to be raising the question of reorganization of the raikom merely "for an exchange of opinions." And the final resolutions referred to the new structure rather tentatively, as something that was needed "at the present stage." This cautious phrasing suggests the possibility that some of Khrushchev's colleagues in the Central Committee had misgivings as to the wisdom of so radical a restructuring of the rural raikom. It seems likely that the reorganization was

* It is worth noting that the zonal secretaries did not, unlike the *zampolity* and politotdel chiefs, have the formal title of deputy directors of the MTS. This omission may perhaps have been a reflection of Khrushchev's disdain for the formalities of the division of functions between state and Party officials. Party officials were expected to intervene even without formal authority to do so.

accepted only on a trial basis. Indeed, the persistent aura of impermanence surrounding the IG's for the entire four years of their existence was an important element in their failure to live up to Khrushchev's expectations.

STAFFING THE INSTRUCTOR GROUPS

As was the case with so many of Khrushchev's organizational innovations, the implementation of the reshaping of the raikom presented serious problems. Perhaps the most difficult of these was the recruitment of sufficient numbers of qualified personnel. At the time of the September Plenum there were 8950 MTS and approximately 94,000 kolkhozes in the USSR.[3] On the average each MTS served slightly more than ten kolkhozes, although there were wide regional variations. Under the formula suggested by Khrushchev each instructor was to supervise "one, or a maximum of two" kolkhozes.[4] This meant that, ideally, a total of almost 55,000 relatively experienced Party workers would be required for minimum staffing of the IG's.* The Party simply did not have that many qualified persons at its disposal, especially since it was also pressing for a massive infusion of managerial and technical specialists into the MTS and the kolkhozes at this time. In fact, as of January 1955, only about 30,000 persons were actually sent to the MTS zones as zonal secretaries and instructors.[5] This figure appears to have been the maximum number of persons comprising the staffs of the zonal groups at any one time during the period of their existence. Thus, the IG's were considerably understaffed in view of the heavy responsibilities Khrushchev envisioned for them.**

The qualitative aspects of the problem were at least equally serious. In certain respects the zonal groups were quite different in conception from the politotdels. Unlike the latter they were not being sent to the village for a short-term, specific purpose, such as wartime mobilization. Rather, they were expressly designed as a long-term institution for insuring the constancy of

---

* 8950 raikom secretaries plus 5 times 8950 instructors.

** However, since the number of kolkhozes continued to decline moderately as the amalgamations proceeded, the situation was at least slightly less serious than the above statement would appear to indicate.

Party influence in the daily life and toil of the village.* It was, therefore, highly desirable that the new cadres possess a good basic knowledge of agriculture and rural life. Khrushchev particularly emphasized the qualitative side of the personnel selection process when he reviewed the progress of the reorganization at the February–March Plenum of the Central Committee in 1954:

In the reconstruction of the rural raikoms of the Party, the primary role is played not only by the quantitative side of the question — how many persons have been selected and where they have been assigned. The main question is the preparation of these persons. It is necessary for the workers of the raikoms to understand well the tasks standing before them, to know kolkhoz production, to know how to work with people . . .[6]

Unfortunately, material on the Party and professional backgrounds of the zonal secretaries and their staffs is very sparse, even in comparison with that for the politotdel staffs and the *zampolity*. Fragmentary data from individual republics and oblasts, however, indicate that a significant number of them, although far less than a majority, came as in the past from urban centers. Owing to the large-scale movements of specialists from urban-based agencies and enterprises to posts in the MTS and the kolkhozes at this time, it would appear unlikely that the Party had very many persons with specialized training available for assignment to the zonal groups. The majority of their personnel, particularly the instructors must, therefore, have been recruited locally. Some, of course, came from the apparatus of the raikoms, but many others were drawn from the various local economic and administrative organs, which usually meant a lower level of formal training. A. I. Kirichenko, then First Secretary of the Ukrainian Central Committee, reported in January 1954 that 4555 Communists in the Ukraine had been sent from city Party organizations to the countryside after the September Plenum. Of these only 338 were accounted for as raikom secretaries and 213 as workers in the apparatus of rural raikoms.[7] At the time there were

* The politotdels may also have originally been conceived as a relatively long-term institution. If so, the conception was soon altered. By mid-1934, it will be remembered, the politotdel had been officially designated as a short-term, single-purpose instrument of Party rule for "backward sectors of the economy."

approximately 800 rural raions and 1396 MTS in the republic.[8] Thus, even if it is assumed that the majority of these persons were assigned to the MTS zones, the great preponderance of IG personnel must have been recruited locally.

In Krasnodar Krai, according to V. Suslov, the First Secretary of the Kraikom, the urban Party organizations sent 190 "experienced Party workers" to the rural raikoms, including 40 persons from the Kraikom apparatus.[9] This would basically have covered the need for zonal raikom secretaries, but the instructors still presumably had to be recruited locally.

The Saratov Obkom, as of April 18, 1954, had succeeded in designating secretaries for all 149 zonal groups in the Oblast and an additional 240 instructors as well.* But it is clear from reports that the instructors were in fact selected locally by the raikoms and simply confirmed by the obkom. The raikoms apparently had some difficulty in finding suitable candidates, however, and one raikom was severely criticized for recruiting persons who had been fired from other jobs in the raion.[10] Similar problems, particularly with finding high level personnel for assignment to the village, were reported in Voronezh.[11]

Now, there is nothing unusual in this manner of recruiting lower level Party cadres, particularly at the instructor rank. Local persons would be expected to have a knowledge of agriculture and to be well acquainted with village life and its problems. Under normal conditions positions at this level would ordinarily be filled from among the most promising young local Party members. However, the massive nature of the levy to staff the IG's placed a severe strain on the available supply of such persons. The result was inevitably a lowering of qualitative standards.

The lack of aggregate background data makes it impossible to offer even the broadest comparisons with earlier MTS political cadres. All that is possible is to list the different types of backgrounds mentioned in individual accounts. From the scattered bits of information available it may be asserted with confidence only that the zonal secretaries and instructors were an extremely heterogeneous group. Among those appointed as secretaries one

* In this oblast not every MTS was given a separate zonal group.

finds former obkom and raikom *apparatchiki* — a significant number, apparently, from the recently liquidated agricultural *otdely* of the raikom (see below) — but also a number of former kolkhoz chairmen. Among the instructors were former kolkhoz chairmen, agronomists from the raizo and the MTS, army political workers, minor raikom *apparatchiki,* bookkeepers, and secretaries of village PPO's.[12] The staffing process, it seems, took on some of the aspects of a mass levy.

THE STRUCTURE AND FUNCTIONING OF THE ZONAL GROUPS

A clear idea of the actual structure of the raikom under the IG plan is indispensable for an understanding of the problems encountered in its operation. As usual there were more or less important regional variations in the structure. The primary seat of authority in the raion continued to be occupied by the first secretary of the raikom. From his office in the raion center he was supposed to exercise overall guidance and supervision of the zonal groups, in addition to his regular duties with respect to the general political, economic, and social affairs of the raion. In most areas there was also a second secretary of the raikom with broad responsibilities complementary to those of the first secretary. The division of labor between them was a matter of mutual agreement and the backgrounds of the individuals themselves.[13] For example, the second secretary might be given charge of ideological and propaganda work, local industry, or even agriculture, depending on the characteristics of the raion or his personal talents and specialties (or lack of same). In Gor'kii Oblast — and probably a few others as well — the second secretary was commonly assigned as a zonal secretary to one of the MTS, presumably the station situated in, or closest to, the raion center.[14] But in the great majority of cases the second secretary was unattached and had all-raion responsibilities.

The central apparatus of the raikom contained two *otdely,* an Organizational Otdel and a Propaganda and Agitation Otdel. The functions of the former included "checking the activities of the primary Party organizations of raion institutions, industrial enterprises, transportation agencies, and kolkhozes; instruction of Party organizations on questions of Party-organizational work; the registration of the membership of the raion Party organizations; and supervision of the state of Party housekeeping affairs." [15] The Propaganda and Agitation Otdel, as the name implies, directed the ideological, agitational, and educational programs of the PPO's and other institutions in the raion.[16] The two *otdely* carried on their work through their own staffs of instructors. Before the September 1953 reorganization there had also been an Agricultural Otdel. Its primary duties were to supervise the activities of all the agricultural institutions in the raion and to serve as the center of planning and operational controls for the raikom leadership in matters of current agricultural business.[17] One of the main reasons for the establishment of the IG system was that the raikom and its Agricultural Otdel had become so bogged down in paper work that they had tended to lose personal control over agricultural affairs. It was hoped that the new arrangement would permit the secretaries and instructors to regain the desired personal contact with production activity. In effect they would serve as a decentralized agricultural *otdel* for the first secretary of the raikom. At the same time, as permanent residents of the MTS zones, the IG's were expected to carry out, on a daily basis, many of the activities falling under the jurisdiction of the two remaining *otdely*.[18] In many respects the new arrangement was a return to the sub-raikom concept briefly tried — and rejected in connection with the initial moves toward the liquidation of the politotdels in 1934. This similarity did not escape the attention of the critics of the IG's in high Party circles.

In the majority of cases a zonal group was established in each MTS, although occasionally a single group would serve two adjacent stations.[19] The raikom normally included from one to four zonal secretaries, in addition to the first and second secretaries, depending, of course, on the number of stations in the raion. The heavier concentrations of zonal Party workers were to be found in the most heavily mechanized regions of the country, such as the Kuban'. Conversely, Party coverage under the new system was weakest in the Northwest and other non-black earth regions, where the MTS/kolkhoz ratio was smallest. On the average there were from two to four instructors in each IG. Each instructor covered from two to four kolkhozes (roughly twice the ideal suggested by Khrushchev).[20]

As noted above, the mission of the zonal groups was to exercise detailed Party supervision, not only over Party affairs, but over all economic and social affairs of the MTS and the kolkhozes of their respective zones. The instructor was a particularly important figure in this mission. His range of responsibilities was significantly broader than that of the instructor of one of the regular raikom *otdely*. Describing these responsibilities a zonal secretary in one of the MTS in Moscow Oblast declared: "In the new conditions it is not enough for the raikom instructor to master questions of Party construction. He must be sufficiently well up on his agronomy and animal husbandry; he must know the most modern methods of agricultural production." [21]

From this and other similar statements it is evident that the ideal IG instructor would be a person with technical skills and general leadership capabilities rather than a specialist in Party organizational or ideological matters, like the instructors of the permanent raikom *otdely*. The difficulty in finding large numbers of such persons was soon a major cause of concern.

An early admission that all was not well with the reorganization was made by Khrushchev himself in his speech at the February–March Plenum of the Central Committee in 1954. "The reconstruction of the work of the rural raikoms of the Party is still far from complete," he declared. Although most of the obkoms had selected sufficient numbers of instructors, the quality of those chosen left much to be desired. Furthermore, the zonal secretaries were not giving the vigorous guidance which the new arrangements required. "Many raikom secretaries visit the machine-tractor stations and the kolkhozes only on the fly, as rare guests. They go there, hold a conference, and run home to the raion center." [22]

The local press offered bountiful evidence in support of Khrushchev's charges. The sheer volume of newspaper coverage of the shortcomings of the new system suggests either a widespread dislike for it among the provincial Party leaders or, more likely, that the problems being encountered were more serious than was usually the case with Party reorganizations. A typical example of the contemporary complaints was the following passage from an editorial in the Saratov Oblast newspaper, *Kommunist,* in January 1954:

> on-the-spot checks and a recent seminar in the obkom for CPSU raikom secretaries for the zones of the MTS have revealed that in the majority of raions the reconstruction of Party leadership on the new basis has been extremely delayed and is being implemented as yet only formally. A significant part of the zonal secretaries has still not gotten down to work to this day.[23]

One of the most serious problems of the reorganization, no doubt a reflection of the uncertainty as to its permanence, was the reluctance of the newly appointed zonal secretaries and instructors to take up residence in their assigned MTS and kolkhozes, far from the relative comforts of the raion centers. S. D. Khitrov, the Second Secretary of the Voronezh Obkom, told an Oblast Party Conference in mid-February 1954 that many secretaries continued to try to direct the MTS zones from the raion centers. He cited the case of several of them who regularly commuted to their assigned stations every day — a distance of 25 to 30 kilometers.[24] The same complaint was heard in other oblasts.[25]

A related charge commonly voiced was that zonal groups were actively being formed only in those MTS that were close to the raion centers, leaving the more remote MTS and kolkhozes without any Party supervision at all.[26] The unpopularity of assignments to the MTS zones, especially the more distant ones, was apparently universal. An amusing example of this attitude was reported in Rostov Oblast. The Second Secretary of the Dubovskii Raikom, Barabash, had officially charged that a distant, chronically backward MTS in the raion had not even been visited by a raikom secretary since the September 1953 reorganization. It subsequently turned out that Barabash and the Third Secretary, Moskalenkov had been carrying on a running fight for three months to avoid assignment to the station.[27]

The widespread attitude toward appointment to a zonal group as a form of exile was apparently reinforced by the reluctance of Party leaders to send their ablest subordinates to the zones.[28]

General awareness of this fact hardly enhanced the prestige of the positions in the eyes of career-minded Party workers.

A direct indication of the unsatisfactory quality and performance of the zonal Party cadres was the high rate of turnover. Fainsod points out that the turnover of raikom secretaries has traditionally been high in comparison with the higher echelons of the Party bureaucracy.[29] This was especially true during the immediate postwar years, as we have seen. But subsequently there had been a tendency toward increasing stability of tenure. The turnover of the zonal raikom secretaries, however, began to approach the postwar rates in many areas. During 1955 alone, 1806 out of a total of 5157 zonal secretaries, or 35 percent, were replaced in the RSFSR.[30] In some oblasts of the republic, such as Novosibirsk, the rates were considerably higher.[31] In the Khmel'-nitskii Oblast of the Ukraine, with 37 rural raions and about 70 MTS, 15 first secretaries, 24 second secretaries, and 44 zonal secretaries were replaced between the spring of 1954 and the spring of 1956.[32]

From the beginning the zonal groups were plagued with "organizational" problems. As had been the case with earlier rural Party reorganizations, the raikoms found it difficult to interpret and adjust to the new mode of operations. Raikom leaders persisted in treating the new personnel — zonal secretaries and instructors alike — in the accustomed manner. They assigned them as plenipotentiaries to the individual kolkhozes and MTS for short-term campaigns and sent them about the raions on general raikom business.[33] A classic description of this practice was given by a dissatisfied instructor in Tambov Oblast in a letter to the editors of *Partiinaia zhizn'* in 1954. It is worth quoting at length.

Our raikom of the Party just cannot seem to give up the habit of sending plenipotentiaries to the kolkhozes. Even MTS instructors end up among the plenipotentiaries. Thus, during the first day of field operations the Second Secretary of the Raikom Comrade Shurlaev, called me and announced that for the entire spring sowing period I am to be attached to the kolkhoz "Dawn of Communism" for the organization of mass political work. The question arises: is this necessary? Even without this I am responsible for that kolkhoz, but I have to do my work in the other kolkhozes assigned to me, too.

They have been undercutting the other instructors in this way, also.

Plenipotentiaries from the raion center were sent to the backward kolkhozes. In my opinion, this, too, is incorrect. It is one thing if, say, they send individual comrades to help an instructor out for a few days. But to attach an instructor to a single kolkhoz, tearing him away from the others — this means to misunderstand the significance of the reconstruction of the work of the rural raikoms.[34]

Sometimes it was the zonal secretaries who "misunderstood" the new arrangements. Reports from Saratov Oblast, for example, complained that some zonal secretaries had begun by shunting the specialists of the MTS about the kolkhozes as plenipotentiaries for the spring sowing campaign. Even the chief agronomist of one MTS was handled in this manner, seriously disrupting the production plans of the zone.[35]

Improper direction of the zonal groups by the raikom remained perhaps the most difficult continuing problem under the new arrangements. There seemed to be a general lack of understanding of the intended division of labor between the central raikom secretaries and the zonal secretaries. According to V. M. Churaev, Head of the Party Organs Department of the newly created Central Committee Bureau of the RSFSR, the raikoms either over-administered the personnel of the zonal groups or ignored them completely. In the former extreme the raikoms squandered the energies of the IG's on secondary matters, such as the direction of village soviets, schools, hospitals, and local trade establishments. "In a word, they view the instructor groups," he wrote, "as some sort of a sub-raikom, called upon to handle everything decisively in the zone of the MTS." [36]

In the other extreme, he complained, the raikoms totally washed their hands of the daily affairs of the MTS zones, arguing that since the zonal secretaries were in charge, close supervision by the central raikom apparatus was unnecessary. The result was a breakdown of communications between the raion centers and the MTS zones. This isolation sometimes reached a point where the zonal personnel were not even invited to sessions of the raikom bureau or conferences of the raikom apparatus, of which they were an important part.[37] When the zonal cadres were persons of little leadership experience or talent, as was often the case, such isolation was bound to decrease the effectiveness of local Party control.

THE LIQUIDATION OF THE ZONAL GROUPS

The weaknesses of the reorganization scheme were fully evident to the top Party leaders. Indeed, by the end of 1955 there were already signs of pressure to eliminate the zonal groups in high Party circles. Khrushchev himself suggested the existence of such sentiments in the course of a speech to central and republic officials in November 1955, when he asked rhetorically: "Are the raikom secretaries for the MTS justifying themselves?" He admitted that there was "some doubt on this score," but expressed his own preference for strengthening the existing system with "the kind of workers who could really get down to business and carry out the mission of the Party." [38]

His wishes were apparently respected for the time being, but opposition persisted on the part of certain unnamed "comrades," as Khrushchev was compelled to admit in his Report to the Twentieth Party Congress. The diffidence with which he treated the subject suggests that the opponents were far from a negligible force.

Some comrades are saying that we ought to change the structure of the Party raikoms again. We should think about this a bit more. It seems to us, it would hardly be expedient to carry out a new reorganization. It would be better to take the path of strengthening these cadres, selecting, where necessary, good organizers capable of working with people for the posts of raikom secretaries.

He concluded by restating his favorite theme on the importance of close Party involvement in production matters: "It is essential to take the line of bringing Party leadership closer to production so that we can finally liquidate depersonalization in Party work." [39]

Again Khrushchev had his way. The entire question was obviously very much involved in his personal struggle for leadership against the spokesmen for more conservative economic policies and more traditional forms of Party and state control at this time. In addition to these considerations of Kremlin intrigue, it is obvious that to Khrushchev the zonal arrangement represented an important principle of Party leadership in the economy. That principle was: to be effective, Party leadership must be closely involved on a continuing basis at the focal points of production. Thus, despite their obvious practical shortcomings the zonal groups were allowed to continue.

The new lease on life extended for another year and a half. The zonal groups finally vanished from the scene with a conspicuous lack of fanfare just a few months before the abolition of the MTS themselves. In the meantime their performance did not markedly improve. A lead editorial in *Partiinaia zhizn'* in March 1957 asserted that many of the groups had "become even weaker than they were in the beginning of their establishment." Turnover of zonal secretaries had remained abnormally high, and some of the more vigorous of them had begun to drift back to the raion centers more or less on their own initiative.[40] As in the case of the politotdels and the *zampolity* there were complaints that the personnel of the zonal groups tended to degenerate into minor economic and managerial functionaries, uninterested in the work of the PPO's.[41]

The experiment had been a dismal failure from beginning to end. The liquidation of the zonal groups and the transfer of Party control in the village back to the regular territorial raikom framework took place in the fall of 1957. A decree of the Central Committee of September 19, 1957, ordered a return to the regular territorial raikom format as of November 15, along with a contraction of raikom staffs.[42]

The IG experiment ended the final attempt to utilize the MTS as centers of political control in the village. In addition to the usual difficulties associated with such efforts this last reorganization suffered from certain special problems of its own. These problems illustrate some of the obstacles to any meaningful reform of the rural Party control structure, which Khrushchev never really seemed to understand. First of all, the zonal raikom plan was based on the erroneous assumption that the authority of an important Party figure, such as the raikom secretary, could be easily transferred or created *de novo,* as it were. Khrushchev had assumed that all that was necessary was to designate an official in the MTS zone as a raikom secretary, and his influence would automatically be commensurate with the title. Experience showed that the zonal secretaries were not able to acquire the authority of full fledged raikom secretaries. This fact was only partially connected with the generally weak backgrounds of the incumbents. In a very real sense, territorial location proved to be an important component of raikom authority. By being removed from the raion centers the zonal secretaries were cut off from the wellsprings of raikom authority. It is difficult to direct from above when one lives side-by-side with the persons he is commanding.

Second, the territorial base and the jurisdictional scope of the zonal secretary were too narrow. The zonal group was essentially a weak politotdel. It had the latter's concentrated production orientation, but lacked the coercive underpinning which had made the politotdel a fairly effective short-term control device. But the politotdel, too, had historically been found to be too narrow in its range of concerns and territorial coverage to serve as an effective long-term Party control agency in the village. The central raikom apparatus under the zonal plan did not seem to be able to provide the necessary coordination, direction, and complementary coverage to make up for the narrowness of the zonal groups. The zonal secretaries were often not even treated as *bona fide* members of the raikom inner circle, despite their nominal status as secretaries, nor, if their reluctance to move to the zones is any indication, did they see themselves as such. There was obviously a subjective dimension to the problem of isolation from the wellsprings of raikom authority.

Finally, another no less important "objective" obstacle to the success of the reform was the changes which had occurred by this time in the requirements of agricultural leadership. Unlike the criteria in the days of the politotdels, the criteria for leadership in the countryside now included a modicum of agricultural expertise. The watchword for Party work was no longer simply Bolshevik organizational talent, but scientific know-how as well. As Khrushchev was to learn, there were not enough Party workers available with the requisite combination of skills.

The end of the zonal groups marked a definite stage in the decline of the MTS. Whether the decision to abolish the zonal arrangement was predicated on the knowledge that the MTS were soon to be liquidated, or the liquidation of the MTS was a result in some way of the failure of the zonal raikom experiment cannot be definitely established without access to Central Committee documents. It seems doubtful, however, that the failure of the zonal groups alone could have prompted Khrushchev to make so momentous a decision. By the same token, the MTS could certainly have continued to exist without the zonal groups, as they had in the past.

Part IV   The Liquidation of the MTS

*Thus, in the course of the construction of a socialist agriculture
and the strengthening of the kolkhozes the socioeconomic
situation in the village has fundamentally changed. Now the kolkhozes
represent developed socialist enterprises, the majority of which
do not need the guidance of the MTS. As a result the presently
existing form of production and technical servicing of the
kolkhozes through the MTS no longer satisfies the requirements of
the growth of kolkhoz production and is beginning to hold
back the development of the productive forces of agriculture.
Therefore, it is essential to find a new form of production and
technical servicing of the kolkhozes, more in conformity
to the contemporary stage of development of the kolkhoz system.*

Khrushchev

13　The Liquidation of the MTS

Khrushchev began his campaign of agricultural reforms firmly committed to the inviolability of the MTS-kolkhoz system. Indeed, one of his first steps had been to strengthen the position of the MTS as the keystone of the entire program. Yet from the very beginning it was clear that Khrushchev's attitude toward the MTS and his approach to agricultural problems in general were quite different from those which had prevailed under Stalin for over twenty years. The difference was essentially a matter of values. For Stalin the primary goal of policy toward the village, in addition, of course, to providing the basic food and fiber needs of the economy, was the maintenance of social and political control. Economic abundance and efficiency of agricultural production were clearly secondary, if desirable at all. For Khrushchev, on the other hand, the primary goals were economic abundance and efficiency, while social and political controls, although still seen as necessary, were not valued so much as ends in themselves. Moreover, they were recognized as being somehow connected with the moral and material welfare of the rural population itself. Thus, while he was by no means free of ideological constraints — witness the "agro-cities" and the campaign against the private plots — Khrushchev differed essentially from Stalin in the extent to which he was willing to pay for social and political control at the expense of economic development.

THE GRADUAL DE-EMPHASIS OF THE MTS

The MTS had been given a series of new responsibilities during the first year of reforms. However, under the new, more pragmatic dispensation each aspect of MTS operations would come under careful scrutiny, to be discarded or retained largely on its economic merits. Thus, the dissolution of the MTS system was not as abrupt or sudden an affair as it is usually thought to have been.

The first element of MTS control over the kolkhozes to be relinquished after failing the test of efficacy was the system of MTS agronomists and zootechnicians permanently assigned to the kolkhozes. In principle, the idea of coordinated scientific agricultural policies throughout the MTS zones represented by these MTS specialists in the kolkhozes had much to recommend it. It was certainly in keeping with the program of agricultural improvement which Khrushchev had selected. In practice, however, it served as merely one more illustration of the weaknesses of Khrushchev's favorite method of problem-solving through structural manipulations. From the outset the MTS specialists found themselves in an untenable position. They had little power to impose their technical advice on the kolkhozes. As in the case of the zonal Party raikom secretaries, the mere designation of the kolkhoz specialists as MTS officials was insufficient to give them the authority to carry out their work. For the most part they were treated as outsiders by the kolkhozes and remained on the fringes of kolkhoz life. If the kolkhoz chairman refused to cooperate with them, there was little they could do. A glaring example was the case of Ploshchadnova, an MTS staff agronomist in a kolkhoz in Saratov Oblast. The kolkhoz chairman consistently refused to assign kolkhozniks to her for the conduct of her work. During the harvest he turned down her request for transportation to inspect field operations. When she invoked the specified obligations to do so in the MTS-kolkhoz contract, the chairman replied coldly: "The contract is a scrap of paper. I told you I won't give you any [transportation], and don't bother me any more." [1]

An MTS agronomist in the Kuban' summed up the difficult position of the MTS specialist in the kolkhoz in the following manner:

Now there exists a dual leadership over the specialists of the MTS. On the one hand, they must carry out the decisions of the artel' management, on the other — their immediate boss is the directorate of the MTS. This leads to a situation where the agronomists sometimes find themselves in an impasse; they don't know what to do, whose instructions to carry out.[2]

Nor did the MTS specialists often receive the support of their parent stations in cases of conflict with kolkhoz management.

Indeed, it sometimes happened that the MTS directors themselves ordered violations of the instructions of their specialists in the kolkhozes. G. A. Denisov, the First Secretary of the Saratov Obkom, asserted that such violations were common and that he did not know of a single instance where an MTS director had been punished for the practice.[3] There were various formal prohibitions against such actions, but the MTS staff specialists did not have the inclination to invoke them and spoil their relations with the MTS and kolkhoz officials.

Characteristically, Khrushchev saw the problem chiefly in terms of material incentives. The specialists were not paid by the kolkhozes, he said, and, consequently, did not work conscientiously to improve kolkhoz crop yields. In a speech in April 1955 he noted with approval several experiments in the Ukraine and certain oblasts of the RSFSR restructuring the system of wage payments to MTS specialists. He suggested that in the future their wages be tied directly to increases in yields and livestock production in their respective kolkhozes. This, he declared, would stop them from "playing around like free Cossacks."[4]

The formal order transferring the MTS agronomists and zoo-technicians to full membership and payroll support in the kolkhozes to which they had been attached was promulgated on August 20, 1955. To help the transferees withstand the obvious financial shock of the change, the decree provided for supplementary state payments for a period of three years. After this they would be dependent solely on their kolkhoz earnings.[5]* Although they continued to be subject for advice to the agronomic department of the MTS, they were for all practical purposes now merely kolkhoz specialists. Thus, within two years of the September Plenum the MTS had already lost an important part of their role in the direction of kolkhoz production.

Perhaps an even more important aspect of the MTS system which was subjected to high-level scrutiny was the old problem of operating costs. For the first time since the middle thirties MTS costs became the subject of serious concern. The issue had been

* Apparently the transfer was not universally well received by the specialists. One raikom in Saratov Oblast, for example, would report that within one year of the promulgation of the decree virtually every specialist transferred had quit the raion ("Povyshat' trebovatel'nost' k kadram," Kommunist [Saratov], November 22, 1956).

raised by Khrushchev himself in 1954, when he discovered that no one really knew just how much money the state was actually paying for the grain it had been receiving for MTS services. In February 1956, after a number of preliminary studies had revealed a serious lack of financial order in MTS affairs, it was decided to transfer the MTS system to a cost-accounting and eventually self-financing basis. The transfer was to be gradual. According to Khrushchev the attainment of the final goal of self-sufficiency might take several years.[6]

The unwonted timidity with which he approached the problem of MTS finances may in part have been a reflection of the high-level political opposition to further tampering with the hallowed MTS system. More likely, it was simply a recognition of the complexity of the technical questions that would necessarily be involved.[7] Under the proposed new cost-accounting system, payments-in-kind income was to be credited in ruble terms to the account of the individual station in Gosbank. (Previously it had gone into the general state procurement fund.) The station would pay all of its expenses out of its Gosbank account, except for certain items of capital expenditures, chiefly for new machinery, which would continue to be paid for out of the state budget. But how were the payments in kind to be valued in ruble terms? At kolkhoz obligatory delivery prices? State purchase prices? Sovkhoz delivery prices? If the kolkhoz obligatory delivery prices were used, the stations would never be able to cover their expenses.

How were MTS costs to be reckoned? The existing system of planning, on which the costs per centner of payments in kind were now being calculated, was based on the old, standard unit of hectares of soft plowing. This was hardly a precise measure of the costs of specific operations. Similarly, how were average cost targets to be determined for planning the operations of the MTS in a given geographical region (assuming, of course, that central operational planning would be continued, and there was no reason to believe that it would not)? The cost patterns of individual stations even in very similar physical circumstances often varied tremendously. For example, in Krasnodar Krai the ratio of costs per centner of *naturoplata* in grain between the best and the worst MTS in 1954 was 1:140. In Leningrad Oblast in 1955 the ratio was 1:600.[8]

These were some of the important questions that had to be answered before a meaningful cost-accounting system could be introduced. As it turned out, the MTS were abolished before the answers could be determined. In the meantime only a few oblasts had made even a start on the conversion process.[9]

The fact that such detailed questions of MTS finances were being discussed by 1955 indicates that important, if at first barely perceptible, changes were taking place in the regime's attitudes toward the MTS. The system was beginning to be evaluated more and more in terms of economic efficiency and less and less in terms of its nonproduction services. Indeed, few of the participants in the discussions on cost-accounting even bothered to pay lip service to the old verities concerning the MTS-kolkhoz relationship. It is perhaps significant as an indication of alarm over these tendencies in certain Party circles that an article in the journal *Kommunist* devoted to problems of *khozraschet* in the MTS found it necessary to remind the debaters:

However, the problem of economic accounting in the machine-tractor stations does not amount simply to self-repayment. Otherwise, it would be necessary to admit that the goal of production activity of the MTS is only the receipt of payments in kind. In this case the MTS would be acting in the role of rental points, in the role of contractors, and not in the role of organizers of kolkhoz production.[10]

Nevertheless, *naturoplata* receipts were in fact becoming the primary criterion of the utility of the MTS. The organizational and political functions associated with the traditional manner of looking at the MTS-kolkhoz relationship were coming to be considered increasingly less relevant. By 1957 the MTS had become a major supplier of agricultural products to the state. Payments in kind for MTS services accounted for more than 50 percent of total state grain procurements, 12–13 percent of meat procurements, and 10 percent of milk procurements.[11] On the surface the importance of the MTS as a procurements agent might seem to guarantee its future. The point is, however, that once the utility of the MTS system was reduced to rubles-and-kopecks terms and the question of economic efficiency became paramount, the MTS became extremely vulnerable. Thus, once Khrushchev was convinced that the MTS was a very inefficient commodity supplier relative to other suppliers (see Table 13-1), its fate was sealed.

Table 13-1. Costs (rubles per centner) of commodities received from kolkhozes, MTS, and sovkhozes.

Commodity	State costs for produce from kolkhozes as obligatory deliveries and purchases	State costs for produce from MTS as *naturoplata*	Cost of sovkhoz produce
Grain	53	85	33
Raw cotton	372	126	158
Sugar beets	24	11	16
Meat	364	848	808
Milk	97	180	127
Wool	2,581	3,028	1,848

Source: N. S. Khrushchev, *Stroitel'stvo Kommunizma v SSSR i razvitie sel'skogo khoziaistva* (Moscow, 1962), II, 522.

The figures in Table 13-1 were given by Khrushchev during the speech to agricultural officials in Belorussia in which he announced his intention to do away with the MTS. Given the artificial nature of Soviet agricultural prices, the data were misleading as a statement of absolute, or even relative, costs. Indeed, no less an authority than Academician S. G. Strumilin would point out exactly three years later that it was impossible to determine the separate shares of the MTS and the kolkhozes in the product of their combined endeavors.[12] The fact is that Khrushchev himself was *convinced* that the MTS were an expensive burden on the state. His control over the prevailing balance of political forces made the absence of really hard data to prove this contention basically irrelevant.

THE RISE OF THE KOLKHOZES

For an understanding of how it was that Khrushchev suddenly found that he could do without the MTS, it is necessary to devote some attention to the rise in the status of the kolkhozes during the period under discussion. Under the orthodox conception of the MTS-kolkhoz relationship, the reader will remember, the kolkhoz had been relegated to the position of an intrinsically inferior, "inconsistently socialist" enterprise. Stalin's agricultural policies had given substance to this ideological conception. Systematically discriminatory practices had kept the kolkhozes in a hopelessly dependent position.

Under Khrushchev's stewardship many of the restrictions on the kolkhozes had been at least partially lifted, albeit in a piecemeal, more or less unconscious manner. As a result of continuing amalgamations the kolkhozes had been physically strengthened. By the end of 1957 the number of kolkhozes had declined to 76,535, as compared with 91,177 at the end of 1953.[13]

As the period progressed there were certain tangible indications of a relative shift in attention to the kolkhozes. An important step in this direction was the appeal in March 1955 for the recruitment of 30,000 experienced managers and technical specialists to go out to the village as kolkhoz chairmen. An unpublished Letter from the Central Committee and the Council of Ministers, dated March 25, was read at Party, office, trade-union, and shop meetings throughout the country to enlist volunteers for the project.[14] These so-called "thirty-thousanders" were given short courses in kolkhoz management and were to be assigned to the kolkhozes by July 1, 1955. In line with Khrushchev's emphasis on material incentives, they were promised good wages and fringe benefits.

According to *Pravda* in mid-January 1956, there were more than 100,000 applicants for the 30,000 positions — a tribute indeed to the Party's mobilization skills.[15] The personal backgrounds of the thirty-thousanders were fairly impressive and are of considerable interest from the standpoint of the subsequent development of relationships in the village. The majority of the new chairmen had no previous agricultural experience. Khrushchev, in his speech in Leningrad in April 1955, had noted that there had been strong arguments in the Central Committee for limiting the selection of chairmen to agronomists and zootechnicians. His own view was that this was not necessary.[16]

The selection process was primarily a local matter. Most of

the candidates were from the cities and raion centers of the oblasts to which the new chairmen were being assigned. A good many were former Party and Komsomol officials of the given or neighboring raion. For example, the five candidates sent to kolkhozes in the Atkar Raion of Saratov Oblast had previously held the positions of Second Secretary of the Atkar Raikom, First Secretary of the Atkar Komsomol Raikom, First Secretary of an urban Komsomol raikom in the oblast, Chief of the supply administration of a Saratov construction trust, and engineer in a Saratov meat-processing plant.[17]

Thus, the new kolkhoz chairmen often came from positions that were at least equal in the Soviet status hierarchy to that of an MTS director. Such persons were unlikely to submit without protest to the arbitary commands of the MTS directors. The potential for friction between the MTS and the kolkhozes was certainly increased by their presence. Indeed, the transfer of the MTS staff specialists to the kolkhozes in August 1955 was probably at least partly motivated by the desire to reinforce the integrity of command of the new chairmen and eliminate an important source of friction with the MTS.

The antagonism between the kolkhoz chairmen and the MTS was brought home with particular forcefulness to the leaders of the Party in the summer of 1956. In July, following a special session of the Supreme Soviet of the USSR devoted to a new pension law, Benediktov called a meeting of those deputies who were kolkhoz chairmen to sound out their opinions and suggestions on current agricultural matters. Benediktov was allegedly much taken aback when at the very beginning of the discussion the assembled chairmen had shouted in chorus: "We've had enough of the MTS!" * This incident may well have been a turning point in the attitude of Party leaders, particularly Khrushchev, toward the MTS and the entire future course of agricultural development. Even if the effects were not this crucial, the timing of the event was such that it must have had considerable impact at a time when important decisions were being made.

* This incident was related to the author by a prominent Soviet agricultural economist.

Meanwhile, significant changes had been taking place in the economic status of the kolkhozes as a result of the reforms introduced at the September Plenum. Rather than rely on massive investments of state funds, it had been decided to finance the development of kolkhoz agriculture chiefly from the funds of the kolkhozes themselves. This meant, of course, a radical change in the discriminatory pricing policy of the Stalin era. Among the steps taken were a reduction in the proportion of procurements to be exacted in the form of low-priced obligatory deliveries and a corresponding increase in the proportion procured at the higher state purchase prices. Improvements were also made in the terms of purchase of kolkhoz animal products. As a result of these and other price changes the kolkhozes rapidly increased their cash incomes and fixed capital funds (indivisible funds).

Table 13-2. Cash income and indivisible funds of kolkhozes. (millions of rubles)

Resources	1953[a]	1956[a]	1957[a]
Total cash income	49,641	94,616	95,213
Indivisible funds	69,841	98,592	101,959

Source: Sel'skoe khoziaistvo SSSR (statistical handbook) (1960), pp. 66, 72–73.
[a] End of year.

Despite this remarkable improvement in their financial condition, the kolkhozes did not invest enough of their funds in the expansion of their operations to suit Khrushchev and his supporters.[18] Rather than supplying the necessary supplements out of state funds, the regime resorted to the tried and tested methods of administrative pressure to get the kolkhozes to increase their own investments. On March 6, 1956, a decree was issued giving the kolkhozes the "right" to make substantial changes in their charters.[19] Although the actual changes suggested involved mainly such matters as the distribution of land for private plots and tightening requirements for the enjoyment of same, the major impact of the decree concerned the disposition of kolkhoz income. Specifically, it opened the way for subsequent pressures to raise the limits on the percentage of annual income to be transferred to the indivisible fund.*

This greater flexibility in the disposition of funds doubtlessly helped some of the wealthiest farms by facilitating the expansion of the production facilities and their income potential. For the majority of weaker farms the measure merely eliminated the legal restrictions on the amount of their income the state could force them to withhold from distribution to the kolkhozniks or other desired purposes. The full implications of the new pressures would be felt in 1959–1960, when the kolkhozes would be compelled to pay for the machinery they had been induced to buy during the summary liquidation of the MTS.

A more immediate illustration of the decision to rely increasingly on the kolkhozes for agricultural finances was the transfer of a large portion of the maintenance of the huge permanent staff of MTS machinery operators to the kolkhozes. The problem of keeping these workers usefully occupied throughout the year had been a matter of concern ever since Khrushchev had announced their transfer to the MTS payroll at the September Plenum. Traditionally winter has been a time of virtual hibernation in the Russian village. Before their transfer to the staff of the MTS, the maintenance of these persons had at least been the responsibility of the kolkhozes. Now about one and a quarter million additional peasants were living, essentially, on a form of state unemployment compensation for several months out of the year — except for the relatively small number of them who could be effectively used on repair and construction work. In March 1954 the economist V. G. Venzher had attempted to come to grips with this new manifestation of MTS inefficiency by suggesting that the total number of permanent workers could be reduced if emphasis was placed on training individuals in several different specialties.[20] Venzher's proposal was immediately rejected, and the very exist-

* Since 1938 the recommended percentage deduction for the indivisible fund, which was written into the charters of the individual kolkhozes, had been not less than 12 and not more than 15 percent for grain kolkhozes and 15-to-20 percent for technical crop and animal raising kolkhozes. In the Ukraine the average percentage for all kolkhozes until 1958 had been about 18.9 percent. In 1958, because of the pressure to purchase MTS machinery, it jumped to 24 percent (P. N. Pershin, ed., *Nedelimye fondy kolkhozov* [Moscow, 1960], p. 109).

ence of the problem was vigorously denied by authoritative Party spokesmen.[21]

The problem of underemployment was allowed to fester for another two years, until the entire question of MTS costs had become a major issue. Then, rather abruptly in late summer of 1956 it was decided to shift the major portion of the burden of wage payments to machinery operators during the agricultural season to the shoulders of the kolkhozes. Ostensibly this was done to increase the material incentives of the "mechanizers" in the expansion of kolkhoz production.[22] But it is quite clear that it was also a means of using the kolkhozes to "bail out" the MTS.

SOME PRELIMINARY EXPERIMENTS

Perhaps the best indication of change in the official attitude toward the inviolability of the traditional MTS-kolkhoz relationship was the increasing readiness to experiment with new forms and relations of production. One of the boldest of these experiments involved the crucial question of the ownership of tractors. Given the increasing pressure on the kolkhozes to invest in their own development, it was only a matter of time before some of the wealthier farms began to demand complex farm machinery of their own, including tractors. For many years it had been possible for the kolkhozes to rent one or two tractors from the MTS for special purposes, such as snow removal or construction, during the off season. This practice had never been formally sanctioned, but at the local level arrangements could sometimes be made. In any case, the question of actual ownership of the tractors was never in dispute.

The first sign of a change in the official attitude to the radical idea of kolkhoz tractor ownership was the publication in *Kommunist* in February 1956 of a request by two kolkhoz chairmen in Moscow Oblast for permission to purchase a few tractors. Their plea was relatively modest. They wanted the tractors merely for intrafarm transport and haulage, especially during the winter months and the spring thaw when it was difficult for the MTS to send its equipment.[23] Given the nature of the Soviet press, the very publication of the chairmen's letter was a signal of tacit approval. Permission was quietly granted, and many kolkhozes began to buy small row-crop tractors, such as the "KhTZ-7" and the "DT-14", through special arrangements with the Consumer Cooperative System.[24] In December 1956 the Council of Ministers issued a decree ordering the Agricultural Supply Administration, "*Glavsel'snab*," to sell tractors and accessory equipment to kolkhozes as well as to the MTS and sovkhozes.[25] Only small garden-type tractors were to be sold to the kolkhozes, however, and the terms of trade were far from attractive. The kolkhozes were required to pay twice the official transfer price recorded for MTS and sovkhoz tractor acquisitions and twice the price for fuel and spare parts.[26] Even at these inflated prices the kolkhozes usually experienced great difficulties in obtaining fuel and parts.[27] The experiment was obviously to be a very limited one. It represented anything but a firm commitment, but the important thing was that the ideological prohibition on kolkhoz tractor ownership had effectively been shattered.

In spite of supply and other difficulties, it appears that the experiment was a rousing success — or at least that the regime was determined to make it appear as such. The kolkhoz-owned tractors invariably performed more efficiently than those of the average MTS. Output per tractor was reported to be higher, and costs of operations were lower, although it should be noted that such claims were made after the decision to abolish the MTS had already been made.[28] Given the limited nature of kolkhoz tractor operations, these comparisons could hardly have been conclusive, but they were useful to Khrushchev in arguing the ability of the kolkhozes to take over the work of the MTS.

Another, more widely publicized, step in the dethroning of the MTS was the initiation of a series of experiments with new forms of production relations between the MTS and the kolkhozes. The first of these forms was the so-called combined or complex tractor-field brigade. As a result of the continuing process of kolkhoz mergers the MTS/kolkhoz ratio had reached the point in several important farming regions where each kolkhoz field brigade was being served by a single MTS tractor brigade. The complex brigade represented a unification of the MTS brigade and the kolkhoz brigade under a single brigadier, usually the head of the MTS tractor brigade. Most sources date the beginning of this experiment in 1956; however, there were apparently several of the complex brigades in operation as early as the spring of 1955 in Rostov Oblast.[29] The practice became fairly widespread in 1957, when there were 3,891 of the brigades at work in 2,228 kolhozes in the RSFSR; that is, in more than 5 percent of the kolkhozes in the republic.[30] Most of them were located in the southeastern regions, such as the North Caucasus, where the MTS/kolkhoz ratio was highest. A conference on wages and farm labor organization in the spring of 1957 suggested that the new form was not applicable in regions such as the non-Black Earth areas of the Center and the Northwest, where tractor brigades still served as many as ten kolkhoz field brigades.[31] Where they were appropriate, the complex brigades offered certain definite advantages, not only in the coordination of field operations, but also in savings on administrative expenses. In Moldavia, for example, it was claimed that the complex brigades had lowered costs by 15–30 percent.[32] But the brigades were feasible only in the relatively few areas where the MTS/kolkhoz ratio was sufficiently high (one-third or better).

An even more radical experiment with combined management was the unification of an MTS and a kolkhoz under a single director. Since this form of organization required an MTS/kolkhoz ratio of 1/1, its applicability was extremely limited. In all of the RSFSR, for example, there were only 110 MTS where the necessary conditions obtained. Forty-one of them were located in Stravropol' Krai, where the experiment was, accordingly, most heavily concentrated.[33]

Interestingly enough, Khrushchev had roundly condemned this form of organization when it had first been proposed in early 1955 at a Plenum of the Ukrainian Central Committee. His criticism of the idea was strikingly orthodox:

It is impossible to agree with the proposal, suggested here, that the chairman of the kolkhoz should simultaneously be the director of the MTS. The collective farm is a cooperative, and, consequently, it has its own charter and its own system, but the MTS is a state enterprise. It is impossible, then, to mix the one with the other.[34]

It was obvious that the suggestion had caught Khrushchev by surprise. In February 1955 he was still clearly unable to conceive of the possibility of basic changes in the nature of the MTS-kol-khoz relationship — which merely serves to underscore the depth of the transformation in his thinking over the next two and one-half years.

In the end, the two main types of experimentation with combined management operated only as a spur to further, more radical measures. Neither form was entirely satisfactory, even in its own terms. Neither proved capable of solving the fundamental problems of the MTS-kolkhoz relationship. The complex tractor-field brigade, for example, did not eliminate the problem of "two bosses on one piece of land," probably the cardinal weakness of the MTS-kolkhoz production system. The separate MTS and kolkhoz managements were still subject to their own distinct, often mutually contradictory, pressures, which were transmitted explicitly or implicitly to their respective subordinate in the combined brigades.

The problem with the integrated MTS-kolkhoz management system was somewhat different. By official order the formal institutional features of the basic MTS-kolkhoz relationship were preserved. For instance, even though one individual managed the affairs of the combined enterprise, he was still required to conclude a contract between the two components and maintain separate systems of accounts.[35] This was the sort of ideological and legalistic hangover that might possibly have been overcome in time had not the MTS been abolished so soon. As it was, the resistance to change seriously detracted from the effectiveness of the experiment. In the meantime, the solution for a number of the combined MTS and kolkhozes was conversion to sovkhozes. However, this, too, was not a universally acceptable answer. On the one hand, the state was reluctant to assume the accompanying financial burden in the form of guaranteed wages, pensions, and capital investments. On the other hand, the members of the wealthiest kolkhozes, which would have been best suited to conversion from the state's point of view, were not always willing to accept so drastic an alteration in their status.[36]

Whatever their specific advantages or shortcomings or even their potential for further development, it was clear that these organizational experiments were of too limited applicability to provide a nationwide solution. Such were, in fact, the conclusions of a Conference on the Organization and Payment of Labor in the Kolkhozes in the spring of 1957, mentioned above. Perhaps the only thing the participants were able to agree upon was that no one solution to the problems of MTS-kolkhoz relations was likely to be universally valid. They asserted that it would be a serious mistake even to attempt to find a single solution. Each region would have to discover its own characteristic organizational forms.[37]

However sensible, conclusions of this sort were hardly likely to appeal to Soviet leaders like Khrushchev, with their penchant for sweeping, universalistic measures and uniform administrative patterns. The newly vague, multiform nature of MTS-kolkhoz relations, was, moreover, difficult to justify in ideological terms. Some clearcut decision had to be made in the near future.

THE DECISION TO ABOLISH THE MTS

Khrushchev appears to have made up his mind to support the growing number of persons in favor of altering the status of the MTS some time in the late spring or early summer of 1957. The relatively long period that elapsed before the issue was brought to a head can only be explained in terms of the powerful opposition that the proposal aroused in conservative circles at the highest echelons of the Party.[38] The question of the future of the MTS was one of the key issues prompting the so-called anti-Party group to press their challenge to Khrushchev in June 1957. Sidney I. Ploss quotes the statement by Minister of Agriculture V. V. Matskevich at the December Plenum of the Central Committee in 1958 that

When the question actually arose of preparing materials for the MTS reorganization, Molotov and Kaganovich literally tried to terrorize the apparatus of the Ministry of Agriculture in order to obtain, or more precisely to concoct, any sort of materials which would discredit this measure.[39]

The ouster of the anti-Party group in June 1957 gave Khrushchev more leeway to proceed, but, as Ploss points out, this freedom was by no means complete. It was not until December that he felt secure enough to come out openly with an expression of support for the liquidation of the MTS.[40]

In the meantime, an important indication of the direction of Khrushchev's thinking was the publication of an article, "for discussion purposes," entitled "Time Does Not Wait" in the November issue of the literary journal *Oktiabr'*. The author was Ivan Vinnichenko, a Ukrainian journalist with past ties to Khrushchev. The article called attention to the extent to which the MTS, in particular the famous Shevchenko station, had been lagging behind the kolkhozes they served in the development of productive capacity in recent years: "So, it turns out, the MTS, that very 'city in the steppe,' which should, ideally, bring the most modern industrial culture to the kolkhozes, is, in fact, already beginning to lag behind them. Yes, it turns out that this is so!" [41]

Vinnichenko recalled a conversation he had with the economists Venzher and Sanina in which the ideological prohibitions on the sale of machinery to the kolkhozes had been discussed. Were not the kolkhozes, too, really socialist enterprises, they had asked? If so, why not build them up to their full potential by allowing them to acquire more of the basic means of production? He concluded that Marxism-Leninism, in reality, posed no fundamental obstacles to the sale of such equipment.[42] In a similar manner he disposed of a number of the other traditional objections to changes in the existing system of relationships in the village, including the position of the MTS in its present form.

In the course of the article he also discussed the strengths and weaknesses of the various experiments with unified management and the rental or sale of farm machinery to the kolkhozes. Where practicable, he said, the idea of forming sovkhozes had much to recommend it, also. In the end, however, Vinnichenko refused to come out for any one particular solution. He concluded, as had the spring conference on kolkhoz organization and wages, that the problem was extremely complex: "What is to be done, then? We must search! But search not for a 'philosopher's stone,' not for some kind of general pattern, but for completely concrete solutions for each zone, for each raion, for each kolkhoz." [43]

By the end of 1957, then, a clearcut decision on the form of the reorganization had still to be made. It is doubtful that Khrushchev had made up his own mind on precise forms or on timing, at this point. An illustration of this indecision was the action taken in December to transfer the financing of the MTS from the All-Union budget to the republic budgets. Discussing this measure at the Budgetary Session of the Supreme Soviet on December 21, Matskevich expressed the hope that it would "facilitate the further improvement" of the financial condition of the MTS.[44] In addition, there was evidence that the response to Vinnichenko's article had not been as favorable as Khrushchev might have wished. A number of articles by kolkhoz chairmen raised serious objections to wholesale changes in the existing system.[45] There were obviously many questions to be answered before almost thirty years of experience with the MTS could be discarded.

Nevertheless, Khrushchev appeared determined to push ahead immediately. It probably seemed to him that he had no choice. The issue was obviously being used as a rallying point for those who continued to oppose him after his incomplete victory at the June Plenum. Thus, the situation posed both a risk and an opportunity to deal the opposition a major blow. Gambler that he was, Khrushchev decided to force a challenge. As far as the author has been able to determine, the first time Khrushchev publicly broached the idea of abolishing the MTS was in the concluding paragraphs of an address at a Plenum of the Ukrainian Central Committee on December 26, 1957. This was, of course, a friendly audience and a good opportunity to test middle-rank Party sentiment. Interestingly, the speech was not published at the time in either the central or republic press, indicating that he was not yet sure of his ground — or, possibly, that he was not yet in sufficient control to be able to force the publication of so controversial a proposal on a divided Party oligarchy. The obvious diffidence with which he injected the issue into his speech lends weight to the impression that he was feeling his way until he could ascertain the reaction of his audience.

Khrushchev: And finally let us take the administrative apparatus. Here, too, there is much waste, both in the kolkhozes and in the machine-tractor stations.

This is where the high costs of kolkhoz production arise, too. Consequently, is it not time to proceed to the transfer of the technology of the MTS to some of the kolkhozes?

Voices from the hall: Right!

Khrushchev: I think it is right. When the land and the equipment are in the hands of a single boss, then all the machines will doubtless be more productively used. In this way we shall unfetter the initiative of the kolkhozniks still more.[46]

Then, obviously reassured by the response, he made it clear that he was not talking about a partial sale of MTS equipment to "some of the kolkhozes" at all, but a wholesale liquidation of the MTS as presently constituted. For he went on to propose that only the few machines that the kolkhozes could not themselves use be retained in the stations, which would be converted to simple rental points (the term he employed).[47]

In the weeks that followed, Khrushchev ordered the convening of a series of conferences of raikom secretaries, kolkhoz chairmen, and MTS directors under the auspices of the Central Committee in order to determine the general reaction to the transfer and, undoubtedly to whip up support for it as well.[48] According to Khrushchev, speaking somewhat later, all who participated in these conferences had agreed at least that the matter was ripe for discussion.[49]

Events were moving rapidly by this time. Toward the end of January 1958 Khrushchev apparently felt confident enough of the outcome to make a public declaration that the MTS were soon to be abolished. The occasion was the Conference of Outstanding Workers of Agriculture in Belorussia on January 22 in the city of Minsk. In the middle of his address he suddenly announced: "I would like to raise for your consideration one of the most important questions of economic construction — the role of the machine-tractor stations under contemporary conditions." [50] He hailed the great positive role the MTS had played in the development of the kolkhoz system, in the mechanization of agriculture, and in the procurement of commodities for the state. In recent years, however, the stations had been unable to maintain their leading role in the village. He presented a catalogue of reasons for this decline that was obviously designed to answer point by point the major objections of the opponents of liquidation.

First, on the question of the quality of leadership cadres in the village, he argued that the kolkhozes had been strengthened with mature leaders "capable of solving any problems." Primary Party Organizations had also been strengthened. And the raikoms were staffed with experienced and well trained cadres capable of providing sound economic guidance. As a result, said Khrushchev, "there is no need to burden the MTS with the role of organizer of production." [51]

Second, as a result of the amalgamation campaign, the kolkhozes were no longer small-scale enterprises unable to use modern technology rationally. Farms of several thousand hectares, he said, were fully capable of managing their technological operations without the assistance of the MTS.[52]

Third, the psychological role of the MTS in transforming the work habits of the peasants had long since been completed:

The MTS have ceased to play that political role which they played in the first stage of kolkhoz construction. There is no one for them to convince now of the superiorities of large-scale, mechanized farming, for our kolkhoz cadres now understand this very well themselves, and the kolkhoznik cannot conceive of his life outside of the kolkhoz.[53]

Fourth, concerning the role of the MTS as a source of commodity procurements, he said that recent price increases and the continuing high levels of overhead and administrative expenditures of the MTS system had made kolkhoz produce received as payments in kind for MTS services even more expensive than sovkhoz produce. In short, the MTS had become a prohibitively costly source of procurements.[54]

Finally, he turned to the traditional problem of friction and conflicting pressures between MTS and kolkhoz management. Obviously, Khrushchev expected this issue to arouse the most popular support for the changes he contemplated.

There are two bosses on one plot of land — the kolkhozes and the MTS. And where there are two bosses, there cannot be good order. In the modern farm everything depends on the work of the tractor and the combine. Yet the kolkhoz has to agree upon and coordinate even such matters as where to put a tractor. All this leads to an irrational use of technology and brings harm to the interests of the state and the kolkhozes.

He concluded by asking, "Is it not better to sell the machines to the kolkhozes and let them use the technology themselves in the interests of the economy?" [55]

Many of these arguments could have been advanced years earlier, particularly the last one. If economic criteria had been emphasized, the utility of the MTS in many areas of the country could have been questioned long ago, as Venzher and others had pointed out. But the quest for uniformity of administration and stringent controls in the countryside had made a pragmatic approach to the farm machinery question impossible. Now the opponents of the MTS had a wonderful champion. However, it is doubtful whether they approved of the enthusiasm and haste with which their pet project was to be carried out.

Khrushchev immediately ordered a special session of the Central Committee to discuss the liquidation of the MTS and to present Theses on the subject for public "debate" prior to the enactment of formal legislation. The Plenum was held on the 25th and 26th of February. The Theses which Khrushchev presented in his report were essentially a detailed restatement of the arguments he had made in Minsk, except that considerably more attention was given to the problem of the ability of the kolkhozes to absorb the MTS equipment. Either because of the continued opposition to the entire proposal or because of genuine recognition of the complexities of the problems involved, Khrushchev found it expedient to stress the gradualness and the basic continuities of the transformation process.

At the same time this is not a question of the liquidation of the MTS. but of their gradual reorganization, to be carried out for the purpose of improving the production and technical service to the kolkhozes with consideration for the peculiarities of different zones and regions and the level of the development of the economy of the individual kolkhozes.[56]

Ostensibly, an important part of the "reorganization" was to be the transformation of a large number of MTS (more than 40 percent of the pre- 1958 total, it turned out) into so-called Repair-and-Technical Stations (RTS). The latter would assume some of the functions of the MTS, such as major repairs of kolkhoz machines, rental of specialized equipment, distribution of fuel, spare parts, chemical fertilizers, and so forth. The RTS were to operate on a strict *khozraschet* basis. The kolkhozes would pay for all services in cash.

Another section of the Theses was devoted to details and conditions of the disposal of MTS machinery. Here, too, the commitment to gradualness and voluntary choice on the part of the kolkhozes was firmly established. General principles for the organization of the sales were to be worked out in each territory by the responsible provincial Party and governmental leaders. It was strongly "recommended," however, that most kolkhozes in the main agricultural regions buy up the machinery they required without delay.[57] Special raion commissions were to be formed to assess the ruble value of the machinery on hand in the MTS. But the kolkhozes were urged to take the machines immediately, without waiting for the completion of the assessment process.

The final section of the Theses concerned "The Tasks of Party and Soviet Organs in Connection with the Reorganization of the MTS." Given the nature of the Soviet system and the tremendous loss of control which the liquidation of the MTS network implied, this section undoubtedly concealed a good deal of heated debate and controversy at the highest levels of the Party apparatus. The solutions presented in the Theses clearly bore the stamp of Khrushchev's personal approach to the problems of administration. The former highly structured control patterns of the nationwide MTS system were to be replaced by the less structured and less specialized leadership of the regular territorial Party organs. Thus, the leading role in the implementation and management of the new system without the MTS was to be played by the provincial and raion Party committees. In addition to propagandizing and explaining the new arrangements, they were given responsibility for deciding which kolkhozes should buy what MTS equipment and when. The raikoms were also given special responsibility for the operations of the new RTS. Evidently, Khrushchev's campaign to bring Party control in the countryside "closer to production" was not to be interrupted by the liquidation of the MTS: "The task is, after the abolition of the instructor groups of the Party raikoms for the MTS zones and after the reorganization of the MTS, to bring leadership of the kolkhozes by Party and Soviet organs still closer to the decisive sectors of production." [58]

The role of the "Soviet organs" under the new system was unclear. Khrushchev himself was apparently not as much interested in creating a formal local link in the chain of the agricultural bureaucracy as were many of his colleagues. For him, the less formal processes of direct Party leadership were sufficient. Many of the formal administrative processes connected with the prevailing agricultural system, such as the confirmation of kolkhoz production and financial plans, were to be entrusted to the *raiispolkom*. The precise format of the administrative arrangements in the raions was to be left for public discussion.[59] However, when it turned out, as he admitted in his speech at the session of the Supreme Soviet on March 27, that many people were in favor of a return to the old raizo system,[60] Khrushchev asserted in no uncertain terms that he would never accept such a proposal.[61] In the end he settled for a system of inspectorates directly attached to the *raiispolkom*. The main burden of local control was clearly to fall to the raikom. Thus, special attention in the Theses was given to the need for strengthening raikom leadership with agricultural expertise. Basically, what Khrushchev had in mind was a return to long-term direct control by the raikom, bolstered by solid knowledge of agricultural science on the part of the raikom secretaries.

Last, and perhaps least, the Theses made the customary mention of the increased role of the PPO's under the new dispensation. One of Khrushchev's selling points in arguing for the abolition of the MTS had been the steady growth in the size and coverage of Party organizations in the kolkhozes. The liquidation of the MTS and the transfer of MTS specialists and machinery operators, many of whom were Communists, would, it was expected, give a substantial boost to the strength of the kolkhoz PPO's.[62]

For all practical purposes, the publication of Khrushchev's Theses represented the end of the MTS system. In spite of the cautious wording of the document itself and the numerous objections raised to many of its details in the ensuing nationwide discussion, the dismantling of the MTS proceeded with amazing rapidity. By the end of 1958 there remained only 345 MTS in the entire country.[63] It is not difficult to agree with Ploss's conclusion that once Khrushchev had made up his mind, he contemplated the speediest possible liquidation.[64] The gradualist language he employed in his arguments was obviously a mere smokescreen for avoiding direct confrontation with his opponents until sufficient popular enthusiasm or, at least, local political support could be generated.

That there was considerable opposition to the dissolution of the MTS, despite the fanfare of approval orchestrated in the mass media, and that this opposition was by no means confined to the high-level political opponents of Khrushchev cannot seriously be doubted. Even among the peasants, for whom the breakup of the MTS system was supposed to be so great a boon, there were important objections, if only to the manner in which the MTS liquidation was to be carried out. It was obvious to all that the transfer of machinery to the kolkhozes would put tremendous financial burdens upon them. An excellent illustration of peasant attitudes and, perhaps, a fitting epitaph for the MTS as well were the words of a country cousin of the hero in Valeriy Tarsis' novelette *The Bluebottle*:

And look what they've thought up. Just because a few kolkhozes are beginning to have a little money, they have to go and take it away. Selling us back our own machinery — tractors made with our money. They stripped us bare to make those tractors; now we have to pay for them again. Do you think we have two lives?[65]

For the MTS the period inaugurated by the September Plenum of the Central Committee in 1953 represented in many respects a return to Markevich's original idea of the "inter-village machine-tractor station." In line with his simplistic, action-oriented formula of bringing leadership "closer to production," Khrushchev attempted to make the MTS zone, rather than the raion, the fundamental unit of economic and political leadership in the countryside. The MTS became centers of planning, procurements, technical supervision, and Party control once again. To be sure, many of the responsibilities now conferred exclusively on the

MTS had been assigned to them in one way or another during past periods. However, in the past there had always been other local agencies, such as the raizo, with similar, or overlapping responsibilities for the kolkhozes. That is, the MTS had in essence been shielded from full accountability for the performance of their zones. Now, for the first time the MTS had the field to themselves.

In the more pragmatic atmosphere of the post-September Plenum years this heightened visibility made the MTS extremely vulnerable. Each aspect of MTS operations came under scrutiny on its merits. Those found wanting were discarded. Proposals which had been rejected in earlier periods on ideological and political grounds now began to receive a sympathetic hearing.

Perhaps the most important change of all was the new attitude toward the kolkhoz. Khrushchev was much less concerned than his predecessor with the maintenance of strict political and administrative control in the village. Stalin's paranoid fear of peasant disloyalty was replaced by an implicit faith that genuine support could be gained in the village by a judicious use of economic incentives, that in the long run such a policy would be cheaper and more effective, in political as well as economic terms. Thus, at the same time that he was strengthening the MTS, Khrushchev began a series of experiments to improve the material position of the kolkhozes. The relative responses of the MTS and the kolkhozes to the new programs were clearly to the advantage of the latter. Many kolkhozes actually began to accumulate significant amounts of capital. Gradually, Khrushchev became aware that the kolkhozes offered greater leverage than the MTS for the rapid improvement of the agricultural sector. The MTS, on the other hand, increasingly appeared as an unnecessary burden on the state.

There can be little doubt that for Khrushchev the fundamental arguments for the liquidation of the MTS were economic. It is equally clear, however, that political infighting at the highest levels of the Party were also heavily involved in the rush to a decision. The function of the conservative political opposition was probably more that of a catalyst in the decision-making process than a principal cause for the decision. The fact that the opposition chose to make the proposal a question of Khrushchev's legitimacy as a ruler forced him to press for the immediate consummation of the liquidation process. In addition, Khrushchev knew from long experience that the agricultural bureaucracy might have delayed the conversion process indefinitely if given the opportunity under a piecemeal approach. There were, of course, many members of the bureaucracy, not to mention the MTS officials themselves, with a vested interest in the preservation of the existing system. Finally, Khrushchev's natural impetuosity also influenced the tempo of the liquidation. Having made up his mind that the MTS were expendable and facing serious problems of resource allocation for his grandiose domestic and foreign plans, he was obviously impatient to disencumber the state of the costs of maintaining the MTS, regardless of the heavy burden that this would place upon the kolkhozes. These various pressures combined to give the liquidation of the MTS an aura of haste and coerciveness which would seriously threaten its efficacy.

14   Conclusions

The foregoing chapters have attempted to accomplish two things: to present the history of an important Soviet institution, the MTS, and to use this history as a source of data and illustrations for a study of various aspects of the Soviet policy process. Because the historical discussion more or less speaks for itself, these concluding remarks will be concerned primarily with the latter of the two problems.

The evidence of the MTS, if nothing else, provides additional confirmation of the truism that policy formulation and policy implementation are inseparably linked. Structural, behavioral, and ideological constraints on the implementation and administration of policy inevitably influence the content of policy itself. Another general conclusion suggested by the history of the MTS is that any monistic, single-factor interpretation of the Soviet policy process is bound to be unsatisfactory if not downright misleading. Situational demands, high-level power struggles, ideology, and personal leadership style were all important factors in the formulation and implementation of agricultural policies during the MTS period. But no single one of these factors can truly be said to have been *the* independent variable in the policy equation on a continuing basis.

In the book a number of these individual factors have been discussed at length and related to specific policy issues involving the MTS. For example, Marxist-Leninist ideology was shown to have performed a number of manifest and latent functions in policy-making. The precise influence of the ideological model of the MTS-kolkhoz relationship on any given agricultural decision is not easy to pinpoint. Sometimes it served merely as an ex post facto rationalization for policies that were determined by situational or personal political considerations. At other times, it had a more independent prescriptive influence, suggesting additional functions for the MTS or a reappraisal of existing functions. In

332

the long run the influence of the model on policy was essentially conservative. The idealized picture of the role of the MTS tended to become a surrogate for its actual role, impeding the search for pragmatic solutions to agricultural problems and absolutely precluding the consideration of non-MTS solutions. In any case it is evident that ideology was basically a conditioning factor, an intervening variable in the policy process rather than a determining factor in its own right.

Another important factor discussed at various points in the book was that of high-level political infighting. The seemingly endless jockeying for political advantage by officials at or near the apex of the Party machine, despite surface impressions of unity, has come to be recognized as one of the characteristic features of the Soviet political system. Although the author does not totally subscribe to the so-called conflict model of Soviet politics, at least in so far as it implies that substantive issues are of minor importance in the decision-making process, the profound impact of the power struggle on many specific policies is impossible to deny.

As a rule, the policy influence of this political competition is strongest during succession crises. At such times the contenders for supreme power are particularly likely to use substantive issues instrumentally, for example in the setting up of "straw men" with whom their opponents are compared. ("Some comrades are of the erroneous opinion . . .") Even when the throne of the dictator is evidently secure, the jockeying for power among his closest subordinates goes on and may exert an important influence on policy. During the Stalin era the extreme delay in the ordering of MTS finances and the reorganization of the agricultural bureaucracy was at least partially the result of the intervention of political considerations. Khrushchev's contest with Andreev over the patently secondary issue of the *zveno* was another good example of this phenomenon under a secure dictatorship.

When the mantle of leadership is not securely worn, the power coloration of the policy process is that much more strongly pronounced. Ploss has presented considerable evidence of the instrumental use of substantive issues during Khrushchev's insecure tenure. The extreme abruptness, bordering on recklessness, with which he pushed through the physical liquidation of the MTS system was largely motivated by his need to smash the opposition that was crystallizing around the MTS "reorganization" issue. As we shall see in the Epilogue, this struggle would carry over to the RTS in the Post-MTS period and would extend to the Ministry of Agriculture itself.

Nevertheless, the political struggle factor should be viewed primarily as a conditioning factor, rather than a direct impetus to policy. There is a certain amount of real skill involved in selecting issues that can serve as effective political rallying points. As any student of American politics must be aware, this is one of the cardinal attributes of the successful politician. However, a substantive issue can rarely be manufactured out of whole cloth for such purposes. The issues must be real and relatively important in themselves.

The third policy factor noted is the personal style of leadership of the Soviet ruler(s). In a highly centralized, authoritarian political system like that of the Soviet Union the personal style of the ruling figure, or figures, is bound to exert a pervasive influence on policy. To be sure, style is not the most tangible of political indicators. Indeed, its importance as an explanatory variable was never fully appreciated in Western Soviet studies until well into the Khrushchev era when some observers began to question a number of the basic assumptions of the standard "totalitarian model." Longitudinal comparisons of specific Soviet institutions, such as the present study of the MTS, however, are particularly sensitive to the operations of the stylistic factor. The history of the MTS clearly shows that there were different Stalinist and Khrushchevian styles of agricultural policy-making and administration. The Epilogue suggests that there is a Brezhnev-Kosygin-? style, as well.

The specific manifestations of these differences of style have been discussed elsewhere in the book and need not be treated here except in very summary fashion. Stalin's cautious, conservative, dogmatic personal style impressed itself on the entire complex of agricultural policies during his reign. His well known abhorrence of spontaneity and his distrust of the peasantry certainly contributed to the elevation of coercive political methods over economic incentives in the achievement of production goals to a greater extent than would seem to have been required even by the "primitive socialist accumulation" model of development. The effects of this style were particularly noticeable also in his use of ideology, which became an impediment, rather than a guide to the formulation and evaluation of policy.

The contrasts of Khrushchev's livelier, more adventurous style can hardly be exaggerated. Ideological norms and verities tended to be handled in a much more flexible, not to say cavalier, manner. Although economic achievements retained their high priority, Khrushchev's great self-confidence and his manifest willingness to rely on peasant initiative permitted much more leeway in the application of various types of incentives — particularly economic incentives — for the attainment of production goals. His style was also reflected in his propensity for experimentation with structural variations in the implementation of policy. It was precisely these stylistic characteristics which led many Western observers during the Khrushchev era to proclaim the accomplishment of an irreversible transformation in the basic nature of the Soviet system. In this case stylistic changes were sometimes confused with basic systemic changes, the real extent of which was probably exaggerated. Thus, if it is incorrect to ignore style, it is probably equally unwise to overemphasize its independent influence as a policy determinant.

By a simple process of elimination, then, we are left with what we have called situational factors as the closest thing to an independent variable in the Soviet policy process. Ultimately it was the concrete requirements of agricultural production and procurements, or specific operational or administrative problems of the MTS system that were the most important factors in the shaping of MTS policy. If this is indeed a general rule of the Soviet system, the question naturally arises how that system really differs from any other modern industrial system. The answer lies, perhaps, in the qualifiers "ultimately" and "most" in the above statement. What is unique about the Soviet policy process is the potency of the intervening factors. Ideology, political infighting, and personal style strongly affect the manner in which situational imperatives are perceived, presented, and acted upon. Throughout the history of the MTS these factors sometimes accelerated, sometimes at-

tenuated, sometimes — in the case of ideology — actually precluded a response to situational demands. On the basis of MTS
experience, then, the conclusion may be drawn that although in
the long run situational requirements will usually be accommodated, the other policy factors discussed will condition the timing
and even many of the specific details of that accommodation.

The main substantive focus of the book has been on administrative aspects of the MTS, particularly those aspects which illustrate the unique division of labor between Party, governmental,
and economic organs in the management of the agricultural system. Generally, the findings tend to confirm the proposition advanced by Hough and others that the officially proclaimed separation of Party and governmental functions does not really exist
in practice. During the most critical phases of the agricultural production cycle the responsible local Party organs — that is, the raikoms — have been expected to intervene in the management of
production affairs. Although the regime has perennially called for
the strengthening of local administrative and managerial agencies,
it has always considered essential the maintenance of a strong
Party reserve force to supply extra pressure and "guidance" during
campaign periods. To a certain extent the same type of Party
intervention may be observed in industry. However, its intensity
has been particularly great in agriculture, perhaps because of
the markedly cyclical nature of the production process, but also
because of the extremely high level of state demands for agricultural output. If in industry there has been a tendency to make
at least minimal concessions to technological and administrative
expertise and the requirements of predictability, there has been
no such tendency, up to the most recent post-Khrushchevian
period, in the agricultural sector. Hence the continuing resort to
direct political pressures.

The MTS system traditionally occupied a prominent position
in the network of political and administrative controls in the village, although the intensity of its involvement in these controls
varied over time. In Chapter 5 it was found that the position of
the MTS system in the successive reorganizations of the agricultural bureaucracy was a good indicator of general policy trends.

The MTS was always a symbol of centralized controls. During periods of intensified agricultural demands or tightened political controls in the countryside the position of the MTS system and of the individual stations was enhanced at the expense of other administrative agencies. This was done chiefly by the concentration of additional administrative and operational responsibilities in the various levels of the MTS hierarchy. Conversely, during periods of relative relaxation some of these responsibilities were transferred from the MTS system to the regular administrative organs, particularly the raizo. These reorganizations followed a roughly cyclical pattern, which was determined primarily by situational factors, but also by the particular administrative styles of the rulers in power. As might be expected, Khrushchev's reorganizations tended to be much more radical than Stalin's.

At the level of the individual station, MTS responsibilities for kolkhoz administration were always considerable, although in practice not necessarily as great as the ideological model suggests. The stations were expected to play a major role in kolkhoz planning and organization, as well as production. They also had important responsibilities for the training of kolkhoz personnel. As in the case of direct production operations, however, the MTS performed these functions at best indifferently. Not only were the stations themselves poorly staffed to provide the necessary leadership, but the relentless pressures for gross output made it often more expedient for the MTS director to try to manipulate "his" kolkhozes for the benefit of the station than to assist them in organizing for their own benefit. As a result, the customary attitude of the kolkhozniks was "the less help from the MTS, the better." Unfortunately, because of physical as well as political reasons the kolkhozes were not often in a position to do without at least some of the services of the MTS, especially after World War II and its disastrous effects on kolkhoz draft animals.

Yet, lest the reader be left with the impression that the MTS was an omnipresent force, darkly lurking behind each hapless kolkhoz village in the country, it might be well to present the picture of a supposedly typical station of the late forties described by Galina Nikolaeva — hardly a critic of the achievements of socialism in the village — in her Stalin-Prize-winning novel, *Harvest*:

It consisted of several old structures and old machinery lying back of the ravine on the edge of the village . . . It was just an MTS as all MTS go. When tilling time came it would give the farm a tractor, when harvesting time [came]—the loan of a combine for several days. Just an ordinary simple thing and of no particular interest.[1]

This picture is undoubtedly somewhat underdrawn, as it was meant to contrast with the grandiose new MTS which was being built in the locality described and which was expected to play a major role in the life of the raion. Nevertheless, it is helpful in maintaining some kind of perspective on the actual influence of the MTS in the daily lives of the peasants in many parts of the country. As is true of so many areas of Soviet life, it is just this divergence between official standards and reality that makes life bearable for the rank-and-file citizen.

A balanced perspective is especially useful where the political functions of the MTS are concerned. Because in the Soviet system political control and leadership are by definition the monopoly of the Communist Party and its organs, the really important questions must center on the extent to which the MTS themselves served as centers, or agencies, of Party control in the village. From a theoretical standpoint the MTS always had great potential as Party activity centers in the countryside. In both the nature of their mission and the composition of their personnel they more closely reflected the industrial-proletarian self-image of the Party than did any other rural institution. Accordingly, the regime sought very early to use the MTS as a means of maximizing the leverage of the weak, scattered Party forces in the village. The MTS support points and the politotdels were particularly clear expressions of this policy. Even under the regular raikom mode of Party control, however, the MTS were given unique status by the assignment to them of special Party officials, the deputy directors for the political sector, whose responsibilities often extended beyond the boundaries of the stations themselves.

Nevertheless, the discussion in Part III presents substantial reasons for questioning whether the types of activity engaged in by the MTS Party organizations really made the stations centers of political control in the village. It was primarily as production institutions that the raikom secretaries were most interested in the MTS. The latter were key instruments in their hands for the attainment of the tremendous production goals sent down from above. To the extent that political work — ideological indoctrination, the maintenance of morale and discipline — in the stations made them more efficient and vigorous in the pursuit of their production tasks the raikom was interested in MTS political work. As we have seen, such activity did not occupy a very high position on the list of raikom priorities; in any case, it had little to do with the use of the MTS as centers of political control in the village. Indeed, it appears that most of the time the MTS were as much the objects as the agents of political activity in the countryside.

During periods of particular stress, it is true, the regime sometimes intensified the level of Party activities in the MTS zones to the extent of attaching autonomous leading Party organs right to the stations. At such times Party control over the kolkhozes did emanate directly from the MTS, rather than from the raion centers. The content of Party activity during these politotdel periods was even more narrowly production oriented than during normal raikom control periods. But even in such cases it is questionable whether the MTS per se can be said to have exercised political control over their zones. Under normal operating conditions the MTS director and the politotdel chief functioned in a complementary fashion in the production process. However, the chief was certainly not subordinate to the director in any political sense. Much of the activity of the politotdels was focussed on eliminating the shortcomings of the stations, often to the dismay of the directors, many of whom were actually removed by the politotdels for supposed economic and/or political failings. The politotdel was a special "Party eye" in the countryside, rather than an agent of the MTS: its gaze fell on MTS and kolkhozes alike.

This conclusion suggests not so much that the prevailing conceptions of the coerciveness of the MTS have been wrong but that the nature of the coerciveness has been imperfectly understood. Its essence lay in the fundamental principles of the MTS-kolkhoz relationship, which was based first and foremost on the economic exploitation of the kolkhozes. The political, administrative, social, and psychological repression of the peasants were superstructural, in a brutally vulgar Marxian sense, to this basic economic fact. The kolkhozes were maintained in a state of helpless infancy by their enforced dependence on the MTS. Political, administrative, and legal controls were merely the instruments for the maintenance of this master-servant relationship and the extortionate procurement policies which underlay it. Aside from the fact that the MTS were part of the procurement machinery, the real coercion of the MTS system lay in its being forced upon the kolkhozes, whether they saw any economic advantage in MTS services or not.

The combination of pious ideological platitudes with the all too obviously coercive and exploitative realities of the MTS-kolkhoz relationship served in the long run thoroughly to discredit the idea of the MTS. This was unfortunate, for in principle the MTS idea made a good deal of sense. It was a uniquely suitable response to the problem of rapid agricultural expansion in the face of acute shortages of farm machinery and skilled technical personnel, such as the Soviet regime confronted in the first decades of the collective farm system. A strong case might even be made for the MTS as an agent of social transformation, since by introducing the backward peasant masses to modern machinery and industrial patterns of labor organization, it certainly helped to prepare them for absorption into a developing urban-industrial society. These facets of the MTS system are obviously relevant to the difficult problems of modernization confronting many developing nations today. Indeed, there is much in Markevich's original conception of the MTS that might be applicable to cooperative agricultural development in resource- and skill-poor traditional societies.

Yet the impact of the MTS idea has been minimal, even in those developing countries which have received Soviet aid, to say nothing of the countries of the so-called Socialist Commonwealth. In the Soviet Union itself the MTS has been so thoroughly discredited that the notion of extending it to other countries is treated with incredulity. When the author described his interest in the practical aspects of the MTS and its possible application elsewhere, he was more than once answered with the wry comment that, yes, the MTS might well be an answer to America's problems of agricultural overproduction!

Although there were many problems resulting from the unseemly haste with which it was carried out, the abolition of the MTS system has obviously brought numerous long-term benefits to Soviet agriculture. Not only has it relieved the kolkhoz — and the state — of a tremendous economic burden, but even more important, it has given kolkhoz leaders much-needed experience in the management of the total production process. This experience has undoubtedly strengthened the capacities of the kolkhoz system for further development; for the lack of local leadership talent has always been a major obstacle to the success of Soviet farm programs. Whether or not the collective farm system itself is worthy of further development is really a value question which a Western observer is not fully competent to judge.

The author was fortunate in having the opportunity to discuss problems of large-scale mechanized farming with many Soviet citizens some five years after the liquidation of the MTS. It is perhaps significant that those persons with at most only a peripheral connection with agriculture were the most vociferous in arguing for a return to the MTS system or some other form of centralized control over the maintenance and use of farm machinery. They argued, with some justification perhaps, that the kolkhozes were unable to use and maintain their expensive equipment properly. Those interviewed who had played a direct role in MTS or kolkhoz operations, however, were overwhelmingly in favor of the new order. They were adamantly against a return to an MTS type of arrangement, regardless of any short-term difficulties. Fortunately for the progress of Soviet agriculture the latter view has apparently prevailed, although, as the Epilogue reveals, there have been some minor elements of a return to centralized control. Party and state controls in the village remain in abundance, but life is certainly easier without the MTS.

15 Epilogue

In retrospect it is obvious that the liquidation of the MTS was not the panacea for the problems of Soviet agriculture that Khrushchev had promised. Although it did help to alleviate some of the more glaring distortions in the agricultural system, its effects on certain other, equally basic difficulties was at best marginal. In the short run, at least, it had many of the negative consequences which Khrushchev's opponents had predicted: it opened once again certain fundamental issues of the future of the kolkhoz system; it seriously complicated the disposition and maintenance of the still far from abundant supplies of farm machinery, leaving many kolkhozes in dire financial straits; and, most important, it thoroughly disrupted the traditional methods of Party and state control over the kolkhozes. Considerations of Kremlin politics apart, Khrushchev had made a major gamble in pressing for the summary liquidation of the MTS: he had gambled that the economic payoff would more than compensate for the inevitable loss of control over the kolkhozes. The record harvest of 1958, largely the result of an unusually favorable distribution of climatic conditions throughout the country, had made the gamble look extremely good. But within a year, with a return to more normal weather patterns and a corresponding decline in crop yields, there were already signs of disaffection in high Party circles.[1] Indeed, if Oleg Penkovskiy is to be believed, Khrushchev himself privately began to question the wisdom of his decision and would gladly have reestablished the MTS but for fear of public humiliation.[2] Whatever the truth of this assertion, one might quite convincingly argue for an interpretation of the remaining years of Khrushchev's reign as a search for institutional substitutes for the MTS. The following pages will trace some of the major steps in this search.

THE CHANGING STATUS OF THE KOLKHOZ

The post-MTS period has been marked by a noticeable tendency toward a decline in the prominence of ideological argumentation in the public treatment of agricultural policies. This is not to say

342

that ideological explanations and theoretical discussions are no longer heard. Past formulas and the exegetical style associated with the theory of the MTS-kolkhoz relationship were bound to leave their mark. However, the lack of a final ideological and political arbiter after Stalin has led to a situation where, in a manner analogous to that in intra-Communist Bloc relations, ideological argument became a mere instrument in the continuing power struggles among the various factions and personalities in the ruling Party oligarchy. Following a sort of Gresham's Law of political theory, bad ideology has tended to drive out the good. The result has been a decline in the general propensity to theorize on concrete agricultural issues.

An interesting example of this decline has been the question of the status of the kolkhoz as a socialist enterprise in the post-MTS period. Both the proponents and opponents of the elimination of the MTS had hastened to advance ideological arguments to justify their respective positions. The conservative opponents turned to the old Stalinist thesis that the sale of machinery to the kolkhozes would place them in an anomalous position among Soviet enterprises, a position incompatible with the general march toward communism. Khrushchev and his supporters had countered by dredging up Lenin's hoary formulations "On Cooperation," asserting that the kolkhozes, as cooperatives, would be no less "socialist" for having their own machinery. Nevertheless, given past ideological conventions, they were clearly hesitant to claim for the kolkhoz a status fully equal to that of the sovkhoz. Instead, they argued that the acquisition of machinery would facilitate the gradual evolution of kolkhoz property towards state property. An important variation on this theme, eventually adopted by the usually conservative Minister of Agriculture Matskevich, was that both the kolkhoz and the sovkhoz contained unique progressive features which would ultimately be fused in a single type of socialist agricultural enterprise.[3] It soon became obvious that this formulation, in Matskevich's hands, was but a thinly disguised argument for the forced conversion of kolkhozes to sovkhozes, or "sovkhozization."

Now, Khrushchev was certainly not opposed to the conversion process per se. He had given it his blessings during the expansion of his pet Virgin Lands program. However, the theoretical argument for "fusion" appears to have been monopolized by Matskevich and a group of Khrushchev opponents in the agricultural bureaucracy.[4] Therefore, while Khrushchev was prepared to go along with the process of sovkhozization as a practical matter, he refused to accept the "fusion" principle as an ideological imperative. Meanwhile, the conversions of kolkhozes to sovkhozes proceeded at a moderately rapid pace.[5]

Khrushchev's counterattack came at the January Plenum of the Central Committee in 1961 when he succeeded in getting rid of Matskevich and smashing the entire agricultural bureaucratic machine (see below). For a while the sovkhozization campaign itself came under attack. At the Plenum Khrushchev's supporter Dimitrii Polianskii charged that local officials had been using the conversions to disencumber themselves of the responsibility for weak kolkhozes in their regions.[6] Special attention was drawn to the high costs of making such kolkhozes wards of the state. Ultimately the entire argument for fusion was condemned as a reflection of the "mistaken idea" that the kolkhozes had outlived their usefulness.[7]

It is interesting to note that the pace of conversions, after a year of near stagnation, picked up once again during the last two years of Khrushchev's reign — further evidence of his lack of objection to the process. It is also worthy of note, although certainly not surprising, that Matskevich's return as Minister of Agriculture signalled a dramatic increase in the rate of conversions.[8] However, there have been no further attempts to provide special ideological formulas for the movement. In domestic affairs, at least, the current leadership appears to seek to avoid straight-jacketing itself with specific ideological prescriptions.[9]

A related issue involving the same general interplay of forces was the question of inter-kolkhoz associations. Even before the abolition of the MTS a number of experiments had been tried with inter-kolkhoz construction associations. These associations maintained construction brigades and subsidiary enterprises to serve the construction requirements of the member kolkhozes. They were financed from the pooled resources of the farms and represented one of the many facets of Khrushchev's program of tapping kolkhoz financial resources for national agricultural investment.

During the "nationwide discussion" of the reorganization of the MTS in early 1958 numerous proposals were made for the extension of the principle of inter-kolkhoz associations to other areas of kolkhoz activity. For the first time in many years there were suggestions that the kolkhoz movement be transformed into a genuine cooperative system with secondary, tertiary, and even national governing organs. Some participants in the discussion called for an outright return to the organizational framework of the late twenties and early thirties under the All-Union *Kolkhoztsentr,* with its republic, oblast, and raion kolkhoz unions. In addition to managing the various specialized inter-kolkhoz enterprises this new network would be expected to assume responsibility for the administration of the entire kolkhoz sector. Some of these schemes and their political ramifications have been amply documented by Ploss.[10] Here it will suffice to note that Khrushchev and his closest associates, such as Polianskii and Nikolai Podgornii, were enthusiastic supporters of the kolkhoz federation idea.[11] Matskevich and his supporters, on the other hand, were decidedly lukewarm to any federations above the raion level, and even there they insisted on full subordination to the provincial agriculture organs.[12] Indeed, it is possible that Matskevich's sponsorship of the sovkhozization campaign was largely motivated by the desire to head off the development of an autonomous kolkhoz sector outside of the control of the agricultural bureaucracy.

Either because he was rebuffed on the issue by a majority of the Central Committee or because he suddenly realized the potential dangers of a nationwide kolkhoz federation for the maintenance of state control over the kolkhozes, Khrushchev abruptly deserted his associates. At the December (1959) Plenum he declared that the establishment of a new *Kolkhoztsentr* was "apparently" out of the question.[13] He did, however, lend his endorsement to further inter-kolkhoz activities on the raion level.

Since that time there has been a proliferation of inter-kolkhoz associations. The number and scale of inter-kolkhoz construction associations, for example, have grown tremendously, and they now account for a significant proportion of total rural construction work, despite frequent complaints of discrimination in the allocation of credits and materials. There are now republic and oblast offices of *Mezhkolkhozstroi* with elaborate networks of subsidiary enterprises.[14] There are also inter-kolkhoz cattle-feeding stations and feed mills, as well as electric power plants. The rapid development of this movement in recent years has aroused concern over the problem of subjecting the new associations to Party and state control. Official penetration has taken the form of including the activities of the associations in local economic plans and placing them under the supervision of local and republic government agencies, although most of their financing continues to come from non-state channels.[15] As was true during the early days of the MTS, the state remains unwilling to countenance the development of any meaningful areas of economic activity outside of its direct control.

FARM MACHINERY CONTROLS

The problem of maintaining some form of supervision over the condition and utilization of farm machinery was surely one of the main preoccupations of the regime in the post-MTS era. As noted earlier, a major concern of the honest critics of the termination of the MTS had been the capacity of the kolkhozes properly to maintain and operate their newly acquired machinery. The RTS were created specifically for the retention of some measure of state control over the care of kolkhoz machinery.

From the very outset, however, there were complaints against the work of the RTS. The kolkhozes considered RTS repair work inordinately expensive and of poor quality. They charged that the RTS, as *khozraschet* enterprises, were more interested in showing a profit than in providing the kinds of service that the kolkhozes needed most.[16] Because the machines were now legally the property of the kolkhozes, it became something of a problem to induce them to abide by the official repair and service norms or to use RTS services. The RTS contained staffs of state technical inspectors to oversee the condition of kolkhoz equipment, but their authority and influence were apparently not very great.[17] Ultimately it became necessary to resort to direct and indirect pressure to compel the kolkhozes to avail themselves of RTS facilities and generally to keep their machines in good working order.[18]

The supply and sales aspects of RTS activities also caused problems. There can be little doubt that the abolition of the MTS had greatly complicated the vital issue of technological innovation in agriculture. Formerly, new equipment and agricultural chemicals had been introduced into production by the simple practice of allocating them to the MTS. Because the MTS were not on *khozraschet,* they were always willing to accept new equipment, whether needed or not. Now that the kolkhozes had to purchase new equipment out of their own meager resources, the state was compelled to undertake a real job of salesmanship in fostering kolkhoz acceptance of technological innovations. The author was told by a number of persons involved in agricultural equipment affairs that this new situation presented a real challenge. The hard-pressed kolkhoz officials were often unwilling to commit themselves to costly purchases unless fully convinced of the profitability of the new equipment.

All of these problems were complicated from the start by the uncertain status of the RTS itself. Toward the end of 1958 approximately 3700 RTS had been established (usually in raion centers) and nearly an equal number of local "affiliates" (in the more remote MTS sites).[19] The new RTS network contained, in addition, a number of factory-type enterprises for the repair of major machinery components and the manufacture of spare parts. The RTS system was undoubtedly too large for the actual work load it was destined to carry, and many stations were operating far below capacity during much of the agricultural year. The result was that they were soon being given substantial amounts of nonagricultural work.[20] Much of their supply activity turned out to be redundant, since the supply agencies of the agricultural machinery industry and the consumer cooperative system continued to operate.

Within six months of the liquidation of the MTS there were voices calling for the total or partial liquidation of the RTS as well. The high costs and low quality of RTS work caused an increasing number of kolkhozes to demand their own fully equipped repair facilities. This tendency was particularly strong in the main agricultural regions of the Southeast, such as the Kuban' and Stavropol', where most RTS served only two or three kolkhozes, but the movement was by no means limited to these areas. Khrushchev himself came out for the sale of RTS to the kolkhozes in the Southeast as early as December 1958.[21] By 1959, at the height of his interest in the kolkhoz federation movement, he was giving warm encouragement to the idea of the transfer of RTS functions to interkolkhoz repair shops. This proposal proved abortive, however, along with other schemes connected with the re-establishment of a national *Kolkhoztsentr*. By January 1961, Khrushchev had apparently done a complete about face on the matter. In line with the reorganization of the agricultural bureaucracy and the establishment of a new All-Union Farm Machinery Association (*Soiuzsel'khoztekhnika*) at the January (1961) Plenum he rejected the idea of transferring repair work to the kolkhozes with the candid statement: "If we now transfer the RTS to the kolkhozes and sovkhozes — and such a tendency existed — then we shall ruin the equipment and arrive at pitiful results in repairing it." [22]

A full explanation of this curious turnabout in Khrushchev's views requires consideration once again of the conflict between the Soviet leader and the agricultural bureaucracy. Matskevich had consistently been less than enthusiastic about the dismantling of the RTS system, which was, after all, an important element of the ministry's administrative apparatus in the village. Khrushchev's change of heart, not very surprisingly, coincided with his victory over Matskevich and the agricultural administrators.

Meanwhile, a good deal of damage had been done to the RTS system by 1961. In 1960 the supply function had been removed from the RTS and transferred to a new national agricultural supply agency under Gosplan. Furthermore, more than 3500 RTS repair shops and plants had been either sold to kolkhozes, transferred to sovkhozes, or handed over to the local Councils of National Economy (*sovnarkhozy*) and taken completely out of agricultural service.[23]

The establishment of the All-Union Farm Machinery Association (FMA) in February 1961 finally brought a degree of stability to Soviet farm machinery repair and supply affairs. Unlike so many of Khrushchev's organizational innovations, the FMA system succeeded in winning fairly widespread acceptance on its own merits, a fact attested to by its survival of the Khrushchev era. It is instructive in this connection that its two chairmen to date, P. Kuchumov and the present incumbent, A. Ezhevskii, are essentially nonpolitical figures with long careers in agricultural machinery administration.

The structure and functions of the new agency reflected the attempt to replace the central coordination and control over the supply, repair, and utilization of agricultural machinery, which had been missing since the demise of the MTS. Organizationally, the All-Union FMA was given the status of a state committee of the USSR Council of Ministers, operating on a *khozraschet* basis. It is a union-republic organization with strong republic links. Where appropriate, there are oblast and krai associations, and finally, there is a broad network of raion and inter-raion associations and departments. The primary functions of the FMA system are the repair of kolkhoz and sovkhoz equipment; the supply of new machinery, spare parts and agro-chemical preparations to the farms; and the provision of certain technical services, such as land improvement, swamp drainage, and the installation of labor-saving devices. The surviving RTS repair shops and plants and the various land improvement, melioration, and animal husbandry stations (LMS, MMS, MZhS), which had existed even during the MTS period, were all transferred to the raion offices of the FMA, as was the inspectorate of state technical supervision.

One of the chief responsibilities of the FMA has been the fostering and introduction of new farm machinery and farming techniques. The local FMA officials are charged with the aggressive solicitation of orders for new machinery from the farms; these orders supposedly serve as the basis for the production plans of the agricultural machinery industry. The All-Union FMA maintains a network of machinery-testing stations, which are responsible for the evaluation and perfection of new models before they are cleared for mass production. It also contains a central Bureau of

Technical Information and Advertising entrusted with the propagation of modern methods of farming and the stimulation of demand for new types of machines.

To the extent that it is possible to centralize repair work and plan for technological innovation the FMA system would appear to be quite well conceived. However, the history of FMA operations has not been notably smoother than that of its predecessors. Many of the problems that plagued the MTS and the RTS continue to cause difficulties, the most common being the low quality and high costs of repair work done in FMA shops.

The uncertain status of the RTS experiment has left a certain ambivalence in official attitudes toward repair work in the kolkhozes. On the one hand, there had been a disposition to accept the principle of a *de facto* division of labor between the kolkhozes and the state repair agencies: the kolkhozes are allowed, if not always actively encouraged, to develop facilities for minor repairs and ordinary servicing, and the state repair enterprises handle the more complicated repair jobs and major overhauls. On the other hand, the fear has remained that the kolkhozes, left to themselves, will try to force out the state enterprises. Indeed, the unhappy record of experience with the performance of RTS and FMA repair work does seem to have reinforced the traditionally strong proclivity of the kolkhozes to make themselves as independent as possible of state services.

However, the majority of kolkhozes remain poorly equipped to handle their own repairs properly. According to Ezhevskii, only one-eighth of them as of mid-1965 had repair shops that met official standards. One-third had no repair shops at all. Yet the FMA system was accounting for only about one-half of the volume of repair work in the country.[24] Given the continuing scarcity of farm machinery and the abundant evidence of wasteful and ineffective repair work in the kolkhozes, it is somewhat understandable that the regime has found it necessary to apply pressure to force the kolkhozes to accept FMA services. In December 1961 the Presidium of the USSR Supreme Soviet issued a decree "On Criminal Liability for Criminal Negligence in the Use or Maintenance of Farm Machinery" with penalties of up to three years' imprisonment for repeated violations.[25] Also in 1961 the FMA began to campaign for a new system of complex servicing of kol-khoz machinery under which the kolkhozes would sign up for a program of year-round preventive maintenance and repair work by FMA mechanics. The pressure for this program has ranged from full-page advertisements in trade journals, such as *Sel'skaia zhizn'* [26] to rather nasty forms of coercion. However, the record of services under the program has not been uniformly inspiring. The local FMA's themselves have often been poorly equipped to carry out the full program of services. Sometimes kolkhozes have found themselves doing most of the work with their own personnel and facilities under the most cursory supervision of the FMA — and paying very dearly for the privilege. Those kolkhozes which attempt to terminate their contracts, as well as those which have refused to sign in the first place, are often discriminated against by the FMA in the allocation of spare parts and materials.[27] Some kolkhozes have evidently found it preferable — and possible — to do without FMA repair services. However, in Moldavia, and perhaps in a few other republics as well, the problem of evasions of this kind has been "solved" by a flat prohibition on any but the simplest repairs and servicing except in the shops of *Moldsel'-khoztekhnika*.[28]

The sales and inspection functions of the FMA have hardly been less troublesome. Because of the continuing, if less acute, short-ages of farm machinery the goal of free sales has not yet been achieved. As a result, the FMA has had to rely, for all intents and purposes, on the traditional system of machinery allocations. Consequently, the old complaints that some farms receive more of a given item than they require while others receive less continue to be heard.

The inspection problem is of a somewhat different nature. Here the old Soviet administrative practice of overlapping jurisdictions remains. The fact that the local inspectorates of technical super-vision were attached to the same agencies that were doing the repair work led to certain difficulties as might be expected. In 1965 it was finally decided to transfer the inspectorates to the local agricultural production administrations of the Ministry of Agriculture. This change does not appear to have made their supervisory work appreciably more effective, however.[29]

One of the most persistently recurring complaints on the work of the FMA system is that it is "divorced from production." [30] To a considerable extent such a charge is probably inevitable and reflects more than a little nostalgia for the rigid patterns of the MTS order. For the fact is that the FMA repair enterprises see themselves as responsible only for the general working condition of the machines sent to them by the kolkhozes and sovkhozes and not for the effectiveness of their utilization in the field. It is hardly surprising that they show little concern for the economy of fuel and spare parts which once occupied so much of the energies of the MTS directors. Because of the pressures on the local FMA manager to show a profit, the greater the number of engine hours logged by a kolkhoz tractor, the happier the manager is likely to be, regardless of the productivity of those hours. There can be no simple solution to this basic conflict of goals, just as there was no real answer to the conflict between the MTS director and the kolkhoz chairman. In giving up the MTS the regime has lost most of its leverage over the utilization of farm machinery. The FMA system does not appear to be particularly well designed to recover much of this leverage, although the regime would obviously like to improve its performance in this direction. As the technological achievements of Soviet agriculture become more satisfactory, it is to be hoped that the often irrational felt need for such control will itself diminish.

CHANGES IN THE SYSTEM OF PARTY AND ADMINISTRATIVE CONTROLS

So far we have confined our attention primarily to the more technical and substantive issues of the post-MTS agricultural system. The administrative and political issues were, if anything, even more volatile and difficult to solve. Thanks to the continuing background of Kremlin infighting and Khrushchev's unique penchant for hit-or-miss organizational experiments, a veritable parade of reorganizations ensued, comprising both old and new permutations of Party-governmental interaction.

Since the abolition of the MTS there have been four well defined periods of organizational arrangement. The first, lasting from April 1958 to January 1961, was a period of decentralized controls during which, in the name of "democratization," the agricultural bureaucracy was laboriously eased out of many of its direct responsibilities for agricultural production. Meanwhile, certain limited compensatory steps were taken to facilitate the involvement of the local and lower Party organs in agricultural operations. The second period, extending from February 1961 to March 1962, was essentially an interregnum. The agricultural bureaucracy had been summarily removed from production matters, but Khrushchev could not manage to combine alternative agencies of Party and state leadership into an effective administrative system. The third period, lasting from March 1962 until Khrushchev's ouster in October 1964, witnessed a major effort at recentralization with the introduction of one of the most radical schemes of reorganization in the history of Soviet public administration. Party and governmental agencies were linked in a manner somewhat reminiscent of the MTS politotdels, and the entire Party and governmental structure at the provincial level was separated into virtually independent agricultural and industrial hierarchies. The fourth period, extending from the removal of Khrushchev to the present, has featured a return to the traditional pre-Khrushchevian patterns of Party and governmental controls in agriculture, including the re-establishment of the raikom mode of Party involvement in agricultural production matters.

The system of local agricultural administration introduced by Khrushchev in April 1958 was fully in keeping with the spirit of decentralization which had informed the decision to liquidate the MTS. In the course of the nationwide "debates" on the latter measure there had been numerous suggestions for a return to the raizo system of administering the kolkhozes. However, Khrushchev was adamant in refusing to revive an institution which he had so often derided as the epitome of bureaucratic management. Whatever his real motives — a genuine distaste for bureaucracy, a desire to foster local initiative, or a less altruistic determination to undermine the direct authority of the Ministry of Agriculture — Khrushchev pressed for a system of substantially loosened state controls at the grass roots. Thus, responsibility for most questions of agricultural production was placed in the hands of a new raion inspectorate for agriculture, an organ of the *raiispolkom,* rather than a part of the regular agricultural apparatus. The chief of the inspectorate was designated ex officio deputy chairman of the *raiispolkom,* and important local service agencies, such as the seed-control laboratories and the agrochemical laboratories, were placed under the inspectorates and financed out of the raion budget instead of the national and republic budgets, as they had been while they were attached to the MTS.[31] A degree of coordination of local agricultural activities was to be achieved by means of a production-technical council under the *raiispolkom.* It was to comprise the chief of the inspectorate and its top specialists, representatives of the RTS, managerial and specialized representatives of the kolkhozes and sovkhozes, officials of the raion planning commission, and other agricultural officials. Past experiences with similar councils under the MTS suggest that its operational authority could not be very great, but that it might perform a fairly useful function in the airing of local grievances.

The looseness of the new administrative setup indicated that a major part of the responsibility for the coordination and control of production activities would devolve once again upon the raikom. However, as Howard Swearer has pointed out, the raikom was structurally ill-equipped to handle these responsibilities.[32] Having scrapped the MTS zonal raikom secretary format in late 1957, Khrushchev had returned to the standard territorial raikom setup, with three secretaries and two traditional *otdely*; organizational and *agitprop.* The eight to ten instructors of the *orgotdel* were now expected to involve themselves in agricultural production matters along with their regular Party organizational work.[33]

At first glance this arrangement appears to conform to the traditional pattern of indirect raikom control, indicating a typical reaction to the politotdel style of involvement represented by the previous zonal raikom arrangement. Yet from the beginning of the post-MTS period it was clear that there was to be no retrenchment, that the raikom was expected to continue its direct involvement in production matters. Thus, the new arrangement may be interpreted in the light of Khrushchev's general movement since the middle fifties away from the highly compartmentalized division of functions in agricultural administration.

There were other developments in the area of Party organization which to a limited extent might have compensated for the structural inadequacies of the 1958 raikom. Party coverage in the village had been increasing steadily, thanks largely to the influx of former MTS personnel and the continuing farm mergers. Virtually every kolkhoz had a PPO; by mid-1960 the average kolkhoz PPO contained twenty-eight members. More than 10 percent of the kolkhozes in the country had PPO's with more than fifty members.[34] In January 1959 the Central Committee decreed the establishment of Party Committees in kolkhozes with PPO's larger than fifty members and in sovkhozes with PPO's larger than one hundred members. In many respects the new plan was similar to the sub-raikom proposals of the middle thirties. The Party Committees were to enjoy the rights of a raikom in membership questions and certain other organizational matters. The Party organizations in kolkhoz brigades and sovkhoz departments where Party Committees existed were subordinate to the latter in the manner of regular PPO's.[35] The Party Committees had final jurisdiction over the placement of Party members throughout the territory of a given farm. All territorial Party organizations in the vicinity of the farm were brought together under the authority of the kolkhoz or sovkhoz production Party organization, greatly increasing the number of cadres available for assignment to production tasks during crucial periods. Where Party Committees did exist — and they were especially likely to be formed in the major agricultural regions, since Party organizations there were large — they unquestionably enhanced the leverage of the raikoms in their efforts to influence production affairs. By working through the Party Committees the raikom instructors could, in theory at least, more effectively influence the disposition of Party forces on the farms. This was particularly important now that the farms had become so large. However, the number of places where Party Committees could legitimately be formed was necessarily limited: in mid-July 1960 there were Party Committees in only 4130 kolkhozes and 1046 sovkhozes.[36] This numerical limitation, combined with the traditionally low esteem in which the rural PPO was held, certainly reduced the extent to which the Party Committee institution made up for the structural weaknesses of the raikom.

The years 1959 and 1960 witnessed a serious decline in the level of moral and legal discipline in the countryside. Party and governmental officials soon responded to Khrushchev's frantic campaigns to increase agricultural output with elaborate conspiracies to falsify production and procurement statistics. Animals were bought from individual peasants and sold to the state in fulfillment of collective farm quotas. Farmers purchased huge quantities of bread in state and cooperative stores and fed it to their cattle, which they then sold at high prices on the free market. Whole raions were swept clean of grain stocks, including seed reserves, so that the authorities could report overfulfillment of plans, only to petition the state a few months later for seed and fodder to tide them over the next crop year. Khrushchev's de-emphasis of grain procurements in the northwestern and central industrial areas was met with so drastic a cutback in grain acreage that the areas were forced to request large imports of grain from state reserves. Symbolic of the general atmosphere of ballyhoo and deceit was the sordid case of Riazan Oblast and its obkom First Secretary, A. N. Larionov. In 1959 Larionov had made the bold promise to triple the scheduled meat procurements from his oblast. At the end of the year the announced results seemed to indicate that the pledge had been fulfilled, and Larionov was praised throughout the country.[37] Months later it was discovered that most of Riazan's achievements had been attained by the delivery of animals that had been purchased on the side, even beyond the boundaries of the oblast.[38] Larionov was reported to have committed suicide after his brief moment of glory.

How much this breakdown of discipline could be attributed to Khrushchev's calculated disruption of local administrative controls and how much it was due to his high-pressure agitation for a great leap forward in agriculture is impossible to determine. As usual, he saw the situation largely in organizational terms. He initiated a process of retightening of controls over production, but again he refused to return to earlier structural patterns. The process began with an extensive purge of provincial Party officials. In the year between October 1960 and October 1961, 55 out of 114 obkom and kraikom first secretaries were removed or transferred.[39] Many of these shifts were related to the intense jockeying for political position that was occurring during this period, but the issue of agricultural performance bulked large in the discussions of personal failures. In February 1961 Khrushchev managed to push through his long-cherished plan to break up the agricultural bureaucratic machine and to recast the Ministry of Agriculture in the role of a scientific and technical coordinating agency without operational responsibilities.[40] The raion agricultural inspectorates were abolished at this time and the RTS transferred to the newly created All-Union Farm Machinery Association.

Khrushchev now took a radically different tack in his search for a new system of operational controls. Following a line he had first broached in the middle fifties, he proposed to entrust a major share of the responsibility for the direction and supervision of kolkhoz production to a greatly strengthened network of procurement organs. On February 26, 1961, he established a new State Committee of Procurements under the USSR Council of Ministers, with republic, oblast, and raion counterparts. A state inspectorate for procurements at the raion level was made responsible not only for the fulfillment of procurement plans, but also for the supervision of kolkhoz operations throughout the agricultural year. The inspectorate was directed to employ the authority of the raikom and *raiispolkom* to secure remedial action.[41]

This new attempt to impose control without resorting to a full-fledged system of administration was no more successful than past efforts. While the procurement agencies were in theory well situated to supervise the production process, it proved difficult in practice to get them to utilize their full authority. Large areas of kolkhoz activity were left partially or wholly untouched. Such important matters as kolkhoz finances and the introduction of new agrotechnical procedures, which had formerly been under the control of the raion agricultural inspectorates, were now left totally in abeyance.[42] The only figures in the raion specifically responsible for the broad range of organizational work in the kolkhozes remained the raikom and the instructors of its *orgotdel*. But, as we have seen, the raikom was inadequately staffed to exercise close control. This organizational hiatus would not be allowed to continue for very long.

The radical reorganizations of March–November 1962 saw a dramatic recentralization of the system of agricultural administration. Khrushchev rammed through an elaborate network of administrative organs, strikingly different from anything that had previously existed under the old ministerial system. It combined a system of strong line-type administrative organs with close Party supervision at each level. At the apex of the new system was an All-Union Agricultural Committee, headed by a first deputy chairman of the USSR Council of Ministers. (The eventual designee was N. G. Ignatov, a Khrushchev supporter who had recently been demoted from the Party Presidium.)[43] It also included the head of the agricultural *otdel* of the Central Committee for union republics, the Minister of Agriculture, the chairman of the FMA system, and the deputy chairman of *Gosplan* for agriculture. There were counterpart committees at the republic, oblast, and krai levels. These committees were headed by the first secretaries of the Party committees of the respective territories and were responsible for policy guidance and Party supervision of all agricultural affairs therein.

More specific administrative duties were assigned to a hierarchy of administrative organs, beginning at the republic level. In the republics there were new Ministries of Production and Procurement of Agricultural Products. Subordinate to them were oblast (krai) Administrations of Production and Procurement of Agricultural Products.[44]

The heart of the reorganization was in the lowest level organs of administration, the so-called Territorial Kolkhoz-Sovkhoz or Sovkhoz-Kolkhoz (whichever type of farm predominated in a given area) Production Administrations (TPA's). Nine hundred and sixty of these bodies were created to serve the 3421 rural raions in existence at the beginning of 1962.[45] The TPA's were directly subordinated to the oblast, krai, or republic production and procurement organs. Their primary working staff consisted of a chief and a group of inspector-organizers, each of whom was assigned to a fixed number of kolkhozes and/or sovkhozes (usually from three to six farms). The individual inspector-organizers were responsible for the full range of production activities in their farms, from planning and accounting to field operations and the introduction of new techniques.[46] Following Khrushchev's conception of the role of the inspector, they were expected to spend the major part of their time in the field and, ordinarily, to live in the vicinity of their assigned farms.

An interesting sidelight of the new format was the inclusion of both kolkhozes and sovkhozes under the same administrative organs. This might have been interpreted as a further step in the direction of sovkhozization. Indeed, an editorial in *Sovetskaia Rossiia* in March 1962 explicitly presented the new arrangements in terms of the principle of the "convergence" of the two forms of socialist property.[47] This argument does not appear to have been widely accepted, however.

Perhaps the most important operative feature of the 1962 reorganization was the role it assigned to the leading Party officials at the various levels in the activities of the new administrative organs. In a memorandum to the Presidium of the Central Committee dated September 10, 1962, Khrushchev declared: "We must establish production as the basis of Party leadership, because it is the main foundation of the building of communism."[48] The pattern of Party and governmental relationships under the 1962–1964 system was fully consistent with this spirit. At the provincial and republic levels the designation of the Party first secretaries as chairmen of the respective agricultural committees was explicitly designed to pinpoint their personal responsibility for agricultural affairs.

The shift to the production principle of Party leadership was reflected with particular clarity at the lowest administrative level. Khrushchev expressly emulated the politotdel patterns of the MTS period by attaching special Party Committees to the TPA's.[49] These Party Committees were headed by so-called Party organizers on the *nomenklatura* of the obkom (kraikom) or republic central committees. The *partorg* had a staff of inspector-Party organizers (IPO's) who, like their counterparts on the TPA staff, were assigned to a fixed number of kolkhozes or sovkhozes (usually five to seven) to direct the PPO's.[50] The duties of the IPO's were in many ways similar to those of the old MTS politotdel workers: to focus a "Party eye" on the production activities of the farms and to involve themselves as directly as necessary in these activities in order to secure compliance with official goals.

Just as had been the case with the politotdels, the new Party

Committees of the TPA's almost immediately came into conflict with the regular Party raikoms. By June 1962 Khrushchev had already decided that the entire raion Party and government apparatus was superfluous.[51] At the next Central Committee Plenum, in November, the raikom was accordingly abolished, and its remaining functions were assumed by the Party Committees of the TPA's. Thus, by the end of 1962 the TPA and its geographical sphere of operations had become the basic territorial-administrative unit in agriculture. The accompanying amalgamation of controls in the countryside was an important part of the drastic reorganization of Party and governmental organs announced at the November Plenum, where, under the rubric of the production principle, the domestic political system was almost entirely split into separate agricultural and industrial hierarchies.

The new scheme represented a major political decision, not to say gamble, on Khrushchev's part. Previously the provincial Party secretaries had played a dual role in the workings of the politico-economic system. On the one hand, they were powerful political satraps — emissaries of the center, entrusted with the maintenance of tight political control over the provinces. As such, they were bound to develop significant local sources of power. On the other hand, they were a vital link in the administration of the national economy. Khrushchev had reinforced and utilized their political power in his own struggles for ascendancy over his rivals in the Presidium and Central Committee. By 1962, however, he had come to realize that their political role was frequently incompatible with their economic role. The local power of the provincial secretaries often served as an impediment to the implementation of Khrushchev's own policies. Having had to fight so hard for his policies against his opponents in Moscow, he was in no mood to brook continuing opposition in the provinces. At the same time, he had long been committed to the principle of the functional relevance of direct Party leadership in the economy. The existing system, with its emphasis on political power, tended to weaken the attention of the middle-level apparatus toward concrete economic problems. The November 1962 reorganization may thus be interpreted as a move to diminish the unique political power of the provincial Party secretaries while enhancing their economic responsibilities.[52] The first secretary of the agricultural obkom of an oblast was certainly a less imposing political figure than the former first secretary of the integral obkom, but his specific responsibility for agricultural performance was obviously much greater. Once again, as in the fifties, Khrushchev was attempting to increase responsibility by enhancing the "visibility" of the officials in charge of a particular area of production.

But alas, the sorry fate of the 1962 changes was but another illustration of the limitations of reorganization as a technique of administration. In an amazingly short time most of the old problems and discredited practices reasserted themselves. Staffing problems seriously undermined the effectiveness of the new organs. Despite optimistic estimates of the number of trained specialists available, the TPA's had difficulty recruiting the necessary complement of inspector-organizers.[53] Many of those actually appointed were poorly trained and incapable of exerting much positive influence on production. Before long, local Party officials were again being accused of being overinvolved in production matters and supplanting the responsible governmental and economic personnel.[54] Some *partorgi* fell back on the old practice of assigning local officials as plenipotentiaries to individual farms during campaign periods, with all the previous disruptive consequences.[55] The TPA's were accused of drifting back to the bureaucratic style and methods of the raizo.[56]

By the summer of 1964 Khrushchev was already reported to be contemplating yet another reorganization of the agricultural administrative system, ostensibly to eliminate these problems.[57] He was overthrown before he had an opportunity to begin a new paroxysm of reforms.

In sharp contrast with the Khrushchev era, the tenure of his successors has been marked by an amazing degree of stability in agricultural policy and administration. This has been the result of an explicit commitment to avoid the dizzying twists and turns of the preceding decade. The fundamental approach of the new "collective leadership" has been a combination of conservatism in organizational matters and pragmatism in concrete policy matters. Within six months of Khrushchev's ouster they had managed to return the system of Party and governmental controls in agriculture to the traditional pre-Khrushchevian patterns. At the November (1964) Plenum the divided provincial Party organizations were reunited, and the standard territorial-production principle of Party structure was fully reinstated. Similarly, the traditional raion Party organizational format was restored in place of the Party Committees of the Territorial-Production Administrations.[58] Moreover, it was made clear that the leadership of the new raikoms was to be far less intensively involved in the management of agricultural production affairs. In short, there was to be another return to the more comfortable patterns of the indirect raikom mode of control described in Part III.

Similar trends were to be observed in the agricultural administrative organs. Matskevich was reinstated as Minister of Agriculture in February 1965. During the ensuing months the Ministry was radically reorganized from top to bottom. At the lowest level the TPA's were replaced by raion agricultural administrations, similar in many ways to the old raizo, with the important exception that they are not subordinate to the *raiispolkom*. By March 1965 there were 2434 rural raions — 611 more than the number of TPA's at the time of Khrushchev's downfall.[59] Above the raion agricultural administrations are the old oblast and krai agricultural administrations and republic ministries of agriculture. These, like the All-Union Ministry at the apex of the system are now organized in accordance with the old production-branch principle, with branch glavks for grain crops, technical crops, potato and vegetable crops, veterinary services, mechanization and electrification, and other areas of agriculture.[60] General administration of operations now begins at the level of the republic ministries — one of the only departures from the pre-Khrushchevian system.

The administrative structure for the agricultural sector, like that for industry since September 1965 and for the Party apparatus as a whole since the Twenty-third Party Congress, reflects a general tendency to return to the tried and tested organizational forms of the Stalin era. Fortunately, this conservative, not to say reactionary, bias has not applied in the more crucial area of policy. As in the case of the so-called Liberman reforms in industry, the new leadership has demonstrated a real appreciation of the importance of material stimuli for the improvement of economic performance. The statements of Brezhnev and others at the March (1965) Plenum suggest that the Soviet leaders have learned a lesson from the experiences of both the Stalin and Khrushchev periods: namely, that one cannot indeed make bricks without straw. In place of the confiscatory, unstable procurement policies of the past, they have instituted a system of realistic plans with firm targets over a five-year period. Prices paid to the farms for their commodities have been raised dramatically, and high premiums for above-plan sales have been introduced to encourage maximum effort.[61] Moreover, Brezhnev has committed the regime to a long-term program of substantially increased investments in agriculture, particularly in the areas of farm machinery and rural construction.[62]

Perhaps the most striking changes in Soviet agriculture have been in the general atmosphere of the policy formulation process and its reflection in public discussion. While Khrushchev made several important preliminary slashes, he was incapable of decisively cutting through the Gordian knot of dogmatism. Rather, he ended by merely replacing the old, pontifical dogmatism of Stalin with an earthy, bombastic dogmatism of his own. One of the really important achievements of the new leaders has been to move the general attitude toward agricultural problems more closely into line with the attitude toward industry, where the objective requirements of science and technology have long been given their due. If Khrushchev's successors are less colorful than he, they appear readier to confront concrete issues with the requisite dispassion. An example was their abrupt reversal of Khrushchev's policy of squeezing out the peasants' private plots. Here they fully recognized the inability of the socialist sector to provide certain types of commodities. Similarly, Brezhnev has indicated that for the foreseeable future the matter of the transformation of kolkhozes to sovkhozes is strictly a non-issue. The important thing is to raise the capacities and attractions of both types of farm, even if this means reducing the size of some kolkhozes (and hence making them less similar to sovkhozes).[63] True, Khrushchev had been forced to draw the same general conclusions, but whereas for him the issue may have had some theoretical importance, the new leaders give the impression of a general lack of interest in the principles involved.

One other item which might be mentioned in connection with the "atmospherics" of the new regime and which is of particular relevance for the present study is a renewal of interest in the MTS concept. Within a short time after Khrushchev's removal it was already possible to discuss the liquidation of the MTS in a more objective light; that is, to stress its negative as well as positive effects. Some officials began to state openly that the liquidation had been premature and that it had left many kolkhozes worse off then before.[64] This view seems to have been especially strong in the Armenian SSR. At the March Plenum in 1965 the Armenian First Secretary, I. N. Zarobian, complained that the abolition of the MTS had left some three hundred small kolkhozes in his republic in desperate straits. He asserted, furthermore, that there were thousands of such farms in the country.[65]

While rejecting — almost reluctantly — any revival of the MTS system per se, Zarobian and others have recommended the establishment of networks of machinery rental stations and even machinery-exploitation stations under the FMA system to perform specific farming and auxiliary service operations for the kolkhozes on a contractual basis.[66] While there is at present no prospect of a return to the old MTS-kolkhoz system, there has been a steady expansion in the number of operational brigades and detachments under the local FMA offices performing work for the kolkhozes in a manner very similar to the MTS.[67]

So far, the post-Khrushchevian leaders seem to have been vindicated in their agricultural policies. Harvests, particularly that of 1966, have been good, and the new system of procurements appears to be working smoothly. Even the less satisfactory agricultural year of 1967 did not cause anything like the disruption of the last two Khrushchev years, when the Soviet Union was forced to buy large quantities of grain from the capitalist West. This is not to say that the new policies have not encountered opposition. So far the long-awaited Third Congress of Kolkhozniks, which Brezhnev had warmly supported in 1965, has yet to be held.

And Dimitrii Polianskii admitted in October 1967 that he and Brezhnev had been compelled to fight a running battle (not completely successfully, it appears) with conservative forces in the planning and administrative bureaucracies to maintain a high rate of agricultural investment.[68]

The struggle for a rational agricultural program is not yet over. While the new methods of planning and administration appear to be relatively stable and effective, one may well wonder what a succession of poor harvests or a sudden increase in demand for nonagricultural investments might bring. A return to the exploitation of the peasants and the imposition of tight political controls in the village unfortunately cannot be ruled out under such circumstances.

Appendix

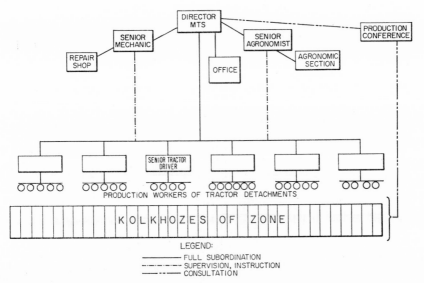

Figure A.1. Internal organization of the MTS, 1929–1931.

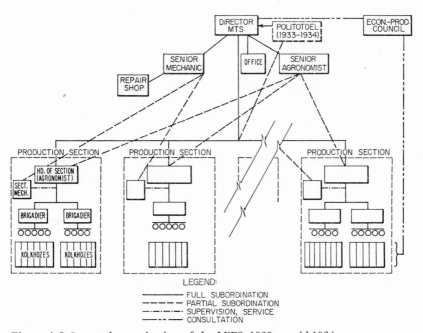

Figure A.2. Internal organization of the MTS, 1932 to mid-1934.

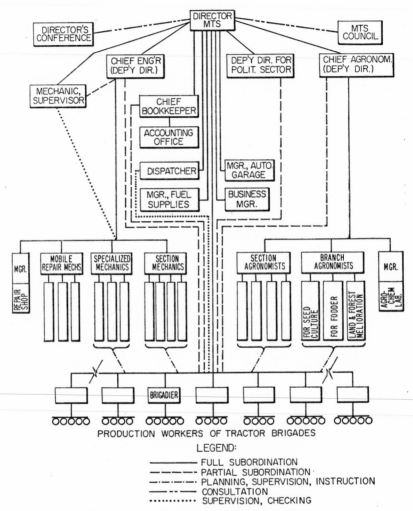

LEGEND:

————————— FULL SUBORDINATION
————————— PARTIAL SUBORDINATION
—·—·—·—· PLANNING, SUPERVISION, INSTRUCTION
——·—— CONSULTATION
············· SUPERVISION, CHECKING

Figure A.3. Internal organization of the MTS, early 1950's.

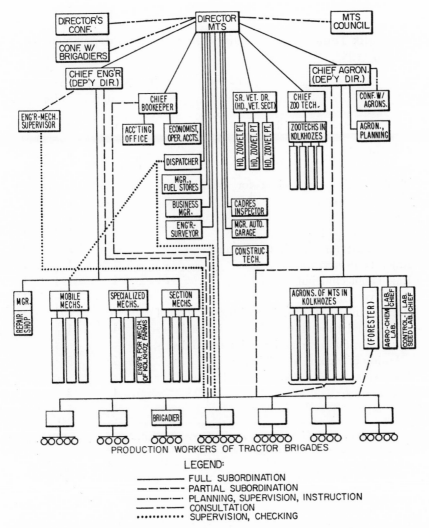

Figure A.4. Internal organization of the MTS, September 1953–1958.

371

Appendix Table. Typical staff of the raion land department (raizo), 1933.

Position	Number of persons by categories of raions		
	I	II	III[a]
Chief of raizo	1	1	1
Instructor for cadres	1	1	1
Planner (also responsible for questions of kolkhoz credit)	—	1	1
Statistician	1	1	1
Raion agronomist	1	1	1
Agronomists for branches of farming	1	2	3
Raion land surveyor	1	1	1
Raion zootechnician	1	1	1
Raion veterinarian	1	1	1
Raizo manager for questions of organization of labor and distribution of income in kolkhozes	1	1	1
Instructors for organization of labor and distribution of income in kolkhozes	2	3	4
Instructors for record keeping and accounts in kolkhozes	1	2	2
Secretary	1	1	1

Source: Decree of the Presidium of the Central Executive Committee, USSR, "On the Establishment of Typical Staffs of Raion Land Departments in Connection with the Liquidation of the Raion Kolkhoz Unions," *Biulleten' finansovogo i khoziaistvennogo zakonodatel'stva,* no. 13 (1933), p. 1.

[a] Generally, raions in category three had no MTS. Thus, the number of certain personnel was larger.

Notes   Index

Notes

CHAPTER ONE

1. Karl Marx, *Capital* (Moscow: Foreign Languages Publishing House, 1961), I, 748–749.

2. Karl Marx, *The Eighteenth Brumaire of Louis Bonaparte,* ed. C. P. Dutt (New York: International Publishers, n.d.), p. 109.

3. Friedrich Engels, *Herr Eugen Dühring's Revolution in Science* (Moscow: Foreign Languages Publishing House, 1947), pp. 434–435, 440–441.

4. Friedrich Engels. *The Peasant Question in France and Germany,* in Karl Marx and Friedrich Engels, *Selected Works in Two Volumes* (Moscow: Foreign Languages Publishing House, 1949), II, 384.

5. *Ibid.,* p. 397.

6. Cited in V. M. Selunskaia, *Bor'ba KPSS za sotsialisticheskoe preobrazovanie sel'skogo khoziaistva* (Moscow, 1961), p. 22.

7. See, for example, Plekhanov's review of Vandervelde's *La Propriété foncière en Belgique* in G. V. Plekhanov, *Sochineniia* (Moscow-Leningrad, 1923–1927), XI, 363–369. See also Lenin's review of Kautsky's *Die Agrarfrage* in V. I. Lenin, *Sochineniia* (4th ed., Moscow, 1941–1962), IV, 78–83.

8. Karl Kautsky, *La Question agraire* (Paris: V. Giard and E. Briére, 1900), pp. xii, 4–6.

9. *Ibid.,* pp. 63–64.

10. Peter I. Lyashchenko, *History of the National Economy of Russia to the 1917 Revolution,* trans. Leon M. Herman (New York: Macmillan Co., 1949), p. 504.

11. Adam B. Ulam, *The Unfinished Revolution* (New York: Random House, 1960).

12. Elsewhere in Europe the commune had long since ceased to exist as a functioning unit. Even in Serbia, where the extended family commune (*zadruga*) was important as late as the nineteenth century, it had undergone a radical shift to permanent distribution of the land to individual households after 1844. See Ranko M. Brashich, *Land Reform and Ownership in Jugoslavia: 1919–1953* (New York: Mid-European Studies Center, Free Europe Committee, 1954), p. 11.

13. Cf. the famous letter of Marx to Vera Zasulich in 1881, where he gave his conditional blessings to the project but announced his skepticism that the process could be effected quickly enough to avoid the capitalist stage (Karl Marx and Friedrich Engels, *Selected Correspondence* [Moscow: Foreign Languages Publishing House, 1953], pp. 411–412). See also Plekhanov, *Sochineniia,* I, 107.

14. For a good account of this period see Arthur P. Mendel, *Dilemmas of Progress in Tsarist Russia: Legal Marxism and Legal Populism* (Cambridge: Harvard University Press, 1961), esp. pp. 119–120.

15. Plekhanov, *Sochineniia,* XI, 363.

16. *Ibid.,* XVI, 281.

17. See, for example, his pamphlet "Zadachi russkikh sotsial'-demokratov," in Lenin, *Sochineniia* (4th ed.), II, esp. pp. 306–307. However, Richard Pipes has recently demonstrated that Lenin's attitude toward the peasantry underwent a number of shifts during this period. His early interest was never fully discarded, suggesting an important reason for Lenin's much greater attention to the details of the agrarian question than was common among the Russian social democratic leaders (Richard Pipes, "The Origins of Bolshevism," in Richard Pipes, ed., *Revolutionary Russia* [Cambridge: Harvard University Press, 1968], pp. 26–52). See also the comments by Sir Isaiah Berlin, *ibid.,* pp. 52–59.

18. Lenin, *Sochineniia* (4th ed.), IV, 82.

19. *Ibid.,* p. 105.

20. *Leninskii sbornik* (Moscow: Politizdat pri TsK VKP(B), 1940), XXXIII, 160.

21. Nicolas Berdyaev, *The Origin of Russian Communism,* trans. R. M. French (London: Goeffrey Bles, 1948), p. 124.

22. At the so-called Stockholm "Unity Congress" of the Russian Social Democratic Workers' Party (RSDRP) in 1906 Lenin was virtually alone in fighting for a more active peasant policy (V. I. Lenin, *Polnoe sobranie sochinenii* [5th ed., Moscow, 1960–1965], XII, 366–367).

23. *Ibid.,* XVI, 277.

24. V. I. Lenin, "Capitalism and Agriculture in the United States," in *Capitalism and Agriculture* (New York: International Publishers, 1946), p. 34.

25. *Ibid.,* pp. 53–54.

26. Lenin, *Polnoe sobranie,* XXXI, 272.

27. V. I. Lenin, *Selected Works in Two Volumes* (Moscow: Foreign Languages Publishing House, 1952), II, pt. 1, 339–340.

28. The initial Decree on Land had had very little effect on the conduct of the peasants in any case. The wave of "repartitions," or seizures of gentry estates, which had begun in the summer of 1917, greatly intensified in the fall and continued at a high pitch throughout 1918. According to E. Kochetovskaia, in an orthodox Stalinist account, the land seizures did not become really widespread until 1918. See Lyashchenko, *History of the National Economy,* p. 778; E. Kochetovskaia, *Natsionalizatsiia zemli v SSSR* (Moscow, 1952), pp. 122–123.

29. For example, see his speech at the Eighth Party Congress in March 1919 (Lenin, *Selected Works in Two Volumes,* II, pt. 2, esp. p. 179). Lenin's attitude may also be inferred from the relatively permissive and gradualistic provisions of the Land Socialization Decree of February 9, 1918, which was mainly concerned — judging from a content analysis of the respective sections — with the distribution of land to individual peasants in accordance with "consumer-labor norms" established by the SR Party (Decree of the All-Russian Central Executive Committee of the Soviets of Workers', Soldiers', and Peasants' Deputies of January 27 [February 9], 1918, "O sotsializatsii zemli," *Direktivy KPSS i Sovetskogo pravitel'stva po khoziaistvennym voprosam* [Moscow, 1957], I, 37–49).

30. The decree bore the imposing title "On the Conferral on the People's Commissariat of Food of Extraordinary Powers for the Struggle with the Village Bourgeoisie, Which Is Concealing Grain Supplies and Speculating in Them," *Direktivy KPSS,* I, 32–34.

31. S. G. Strumilin, ed. *Ekonomicheskaia zhizn' SSSR* (Moscow, 1961), p. 28. On Party relations with the *kombedy* see S. S. Korkin, "Iz istorii partiinogo rukovodstva kombedami," *Voprosy istorii KPSS,* no. 6 (1959), pp. 66–79.

32. Korkin, "Iz istorii," pp. 67, 76.

33. See, for example, Korkin, "Iz istorii."

34. *Ibid.,* p. 79. The fact that peasant resistance to the Food Army and the *kombedy* was vigorous may be seen in the casualty figures reported. From May to December 1918 the Food Army lost 7309 men killed, wounded, or otherwise incapacitated, out of a total strength of close to 37,000 ("Prodovol'-stvennaia armiia," *Pravda,* December 27, 1918).

35. Interview with A. G. Shlikhter, *Ekonomicheskaia zhizn',* November 23, 1918.

36. Lenin, *Selected Works in Two Volumes,* II, pt. 2, 179.

37. *VKP(B) v rezoliutsiiakh i resheniiakh s"ezdov, konferentsii i plenumov TsK* (Moscow, 1936), pt. 1, pp. 300–301.

38. Strumilin, *Ekonomicheskaia zhizn' SSSR,* p. 13.

39. Lenin, *Selected Works in Two Volumes,* II, pt. 2, 189.

40. See, for example, "Ugrozhaiushchee polozhenie v sel'skom khoziaistve," *Ekonomicheskaia zhizn',* April 17, 1919.

41. P. Sereda, then Commissar of Agriculture, complained in the spring of 1919 that all levels of the agricultural bureaucracy were weak, with the result that policy coordination was extremely difficult. "Owing to the lack of guidance from the *guberniia* center," he said, "each *uezd* has its own policy" ("V Komitete po posevnoi ploshchadi," *Ekonomicheskaia zhizn',* April 29, 1919).

42. *Direktivy KPSS,* I, 225–227.

43. Lenin, *Selected Works in Two Volumes,* II, pt. 2, 542.

44. *Ibid.,* p. 543.

45. Decree of the Ninth All-Russian Congress of Soviets of December 26, 1921, "Po voprosu o vosstanovlenii i razvitii sel'skogo khoziaistva," *Direktivy KPSS,* I, 286.

46. "Zakon o trudovom zemlepol'zovanii," adopted by the Central Executive Committee on May 22, 1922, *Direktivy KPSS,* I, 334–335.

47. Decree of the Council of People's Commissars of May 24, 1921, "O poriadke ispol'zovaniia i raspredeleniia sel'sko-khoziaistvennykh mashin i orudii" in Strumilin, *Ekonomicheskaia zhizn' SSSR,* p. 79.

48. V. P. Miliutin, *Agrarnaia politika SSSR* (3rd ed., Moscow, 1929), p. 162.

49. Naum Jasny, *The Socialized Agriculture of the USSR: Plans and Performance* (Stanford: Stanford University Press, 1949), p. 787 (tables).

50. I. A. Gladkov, ed., *Sovetskoe narodnoe khoziaistvo v 1921–1925 gg.* (Moscow, 1961), pp. 412–413.

51. N. P. Gorbunov and A. V. Stoklitskii, eds., *SSSR: god raboty pravitel'-stva (1924/1925 biudzhetnyi god)* (Moscow, 1926), p. 259.

52. *VKP(B) v rezoliutsiiakh,* pt. 1, pp. 557–560.

53. Decree of the Third Congress of Soviets of the USSR of May 20, 1925, "O meropriiatiiakh po podniatiiu i ukrepleniiu krest'ianskogo khoziaistva," *Direktivy KPSS*, I, 531.

54. *Ibid.*, p. 533.

55. Quoted in Alexander Erlich, *The Soviet Industrialization Debate, 1924–1928* (Cambridge: Harvard University Press, 1960), p. 16.

56. See, for example, A. M. Bol'shakov, *Derevnia, 1917–1927* (Moscow, 1927), p. 128 *et passim;* V. P. Danilov, "Zemel'nve otnosheniia v sovetskoi dokolkhoznoi derevne," *Istoriia SSSR*, no. 3 (1958), p. 98; D. J. Male, "The Village Community in the USSR: 1925–1930," *Soviet Studies*, XIV, no. 3 (January 1963), 225–248; Moshe Lewin, *La Paysannerie et le pouvoir soviétique 1928–1930* (Paris: Mouton et Cie., 1966), pp. 41–42.

57. Iu. Larin, *Sovetskaia derevnia* (Moscow, 1925), p. 40.

58. N. Rotenberg, "O rabote sel'skikh iacheek," *Pravda*, February 21, 1923; for similar occurrences see Male, "Village Community," pp. 237–239.

59. M. I. Bakhtin, "Ukreplenie partiinykh organizatsii v derevne v vosstanovitel'nyi period (1921–1925)," *Voprosy istorii*, no. 11 (1954), p. 86.

60. M. Khataevich, "O sostoianii i rabote partiinoi iacheiki v derevne," *Bol'shevik*, no. 3–4 (February 1925), p. 74.

61. Bakhtin, "Ukreplenie partiinykh organizatsii," pp. 86–87.

62. Merle Fainsod, *How Russia Is Ruled* (rev. ed., Cambridge: Harvard University Press, 1963), p. 253 (table).

63. *VKP(B) v rezoliutsiiakh*, pt. 1, pp. 464, 512.

64. *Ibid.*, pt. 2, p. 44.

65. For example, Rotenberg, "O rabote sel'skikh iacheek."

66. Bakhtin, "Ukreplenie partiinykh organizatsii," p. 92; Khataevich, "O sostoianii," pp. 75–76. Khataevich concedes that much of this early missionary work had little effect.

67. Lenin, *Selected Works in Two Volumes*, II, pt. 2, pp. 750–751.

68. See, for example, V. M. Selunskaia, "Razrabotka V. I. Leninym kooperativnogo plana," *Voprosy istorii KPSS*, no. 2 (1960), p. 114.

69. Lenin, *Selected Works in Two Volumes*, II, pt. 2, 715.

70. *Ibid.*, p. 718.

71. For a more detailed account of develpoments in the theory and practice of the Soviet cooperatives see Miliutin, *Agrarnaia politika SSSR*, pp. 188–239; Larin, *Sovetskaia derevnia*, ch. 6 (pp. 233–331); V. P. Danilov, *Sozdanie material'no-tekhnicheskikh predposylok kollektivizatsii sel'skogo khoziaistva v SSSR* (Moscow, 1957), pp. 136–145.

72. "O kooperatsii, Tezisy tov. Andreeva, utverzhdennye TsK RKP(B)," *Ekonomicheskaia zhizn'*, May 14, 1924.

73. A. Petrov, "Nedostatki v raspredelenii kreditov," *Pravda*, September 11, 1926.

74. Decree of the Central Executive Committee and the Council of People's Commissars of the USSR of August 22, 1924, "O sel'sko-khoziaistvennoi kooperatsii," *Direktivy KPSS*, I, 492.

75. "O kooperatsii, Tezisy tov. Andreeva."

76. Ch. Toroshelidze, "Soglasovanie deiatel'nosti otdel'nykh vidov kooperatsii," *Ekonomicheskaia zhizn'*, September 14, 1924.

77. *Ibid.* See also P. Sadyrin, "Vzaimootnosheniia mezhdu sel'skokhoziaist-

vennoi i potrebitel'noi kooperatsiei," *Ekonomicheskaia zhizn'*, September 21, 1924.

78. Gorbunov and Stoklitskii, *SSSR*, p. 332.

79. In some of the most important, wealthiest agricultural areas, such as the North Caucasus, well-to-do peasants owned more than 25 percent of the total number of tractors (Danilov, *Sozdanie*, p. 302).

80. Decree of the Council of Labor and Defense of July 17, 1926, "O traktoroispol'zovanii," in N. D. Kazantsev, ed., *Istoriia kolkhoznogo prava, sbornik zakonodatel'nykh materialov SSSR i RSFSR, 1917–1958 gg.* (Moscow, 1959), I, 90.

81. Ia. Iakovlev, "Traktorosnabzhenie v 1926–27 g.," *Pravda*, September 22, 1926.

82. Quoted in Danilov, *Sozdanie*, p. 303.

83. Danilov, *Sozdanie*, pp. 227, 415.

84. Quoted in "Materialy po sel'skomu i lesnomu khoziaistvu na 1926–1927 god," in Narodnyi komissariat zemledeliia RSFSR, *Trudy zemplana* (Moscow, 1927), pt. 11, p. 304.

85. I. S. Malyshev, ed., *Sel'skoe khoziaistvo SSSR, statisticheskii sbornik* (Moscow, 1960), p. 8.

86. Narodnyi Komissariat, *Trudy zemplana*, p. 42.

87. Danilov, *Sozdanie*, p. 229.

88. *Piatnadtsatyi s"ezd VKP(B), stenograficheskii otchet* (Moscow, 1962), II, 1196.

89. *Ibid.*, I, 569 (speech by Iakovlev).

90. *Ibid.*, II, 1210 (speech by Molotov).

91. *Ibid.*, I, 64–65 (speech by Stalin).

CHAPTER TWO

1. F. R. Dunaevskii, "Mekhanizatsiia polevodstva i general'noe planirovanie," *Planovoe khoziaistvo*, no. 12 (December 1927), p. 62.

2. *Ibid.*, p. 63. See also K. F. Dudin, *Organizatsiia traktornykh kolonn* (Moscow, 1929), p. 11.

3. Dunaevskii, "Mekhanizatsiia polevodstva," p. 68.

4. V. P. Danilov, *Sozdanie material'no-tekhnicheskikh predposylok kollektivizatsii sel'skogo khoziaistva v SSSR* (Moscow, 1957), pp. 245–247; and I. A. Gladkov, ed., *Postroenie fundamenta sotsialisticheskoi ekonomiki v SSSR, 1926–1932 gg.* (Moscow, 1960), p. 266.

5. Dudin, *Organizatsiia traktornykh kolonn*, p. 12.

6. *Ibid.*, pp. 12–14.

7. See, for example, I. I. Shiriaev, "Organizuiushchaia rol' kommunisticheskoi partii v stroitel'stve mashinno-traktornykh stantsii v gody pervoi piatiletki," (Kandidat dissertation, Moscow, 1959), p. 79. Shiriaev is generally scornful of the contribution of the tractor columns.

8. A. M. Markevich, *Mezhselennye mashinno-traktornye stantsii* (Moscow, 1929).

9. Danilov, *Sozdanie*, p. 380.

10. *Ibid.*, p. 364.

11. *Ibid.*, p. 365; see also Iu. V. Arutiunian and M. A. Vyltsan, *Istoricheskaia rol' MTS i ikh reorganizatsiia* (Moscow, 1958), p. 14; and M. A.

Kraev in Gladkov, *Postroenie fundamenta*, p. 330. Although many Soviet writers mention the group unions in connection with the MTS, the author has found evidence of only three actual MTS based on such unions.

12. Kraev, in Gladkov, *Postroenie fundamenta*.

13. Markevich, *Mezhselennye*, p. 274.

14. See, for example, the remarks of I. M. Vareikis and G. N. Kaminskii at the Sixteenth Party Conference, *Shestnadtsataia konferentsiia VKP(B): stenograficheskii otchet* (Moscow, 1962), pp. 335–336, 393–394. Additional details of the debates before, during, and after the Sixteenth Party Conference are discussed in Chapter 3 of the present volume.

15. *Ibid.*, p. 631.

16. Decree of the Council of Labor and Defense of June 5, 1929, "Ob organizatsii mashinno-traktornykh stantsii," in N. D. Kazantsev, ed., *Istoriia kolkhoznogo prava, sbornik zakonodatel'nykh materialov SSSR i RSFSR, 1917–1958 gg.* (Moscow, 1959), I, 137–138. A subsequent decree in December 1929 set a target of 102 MTS to be constructed by the spring sowing campaign of 1930. Decree of the Council of People's Commissars of the USSR (CPC USSR) of December 23, 1929, "O vesennei posevnoi kampanii 1930 goda," *ibid.*, pp. 154–157.

17. Decree of June 5, 1929, in Kazantsev, *Istoriia kolkhoznogo prava*, I, 154–157.

18. J. Stalin, *Leninism* (New York: International Publishers, n.d.), II, 191.

19. Decree of the CC AUCP(B) of January 5, 1930, "O tempe kollektivizatsii i merakh pomoshchi gosudarstva kolkhoznomu stroitel'stvu," in P. N. Sharova et al., eds., *Kollektivizatsiia sel'skogo khoziaistva: vazhneishie postanovleniia kommunisticheskoi partii i Sovetskogo pravitel'stva, 1927–1935* (Moscow, 1957), pp. 258–260. The increase in the number of kolkhozes so far outstripped the supply of tractors that it was not until some time in 1935 that the number of tractors equaled the number of kolkhozes! (Iu. V. Arutiunian, *Mekhanizatory sel'skogo khoziaistva SSSR v 1929–1957 gg.* [Moscow, 1957], p. 11, n. 1.)

20. Decree of the CC AUCP(B) of September 10, 1930, "O stroitel'stve i rukovodstve mashinotraktornymi stantsiiami," Sharova et al., *Kollektivizatsiia*, p. 322.

21. Decree of the CC AUCP(B) of December 29, 1930, "O proizvodstvennoi programme Traktorotsentra na 1931 g.," *ibid.*, pp. 347–349.

22. Decree of the CC AUCP(B) of January 5, 1930, *ibid.*, pp. 258–260.

23. Decree of the CPC USSR and the CC AUCP(B) of January 21, 1931, "O kontraktatsii iarovykh posevov," Sharova et al., *Kollektivizatsiia*, pp. 356–360.

24. Arutiunian and Vyltsan, *Istoricheskaia, rol' MTS*, p. 25.

25. *KPSS v rezoliutsiiakh i resheniiakh s"ezdov, konferentsii i plenumov TsK* (7th ed., Moscow, 1954–1960), pt. 2, p. 646.

26. L. I. Dembo, *Kolkhoznoe stroitel'stvo i ego pravovye formy* (Leningrad, 1930), p. 56; see also, "K itogam vsesoiuznogo soveshchaniia MTS," *Sel'skokhoziaistvennaia zhizn'*, no. 37 (1929), p. 18. For a more recent discussion of problems of MTS location see B. N. Polikarpov, "Ekonomicheskoe obosnovanie razmeshcheniia khoziaistvennogo tsentra (usad'by) MTS i ee proisvodstvennykh

postroek," in P. N. Pershin, ed., *Ekonomicheskie voprosy planirovki khoziaistvennykh tsentrov kolkhozov i MTS* (Moscow, 1957), esp. pp. 97–98.

27. Decree of the CC AUCP(B) of July 30, 1930, "O reorganizatsii kolkhozno-kooperativnoi sistemy," Sharova et al., *Kollektivizatsiia*, pp. 314–315.

28. Decree of the Commission of the People's Commissariat of Agriculture USSR, the All-Union Union of Agricultural Cooperation, and Kolkhoztsentr USSR of August 23, 1930, "O reorganizatsii kolkhozno-kooperativnoi sistemy," *Biulleten' finansovogo i khoziaistvennogo zakonodatel'stva*, no. 28 (1930), pp. 24–25.

29. S. G. Strumilin, ed., *Ekonomicheskaia zhizn' SSSR* (Moscow, 1961), p. 277.

30. Shiriaev, "Organizuiushchaia," p. 235.

31. Decree of the Presidium of the Central Control Commission and the Collegium of the People's Commissariat of Workers' and Peasants' Inspection, "O proverke raboty mashinno-traktornykh stantsii i Traktorotsentra," in *Postanovlenie Kolkhoztsentra, prezidiuma TsKK i kollegii NKRKI o rabote mashinno-traktornykh stantsii i oplate truda traktorista* (Moscow, 1932), pp. 76–78.

32. I. A. Benediktov, "Nepobedimyi kolkhoznyi stroi," *Pravda*, December 24, 1945.

33. Arutiunian and Vyltsan, *Istoricheskaia rol' MTS*, p. 76. On war production problems see also, N. Voznesenskii, *Voennaia ekonomika SSSR v period Otechestvennoi voiny* (Moscow, 1948), pp. 92–93.

34. For example, the Decree of the CPC USSR and the CC AUCP(B) of January 23, 1943, "O meropriiatiiakh po vosstanovleniiu MTS i kolkhozov v raionakh, osvobozhdaemykh ot nemetskofashistskikh okkupantov," *Direktivy KPSS i Sovetskogo pravitel'stva po khoziaistvennym voprosam* (Moscow, 1957), II, 746–750; the Decree of the CPC USSR and the CC AUCP(B) of March 18, 1943, "O meropriiatiiakh po vosstanovleniiu proizvodstva sel'skokhoziaistvennykh mashin i orudii," *ibid.*, pp. 753–755; and the Decree of the CPC USSR and the CC AUCP(B) of August 21, 1943, "O neotlozhnykh merakh po vosstanovleniiu khoziaistva v raionakh, osvobozhdennykh ot nemetskikh okkupantov," *ibid.*, pp. 765–802, esp. Section VI on the MTS, pp. 780–789.

35. A. S. Novik, "Vosstanovlenie i razvitie MTS na Ukraine i ikh rol' v vozrozhdenii sel'skogo khoziaistva v chetvertoi piatiletke (1946–1950 gg.)," (Kandidat dissertation, Kiev State University, 1957), p. 7.

36. Strumilin, *Ekonomicheskaia zhizn' SSSR*, p. 415.

37. *Ibid.*, p. 437.

38. Novik, "Vosstanovlenie," p. 8.

39. Arutiunian and Vyltsan, *Istoricheskaia rol' MTS*, p. 76.

40. "Plenum Rostovskogo obkoma VKP(B)," *Pravda*, July 19, 1945.

41. For example, the report from Stavropol' Krai on the problems of repairs and operational planning caused by the multiplicity of types of tractors in the MTS (A. Chupeev, "Ob odnoi pomekhe v rabote MTS," *Pravda*, October 24, 1945).

42. Arutiunian and Vyltsan, *Istoricheskaia rol' MTS*, p. 91. See also V. Khalturin, "O roli mashinno-traktornykh stantsii v poslevoennyi period," *MTS*, no. 3 (March 1947), p. 7.

43. For a general account of war-induced problems see "Vysokoproizvoditel'no ispol'zovat' mashinno-traktornyi park" (lead editorial), *Sotsialisticheskoe zemledelie* (hereafter *Sots. zem.*), April 14, 1946.

44. Decree of the Council of Ministers USSR and the CC AUCP(B) of October 20, 1948, "O plane polezashchitnykh lesonasazhdenii, vnedreniia travopol'nykh sevooborotov, stroitel'stva prudov i vodoemov dlia obespecheniia vysokikh i ustoichivykh urozhaev v stepnykh raionakh evropeiskoi chasti SSSR" in Kazantsev, *Istoriia kolkhoznogo prava,* II, 323–327. The first 58 LZS were supposed to be operational in the spring of 1948. The three-year target was 570 LZS ("Lesozashchitnye stantsii pered pervoi vesnoi" [lead editorial], *Sots. zem.,* February 1, 1949).

45. Decree of the CM USSR and the CC AUCP(B) of April 18, 1949, "Trekhletnii plan razvitiia obshchestvennogo kolkhoznogo i sovkhoznogo produktivnogo zhivotnovodstva (1949–1951 gg.)" in *Direktivy KPSS,* III, 341–368, esp. pp. 353–355.

46. A. Savin, "Voprosy ukrupneniia kolkhozov," *Voprosy ekonomiki,* no. 9 (September 1950), pp. 96–97.

47. *Ibid.*

48. V. T. Kolomiichuk, "Bor'ba KPSS za povyshenie roli MTS v kolkhoznom proizvodstve v 1951–1954 gg." (Kandidat dissertation, Kiev State University, 1955), p. 40.

49. Arutiunian and Vyltsan, *Istoricheskaia rol' MTS,* p. 95; *Sel'skoe khoziaistvo SSSR* (statistical handbook) (Moscow, 1960), p. 51; G. M. Malenkov (speech at the Nineteenth Party Congress), *Pravda,* October 6, 1952.

50. Rough calculations by the author from data in Arutiunian, *Mekhanizatory,* p. 106, and *Sel'skoe khoziaistvo SSSR* (statistical handbook), pp. 51, 75.

51. J. Stalin, *Economic Problems of Socialism in the USSR* (Moscow: Foreign Languages Publishing House, 1952), pp. 93–94.

52. Malenkov, *Pravda,* October 6, 1952.

CHAPTER THREE

1. Zbigniew K. Brzezinski, *Ideology and Power in Soviet Politics* (New York: Frederick A. Praeger, 1962), pp. 4–5. Emphasis in original.

2. Zbigniew K. Brzezinski and Samuel P. Huntington, *Political Power: USA/USSR* (New York: Viking Press, 1965), p. 21.

3. J. Stalin, *Works* (Moscow: Foreign Languages Publishing House, 1955), XII, 148.

4. Brzezinski and Huntington also mention legitimation and conservation as functions of Soviet ideology (*Political Power,* pp. 45–53). My use of the terms is in some respects similar to theirs, as far as they go. In general, I have attempted to show the various functions in their relationships as they apply to specific policy-making situations, namely, to specific moments in the history of MTS policies. Because of the relatively standardized connotations of the terms themselves, I have not attempted to invent new terms for these functions, despite my differences in emphasis.

5. Robert K. Merton, *Social Theory and Social Structure,* rev. and enl. ed. (New York: Free Press, 1957), p. 51. In the above discussion I have not fully adhered to Merton's definition of "social functions" as such, since I find his concentration on objective consequences too restrictive for my purposes.

Nevertheless, the concepts "manifest" and "latent" may, I think, be used meaningfully in this broader context as well.

6. Merton notes the case in which latent functions may be transformed into manifest functions (Merton, *Social Theory and Social Structure*, p. 51). His disinclination to consider "subjective dispositions," however, somewhat detracts from the usefulness of his analysis for dualistic situations such as the rationalizing function under discussion here. Amitai Etzioni's distinction between real and stated goals of an organization is obviously of considerable relevance here. See his discussion of the problem of unawareness of the discrepancy between real and stated goals in Amitai Etzioni, *Modern Organizations* (Englewood Cliffs, New Jersey: Prentice-Hall, Inc., 1964), p. 7.

7. A. M. Markevich, *Mezhselennye mashinno-traktornye stantsii* (Moscow, 1929), p. 249, table pp. 250–251; also, "K itogam vsesoiuznogo soveshchaniia MTS," *Sel'sko-khoziaistvennaia zhizn'*, no. 37 (September 16, 1929), p. 19.

8. V. P. Danilov, *Sozdanie material'no-tekhnicheskikh predposylok kollektivizatsii sel'skogo khoziaistva* (Moscow, 1957), p. 395. See also, Dana G. Dalrymple, "The American Tractor Comes to Soviet Agriculture: The Transfer of a Technology," *Technology and Culture*, V, no. 2 (Spring 1964), p. 212, table.

9. K. F. Dudin, *Organizatsiia traktornykh kolonn* (Moscow, 1929), p. 6; also, K. Dem'ianenko, "Mashinno-traktornye stantsii i kollektivizatsiia krest'-ianskikh khoziaistv," *Khoziaistvo Ukrainy*, no. 11 (November 1928), pp. 104–105.

10. N. Gordienko, "Protiv traktornykh kolonn," *Khoziaistvo Ukrainy*, no. 11 (November 1928), p. 98.

11. *Ibid.*, p. 101.

12. For example, Dem'ianenko, "Mashinno-traktornye stantsii," p. 101.

13. Gordienko, "Protiv traktornykh kolonn," p. 101.

14. A. Lozovyi, "Mashinno-traktornye stantsii i ikh rol' v obobshchestvlenii krest'ianskogo khoziaistva," *Na agrarnom fronte*, no. 4 (April 1929), p. 36.

15. M. Anisimov, "O traktornykh kolonnakh," *Bol'shevik*, no. 1 (January 1929), pp. 51–52.

16. Markevich, *Mezhselennye*, pp. 17–18.

17. *Ibid.*, p. 29.

18. *Ibid.*, p. 21.

19. *Ibid.*, p. 60.

20. *Ibid.*, p. 269.

21. *Ibid.*, p. 271.

22. *Ibid.*, pp. 274–275.

23. *Ibid.*, pp. 281, 289.

24. *Ibid.*, p. 58.

25. *Ibid.*, p. 65.

26. *Ibid.*, p. 284.

27. *Shestnadtsataia konferentsiia VKP(B): stenograficheskii otchet* (Moscow, 1962), p. 291.

28. *Ibid.*, pp. 306–307.

29. *Ibid.*, pp. 335–336.

30. *Ibid.*, pp. 393–394.

31. *Ibid.*, p. 631.

32. Iu. V. Arutiunian and M. A. Vyltsan, *Istoricheskaia rol' MTS i ikh reorganizatsiia* (Moscow, 1958), pp. 15–16.

33. Stalin, *Works,* XII, 148.

34. S. Leikin, "Protiv opportunizma v rabote MTS," *Bol'shevik,* no. 20 (October 1929), pp. 65–66.

35. M. Golendo, "Organizatsiia mashinno-traktornykh stantsii," *Na agrarnom fronte,* no. 2 (February 1930), pp. 10–11.

36. Ia. Nikulikhin, "Problema agroindustrial'nykh kombinatov," *Na agrarnom fronte,* no. 1 (January 1930), pp. 39–40, and no. 3 (March 1930), p. 39, where he elaborates on the theory of the AIK. Nikulikhin foresees the AIK as an inevitable result of collectivization with the MTS.

37. Golendo, "Organizatsiia," pp. 10–11.

38. Nikulikhin, "Problema" (January 1930) pp. 38–39.

39. For example, A. F. Cheshkov, "Mashinno-traktornye stantsii na poroge novykh istoricheskikh zadach," *Sotsialisticheskaia rekonstruktsiia sel'skogo khoziaistva,* no. 1 (January 1933), p. 47.

40. Stalin, *Works,* XII, 287. Emphasis in original.

41. L. I. Dembo, *Kolkhoznoe stroitel'stvo i ego pravovye formy* (Leningrad, 1930), p. 61. Some MTS included a sales agreement in their contracts with peasant unions. Danilov, *Sozdanie,* p. 378

42. In a recent article devoted to setting the record straight on collectivization M. L. Bogdenko and I. E. Zelenin note that "acrimonious discussions" on the MTS went on well into 1930. They refer to a sharp exchange in Traktorotsentr between cooperative spokesmen, demanding the transfer of MTS machinery to the kolkhozes, and T. A. Iurkin and Markevich, who insisted on retaining the state MTS formula (M. L. Bogdenko and I. E. Zelenin, "Istoriia kollektivizatsii sel'skogo khoziaistva v sovremennoi sovetskoi istoriko-ekonomicheskoi literature," *Istoriia SSSR,* no. 4 [1962], p. 136).

43. P. Savchuk, "Rol' MTS v sotsialisticheskom pereustroistve derevni," *Bol'shevik,* no. 3–4 (February 1930), p. 48.

44. Stalin, *Works,* XII, 171.

45. Decree of the Central Committee of the AUCP (B) of December 29, 1930, "O proizvodstvennoi programme Traktorotsentra na 1931 g.," in P. N. Sharova et al., *Kollektivizatsiia sel'skogo khoziaistva: vazhneishie postanovleniia kommunisticheskoi partii i Sovetskogo pravitel'stva, 1927–1935* (Moscow, 1957), p. 347.

46. V. I. Lenin, *On Cooperation* (Moscow: Foreign Languages Publishing House, 1951), pp. 12–13.

47. M. Vlasov, "Sotsialisticheskaia rekonstruktsiia sel'skogo khoziaistva v raionakh MTS," *Narodnoe khoziaistvo SSSR,* no. 1–2 (1932), pp. 104–105, 106.

48. P. Piatnitskii, "Dogovor mashinno-traktornykh stantsii s kolkhozami," *Sotsialisticheskaia iustitsiia,* no. 11 (1938), p. 5.

49. A. A. Ruskol and N. G. Salishcheva, *Pravovoe polozhenie mashinno-traktornoi stantsii i kharakter ee dogovornykh otnoshenii s kolkhozami* (Moscow, 1956), pp. 133–134.

50. V. M. Molotov, Speech at Conference of Agricultural Officials on February 21, 1938, *Pravda,* February 24, 1938.

51. I. T. Kuznetsov, "Khozraschet i povyshenie rentabel'nosti MTS," in

P. P. Grebtsov, ed., *V pomoshch' izuchaiushchim ekomomiku MTS* (Moscow, 1956), p. 77.

52. Karl Marx, *Capital* (Moscow: Foreign Languages Publishing House, 1962), III, chaps. 38–43.

53. For example, see remarks of Professors Kovaleva and Pashkov in P. Malyshev (rapporteur), "Differential Rent Under Socialism: A Scientific Conference at Moscow University," *Problems of Economics*, II, no. 10 (February 1960), pp. 5–9. See also, M. Bronshtein, "Distribution of Differential Rent Under Socialism," *Problems of Economics*, III, no. 3 (July 1960), pp. 37–38. Professor S. G. Strumilin took an important part in these debates.

54. V. Ovchinnikova, "O proizvodstvennykh i khoziaistvennykh uspekhakh ukrupnennykh kolkhozov," *Voprosy ekonomiki*, no. 4 (April 1953), p. 104.

55. V. G. Venzher, "Vysokoproizvoditel'noe ispol'zovanie tekhniki v kolkhozakh," *Voprosy ekonomiki*, no. 3 (March 1951), pp. 29–31.

56. The author held an extended interview with Professor Venzher in Moscow on March 1, 1963, during which a number of questions on the history of Soviet agriculture were discussed. On the MTS liquidation scheme, Venzher asserted that their proposals were not merely theoretical but were based on extensive experiments lasting several years conducted by him and others in Krasnodar Krai. The author received the impression that such relatively radical experiments, on a small, semisecret basis, were fairly common even under Stalin.

57. J. Stalin, *Economic Problems of Socialism in the USSR* (Moscow: Foreign Languages Publishing House, 1952), p. 63.

58. *Ibid.*, p. 68.

59. *Ibid.*, pp. 68–69.

60. *Ibid.*, pp. 69–70.

61. "Velikii vklad v sokrovishchnitsu marksizma-leninizma" (lead editorial), *Voprosy ekonomiki*, no. 10 (October 1952), p. 16.

62. V. Venzher, "Voprosy kompleksnoi mekhanizatsii sel'skogo khoziaistva SSSR," *Voprosy ekonomiki*, no. 6 (June 1952), p. 4.

63. See, for example, Eugenia Semyonovna Ginzburg, *Journey into the Whirlwind*, trans. Paul Stevenson and Max Hayward (New York: Harcourt, Brace and World, 1967), p. 75. In this remarkable book Madame Ginzburg, the wife of a high Party official in the Tatar Republic and herself a prominent Party member, describes how she and others of similar social and political status fully accepted the Party line on industrialization and collectivization despite their suspicions concerning Stalin's personal motives.

CHAPTER FOUR

1. See, for example, Alfred G. Meyer, *The Soviet Political System: An Interpretation* (New York: Random House, 1965), chap. 8. Note also the inclusion of two selections on Soviet bureaucracy and one on Chinese bureaucracy in a recent reader on comparative public administration: Nimrod Raphaeli, ed., *Readings in Comparative Public Administration* (Boston: Allyn and Bacon, 1967), pp. 148–198.

2. Meyer, *The Soviet Political System*, p. 216.

3. See, for example, M. P. Kareva, "Teoreticheskoe znachenie opyta

Sovetskogo sotsialisticheskogo gosudarstva," in P. E. Orlovskii et al., eds., *Voprosy Sovetskogo gosudarstva i prava, 1917–1957* (Moscow: Izdatel'stvo Akademii nauk SSSR, 1957), pp. 89–90; also, D. M. Gvishiani, *Sotsiologiia biznesa: Kriticheskii ocherk amerikanskoi teorii menedzhmenta* (Moscow: Izdatel'stvo sotsial'no-ekonomicheskoi literatury, 1962). Gvishiani makes the following assertion: "Thus, the rise of a system of management is conditioned, on the one hand, by the objective preconditions proceeding from the laws of development of contemporary social production, from the ever greater complexity of the functions of administration as the social character of production increases, and, on the other hand, by the specific demands and peculiarities of the capitalist system of economy . . ." (p. 44).

4. James G. March and Herbert A. Simon, *Organizations* (New York: John Wiley and Sons, 1958), p. 169.

5. For example, A. A. Ruskol and N. G. Salishcheva, *Pravovoe polozhenie mashinno-traktornoi stantsii i kharakter ee dogovornyk otnoshenii s kolkhozami* (Moscow, 1956), pp. 75–76; S. V. Fraer, *Organizatsiia raboty MTS v kolkhozakh* (Moscow, 1952), chap. 11; B. A. Voronkov, "Organizatsiia upravleniia v mashinno-traktornoi stantsii," (Kandidat dissertation, Moscow, 1955), p. 164.

6. Ruskol and Salishcheva (*Pravovoe polozhenie*, pp. 75–76) place the brigadiers in the first group, which they call the administration (*administratsiia*) of the MTS.

7. *Ibid.*, p. 81.

8. *Ibid.*, p. 75.

9. For the Soviet interpretation of *edinonachalie* see the *Bol'shaia Sovetskaia entsiklopediia*, 2nd ed. (Moscow, 1952), XV, 475–476; also, I. N. Ananov, *Ministerstva v SSSR* (Moscow, 1960), pp. 154–161. For a Western treatment see Meyer, *The Soviet Political System*, esp. pp. 210–215.

10. For an interesting discussion of the ambiguity of *edinonachalie* in the industrial sector, see Jerry F. Hough, "The Soviet Concept of the Relationship between the Lower Party Organs and the State Administration," *Slavic Review*, XXIV (June 1965), 215–240.

11. Ruskol and Salishcheva, *Pravovoe polozhenie*, p. 35.

12. *Ibid.*, pp. 76–78; Fraer, *Organizatsiia raboty MTS*, pp. 386–387.

13. Voronkov, *Organizatsiia upravleniia*, pp. 173, 178; Ruskol and Salishcheva, *Pravovoe polozhenie*, p. 79.

14. See the 1939 version of the Model Contact in N. D. Kazantsev, ed., *Istoriia kolkhoznogo prava, sbornik zakonodatel'nykh materialov SSSR i RSFSR, 1917–1958 gg.* (Moscow, 1959), II, 67; also, Ruskol and Salishcheva, *Pravovoe polozhenie*, p. 140.

15. For example, see Daniel Katz and Robert L. Kahn, *The Social Psychology of Organizations* (New York: John Wiley and Sons, 1966), pp. 371, 380 *et passim*.

16. See, for example, the accounts of such meetings in Soviet literature on village life. Good illustrations may be found in Galina Nikolaeva's *Harvest* (Moscow: Foreign Languages Publishing House, 1952); and the sketches "Raionnye budni" by Valentin Ovechkin in *Izbrannye proizvedeniia v dvukh tomakh* (Moscow, 1963), II.

17. Fraer, *Organizatsiia upravlenie*, p. 387.

18. Ruskol and Salishcheva, *Pravovoe polozhenie,* pp. 81–82.

19. *Ibid.,* pp. 83–84.

20. *Postanovlenie Kolkhoztsentra, Prezidiuma TsKK i Kollegii NKRKI o rabote Mashinnotraktornykh stantsii i oplate truda traktorista* (Moscow, 1932), p. 1; Fraer, "Organizatsiia traktornykh brigad v MTS," in P. P. Grebtsov, ed., *V pomoshch' izuchaiushchim ekonomiku MTS* (Moscow, 1956), p. 176; M. Vainer and S. Demidov, "Voprosy traktornykh otriadov na veseniuiu posevnuiu kampaniiu zernovykh MTS," *Sotsialisticheskaia rekonstruktsiia sel'skogo khoziaistva,* no. 2 (February 1933), p. 130. The authors of the last article note, with approval, that the original detachments of seven to nine tractors had been reduced to three to five tractors.

21. Fraer, in Grebtsov, *V pomoshch',* p. 176.

22. Decree of the Council of Labor and Defense of September 21, 1933, "Ob organizatsii ispol'zovaniia traktornogo parka," in P. N. Sharova et al., eds., *Kollektivizatsiia sel'skogo khoziaistva: vazhneishie postanovleniia kommunisticheskoi partii i Sovetskogo pravitel'stva, 1927–1935* (Moscow, 1957), p. 472.

23. Decree of the Secretariat of the All-Union Central Union of Trade-Unions of January 8, 1937, "O sotsial'nom strakhovanii nekotorykh rabotnikov MTS," *Finansovoe i khoziaistvennoe zakonodatel'stvo,* no. 12 (1937), p. 30.

24. N. S. Khrushchev, *Stroitel'stvo kommunizma v SSSR i razvitie sel'skogo khoziaistva* (Moscow, 1962–1963), I, 54–55. Text of the relevant passage of the decree "O merakh po dal'neishemu uluchsheniiu raboty mashinnotraktornykh stantsii," Decree of the Council of Ministers, USSR and the CC CPSU of September 21, 1953, in Kazantsev, *Istoriia kolkhoznogo prava,* II, 395.

25. Ruskol and Salishcheva, *Pravovoe polozhenie,* p. 90.

26. Iu. V. Arutiunian, *Mekhanizatory sel'skogo khoziaistva SSSR v 1929–1957 gg.* (Moscow, 1960), p. 15, n. 12.

27. Iu. Gololobov, "Na pervom etape stroitel'stva MTS," *Na agrarnom fronte,* no. 6 (June 1930), pp. 122–123.

28. Arutiunian, *Mekhanizatory,* p. 15.

29. "Dogovor mashino-traktornoi stantsii 'Traktorotsentra' s kolkhozami," accepted by Traktorotsentr and Kolkhoztsentr and confirmed by the PCA, USSR on October 13, 1930, in A. Likhachev, compiler, *Sbornik zakonov i rasporiazhenii o mashinotraktornykh stantsiiakh, deistvuiushchikh na 1 noiabria 1931 g.* (Moscow, 1931), p. 48.

30. Decree of the CC AUCP(B) of October 16, 1930, "O partiino-massovoi rabote v raionakh deiatel'nosti MTS," Sharova et al., *Kollektivizatsiia,* p. 336.

31. M. A. Vyltsan, *Ukreplenie material'no-tekhnicheskoi bazy kolkhoznogo stroia vo vtoroi piatiletke (1933–1937 gg.)* (Moscow, 1958), p. 53.

32. L. M. Kaganovich, "Tseli i zadachi politicheskikh otdelov MTS i sovkhozov," *Bol'shevik,* no. 1–2 (January 1933), p. 30.

33. "Ne pozvolim opportunistam i bezdel'nikam sorvat' khlebozagotovki," *Proletarii,* September 20, 1931.

34. B. Markovich, "Reshitel'no izzhit' tekuchest' raionnykh kadrov," *Partiinoe stroitel'stvo,* no. 19 (October 1933), p. 42.

35. A. Shteingart, "Politotdely Severnogo Kavkaza za rabotoi," *Pravda,* May 9, 1933.

36. Ia. A. Iakovlev, "Zadachi komandnogo sostava novostroiashchikhsia MTS," address delivered on July 3, 1933, in Iakovlev, *Voprosy organizatsii*

sotsialisticheskogo sel'skogo khoziaistva, 2nd ed. (Moscow, 1935), pp. 134, 144–145.

37. D. Krinitskii, "O tekh, kto vozglavliaet MTS," *Sots. zem.,* March 28, 1937.

38. *Ibid.* See also, Vyltsan, *Ukreplenie,* p. 60; A. Zalikin, "Novye kadry rukovoditelei sel'skogo khoziaistva," *Partiinoe stroitel'stvo,* no. 3 (February 1938), pp. 60–61; M. N. Shamis, "Podmena i obezlichivanie direktorov MTS i zav. raizo," *Sots. zem.,* March 15, 1937.

39. "Vydvizhenie kadrov v zemel'nykh organakh" (lead editorial), *Sots. zem.,* August 12, 1937.

40. D. Krinitskii, "O tekh, kto vozglavliaet MTS."

41. "Vydvizhenie kadrov," *Sots. zem.*

42. I. A. Benediktov, "Na poroge novogo goda," *Sots. zem.,* January 1, 1939.

43. Vyltsan, *Ukreplenie,* p. 59.

44. D. Krinitskii, "O tekh, kto vozglavliaet MTS."

45. Vyltsan, *Ukreplenie,* p. 58.

46. Ia. A. Iakovlev, speech on December 29, 1935, *Pravda,* January 4, 1936.

47. Benediktov, "Na poroge."

48. S. Matskevich, "Kadry MTS," *Problemy ekonomiki,* no. 1 (January 1937), p. 178.

49. Computed by author from data in B. Khalturin, "O roli mashinno-traktornykh stantsii v pod"eme sel'skogo khoziaistva v poslevoennyi period," *MTS,* no. 3 (March 1947), p. 9; and I. S. Malyshev, ed., *MTS vo vtoroi piatiletke* (Moscow-Leningrad, 1939), p. 90.

50. Khalturin, "O roli mashinno-traktornykh stantsii," p. 9.

51. A. A. Andreev, "O merakh pod"ema sel'skogo khoziaistva v poslevoennyi period," address at the February (1947) Plenum of the CC AUCP(B), *Sots. zem.,* March 7, 1947.

52. *Ibid.* For a description of the situation in Kuibyshev Oblast see "Kogda zhe agronomy i zootekhniki pereidut na proizvodstvo?" *Sots. zem.,* April 16, 1947.

53. Decree of the February Plenum of the CC AUCP(B), February 1947, "O merakh pod"ema sel'skogo khoziaistva v poslevoennyi period," *KPSS v rezoliutsiiakh i resheniiakh s"ezdov, konferentsii i plenumov TsK* (Moscow, 1954–1960) pt. 3, p. 536.

54. A. Kuropatkin, "O prevrashchenii selsko-khoziaistvennogo truda v raznovidnost' truda industrial'nogo," *Bol'shevik,* no. 5 (March 1949), p. 53.

55. Calculated by the author from Arutiunian, *Mekhanizatory,* p. 108; and *Sel'skoe khoziaistvo SSSR: Statisticheskii sbornik* (Moscow, 1960), pp. 51, 75.

56. I. A. Benediktov, "MTS v bor'be za novyi pod"em sel'skogo khoziastva," *Bol'shevik,* no. 5 (March 1951), p. 16.

57. Khrushchev, *Stroitel'stvo kommunizma,* I, 64–65.

58. *Ibid.,* p. 56.

59. I. S. Kuvshinov, *MTS — reshaiushchaia sila kolkhoznogo proizvodstva* (Moscow, 1955), p. 13.

60. Khrushchev, *Stroitel'stvo kommunizma,* p. 65.

61. I. A. Benediktov, speech at All-Union Conference of MTS Workers, reported in *Kommunist* (Saratov), January 27, 1924.

62. Khrushchev, *Stroitel'stvo kommunizma,* p. 425.

63. See, for example, the article "Usilit' otbor i napravlenie spetsialistov na proizvodstvo" in *Kolkhoznoe zemledelie* (house organ of the Ministry of Agriculture, USSR), October 22, 1953.

64. Decree of the CC CPSU and the Council of Ministers, USSR of August 20, 1955, "O merakh po dal'neishemu uluchsheniiu agronomicheskogo i zootekhnicheskogo obsluzhivaniia kolkhozov" in B. A. Boldyrev, ed., *Sbornik zakonodatel'nykh i vedomstvennykh aktov po sel'skomu khoziaistvu* (Moscow, 1957), I, 182–187.

65. Likhachev (compiler), *Sbornik zakonov,* p. 48.

66. Arutiunian, *Mekhanizatory,* pp. 120–121.

67. Khrushchev, *Stroitel'stvo kommunizma,* I, 54.

68. KPSS v rezoliutsiiakh, pt. 3, pp. 640–641.

69. Arutiunian, *Mekhanizatory,* p. 215, table.

70. A. F. Cheshkov, "Mashinno-traktornye stantsii na poroge novykh istoricheskikh zadach," *Sotsialisticheskaia rekonstruktsiia sel'skogo khoziaistva,* no. 1 (January 1933), p. 55.

71. Arutiunian, *Mekhanizatory,* p. 32.

72. Decree of the Council of Labor and Defense of September 21, 1933, Sharova et al., *Kollektivizatsiia,* p. 471.

73. Arutiunian, *Mekhanizatory,* p. 48.

74. "Za dal'neishee uluchshenie raboty mashinno-traktornykh stantsii" (lead editorial), *Sots. zem.,* January 14, 1939.

75. Calculated by the author from data in Naum Jasny, *The Socialized Agriculture of the USSR: Plans and Performance* (Stanford: Stanford University Press, 1949), pp. 284–285.

76. Decree of the Council of People's Commissars, USSR and the CC AUCP(B) of January 13, 1939, "O poriadke nachisleniia naturoplaty za raboty MTS po zernovym kul'turam" in Kazantsev, *Istoriia kolkhoznogo prava,* II, 60.

77. Ia. A. Iakovlev, Speech to the First All-Union Congress of Kolkhoznik-Shock Workers, in *Pervyi vsesoiuznyi s"ezd kolkhoznikov-udarnikov, 15–19 fevralia 1939 g.* (Moscow and Leningrad, 1933), p. 113.

78. Arutiunian, *Mekhanizatory,* pp. 48–49.

79. *Ibid.,* p. 58.

80. *Ibid.,* p. 96.

81. *KPSS v rezoliutsiiakh,* pt. 3, p. 533.

82. Decree of the Council of Ministers, USSR of September 29, 1951, "O merakh po uluchsheniiu raboty mashinno-traktornykh stantsii," in *Direktivy KPSS i Sovetskogo pravitel'stva po khoziaistvennym voprosam* (Moscow, 1957), III, 593–607.

83. Arutiunian, *Mekhanizatory,* p. 134.

84. Khrushchev, *Stroitel'stvo kommunizma,* I, 427.

85. Arutiunian, *Mekhanizatory,* p. 142, table 21.

86. Khrushchev, *Stroitel'stvo kommunizma,* I, 53.

87. *Ibid.*

88. *Ibid.,* p. 55.

89. *Ibid.*, p. 229. (Speech at the February–March [1954] Plenum of the Central Committee.)

90. Decree of the Council of Ministers, USSR and the CC CPSU of September 21, 1953, "O merakh po dal'neishemu uluchsheniiu raboty mashinno-traktornykh stantsii," Kazantsev, *Kollektivizatsiia*, II, 394–408, esp. p. 397.

91. Peter M. Blau and W. Richard Scott, *Formal Organizations: A Comparative Approach* (San Francisco: Chandler Publishing Co., 1962), p. 172.

92. Markevich, *Mezhselennye mashinno-traktornye stantsii* (Moscow, 1929), pp. 53–55.

93. Decree of the Commission of the PCI, the All-Union Union of Agricultural Cooperation and Kolkhoztsentr, USSR on the Reorganization of the Kolkhoz-Cooperative System of August 23, 1930, "O postroenii kolkhoznoi sistemy," A. M. Turubiner and A. B. Fridenshtein, *Osnovnye direktivy po sotsialisticheskoi rekonstruktsii sel'skogo khoziaistva* (Moscow, 1931), pp. 97–106, esp. p. 103.

94. For example, the Government of the RSFSR tacitly admitted the absence of any systematic agronomic work by ordering "all sovkhozes, kolkhozes and MTS . . . to designate special persons as organizers and leaders responsible for the conduct of agrotechnical measures in agricultural production" (Decree of the Council of People's Commissars of the RSFSR of January 27, 1932, "O poriadke provedeniia meropriiatii po agrotekhnike v sel'skokhozizistvennom proizvodstve," Kazantsev, *Istoriia kolkhoznogo prava*, I, 335).

95. "Zakrepit' traktornyi otriad za kazhdym uchastkom MTS" (signed: Chairman of the Board of Traktorotsentr, Markevich), in *Postanovlenie Kolkhoztsentra*, p. 1. See also, the Decree of the CC Communist Party (B) Ukraine of February 1932, "O rabote Shevchenkovskoi MTS," *Proletarii*, February 29, 1932; M. S. Romanov, "Rol' proizvodstvennykh uchastkov v MTS v bor'be za ukreplenie kolkhozov, za pod"em urozhainosti v nikh," *Sotsialisticheskaia rekonstruktsiia sel'skogo khoziaistva*, no. 2 (February 1933), p. 117; and the Decree of the Council of People's Commissars, USSR of May 8, 1932, "Po otchetnomu dokladu Traktorotsentra za 1931 g.," Sharova et al., *Kollektivizatsiia*, pp. 413–414. These decrees and articles are concerned with the structure and functions of the MTS production sections.

96. Speech by Kaganovich in J. Stalin, Molotov, Kaganovich, et al. [sic], *Socialism Victorious* (New York: International Publishers, 1934), pp. 154–155.

97. Decree of the Central Executive Committee and the Council of People's Commissars, USSR of April 4, 1934, "O reorganizatsii Narodnogo komissariata zemledeliia Soiuza SSR, respublikanskikh i mestnykh zemel'nykh organov," Kazantsev, *Istoriia kolkhoznogo prava*, I, 399–402.

98. Voronkov, *Organizatsiia upravleniia*, App. 1 to p. 169.

99. See, for example, I. A. Benediktov, "Za korennoe ulushchenie raboty MTS," *MTS*, no. 4 (April 1947), p. 3.

100. Khrushchev, *Stroitel'stvo kommunizma*, I, 51.

101. *Ibid.*, p. 65.

102. Voronkov, *Organizatsiia upravleniia*, p. 178.

103. Khrushchev, *Stroitel'stvo kommunizma*, I, 65. See the Decree of the Council of Ministers, USSR and the CC CPSU of September 21, 1953, "O

merakh po dal'neishemu uluchsheniiu mashinno-traktornykh stantsii,"
Kazantsev, *Istoriia kolkhoznogo prava,* II, 405.

CHAPTER FIVE

1. For an authoritative Soviet discussion of these principles see I. N.
Ananov, *Ministerstva v SSSR* (Moscow, 1960), pp. 188–189, 200–201. There
is a description of their application to changes in the structure of the Party
apparatus, with interesting chronological parallels in Merle Fainsod, *How
Russia Is Ruled,* rev. ed. (Cambridge: Harvard University Press, 1963), pp.
190–204 *passim.*

2. For example, Peter M. Blau and W. Richard Scott, *Formal Organizations*
(San Francisco: Chandler Publishing Co., 1962), pp. 173–176; also, Charles
A. Myers and John G. Turnbull, "Line and Staff in Industrial Relations," in
Joseph A. Litterer, ed., *Organizations: Structure and Behavior* (New York:
John Wiley and Sons, 1963), pp. 308–316.

3. Decree of the CC AUCP(B) of September 10, 1930, "O stroitel'stve i
rukovodstve mashinnotraktornymi stantsiiami," in P. N. Sharova et al., eds.,
*Kollektivizatsiia sel'skogo khoziaistva: vazhneishie postanovleniia kommu-
nisticheskoi partii i Sovetskogo pravitel'stva, 1927–1935* (Moscow, 1957),
p. 322.

4. Decree of the CC AUCP(B) of July 30, 1930, "O reorganizatsii kolkhozno-kooperativnoi sistemy," *ibid.,* pp. 314–315.

5. Decree of the Commission of the PCA USSR, the All-Union Union of
Agricultural Cooperation, and Kolkhoztsentr USSR of August 23, 1930, "O
reorganizatsii kolkhozno-kooperativnoi sistemy," *Biulleten' finansovogo i
khoziaistvennogo zakonodatel'stva,* no. 28 (1930), pp. 24–25.

6. Decree of the CC CP(B)U, "O rabote Shevchenkovskoi MTS,"
Proletarii, February 29, 1932.

7. L. I. Dembo, *Kolkhoznoe stroitel'stvo i ego pravovye formy* (Leningrad,
1930), p. 13.

8. Decree of the Presidium of the Central Control Commission and the
Collegium of the People's Commissariat of Workers' and Peasants' Inspection,
"O proverke raboty mashinno-traktornykh stantsii i Traktorotsentra," in
*Postanovlenie Kolkhoztsentra, prezidiuma TsKK i kollegii NKRKI o rabote
Mashinno-traktornykh stantsii i oplate truda traktorista* (Moscow, 1932),
pp. 76–78.

9. I. Goretskii, "MTS i ikh rol' v sotsialisticheskoi rekonstruktsii derevni,"
Sovetskoe stroitel'stvo, no. 4 (81), (1963), p. 37.

10. Decree of the Central Executive Committee of the USSR of October 1,
1932, "Ob obrazovanii Narodnogo komissariata zernovykh i zhivotnovod-
cheskikh sovkhozov Soiuza SSR," in Upravelenie delami Soveta narodnykh
komissarov Soiuza SSR i Soveta truda i oborony, *Sobranie zakonov i rasporiazhenii Rabochekrest'ianskogo pravitel'stva SSSR* (hereafter referred to
as SZ), no. 71–435 (October 5, 1932), p. 713.

11. *Ibid.;* see also, Iu. V. Arutiunian and M. A. Vyltsan, *Istroricheskaia
rol' MTS i ikh reorganizatiia* (Moscow, 1958), p. 21.

12. *Ibid.*

13. A. A. Ruskol and N. G. Salishcheva, *Pravovoe polozhenie mashinno-*

traktornoi stantsii i kharakter ee dogovornykh otnoshenii s kolkhozami (Moscow, 1956), pp. 53–55. On the principle of "dual subordination" see Ananov, *Ministerstva,* pp. 212–213.

14. P. P. Postyshev, speech at meeting of the Khar'kov Oblast and City Party *aktiv* on February 16, 1934, *Proletarii,* February 22, 1934.

15. *XVII s"ezd vsesoiuznoi kommunisticheskoi partii (B): stenograficheskii otchet* (Moscow, 1934), p. 154.

16. *Ibid.,* p. 540.

17. *Ibid.,* p. 542.

18. Decree of the CEC and the CPC USSR of April 4, 1934, "O reorganizatsii Narodnogo komissariata zemledeliia Soiuza SSR, respublikanskikh i mestnykh organov" in N. D. Kazantsev, ed., *Istoriia kolkhoznogo prava, sbornik zakodatel'nykh materialov SSSR i RSFSR, 1917–1958 gg.* (Moscow, 1959), I, 399–400.

19. *Ibid.,* p. 402.

20. *Ibid.*

21. Decree of the CPC USSR of December 30, 1929, "Ob obespechenii planomernogo uchastiia sredstv krest'ianskogo naseleniia v stroitel'stve mashinotraktornykh stantsii i traktornykh kolonn," Sharova et al., *Kollektivizatsiia,* pp. 257–258; also, L. Apresiants, *MTS i kolkhozy* (Moscow-Leningrad, 1931), p. 22.

22. Arutiunian and Vyltsan, *Istoricheskaia rol' MTS,* p. 20.

23. Decree of the CPC USSR of May 8, 1932, "O razmeshchenii aktsii Traktorotsentra dlia obespecheniia plana stroitel'stva mashinotraktornykh stantsii v 1932 g.," Sharova et al., *Kollektivizatsiia,* pp. 414–415.

24. Decree of the CC CP(B)U and the CPC Ukrainian SSR, "Po-bol'-shevistski mobilizovat' vse sily na uspeshnoe provedenie poseva," *Proletarii,* February 21, 1931; also "MTS — moshchnyi rychag sploshnoi kollektivizatsii," *Proletarii,* April 3, 1931. In each case five MTS were to be transferred.

25. Decree of the Presidium of the Central Control Commission and the Collegium of the People's Commissariat of Workers' and Peasants' Inspection, *Postanovlenie Kolkhoztsentra,* pp. 71, 77.

26. S. Trapeznikov, *Istoricheskii opyt KPSS v sotsialisticheskom preobrazovanii sel'skogo khoziaistva* (Moscow, 1959), p. 254.

27. A. Odintsov, "Rabotat' po-stakhanovskii," *Molot* (Rostov-on-Don), October 29, 1935.

28. R. W. Davies, *The Development of the Soviet Budgetary System* (Cambridge, Eng.: Cambridge University Press, 1958), pp. 174, 262–264.

29. M. A. Vyltsan, *Ukreplenie material'no-tekhnicheskoi bazy kolkhoznogo stroia vo vtoroi piatiletke (1933–1937 gg.)* (Moscow, 1958), p. 109.

30. *Ibid.,* p. 111.

31. N. Nikitin and P. Prigolovko, "Novyi poriadok finansirovaniia MTS," *Sots. zem.,* February 10, 1938.

32. Quoted in A. A. Ruskol, "Nekotorye voprosy dogovornoi praktiki MTS s kolkhozami," *Arbitrazh,* no. 8 (1936), p. 18.

33. Speech by People's Commissar of Agriculture Robert I. Eikhe, *Molot,* January 22, 1938.

34. *Vtoroi Vsesoiuznyi s"ezd kolkhoznikov-udarnikov: stenograficheskii otchet* (Moscow, 1935), p. 102.

35. M. A. Chernov, "Plan 1936 goda i zadachi mashinno-traktornykh stantsii," *Sotsialisticheskaia rekonstruktsiia sel'skogo khoziaistva,* no. 2 (February 1936), p. 35.

36. "Navesti bol'shevistskii poriadok v finansovom khoziaistve MTS!" *Sots. zem.,* September 29, 1937.

37. M. A. Chernov, "O proizvodstvenno-finansovoi deiatel'nosti MTS," *Pravda,* January 8, 1936. See also, N. Tkachev, "Privedem v poriadok finansovoe khoziaistvo MTS," *Molot,* June 21, 1935.

38. V. A. Zaslavskii, "O goriuchem i rentable'nosti MTS," *Molot,* April 9, 1936. One of the reasons for the large specific weight of fuel expenses was the artificially high price of fuel to the MTS. By a decree of December 22, 1933, fuel prices for the MTS and sovkhozes were increased by a factor of ten, requiring these important users to pay the inflated (by the turnover tax) retail price. See Naum Jasny, *The Socialized Agriculture of the USSR: Plans and Performance* (Stanford: Stanford University Press, 1949), p. 256.

39. E. I. Riabinin, Speech at Voronezh oblast conference of raikom secretaries, *Kommuna* (Voronezh), May 26, 1935.

40. Chernov, *Pravda,* January 8, 1936; Vyltsan, *Ukreplenie,* p. 110.

41. R. I. Eikhe, "O plane sel'sko-khoziaistvennykh rabot na 1938 god," *Sots. zem.,* January 22, 1938. On the general problem see F. Iur'ev, "Zateriavshiisia opyt bezubytochnykh MTS," *Sots. zem.,* February 15, 1937.

42. Vyltsan, *Ukreplenie,* p. 129.

43. V. Belousov, "Poroki struktury zemel'nykh organov," *Pravda,* August 27, 1938.

44. Chernov, *Pravda,* January 8, 1936.

45. *Ibid.*

46. V. Ia. Chubar', *Prevratim mashinno-traktornye stantsii v obraztsovye predpriiatiia* (pamphlet) (Moscow: Partizdat TsK VKP(B), 1936), p. 10. N. K. Antipov, "Soveshchanie rukovodiashchikh rabotnikov MTS i zemel'nykh organov s rukovoditeliami partii i pravitel'stva," *Pravda,* January 9, 1936. Antipov proposed to give the projected territorial administrations control over the whole range of MTS affairs — planning, finance, cadres, operations, etc. That is, he wanted to eliminate functionalism completely.

47. Chubar', *Prevratim,* Ia. A. Iakovlev, *Pravda,* January 10, 1936.

48. "Na sobranii aktiva Narkomzema Soiuza," *Sots. zem.,* May 29, 1937.

49. "Informatsionnoe soobshchenie," *Pravda,* June 30, 1937.

50. Narkomzem SSSR, *"O merakh uluchsheniia raboty mashinno-traktornykh stantsii," Proekt NKZ'a SSSR* (Ioshkar-Ola: Margiz, 1937). A copy with the same title can be found in the *Smolensk Archive,* Harvard University Library, WKP 238, pp. 253–256. The circular is mentioned by Merle Fainsod in *Smolensk Under Soviet Rule* (Cambridge: Harvard University Press, 1958), p. 293.

51. Narkomzem SSSR, *"O merakh uluchsheniia."*

52. For example, "Uporiadochit' finansovoe khoziaistvo MTS," *Sots. zem.,* December 26, 1937.

53. See footnote on page 89 above. At least one member of the group of economists who made these suggestions in 1937 managed to survive the purges and continue the struggle against the irrationalities of the agricultural system. When the author questioned Professor V. G. Venzher on the matter of dissent

in economic affairs during the Stalin era, he replied: "After all, people continued to think and hold opinions even under Stalin" (Interview in Moscow, March 1, 1963).

54. "Vystuplenie tov. V. M. Molotova na soveshchanii zemel'nykh rabotnikov," *Pravda,* February 24, 1938.

55. Decree of the CPC USSR of February 5, 1938, "O poriadke finansirovaniia mashinno-traktornykh stantsii," Kazantsev, *Istoriia kolkhoznogo prava,* II, 35–36.

56. Decree of the CPC USSR of January 13, 1939, "O rabote mashinno-traktornykh stantsii," *ibid.,* II, 61–63.

57. N. A. Paskutskii, speech at meeting of the *aktiv* of the PCA USSR, *Sots. zem.,* October 5, 1937.

58. Belousov, *Pravda,* August 27, 1938.

59. *Ibid.*

60. N. Nazartsev, "O strukture zemel'nykh organov," *Sots. zem.,* December 12, 1938. Also, M. Peregudova and M. Morev, "Organizatsionnaia nerazberikha v oblastnom zemel'nom otdele," *Kommuna,* June 3, 1938; and the report by the Voronezh *Oblzu* on the status of tractor repairs, *ibid.,* March 24, 1939.

61. Peregudova and Morev, *Kommuna,* June 3, 1938.

62. For example, Belousov, *Pravda,* August 27, 1938; P. Lapaev, "O strukture Narkomzema SSSR," *Sots. zem.,* September 21, 1938; O. Kotov, "O perestroike apparata Narkomzema SSSR," *ibid.,* September 29, 1938; Nazartsev, *Sots. zem.,* December 12, 1938.

63. Decree of the CC AUCP(B) and the CPC USSR of December 5, 1939, "O strukture Narkomzema SSSR, narkomzemov RSFSR i USSR, narkomzemov avtonomnykh respublik, kraevykh, oblastnykh, i raionnykh zemel'nykh otdelov," Kazantsev, *Istoriia kolkhoznogo prava,* II, 120–126.

64. *Ibid.,* II, 125–126.

65. I. N. Ananov and S. M. Bertsinskii, *Sovetskoe administrativnoe pravo: Uchebnik* (Moscow, 1940), p. 258.

66. Nazartsev, *Sots. zem.,* December 12, 1938.

67. Ananov and Bertsinskii, *Sovetskoe administrativnoe pravo.*

68. Decree of December 5, 1939, Kazantsev, *Istoriia kolkhoznogo prava,* p. 126.

69. Decree of the CPC USSR of November 11, 1945, "Voprosy organizatsii Narodnogo Komissariata Tekhnicheskikh Kul'tur Soiuza SSR," *Sobranie postanovlenii i rasporiazhenii pravitel'stva Soiuza sovetskikh sotsialisticheskikh respublik* (hereafter referred to as *SP and R SSSR*), *1945,* no. 10–132, (December 30, 1945), pp. 198–199.

70. Edict of the Presidium of the Supreme Soviet of the USSR of March 26, 1946, "O razdelenii Ministerstva zemledeliia SSSR na dva ministerstva — Ministerstvo zemledeliia SSSR i Ministerstvo zhivotnovodstva SSSR," Strumilin, *Ekonomicheskaia zhizn' SSSR,* pp. 441–442. The People's Commissariats were renamed "Ministries" on March 15, 1946.

71. Edict of the Presidium of the Supreme Soviet of the USSR of February 4, 1947, "Ob ob"edinenii Ministerstva zemledeliia, Ministerstva tekhnicheskikh kul'tur i Ministerstva zhivotnovodstva v Ministerstvo sel'skogo khoziaistva SSSR," *Izvestiia,* February 5, 1947.

72. I. A. Benediktov, speech at Budgetary Session of the Supreme Soviet, USSR, *Izvestiia*, February 22, 1947.

73. Decree of the Plenum of the CC AUCP(B), February 1947, "O merakh pod"ema sel'skogo khoziaistva v poslevoennyi period," *KPSS v rezoliutsiiakh i resheniiakh s"ezdov, konferentsii i plenumov TsK* (Moscow, 1954–1960), pt. 3, p. 536.

74. A. A. Andreev, "O merakh pod"ema sel'skogo khoziaistva v poslevoennyi period" (speech at February Plenum), *Sots. zem.*, March 7, 1947.

75. *KPSS v rezoliutsiiakh*, pt. 3, pp. 545, 532.

76. Decree of the Council of Ministers, USSR of August 9, 1947, "O gosudarstvennykh inspektorakh po kontroliu za kachestvom traktornykh rabot machinno-traktornykh stantsii," *SP and R SSSR, 1947*, no. 5–92, (September 12, 1947), pp. 86–87.

77. Decree of the Council of Ministers, USSR and the CC AUCP(B) of April 18, 1949, "Trekhletnii plan razvitiia obshchestvennogo kolkhoznogo i sovkhoznogo produktivnogo zhivotnovodstva (1949–1951 gg.)," in *Direktivy KPSS i Sovetskogo pravitel'stva po khoziastvennym voprosam* (Moscow, 1957), III, 341–368.

78. "O khoziaistvennom raschete v MTS," *Sots. zem.*, July 10, 1947.

79. See, for example, L. Galimon, "Nazrevshie voprosy finansirovaniia MTS," *MTS*, no. 10 (October 1950), pp. 8–12.

80. Decree of the Council of Ministers, USSR and the CC CPSU of September 21, 1953, "O merakh po dal'neishemu uluchsheniiu raboty mashinno-traktornykh stantsii," Kazantsev, *Istoriia kolkhoznogo prava*, II, 405.

81. See, for example, I. F. Pokrovskii, *MTS — opornyi punkt gosudarstvennogo rukovodstva kolkhozami* (Moscow, 1957), p. 40.

82. N. S. Khrushchev, *Stroitel'stvo kommunizma v SSSR i razvitie sel'skogo khoziaistva* (Moscow, 1962–1963) I, 63–64.

83. Resolution of the September Plenum, September 7, 1953, "O merakh dal'neishego razvitiia sel'skogo khoziaistva SSSR," *KPSS v rezoliutsiiakh*, pt. 3, pp. 646–647.

84. Ruskol and Salishcheva, *Pravovoe polozhenie*, pp. 17–18, 20.

85. *Ibid.*, see also, "Struktura Ministerstva sel'skogo khoziaistva SSSR," Order (*prikaz*) of the Ministry of Agriculture, USSR, No. 1029, December 9, 1953, *Kolkhoznoe zemledelie*, December 17, 1953.

86. Khrushchev, *Stroitel'stvo kommunizma*, vol. 1, p. 482.

87. V. Safonov, "Struktura novaia, a metody starye," *Partiinaia zhizn'* (hereafter *Part. zhizn'*) no. 6 (March 1956), pp. 56, 58. From the title of the article ("The Structure is New, but the Methods are Old") it would appear that the reorganization was not universally effective.

88. Pokrovskii, *MTS — opornyi punkt*, pp. 35–38.

89. T. L. Basiuk, *MTS — reshaiushchaia sila v razvitii kolkhoznogo proizvodstva* (Moscow, 1954), p. 186.

90. See, for example, letters published in *Partiinaia zhizn'*, no. 13 (July 1956), pp. 59, 61; *ibid.*, no. 16 (August 1956), p. 18.

91. P. S. Kuchumov, "Po-khoziaiski ispol'zovat' moguchuiu tekhniku MTS," *Kommunist*, no. 3 (February 1954), p. 51.

92. For example, P. V. Nikolaenko, "Za pod"em obshchestvennogo kho-

ziaistva kolkhozov" in P. P. Grebtsov, ed., *MTS v bor'be za pod"em kolkhoznogo proizvodstva* (Moscow, 1954), p. 118.

93. Khrushchev, *Stroitel'stvo kommunizma*, I, 304–305.

94. See the following articles: I. Skvortsov, "O sebestoimosti traktornykh rabot," *Part. zhizn'*, no. 8 (July 1954), pp. 17–23; "Podchinim vsiu rabotu apparata ministerstva vypolneniiu iiun'skogo Plenuma TsK KPSS," (report of a Party meeting in the Ministry of Agriculture, USSR, addressed by Benediktov), *Kolkhoznoe zemledelie*, July 10, 1954; V. Petrovskii and S. Romanov, "O ser'eznykh nedostatkakh v rabote finansovogo upravleniia," *ibid.*, May 31, 1955; "Glubzhe izuchat' ekonomiku sel'skogo khoziaistva" (editorial), *Kommunist*, no. 1 (January 1956), p. 18.

95. *KPSS v rezoliutsiiakh*, pt. 4, p. 174.

96. Decree of the CPC USSR and the CC AUCP(B) of January 19, 1933, "Ob obiazatel'noi postavke zerna gosudarstvu kolkhozami i edinolichnymi khoziaistvami," Sharova et al., *Kollektivizatsiia*, pp. 441–445.

97. See for example, the plan for the spring sowing campaign of 1937: Decree of the CPC USSR of February 2, 1937, "O gosudarstvennom plane vesennego poseva 1937 goda," Kazantsev, *Istoriia kolkhoznogo prava*, II, 3–5.

98. Kaganovich made this complaint in his speech at the Seventeenth Party Congress, reported in *Proletarii*, February 13, 1934.

99. P. S. Kuchumov, the Deputy Minister of Agriculture in charge of MTS affairs, revealed that as late as 1953 this system was still being used. Forty-four basic operations performed by the MTS were still being centrally planned at that time. *Vsesoiuznoe soveshchanie rabotnikov mashinno-traktornykh stantsii* (Moscow, 1954), p. 197.

100. Institut Krasnoi Professury, *MTS i ee politotdel: Opyt raboty Veselokutskoi MTS, Odesskoi oblasti, SSSR* (Moscow-Leningrad, 1934), p. 129.

101. *Ibid.*

102. Antipov, "Soveshchanie," *Pravda*, January 9, 1936.

103. Chernov, *Pravda*, January 8, 1936.

104. S. V. Kossior, speech at May (1936) Plenum of the Ukrainian Party Central Committee, in *Sotsialisticheskaia rekonstruktsiia sel'skogo khoziaistva*, no. 6 (June 1936), p. 21.

105. Khrushchev, *Stroitel'stvo kommunizma*, I, 63.

106. V. G. Venzher, *Voprosy kompleksnoi mekhanizatsii kolkhoznogo proizvodstva* (Moscow, 1955), p. 98.

107. Kuchumov, *Vsesoiuznoe soveshchanie*, p. 196.

108. Khrushchev, *Stroitel'stvo kommunizma*, I, 63.

109. *KPSS v rezoliutsiiakh*, pt. 3, p. 667.

110. Decree of the CC CPSU and the Council of Ministers, USSR, of March 9, 1955, "Ob izmenenii praktiki planirovaniia sel'skogo khoziaistva," Kazantsev, *Istoriia kolkhoznogo prava*, II, 441–444.

111. See for example, Pokrovskii, *MTS — opornyi punkt*, pp. 38–39.

112. See Contract in Markevich, *Mezhselennye*, App., pp. 298–301.

113. *Pervyi vsesoiuznyi s"ezd kolkhoznikov-udarnikov, 15–19 fevralia 1933 g.* (Moscow-Leningrad, 1933), p. 114.

114. Decree of the CPC USSR of February 5, 1933, "O primernom dogovore mashinno-traktornoi stantsii s kolkhozami," Kazantsev, *Istoriia kolkhoznogo prava*, I, 357–359.

4. See for example, the powerful story of the impact of collectivization in a Siberian village by S. Zalygin, "Na Irtyshe," *Novyi mir*, no. 2 (February 1964), pp. 3–80.

5. Additional, if indirect, confirmation of this stratified pattern may be found in the fragmentary data on the social composition of the labor force of the early MTS. Arutiunian presents *Gosplan* figures for five MTS in 1930 showing the social origins of the labor force as follows: industrial workers — 24.9 percent, agricultural laborers — 7.0 percent, white collar workers — 6.1 percent, poor peasants — 40.6 percent, middle peasants — 12.7 percent, kulaks — 0.4 percent, tradesmen — 7.9 percent, others — 0.4 percent (Iu. V. Arutiunian, *Mekhanizatory sel'skogo khoziastva SSSR v 1929–1957 gg.* [Moscow, 1960] p. 16).

6. *MTS k XVI Parts"ezdu*, p. 71.

7. N. Datiuk, "Prakticheskie voprosy kollektivizatsii," *Bol'shevik*, no. 13–14 (July 31, 1929), p. 52.

8. I. I. Shiriaev, "Organizuiushchaia rol' kommunisticheskoi partii v stroitel'stve mashinno-traktornykh stantsii v gody pervoi piatiletki" (Kandidat dissertation, Moscow, 1959), p. 60.

9. B. A. Abramov, "Nekotorye voprosy organizatsionno-massovoi raboty partii sredi krest'ianstva v 1928–1929 gg." in N. I. Nemakov and A. D. Kliueva, eds., *KPSS v bor'be za sotsialisticheskoe preobrazovanie sel'skogo khoziaistva* (Moscow, 1961), p. 18.

10. P. Savchuk, "Rol' MTS v sotsialisticheskom pereustroistve derevni," *Bol'shevik*, no. 3–4 (February 28, 1930), p. 57.

11. A. Lozovyi, "Mashinno-traktornye stantsii i ikh rol' v obobshchestvlenii krest'ianskogo khoziaistva," *Na agrarnom fronte*, no. 4 (April 1929), p. 38. For similar rumors see S. Leikin, "Protiv opportunizma v rabote MTS," *Bol'shevik*, no. 20 (October 1929), p. 70.

12. *MTS k XVI Parts"ezdu*, p. 67.

13. M. Anisimov, "O traktornykh kolonnakh," *Bol'shevik*, no. 1 (January 1929), p. 49.

14. Shiriaev, "Organizuiushchaia rol'," pp. 61–62.

15. Leikin, "Protiv opportunizma," p. 69.

16. R. Lavrov and F. Gavrilov, "Pervaia mashinno-traktornaia stantsiia v RSFSR," *Sel'sko-khoziaistvennaia zhizn',* no. 32–33 (August 1929), p. 9.

17. Anisimov, "O traktornykh kolonnakh," p. 50.

18. See for example, M. L. Bogdenko and I. E. Zelenin, "Osnovnye problemy istorii kollektivizatsii sel'skogo khoziaistva i kolkhoznogo stroitelstva v sovetskoi literature" in M. P. Kim, ed., *Istoriia sovetskogo krest'ianstva i kolkhoznogo stroitel'stva v SSSR* (Moscow, 1963), p. 202.

19. P. N. Sharova, et al., eds., *Kollektivizatsiia sel'skogo khoziaistva: vazhneishie postanovleniia kommunisticheskoi partii i Sovetskogo pravitel'stva, 1927–1935* (Moscow, 1957), p. 347.

20. *Ibid.*, p. 364.

21. For example, Shiriaev, "Organizuiushchaia rol'," p. 235.

22. V. V. "Rost partii v derevne," *Partiinoe stroitel'stvo*, no. 11–12 (June 1932), p. 46. If the data in the V. V. article are correct, it would appear that the number of MTS Party cells was greater than the number of MTS at the end of 1931. This paradox may possibly be explained by the fact that many

115. A leading expert on MTS contract relations noted this practice in an article in 1934. The tendency to shirk concrete obligations extended up to the oblast and krai MTS administrations, which apparently condoned the practice on the part of their subordinate MTS (A. M. Turubiner, "O dogovorakh MTS s kolkhozami," *Biulleten' Gosarbitrazha*, no. 6 (1934), p. 4.

116. Decree of the CPC USSR of February 17, 1934, "O primernom dogovore mashinno-traktornoi stantsii s kolkhozami," Kazantsev, *Istoriia kolkhoznogo prava*, I, 387–391.

117. *Ibid.*, p. 389.

118. Decree of the CPC USSR and the CC AUCP(B) of January 13, 1939, "O poriadke nachisleniia naturoplaty za raboty MTS po zernovym kul'turam," *ibid.*, II, 60; and Decree of the CPC USSR of January 14, 1939, "Tipovoi dogovor mashinno-traktornoi stantsii s kolkhozami," *ibid.*, pp. 63–67.

119. "Plody politicheskoi blizorukosti" (lead editorial), *Sots. zem.*, March 14, 1937.

120. For example, L. Agafonov, "Mitrofanovskaia MTS nakanune seva," *Kommuna*, March 17, 1937.

121. "Plody politicheskoi blizorukosti," *Sots. zem.*, March 14, 1937.

122. *Bol'shaia Sovetskaia entsiklopediia*, 2nd ed. (1952), XIV, 623.

123. For example, S. L. Fuks, "K voprosu o primenenii p. 15 primernogo dogovora MTS s kolkhozami," *Arbitrazh*, no. 4 (1936), p. 4.

124. A. Ruskol, "Nekotorye voprosy dogovornoi praktiki MTS s kolkhozami," *Arbitrazh*, no. 8 (1936), pp. 19–20.

125. For a while, during the thirties, even the kolkhozes, not to speak of the local procurement agents, tended to view *naturoplata* obligations as secondary to the fulfillment of obligatory deliveries. The result was that payments to the MTS were often considerably in arrears, forcing the MTS to go to court to collect (A. Ruskol, "Imushchestvennye spory kolkhozov v organakh Gosarbitrazha," *Arbitrazh*, no. 7 (1936), p. 2.

126. According to one writer, 40 percent of total grain procurements in a given raion were arbitrarily set aside as the share to be collected as payments in kind for MTS services, regardless of the actual services performed (N. Nikitin, "Pol'nost'iu i v srok sobrat' naturoplatu," *MTS*, no. 7–8 [1946], p. 9).

127. A. A. Andreev, "O merakh pod"ema sel'skogo khoziaistva v poslevoennyi period," *Sots. zem.*, March 7, 1947.

128. *KPSS v rezoliutsiiakh*, pt. 3, pp. 533–534.

129. Decree of the Council of Ministers, USSR of January 27, 1948, "O tipovom dogovore mashinno-traktornoi stantsii s kolkhozami," Kazantsev, *Istoriia kolkhoznogo prava*, II, 301–308.

130. A. Ruskol, *Dogovornye otnosheniia MTS s kolkhozami* (Moscow, 1948), pp. 37, 41–42.

131. P. A. Malyshev, "Proizvodstvennye vzaimootnosheniia MTS s kolkhozami na sovremennom etape" (Kandidat dissertation, Moscow, 1956), pp. 266–268.

132. Khrushchev, *Stroitel'stvo kommunizma*, I, 60.

133. Decree of the Council of Ministers, USSR of February 20, 1954, "O tipovom dogovore mashinno-traktornoi stantsii s kolkhozom," Kazantsev, *Istoriia kolkhoznogo prava*, II, 413–419.

134. P. A. Malyshev, *Proizvodstvennye vzaimootnosheniia*, p. 297, table.

135. See for example, A. Emel'ianov, "Ekonomicheskie stimuly i upravlenie sel'skim khoziaistvom," *Planovoe khoziaistvo*, no. 1 (January 1966), p. 74.

CHAPTER SIX

1. L. Slepov, *O stile v partiinoi rabote* (Moscow, 1953), p. 30.

2. *Ibid.*

3. L. Slepov, *Mestnye partiinye organy* (Moscow, 1954), p. 10. For an interesting Western treatment of the involvement of Party officials in the affairs of the industrial plant see Jerry F. Hough, "The Soviet Concept of the Relationship between the Lower Party Organs and the State Administration," *Slavic Review*, XXIV, no. 2 (June 1965), pp. 215–240.

4. S. V. Kossior, speech at May (1936) Plenum of the CC CP(B)U, "Ob uborke i zagatovkakh zernovykh," in *Sotsialisticheskaia rekonstruktsiia sel'skogo khoziaistva*, no. 6 (1936), p. 22.

5. Roy D. Laird, Darwin E. Sharp, and Ruth Sturtevant, *The Rise and Fall of the MTS as an Instrument of Soviet Rule*, (Lawrence, Kansas: The University of Kansas Publications, 1960), esp. pp. 68–73.

6. *Shestnadtsataia konferentsiia VKP(B), aprel' 1929 goda, stenograficheskii otchet* (Moscow, 1962), p. 665.

7. S. F. Markov, "Ukreplenie sel'skikh partiinykh organizatsii v period podgotovki massovogo kolkhoznogo dvizheniia (1928–1929 gg.)," *Voprosy istorii KPSS*, no. 3 (1962), p. 114.

8. *Ibid.*

9. Moshe Lewin, *La Paysannerie et le pouvoir Soviétique, 1928–1930* (Paris: Mouton et Cie., 1966), p. 116.

10. A. Gaister and A. Levin, "O sostave derevenskikh partiinykh organizatsii," *Bol'shevik*, no. 9–10 (May 31, 1929), pp. 78, 81.

11. Lewin, *La Paysannerie*, also, I. I. Shiriaev, "Organizuiushchaia rol' kommunisticheskoi partii v stroitel'stve mashinno-traktornykh stantsii v gody pervoi piatiletki" (Kandidat dissertation, Moscow, 1959), p. 238; V. M. Selunskaia, *Bor'ba KPSS za sotsialisticheskoe preobrazovanie sel'skogo khoziaistva* (Moscow, 1961), p. 116.

12. *KPSS v rezoliutsiiakh i resheniiakh s"ezdov, konferentsii i plenumov TsK* (Moscow, 1954–1960), pt. 2, pp. 661–662.

13. S. V. Voronkova, "Bor'ba Kommunisticheskoi partii Sovetskogo Soiuza za ukreplenie Sovetov v derevne v period kollektivizatsii sel'skogo khoziaistva (1923–1931 gg.)" in N. I. Nemakov and A. D. Kliueva, eds., *KPSS v bor'be za sotsialisticheskoe preobrazovanie sel'skogo khoziaistva* (Moscow, 1961), p. 80.

14. *KPSS v rezoliutsiiakh*, pt. 2, p. 648.

15. E. I. Lar'kina, *Podgotovka kolkhoznykh kadrov v period massovoi kollektivizatsii* (Moscow, 1960), p. 21.

16. *Ibid.*, p. 23 (table).

17. Markov, "Ukreplenie," pp. 114–115.

18. Decree of the CC AUCP(B) of September 9, 1929, "O massovoi rabote v raionakh organizatsii mashinotraktornykh stantsii," in P. N. Sharova, et al., eds. *Kollektivizatsiia sel'skogo khoziaistva: vazhneishie postanovleniia kommunisticheskoi partii i Sovetskogo pravitel'stva, 1927–1935* (Moscow, 1957), pp. 199–200.

19. See, for example, Abdurakhman Avtorkhanov, [...] *Apparatus* (Chicago: Henry Regnery Co., 1966), p. 135.

20. See the 1934 and 1939 versions of the Party Ch[...] *tsiiakh*, pt. 3, p. 240 (1934 Charter), p. 390 (1939 Charte[...]

21. Avtorkhanov, *The Communist Party Apparatus*, [...] Sidney Harcave, *Structure and Functioning of the Lowe[...] in the Soviet Union* (Maxwell Air Force Base, Alabam[...] Research Institute, 1954), p. 11.

22. For a brief but interesting discussion of Party per[...] see Slepov, *Mestnye partiinye organy*, pp. 51–52.

23. For other functions of the raikom see Merle Fain[...] *Ruled* (rev. ed., Cambridge, Mass.: Harvard University Pr[...] 229.

24. Slepov, *Mestnye partiinye organy*, p. 57.

25. Valentin Ovechkin, "Raionnye budni," in *Izbrann[...] dvukh tomakh* (Moscow, 1963), vol. II.

26. N. S. Khrushchev, "Respublikanskoe soveshchanie sek[...] okruzhkomov KP(B)U, predsedatelei ispolkomov raionny[...] sovetov deputatov trudiashchikhsia," *Pravda Ukrainy*, Febru[...]

27. *KPSS v rezoliutsiiakh*, pt. 3, p. 591. This list of PPO [...] the 1952 Charter. It is almost identical to Article 60 of tl[...] *ibid.*, p. 392.

28. *Ibid.*, pp. 374, 379.

29. Fainsod, *How Russia Is Ruled*, p. 537.

30. L. Mel'nikov, "Partiinye organizatsii ukrupnennykh kolk[...] vik, no. 4 (February 1951), p. 50.

31. For example, see I. Mar'ianskii, "Za boesposobnuiu part[...] MTS," *Partiinoe stroitel'stvo*, no. 13 (July 1932), p. 23; and Iu.[...] *Mekhanizatory sel'skogo khoziaistva SSSR v 1929–1957 gg.* (Mo[...] 164.

32. V. Suslov, "Partiinye organizatsii i voprosy dal'neishego [...] skogo khoziaistva," *Kommunist*, no. 5 (March 1953), p. 59.

33. "Partiinye organizatsii i khoziaistvennoe stroitel'stvo" (le[...] *Kommunist*, no. 17 (November 1966), p. 9.

34. For a more detailed treatment of the politotdel mode se[...] "The Politotdel: A Lesson from the Past," *Slavic Review*, [...] (September 1966), 475–496.

CHAPTER SEVEN

1. For typical examples see the following: M. A. Kraev, [...] *khoznogo stroia v SSSR* (Moscow, 1954); S. P. Trapeznikov, *Istoric[...] KPSS v sotsialisticheskom preobrazovanii sel'skogo khoziaistva[...]* 1959); V. M. Selunskaia, *Bor'ba KPSS za sotsialisticheskoe preobraz[...] skogo khoziaistva* (Moscow, 1961).

2. For a definitive account of the nature and effects of social str[...] in the village on the eve of collectivization see Moshe Lewin, *La Pa[...] et le pouvoir soviétique, 1928–1930* (Paris: Mouton et Cie.)

3. *Mashinno-traktornye stantsii k XVI Parts"ezdu* (Moscow-Le[...] 1930), p. 67.

village cells which came under the jurisdiction of the Partkoms of the MTS support points may have been counted as MTS cells.

23. During 1931 the number of MTS increased 3.9 times; kolkhozes, 1.4 times; sovkhozes, 1.5 times. These calculations were made by the author from data in Table 7-1, a larger table in the V. V. article (*Partiinoe stroitel'stvo*, p. 47), and *Sel'skoe khoziaistvo SSSR* (Moscow, 1960), pp. 9, 41.

24. I. Mar'ianskii, "Za boesposobnuiu partorganizatsiiu v MTS," *Partiinoe stroitel'stvo*, no. 13 (July 1932), p. 23; calculations also from data in sources cited in note 23 above.

25. Shiriaev, p. 238. By omitting references to the sovkhozes and the large kolkhozes Shiriaev incorrectly implies that the support-point decree applied only to the MTS. In general, he follows the old line of exaggerating the political importance of the MTS during the collectivization period, a line which has begun to change, thanks to the revelations of writers such as Zelenin, cited below.

26. *Ibid.*, p. 239.

27. *Ibid.*, p. 241.

28. "Voprosy orgpartraboty v derevne" (letters to the editor), *Partiinoe stroitel'stvo*, no. 13 (July 1932), p. 27.

29. Mar'ianskii, "Za boesposobnuiu," p. 23.

30. *Ibid.*, p. 24.

31. *Ibid.*

32. *Ibid.*

33. "Ukrepit' orgpartrabotu v derevne" (lead editorial), *Partiinoe stroitel'-stvo*, no. 5 (March 1932), p. 3.

34. For an interesting account of the famine see Dana G. Dalrymple, "The Soviet Famine of 1932–1934," *Soviet Studies*, XV, no. 3 (January 1964), pp. 250–284.

35. "MTS ne vozglavili bor'by za sev," *Proletarii*, September 15, 1932.

36. *Proletarii*, December 12, 1932.

37. "Postanovlenie prezidiuma TsKK i Kollegii NKRKI SSSR, 'O proverke raboty mashinno-traktornykh stantsii i "Traktorotsentra" ' " in *Postanovlenie Kolkhoztsentra, Prezidiuma TsKK i Kollegii NKRKI SSSR o rabote Mashinno-traktornykh stantsii i oplate truda traktorista* (Moscow, 1932), p. 64. M. M. Khataevich, at the time the Ukrainian Central Committee's leading agricultural spokesmen, told an audience at the Higher Agricultural School that although on the average seventy new tractors were being delivered in the Ukraine each day, more than seventy were going out of commission for one reason or another (M. M. Khataevich, "Itogi Plenumov TsK VKP(B) i TsK KP(B)U i zadachi bol'shevikov Ukrainy," *Proletarii*, October 27, 1932).

38. S. V. Kossior, speech at the Third All-Ukrainian Party Conference, *Proletarii*, July 15, 1932.

CHAPTER EIGHT

1. Resolution of the Joint Plenum of the CC and the CCC AUCP(B) of January 11, 1933, "Tseli i zadachi politicheskikh otdelov MTS i sovkhozov," *KPSS v rezoliutsiiakh i resheniiakh s"ezdov, konferentsii i plenumov TsK* (Moscow, 1954–1960), pt. 3, pp. 187–198. Actually, politotdels began to be set up towards the end of 1932. M. M. Khataevich reported to a group of agri-

cultural officials in Kharkov in late December 1932 that politotdels were already being introduced in the Steppe regions of the Ukraine (*Proletarii*, January 9, 1933). Also, Kaganovich, in his speech at the Joint Plenum, announced that the first thousand politotdel officials had already been selected (L. M. Kaganovich, "Tseli i zadachi politicheskikh otdelov MTS i sovkhozov," *Bol'shevik*, no. 1–2 [January 1933], p. 21).

2. K. E. Voroshilov, *Stat'i i rechi* (Moscow, 1937), p. 505.

3. J. Stalin, *Works* (Moscow: Foreign Languages Publishing House, 1952–1955), XIII, 229.

4. *Ibid.*, pp. 229–230.

5. Kaganovich, "Tseli i zadachi," p. 18.

6. *KPSS v rezoliutsiiakh*, pt. 3, p. 190.

7. *Ibid.*, p. 189.

8. *Ibid.*, pp. 191–192. On links with the Procuracy see, for example, "V kollegii NKIu," *Sovetskaia iustitsiia*, no. 7 (1933), p. 24; and S. Galitskii, "Sovmestnaia rabota organov iustitsii s politotdelami Leningradskoi oblasti," *Sovetskaia iustitsiia*, no. 16 (1934), p. 4.

9. *KPSS v rezoliutsiiakh*, pt. 3, p. 197.

10. *Ibid.*, p. 196.

11. "Novyi otriad poslantsev partii v derevniu," *Pravda*, August 15, 1933.

12. Iu. S. Borisov, "Dokumenty o deiatel'nosti politotdelov sovkhozov v 1933–1935 gg." in D. A. Chugaev et al., eds., *Materialy po istorii SSSR: Dokumenty po istorii Sovetskogo obshchestva* (Moscow: Akademiia nauk SSSR, 1959), VII, 354.

13. Merle Fainsod, *Smolensk Under Soviet Rule* (Cambridge: Harvard University Press, 1958), p. 286. See also, S. Trapeznikov, *Istoricheskii opyt KPSS v sotsialisticheskom preobrazovanii sel'skogo khoziaistva* (Moscow, 1959), p. 277. Trapeznikov refers to the OGPU deputy as the "deputy director [of the MTS] for special work [*spetsrabota*]," indicating a formal status perhaps equal to that of the politotdel chief himself. I have not seen this formulation used elsewhere, however.

14. I. E. Zelenin, "Politotdely MTS (1933–1934 gg.)" in *Istoricheskie zapiski* (Moscow: Institut istorii AN SSSR, no. 76, 1965), p. 54.

15. On the parallel hierarchies and the meaning of the separation in practice see Jerry F. Hough, "The Soviet Concept of the Relationship Between the Lower Party Organs and the State Administration," *Slavic Review*, XXIV, no. 2 (June 1965), pp. 215–240.

16. Borisov, "Dokumenty," p. 350. Also, Zelenin, "Politotdely MTS," pp. 44–45.

17. *KPSS v rezoliutsiiakh*, pt. 3, p. 195.

18. *Itogi raboty mashinno-traktornykh stantsii za 1933 goda* (Moscow, 1936), p. vi.

19. P. D. Indychenko, "Pervyi opyt raboty politotdelov MTS i sovkhozov," *Sovetskoe stroitel'stvo*, no. 9 (September 1933), p. 19.

20. "Derevenskaia partorganizatsiia pered litsom novykh zadach," *Partiinoe stroitel'stvo*, no. 13–14 (July 1933), p. 26.

21. For example, "Vsemernuiu pomoshch' politotdelam MTS i sovkhozov," *Pravda*, June 12, 1933.

22. Decree of the CC AUCP(B) of June 15, 1933, "O rabote politotdelov

MTS, o kolkhoznoi iacheike i o vzaimootnosheniiakh politotdelov i raikomov," P. N. Sharova, et al., eds., *Kollektivizatsiia sel'skogo khoziaistva: vazhneishie postanovleniia kommunisticheskoi partii i Sovetskogo pravitel'stva, 1927–1935* (Moscow, 1957), p. 461.

23. Zelenin, "Politotdely MTS," p. 45.

24. *Ibid.*, p. 45, n. 14.

25. Ia. A. Iakovlev, "Zadachi komandnogo sostava novostroiashchikhsia MTS," in Ia. A. Iakovlev, *Voprosy organizatsii sotsialisticheskogo sel'skogo khoziaistva* (Moscow, 1935), p. 144.

26. V. Markovich, "Derevnia poluchila moguchii otriad Bol'shevikov," *Partiinoe stroitel'stvo,* no. 13–14 (July 1933), pp. 62–63.

27. L. Kaganovich, "Report on Organizational Problems," in J. Stalin, Molotov, Kaganovich, et al., *Socialism Victorious* (New York: International Publishers, 1934), p. 115.

28. Markovich, "Derevnia poluchila," pp. 62–63.

29. Zelenin, "Politotdely MTS," p. 46.

30. *Ibid.* Compare these percentages with those for the Party as a whole given in Fainsod, *How Russia Is Ruled* (rev. ed., Cambridge, Mass.: Harvard University Press, 1963), p. 268.

31. Markovich, "Derevnia poluchila," p. 64.

32. For example, by Krinitskii in *Pervyi vsesoiuznyi s"ezd kolkhoznikov-udarnikov, 15–19 fevralia 1933 g.* (Moscow-Leningrad, 1933), p. 222. See also, Victor Kravchenko, *I Chose Freedom* (New York: Charles Scribner's Sons, 1946), esp. pp. 115–116.

33. Kravchenko, *I Chose Freedom,* pp. 111–112.

34. There were the customary delays in certain areas, such as Kharkov Oblast. See, for example, the speech by Obkom Secretary Il'in at a Conference of politotdel chiefs in *Proletarii,* March 10, 1933.

35. Trapeznikov, *Istoricheskii opyt,* p. 276.

36. Decree of the CC and the CCC AUCP(B), "O chistke partii," *Pravda,* April 29, 1933.

37. Krinitskii, in *XVII s"ezd Vsesoiuznoi kommunisticheskoi partii (B): Stenograficheskii otchet* (Moscow, 1934), p. 139.

38. V. F. Larin, speech, *Molot* (Rostov-on-Don), January 30, 1934.

39. The title of a lead editorial in *Pravda* on the problem of resistance to the politotdel chief is suggestive: "For Slander of the Politotdel — Severe Party Punishment," *Pravda,* July 3, 1933.

40. Iu. V. Arutiunian and M. A. Vyltsan, *Istoricheskaia rol' MTS i ikh reorganizatsiia* (Moscow, 1958), p. 45.

41. Once again the impact of the purge was especially severe in the North Caucasus. There 47.9 percent of the kolkhoz chairmen, 38.9 percent of the field brigadiers, and 57.3 percent of the *zavkhozy* were replaced. Only 133 of the 777 kolkhozes in the newly formed North Caucasus Krai did not have at least one change of chairman during 1933 (V. F. Larin, *Molot* (Rostov-on-Don), January 30, 1934).

42. Zelenin, "Politotdely MTS," p. 53.

43. Kravchenko, *I Chose Freedom,* pp. 123–124.

44. "V kolegii NKIu," *Sovetskaia iustitsiia,* no. 7 (1933), p. 24.

45. *Sovetskaia iustitsiia,* no. 8 (1933), p. 8.

46. S. Galitskii, "Sovmestnaia rabota," p. 4.

47. Zelenin, "Politotdely MTS," p. 49.

48. Fainsod, *Smolensk*, p. 289.

49. Sharova et al., *Kollektivizatsiia*, p. 460.

50. B. Ruban, "God bor'by za bol'shevistskie kolkhozy," *Na agrarnom fronte*, no. 1 (January 1934), p. 121.

51. Trapeznikov, *Istoricheskii opyt*, p. 302.

52. Zelenin, "Politotdely MTS."

53. *Ibid.*

54. Decree of the CC CP(B)U of April 29, 1933, "O rabote kolkhoznoi iacheiki," *Proletarii*, May 4, 1933.

55. Kravchenko, *I Chose Freedom*, pp. 110–130, *passim*.

56. F. I. Anastasenko and I. A. Malashenkov, *Dogovornye otnosheniia MTS s kolkhozami* (Moscow-Leningrad, 1934), pp. 14–15.

57. Institut Krasnoi Professury, *MTS i ee politotdel: opyt raboty Veselokutskoi MTS, Odesskoi oblasti, SSSR* (Moscow-Leningrad, 1934), pp. 33–34. This arrangement was not necessarily typical. Many politotdels apparently employed their staffs on fixed assignments.

58. *Ibid.*, pp. 39–40.

59. *Ibid.*, pp. 49–50.

60. Quoted in A. Shteingart, "Politotdely Severnogo Kavkaza za rabotoi," *Pravda*, May 9, 1933.

61. Fainsod, *Smolensk*, p. 282.

62. Stalin, in *XVII s"ezd*, pp. 22–23.

63. *Ibid.*, pp. 138–139.

64. *Ibid.*

65. Zelenin, "Politotdely MTS," p. 53.

66. Kaganovich, in *XVII s"ezd*, p. 542.

67. *Ibid.*, p. 150.

68. *Pravda*, December 31, 1933.

69. *XVII s"ezd*, pp. 560–561.

70. *KPSS v rezoliutsiiakh*, pt. 3, pp. 227–228.

71. *Ibid.*

72. Larin, *Molot*, January 30, 1934.

73. *Proletarii*, February 22, 1934.

74. "Vstretit' uborku khoroshimi taborami," *Molot*, June 15, 1934.

75. "Vse usloviia dlia rosta pogolov'ia est'," *Molot*, September 3, 1934.

76. "Lesonosazhdenie — zashchita urozhaia," *Pravda*, May 21, 1934.

77. See, for example, the decree of the Azov–Black Sea Kraikom, "O vypolnenii plana khlebosdachi po otstaiushchim raionam i MTS kraia," *Molot*, October 12, 1934.

78. A. Charkin, "Iz praktiki partiinogo instruktazha v politsektore MTS," *Partiinoe stroitel'stvo*, no. 12 (June 1934), p. 33.

79. "Inzhenery sotsialisticheskikh polei," *Pravda*, May 18, 1934.

80. Zelenin, "Politotdely MTS," pp. 56–57.

81. For example, "Materialy soveshchaniia zavotdelami rukovodiashchikh partorganov," *Partiinoe stroitel'stvo*, no. 18 (September 1934), p. 28. See also, A. Sokolov, "Instruktor raikoma funktsioniruet," *Molot*, March 23, 1934.

82. L. M. Kaganovich, "O vnutripartiinoi rabote i otdelakh rukovodiashchikh partiinykh organov," *Pravda*, November 23, 1934.

83. *KPSS v rezoliutsiiakh*, pt. 3, p. 263.

84. *Ibid.*, pp. 263–264.

85. *Ibid.*, p. 264.

86. *Ibid.*

87. L. M. Kaganovich, "Itogi noiabr'skogo Plenuma TsK VKP(B)," *Partiinoe stroitel'stvo*, no. 1–2 (January 1935), p. 15.

88. *KPSS v rezoliutsiiakh*, pt. 3, p. 238.

CHAPTER NINE

1. Malinov, formerly Second Secretary of the Kraikom, was named Chief of the *Kraizu* in February, 1937 *(Molot,* February 14, 1937). He was arrested and condemned as an "enemy of the people" in May or June. (See speech by Evdokimov, the new First Secretary of the Kraikom, *Molot,* June 5, 1937.) There were similar circumstances in other agricultural regions.

2. "Rabotu zemel'nykh organov — na vysshuiu stupen'" (lead editorial), *Sotsialisticheskaia rekonstruktsiia sel'skogo khoziaistva,* no. 4 (April 1937), pp. 8–9.

3. A. Berezin, "O rabote sel'skikh raikomov partii," *Molot,* June 16, 1935.

4. For example, E. I. Riabinin, "O zadachakh i metodakh partiinogo rukovodstva," *Kommuna* (Voronezh), June 1, 1935. Contrast the tone of this article with that of the Berezin article, above.

5. B. Rudnev, "Oshibki i nedochety v rukovodstve sel'raikomov," *Partiinoe stroitel'stvo,* no. 15 (August 1935), p. 28.

6. Even here there were fairly wide regional variations. Kossior in the Ukraine, for example, continued to press for a high level of economic interference by the rural raikoms. See S. V. Kossior, "Ob uborke i zagotovkakh zernovykh," *Sotsialisticheskaia rekonstruktsiia sel'skogo khoziaistva,* no. 6 (June 1936), p. 22.

7. For example, L. Slepov, *O stile v partiinoi rabote* (Moscow, 1953), pp. 28–29. Slepov presents the argument purely in terms of the need for strengthening the ideological level of leadership personnel. He says nothing of the special exception made for Party work in agriculture.

8. J. V. Stalin, "O nedostatkakh partiinoi raboty v merakh likvidatsii trotskistskikh i inykh dvurushnikov," speech at the February–March (1937) Plenum of the CC AUCP(B), *Pravda,* March 29, 1937. The speech was actually delivered on March 3. It was published at the end of a month-long campaign in the press against "Trotskyites" in the Soviet economy.

9. For an excellent account of Stalin's development of a new corps of "red specialists" to staff the industrialization drive see Jeremy R. Azrael, *Managerial Power and Soviet Politics* (Cambridge: Harvard University Press, 1966), esp. chaps. 4 and 5.

10. "Zemel'nye organy pered litsom novykh zadach" (lead editorial), *Pravda* March 9, 1937.

11. "Zemel'nye organy pered litsom novykh zadach" (lead editorial), *Sots. zem.,* March 17, 1937.

12. *KPSS v rezoliutsiiakh i resheniiakh s"ezdov, konferentsii i plenumov TsK* (Moscow, 1954–1960), pt. 3, p. 372.

13. "Za bol'shevistskoe rukovodstvo kolkhozami" (lead editorial), *Partiinoe stroitel'stvo,* no. 11 (June 1939), p. 25.

14. Fainsod, *How Russia Is Ruled* (rev. ed., Cambridge: Harvard University Press, 1963), p. 249, table.

15. A. A. Andreev, speech at the Eighteenth Party Congress, *Pravda,* March 14, 1939.

16. See, for example, P. Titov, "Kolkhoznaia partorganizatsiia i raikom," *Kommuna,* April 28, 1938.

17. "Ob instruktore raikoma," *Molot,* February 12, 1938.

18. M. N. Shamis, "Podmena i obezlichivanie direktorov MTS i zaveduiushchikh raizo," *Sots. zem.,* March 15, 1937.

19. F. Klimov, "Budni odnogo kraizemotdela," *Sots. zem.,* December 22, 1938.

20. N. Nazartsev, "O strukture zemel'nykh organov," *Sots. zem.,* December 12, 1938.

21. *KPSS v rezoliutsiiakh,* pt. 3, p. 264.

22. Decree of the Kiev Obkom CP(B)U, "O partiino-massovoi rabote na sele," *Proletarii,* June 4, 1935.

23. *Ibid.*

24. "V Obkome VKP(B): 'O perestroike partraboty v MTS,'" *Kommuna,* June 21, 1935.

25. Ia. Osipov, "Zamestitel' direktora MTS po politchasti — boevoi organizator mass," *Partiinoe stroitel'stvo,* no. 16 (August 1935), p. 29.

26. *Ibid.*

27. N. Baryshev, "Zamestitel' direktora MTS — politicheskii organizator mass," *Partiinoe stroitel'stvo,* no. 3 (February 1936), p. 32.

28. "Rabotu zemel'nykh organov — na vysshuiu stupen'," pp. 8–9.

29. Baryshev, "Zamestitel' direktora MTS," p. 31.

30. *Ibid.*

31. I. Iarygin, "Partiino-massovaia rabota v MTS," *Partiinoe stroitel'stvo,* no. 19 (October 1936), p. 27.

32. Osipov, "Zamestitel' direktora MTS po politchasti," p. 28.

33. Baryshev, "Zamestitel' direktora MTS," p. 31.

34. Resolution of the Voronezh Obkom, AUCP(B), "Itogi obmena partdokumentov i zadachi partiinykh organizatsii," *Kommuna,* November 20, 1936.

35. N. Ianin, "Gotovilis' slabo," *Kommuna,* April 24, 1935. Urban Party organizations continued to serve as a major source of cadres for rural leadership posts throughout this period. (See above, Chapter 4.)

36. Speech by the secretary of the Nikitovskii Raikom at the First Voronezh Oblast Party Conference, "Na oblastnoi partiinoi konferentsii," *Kommuna,* June 9, 1937.

37. "Vybory rukovodiashchikh partiinykh organov" (lead editorial), *Kommuna,* April 1, 1938.

38. V. Dudarev, "Vospitanie partiinykh kadrov," *Molot,* December 21, 1936.

39. V. Kudriavtsev, "Za dal'neishii pod"em partiinoi raboty," *Molot,* December 16, 1935.

40. See, for example, the case of a Comrade Dorokhov, a *zampolit* mentioned in a decree of the Voronezh Obkom and Oblispolkom, "O remonte traktorov v Shchuchenskoi MTS" (*Kommuna*, February 12, 1939). Dorokhov was assigned to replace the previous MTS director, who had been fired for the chaotic condition of repair work at the station. The assignment was to be temporary, Dorokhov being given a specific date by which to complete tractor repairs.

41. Quoted in K. Sholokhov, "Korni otstavaniia," *Molot*, August 1, 1937.

42. See, for example, Roy D. Laird, Darwin E. Sharp, and Ruth Sturtevant, *The Rise and Fall of the MTS as an Instrument of Soviet Rule* (Lawrence, Kansas: The University of Kansas Publications, 1960), p. 71.

CHAPTER TEN

1. Iu. V. Arutiunian, *Sovetskoe krest'ianstvo v gody Velikoi Otechestvennoi voiny* (Moscow: Izdatel'stvo Akademii nauk SSSR, 1963), pp. 53–54.

2. "O nagrazhdenii ordenami e medaliami rabotnikov Narodnogo Kommissariata Zemledeliia SSSR," *Pravda*, September 12, 1945. Benediktov, incidentally, had been dropped from the Central Committee for certain unspecified failures at the Eighteenth Party Conference on the eve of the German invasion ("Ob obnovlenii tsentral'nykh organov VKP(B)," *Pravda*, February 21, 1941). Had it not been for the war, it is conceivable that he would have shared the fate of his predecessors.

3. Arutiunian, *Sovetskoe krest'ianstvo*, p. 54.

4. *Pravda*, July 17, 1941.

5. V. Ia. Ashanin, "Politotdely MTS v gody Velikoi Otechestvennoi voiny," *Voprosy istorii KPSS*, no. 4 (1960), p. 52.

6. Arutiunian, *Sovetskoe krest'ianstvo*, p. 51.

7. *Ibid.*, p. 56; also, B. A. Voronkov, "Organizatsiia upravleniia v mashinno-traktornoi stantsii" (Kandidat, dissertation, Moscow, 1955), p. 188.

8. Ashanin, "Politotdely MTS," p. 52.

9. Iu. V. Arutiunian, "Iz istorii MTS v period Velikoi Otechestvennoi voiny 1941–1945 gg.," *Voprosy istorii*, no. 8 (August 1958), p. 85, n. 12.

10. Ashanin, "Politotdely MTS," p. 52.

11. Arutiunian, *Sovetskoe krest'ianstvo*, p. 393, table.

12. *Ibid.*, p. 56, n. 112.

13. *Ibid.*, p. 394, table.

14. *Ibid.*

15. N. Itskov, "Zadachi politotdelov MTS i sovkhozov," *Partiinoe stroitel'stvo*, no. 4 (February 1942), p. 14.

16. Ashanin, "Politotdely MTS," p. 53.

17. *Ibid.*

18. Arutiunian, "Iz istorii," pp. 88–89.

19. *Ibid.*, p. 91.

20. For example, Itskov, "Zadachi politotdelov," p. 14.

21. A. Grigor'ev, "Neskol'ko vyvodov iz opyta raboty politotdelov MTS," *Partiinoe stroitel'stvo*, no. 17–18 (September 1942), p. 20.

22. Iu. V. Arutiunian and M. A. Vyltsan, *Istoricheskaia rol' MTS i ikh reorganizatsiia* (Moscow, 1958), p. 77.

23. Grigor'ev, "Neskol'ko vyvodov," pp. 20–21.

24. Arutiunian, *Sovetskoe krest'ianstvo,* p. 59.

25. Grigor'ev, "Neskol'ko vyvodov," p. 26. See also, "Sel'skii raikom partii" (lead editorial), *Partiinoe stroitel'stvo,* no. 5–6 (March 1943), p. 5.

26. Ashanin, "Politotdely MTS," p. 61.

27. *Ibid.* See also, Arutiunian, *Sovetskoe krest'ianstvo,* p. 59, although Arutiunian also shows some of the negative features of the politotdel and suggests tacitly that they may have had something to do with the abolition.

28. "Ocherednye zadachi partorganizatsii v sel'skom khoziaistve" (lead editorial), *Partiinoe stroitel'stvo,* no. 11 (June 1943), p. 9.

CHAPTER ELEVEN

1. Fedor Belov writes that his kolkhoz, which had been well enough supplied with horses and oxen before the war to be only minimally dependent on the MTS, found itself almost totally reliant on the latter after the war as a result of the depletion of its work stock by more than 80 percent (Fedor Belov, *The History of a Soviet Collective Farm* (New York: Praeger, 1955), pp. 124–125). An interesting admission of the questionable value of MTS services to the kolkhozes was made by Andreev at the February (1947) Plenum, when he noted that kolkhozes not served by the MTS were paying 40–50 percent less in crops to the state than were comparable farms served by the stations. For the sake of "justice" Andreev suggested that the rates of obligatory deliveries be raised for farms not served. This was a novel application of the theory of differential rent! However, it should be noted that as early as 1933 farms served by MTS were given special reductions in the size of their obligatory delivery quotas (A. A. Andreev, "O merakh pod"ema sel'skogo khoziaistva v poslevoennyi period," *Pravda,* March 7, 1947.)

2. *KPSS v rezoliutsiiakh i resheniiakh s"ezdov, konferentsii i plenumov TsK* (Moscow, 1954–1960), pt. 3, pp. 495–500. The Council was chaired by Andreev and included high-ranking Party and secret police officials, such as Khrushchev and S. D. Ignat'ev, as well as a sprinkling of kolkhoz chairmen and other representatives of the rural populace. Operationally, the Council was to function through a corps of inspectors independent of the local Party and state authorities who were empowered to give the latter binding orders to rectify violations on the spot. The Council was also given the responsibility for formulating general policies on rural affairs for the approval of the Politburo and the Council of Ministers (Decree of the CC AUCP(B) and the Council of Ministers, USSR of October 8, 1946, "O Sovete po delam kolkhozov," *S P and R SSSR 1946,* no. 13, pp. 232–233; and Decree of the Council of Ministers, USSR of October 22, 1946, "Ob utverzhdenii Polozheniia o Sovete po delam kolkhozov pri Pravitel'stve SSSR," *ibid.,* no. 14, pp. 242–245.)

3. For example, P. Koval'chick, "Samodur," *Sots. zem.,* May 31, 1946, where an MTS director punished a kolkhoz chairman for complaining about MTS appropriation of kolkhoz land by withholding tractor brigade services during the spring plowing. See, also, the admissions of bribery of MTS officials by a woman kolkhoz chairman in M. Grek, "V ukrainskom kolkhoze," *Pravda,* September 22, 1946.

4. Arutiunian, *Sovetskoe krest'ianstvo v gody Velikoi Otechestvennoi voiny* (Moscow, 1963) p. 55, n. 106.

5. *Ibid.*, n. 107.

6. For example, the instructions to the raikom in the "Letter from a Liberated Raion" in the fall of 1945 declared: "In order to direct business surely, to lead successfully, it is necessary to know the concrete circumstances of each individual kolkhoz, to interfere actively in all details of the production process . . ." (A. Zemtsov, "O praktike rukovodstva sel'skim khoziaistvom," *Pravda,* October 5, 1945).

7. N. S. Khrushchev, "Uluchshit' podbor, rasstanovku, i vospitanie kadrov," *Pravda,* January 12, 1947.

8. "Sel'skii raikom partii" (lead editorial), *Pravda,* August 26, 1946.

9. See, for example, "Vazhneishaia zadacha partorganizatsii MTS" (lead editorial), *Pravda,* January 12, 1947.

10. *KPSS v rezoliutsiiakh,* pt. 3, p. 549.

11. *Ibid.*

12. N. S. Khrushchev, Speech at republican conference of secretaries of rural raikoms and okruzhkoms of the CP(B)U and chairmen of raion and okrug executive committees, *Pravda Ukrainy,* February 22, 1948.

13. N. S. Khrushchev, "S chest'iu vypolnit' obiazatel'stva, vziatye rabotnikami sel'skogo khoziaistva Ukrainy v pis'me tovarishchu Stalinu," *Bol'shevik,* no. 10 (May 1948), pp. 12, 18.

14. L. Slepov, "O bol'shevistskom metode rukovodstva khoziaistvennymi organami," *Bol'shevik,* no. 2 (January 1951), p. 49.

15. *Ibid.*

16. For example, see M. Domrachev, "Nekotorye voprosy rukovodstva pervychnymi partiinymi organizatsiiami," *Bol'shevik,* no. 4 (February 1952), pp. 64–65.

17. P. Doronin, "Pervyi opyt raboty zamestitelei direktorov MTS po politchasti," *Pravda,* May 13, 1947.

18. *KPSS v rezoliutsiiakh,* pt. 3, p. 549.

19. *Partiinaia zhizn',* no. 13 (July 1947), p. 37, cited in Sidney Harcave, *Structure and Functioning of the Lower Party Organizations in the Soviet Union* (Maxwell Air Force Base, Alabama: Human Resources Research Institute, 1954), p. 19.

20. Doronin, "Pervyi opyt."

21. P. Vorontsov, "Partiinye organizatsii i sorevnovanie v derevne," *Pravda,* May 4, 1947.

22. K. Zhukov, "O partiino-politicheskoi rabote v MTS," *Bol'shevik,* no. 5 (March 1951), p. 54.

23. "Povysit' boesposobnost' partiinykh organizatsii MTS" (lead editorial), *Sots. zem.,* March 25, 1947.

24. See, for example, "Zamestitel' direktora MTS po politicheskoi chasti" (lead editorial), *Sots. zem.,* April 20, 1947.

25. "Zamestitel' direktora MTS po politicheskoi chasti" (lead editorial), *Pravda,* May 11, 1947.

26. *Ibid.*

27. N. Bolkunov, "Zamestitel' direktora MTS po politchasti pristupil k rabote," *Pravda,* May 11, 1947.

28. Doronin, "Pervyi opyt." Doronin was the First Secretary of the Kursk Obkom. He was later condemned for "distortions" during the "zveno" controversy for having supported the use of the "link" in sugar-beet production in his oblast — a rational position in light of the level of mechanization at the time.

29. S. V. Fraer, *Organizatsiia raboty MTS v kolkhozakh* (Moscow, 1952), p. 388.

30. Belov, *The History of a Soviet Collective Farm.*

31. B. Rybin, "Raikom i partiinaia organizatsiia otstaiushchei MTS," *Molot,* July 4, 1953.

32. Iu. V. Arutiunian, *Mekhanizatory sel'skogo khoziaistva SSSR v 1929–1957 gg.* (Moscow, 1960), p. 173.

33. *Ibid.*

34. Harcave, *Structure,* p. 19.

35. However, the provincial Party committees did occasionally devote a certain amount of attention to them by summoning them to special conferences on political and economic problems (Arutiunian, *Mekhanizatory,* p. 173). See also, K. Zhukov, "O partiino-politicheskoi rabote," p. 59.

36. See, for example, "Pravil'no sochetat' politicheskuiu i khoziaistvennuiu rabotu," *Molot,* August 16, 1952.

37. See, for example, Zhukov, "O partiino-politicheskoi rabote," p. 59; and A. Gryza, "Partiino-politicheskaia rabota v mashinno-traktornykh stantsiiakh," *Bol'shevik,* no. 19 (October 1950), p. 59.

38. Zhukov, "O partiino-politicheskoi rabote," p. 60.

39. They might, for example, pressure kolkhoz chairmen to accept unsatisfactory tractor work (*ibid.,* p. 59). Or they might help to conceal illegal levies on the kolkhozes for machinery repairs that were the responsibility of the MTS (Speech by kolkhoz chairman Skliadneva, "Ser'eznye pretenzii k MTS," *Kommuna,* February 21, 1953).

40. "Protiv izvrashchenii v organizatsii truda v kolkhozakh," *Pravda,* February 19, 1950.

41. N. S. Khrushchev, speech at meeting of voters of the Kalinin Electoral District in Moscow, *Pravda,* March 8, 1950.

42. M. Kraev, "Postoiannaia proizvodstvennaia brigada — osnovnaia forma organizatsii truda v kolkhozakh," *Bol'shevik,* no. 11 (June 1950), p. 55.

43. L. Mel'nikov, "Partiinye organizatsii ukrupnennykh kolkhozov," *Bol'shevik,* no. 4 (February 1951), p. 50.

44. N. S. Khrushchev, *Stroitel'stvo kommunizma v SSSR i razvitie sel'skogo Khoziaistva* (Moscow, 1962–1963), I, p. 72; also, Fainsod, *How Russia Is Ruled* rev. ed. (Cambridge: Harvard University Press, 1963), p. 249, table.

45. Khrushchev, *Stroitel'stvo kommunizma,* pp. 8, 72 (calculations by author).

46. Valentin Ovechkin, "Raionnye budni," in *Izbrannye proizvedeniia v dvukh tomakh* (Moscow, 1963), pp. 17–18.

CHAPTER TWELVE

1. N. S. Khrushchev, *Stroitel'stvo kommunizma v SSSR i razvitie sel'skogo khoziaistva* (Moscow, 1962–1963), I, 79.

2. *KPSS v rezoliutsiiakh i resheniiakh s"ezdov, konferentsii i plenumov TsK* (Moscow, 1954–1960), pt. 3, p. 652.

3. Khrushchev, *stroitel'stvo kommunizma*, p. 8.

4. *Ibid.*, p. 79.

5. *Ibid.*, p. 490.

6. *Ibid.*, p. 279.

7. A. I. Kirichenko, "Povysit' uroven' organizatorskoi raboty v massakh," *Pravda,* January 6, 1954.

8. *Sel'skoe khoziaistvo SSSR* (statistical handbook) (1960), p. 75.

9. V. Suslov, "V bor'be za dal'neishii pod"em sel'skogo khoziaistva," *Sovetskaia Kuban'* (Krasnodar), August 2, 1955.

10. "Pravil'no podbirat' i vospityvat' partiinye kadry" (lead editorial), *Kommunist* (Saratov), April 18, 1954.

11. N. G. Ignatov, speech at the Second Plenum of the Voronezh Obkom, *Kommuna,* May 18, 1954.

12. Among the sources used to compile this list were the following: "O rabote instruktorskikh grupp sel'skikh raikomov partii" (survey of letters to the editor), *Part. zhizn',* no. 5 (June 1954), p. 29; G. Pogodin, "Gruppy instruktorov raikoma KPSS," *Kommuna,* February 25, 1954; N. Deriabin, "Raikom, MTS, kolkhoz," *Kommunist* (Saratov), November 17, 1954; *idem.* "Budni instruktorskoi gruppy," *Kommunist* (Saratov), January 15, 1955; A. Gordeev, "Na odnom zasedanii biuro raikoma," *Kommunist* (Saratov), April 13, 1954; V. Vanin, "Iz opyta instruktorskoi gruppy raikoma partii po zone MTS," *Kommunist,* no. 8 (May 1954), p. 56.

13. For a discussion of the division of labor among the secretaries of the raikom see Sidney Harcave, *Structure and Functioning of the Lower Party Organizations in the Soviet Union* (Maxwell Air Force Base, Alabama: Human Resources Research Institute, 1954), p. 14. In some areas there was also a third secretary, although the formal title was not always used.

14. See, for example, "Glubzhe vnikat' v ekonomiku kolkhozov i MTS," *Gor'kovskaia Pravda* (Gor'kii), December 22, 1953; also, "Rukovidit' konkretno i so znaniem dela," *Gor'kovskaia Pravda,* January 7, 1954.

15. Ia. Storozhev (Deputy Head of the Party Organs Department of the CC CPSU for the RSFSR), "Nekotorye voprosy raboty sel'skikh raikomov," *Part. zhizn',* no. 9 (May 1955), p. 19.

16. *Ibid.*

17. Harcave, *Structure,* p. 11; also, Khrushchev, *Stroitel'stvo kommunizma,* II, 8.

18. L. Slepov, *Mestnye partiinye organy,* (Moscow, 1954), p. 57.

19. For example, M. Efremov, "O rabote sel'skogo raikoma partii," *Kommunist,* no. 7 (May 1954), p. 80; also, A. Gordeev, "Na odnom zasedanii," and "Plenum Saratovskogo obkoma KPSS," *Kommunist* (Saratov), April 4, 1954.

20. For example, Vanin, "Iz opyta," where an MTS in Vinnitsa Oblast had four instructors for the fifteen kolkhozes in its zone; A. Chibisov, "Starymi metodami," *Kommuna,* August 12, 1954, where a Voronezh Oblast MTS had three instructors, each one responsible for two or three kolkhozes; E. Stroitelev, "Sovershenstvovat' metody partiinogo rukovodstva," *Partiinaia rabota v MTS* (Moscow, 1954), p. 25, where an MTS in Moscow Oblast had

four instructors for the sixteen kolkhozes of its zone. By way of exception, however, the Tbilisskaia MTS in Krasnodar Krai maintained a full group of instructors for the one kolkhoz served by the station ("Pochemu slabo rabotaet nasha partiinaia organizatsiia," *Sovetskaia Kuban'*, February 22, 1955).

21. Stroitelev, "Sovershenstvovat' metody," p. 33.

22. Khrushchev, *Stroitel'stvo kommunizma*, I, 277–278.

23. "Blizhe k zhizni, k sel'sko-khoziaistvennomu proizvodstvu" (lead editorial), *Kommunist* (Saratov), January 19, 1954.

24. S. D. Khitrov, speech at the Eighth Oblast Party Conference, *Kommuna*, February 11, 1954.

25. For example, in Gor'kii Oblast ("Likvidirovat' obezlichku v rukovodstve kolkhozami i MTS" [lead editorial], *Gor'kovskaia Pravda*, January 26, 1954).

26. *Ibid.*

27. "Rukovodit' MTS konkretno, operativno," Report of a raion Party conference, *Molot*, December 18, 1953.

28. "Rabota s liud'mi — osnova uspekhov v sel'skom khoziaistve" (lead editorial), *Part. zhizn'*, no. 1 (January 1956), p. 10.

29. Merle Fainsod, *How Russia Is Ruled*, rev. ed. (Cambridge: Harvard University Press, 1963), p. 229.

30. V. Churaev, "Rukovodstvo khoziaistvom Rossiiskoi federatsii i voprosy partiino-organizatsionnoi raboty," *Kommunist*, no. 7 (May 1956), p. 78.

31. *Ibid.*; also, Storozhev, "Nekotorye voprosy," p. 18.

32. "Plenum obkoma o rabote s kadrami," *Part. zhizn'*, no. 9 (May 1956), p. 78; *Bol'shaia Sovetskai entsikolpediia*, 2nd ed., XIX, 485; XLIV, 67. The two-year turnover rates were: First secretaries — 40 percent; second secretaries — 65 percent; zonal secretaries — 63 percent.

33. A. Snechkus, "Perestroika raboty sel'skogo raikoma partii," *Part. zhizn',* no. 4 (May 1954), p. 16; also, "Pod znakom ostroi kritiki," Report from a raion Party conference, *Gor'kovskaia Pravda*, January 14, 1954.

34. "O rabote instruktorskikh grupp sel'skikh raikomov partii" (survey of letters to the editor), *Part. zhizn'*, no. 5 (June 1954), p. 29.

35. G. Grigor'ev, "Formalizm v rukovodstve politicheskoi rabotoi," *Kommunist* (Saratov), April 27, 1954.

36. Churaev, "Rukovodstvo khoziaistvom," p. 22.

37. *Ibid.*

38. Khrushchev, *stroitel'stvo kommunizma*, II, 172.

39. *Ibid.*, p. 219.

40. "Boevaia zadacha sel'skikh raikomov" (lead editorial), *Part. zhizn'*, no. 5 (March 1957), p. 8.

41. *Ibid.*

42. Decree of the CC CPSU of September 19, 1957, "Ob izmenenii struktury sel'skikh raikomov partii," *Spravochnik partiinogo rabotnika*, (Moscow, 1961), pt. 2, pp. 545–546.

CHAPTER THIRTEEN

1. P. Vedeneev, "Agronomy," *Kommunist* (Saratov), August 20, 1954.

2. N. K. Mironenko, "Nashe mesto — v kolkhoze," *Sovetskaia Kuban'*, September 15, 1955. A similar description of working conditions under the

post-1953 setup was given to the author by a kolkhoz agronomist who had served as an MTS sector agronomist in a kolkhoz during this period.

3. G. A. Denisov, Speech at Plenum of the Saratov Obkom, *Kommunist* (Saratov), May 29, 1955.

4. Khrushchev, *Stroitel'stvo kommunizma v SSSR i razvitie sel'skogo khoziaistva* (Moscow, 1962–1963), II, 122.

5. Decree of the CC CPSU and the Council of Ministers, USSR, of August 20, 1955, "O merakh po dal'neishemu uluchsheniiu agronomicheskogo i zootekhnicheskogo obsluzhivaniia kolkhozov," in B. A. Boldyrev, ed., *Sbornik zakonodatel'nykh i vedomstvennykh aktov po sel'skomu khoziaistvu* (Moscow, 1957), I, 182–187.

6. Khrushchev, *Stroitel'stvo kommunizma*, II, p. 203.

7. For discussions of some of the problems of cost accounting in the MTS see the following: I. T. Kuznetsov, "O khozraschete v MTS," *Voprosy ekonomiki MTS* (Moscow, 1955), pp. 112–135; V. Dolzhnykh, "K voprosu o perevode MTS na khoziaistvennyi raschet," *Kommunist*, no. 4 (March 1956), pp. 44–56; P. Zhevtiak, "O perevode MTS na khoziaistvennyi raschet," *Finansy SSSR*, no. 6 (June 1956), pp. 31–40.

8. Zhevtiak, "O perevode MTS," p. 37.

9. Benediktov noted in December 1957 that the RSFSR Ministry of Agriculture had taken measures for the introduction of "elements of *khozraschet*" in the MTS of Vladimir, Saratov, and Gor'kii Oblasts and Stavropol' and the Maritime Krais (I. A. Benediktov, "Maksimal'no ispol'zovat' rezervy sel'skogo khoziaistva," *Kommunist*, no. 18 [December 1957], p. 58).

10. Dolzhnykh, "K voprosu," p. 50. For similar comments see A. A. Ruskol and N. G. Salishcheva, *Pravovoe polozhenie mashinnotraktornoi stantsii i kharakter ee dogovornykh otnoshenii s kolkhozami* (Moscow, 1956), p. 73.

11. Benediktov, "Maksimal'no ispol'zovat'," p. 58.

12. S. G. Strumilin, *Problemy sotsializma i kommunizma v SSSR* (Moscow: Izd. ekonomicheskoi literatury, 1961), p. 329.

13. *Sel'skoe khoziaistvo SSSR* (statistical handbook) (1960), p. 51.

14. Mentioned by Khrushchev, *Stroitel'stvo kommunizma*, II, 52. The text of the letter, under the title "Ob okazanii pomoshchi kolkhoznoi derevne v ukreplenii otstaiushchikh kolkhozov rukovodiashchimi kadrami," dated March 25, 1955, appears in *Direktivy KPSS i Sovetskogo pravitel'stva po khoziaistvennym voprosam* (Moscow, 1957), IV, 372–392.

15. "Predsedatel' kolkhoza" (lead editorial), *Pravda*, January 12, 1956.

16. Khrushchev, *Stroitel'stvo kommunizma*, II, 111.

17. V. Morozov, "Raikom i novye predsedateli kolkhozov," *Kommunist* (Saratov), September 29, 1955.

18. For an interesting discussion of agricultural pricing and investment policies under the 1953 reforms see James Robert Millar, "Price and Income Formation in the Soviet Collective Farm Sector since 1953" (Ph.D. Dissertation, Cornell University, 1965), esp. chaps. 7 and 8.

19. Decrees of the CC CPSU and the Council of Ministers, USSR, of March 6, 1956, "Ob Ustave sel'sko-khoziaistvennoi arteli i dal'neishem razvitii initsiativy kolkhoznikov v organizatsii kolkhoznogo proizvodstva i upravlenii

delami arteli" and (same date) "O ezhemesiachnom avansirovanii kolkhoznikov i dopolnitel'noi oplate truda v kolkhozakh," N. D. Kazantsev, ed., *Istoriia kolkhoznogo prava, sbornik zakonodatel'nykh materialov SSSR i RSFSR, 1917–1958 gg.* (Moscow, 1959), II, 449–452, 452–454.

20. V. Venzher, "O razvitii i ukreplenii ekonomicheskikh sviazei MTS i kolkhozov," *Voprosy eknomiki,* no. 3 (March 1954), pp. 47–55.

21. "Resheniia iiunskogo Plenuma TsK KPSS i zadachi ekonomicheskoi nauki v oblasti sel'skogo khoziaistva" (lead editorial), *Voprosy ekonomiki,* no. 8 (August 1954), pp. 13–14.

22. Decree of the CC CPSU and the Council of Ministers, USSR, of August 23, 1956, "Ob oplate truda traktoristov i drugikh mekhanizatorskikh kadrov MTS," Boldyrev, *Sbornik,* I, 382–384.

23. E. Kolesnikov and L. Petrov, "O nekotorykh voprosakh organizatsii kolkhoznogo proizvodstva," *Kommunist,* no. 3 (February 1956), p. 125.

24. See, for example, D. Shipaev, "Chto nas volnuet," *Gor'kovskaia Pravda,* March 12, 1958.

25. Decree of the Council of Ministers, USSR, of December 10, 1956, "O merakh uluchsheniia snabzheniia sel'skogo khoziaistva," Boldyrev, *Sbornik,* I, 242–248.

26. Shipaev, "Chto nas volnuet."

27. Iu. V. Arutiunian and M. A. Vyltsan, *Istoricheskaia rol' MTS i ikh reorganizatsiia,* (Moscow, 1958), p. 130.

28. See, for example, Z. T. Serdiuk, "Problemy vydvinutye zhizn'iu" in *Vsenarodnoe obsuzhdenie voprosa o dal'neishem razvitii kolkhoznogo stroia i reorganizatsii mashinno-traktornykh stantsii* (Moscow, 1958), p. 98.

29. G. Sverdlin, "Nashi zamechaniia," *Molot,* March 8, 1958.

30. Arutiunian and Vyltsan, *Istoricheskaia rol' MTS,* p. 128.

31. V. Voropaev and A. D'iakov, "Soveshchanie po organizatsii i oplate truda v kolkhozakh," *Voprosy ekonomiki,* no. 5 (May 1957), pp. 142–143.

32. Serdiuk, "Problemy," p. 98.

33. Arutiunian and Vyltsan, *Istoricheskaia rol' MTS,* p. 127. See, also, "Za dal'neishee razvitie i ukreplenie kolkhoznogo stroia" (lead editorial), *Sovestkaia Kuban',* March 2, 1958, where the operation of one of these combined MTS-kolkhoz joint enterprises is described.

34. Khrushchev, *Stroitel'stvo kommunizma,* II, 6.

35. Ivan Vinnichenko, "Vremia ne zhdet," *Oktiabr',* no. 11 (November 1957), p. 223.

36. *Ibid.,* p. 221.

37. Voropaev and D'iakov, "Soveshchanie," p. 143.

38. See the thoroughly documented account in Sidney I. Ploss, *Conflict and Decision-Making in Soviet Russia: A Case Study of Agricultural Policy, 1953–1963* (Princeton, N.J.: Princeton University Press, 1965), esp. pp. 103–153. This important book provides some valuable contributions to our knowledge of the political infighting that accompanied the debates on the MTS. In my opinion, however, Ploss does not devote sufficient attention to the substantive agricultural issues that were involved. While the political struggles were certainly important, they do not begin to exhaust the subject of the reasons for the decision. Indeed, any decision-making model which does not give full weight to the material content of particular decisions and the

perceptions thereof by the individual decision makers cannot be fully satis-factory.

39. *Ibid.,* pp. 106–107.

40. *Ibid.,* p. 113.

41. Vinnichenko, "Vremia ne zhdet," p. 207.

42. *Ibid.,* p. 212.

43. *Ibid.,* p. 219.

44. *Izvestiia,* December 22, 1957.

45. Ploss, *Conflict and Decision-Making,* pp. 118–119.

46. Khrushchev, *Stroitel'stvo kommunizma,* II, 500.

47. *Ibid.*

48. Khrushchev referred to these conferences in his speech in Minsk in January 1958, *ibid.,* II, 522–523.

49. *Ibid.*

50. *Ibid.,* p. 520.

51. *Ibid.,* p. 521.

52. *Ibid.*

53. *Ibid.*

54. *Ibid.*

55. *Ibid.*

56. *Ibid.,* III, 65. The text of the Theses can be found in *KPSS v rezoliu-tsiiakh i resheniiakh s''ezdov, konferentsii i plenumov TsK* (Moscow, 1954–1960), pt. 4, p. 319.

57. Khrushchev, *Stroitel'stvo kommunizma,* III, p. 72.

58. *Ibid.,* p. 79.

59. *Ibid.,* p. 81.

60. *Ibid.,* p. 141.

61. *Ibid.,* p. 259.

62. "Theses," *ibid.,* p. 82.

63. *Sel'skoe khoziaistvo SSSR* (statistical handbook), 1960, p. 41.

64. Ploss, *Conflict and Decision-Making,* p. 126.

65. Valeriy Tarsis, *The Bluebottle,* trans. Thomas Jones (New York: Alfred A. Knopf, 1963), p. 34.

CHAPTER FOURTEEN

1. Galina Nikolaeva, *Harvest* (Moscow: Foreign Languages Publishing House, 1952), p. 306.

CHAPTER FIFTEEN

1. Sidney I. Ploss, *Conflict and Decision-Making in Soviet Russia: A Case Study of Agricultural Policy, 1953–1963* (Princeton, N.J.: Princeton University Press, 1965), chap. 4.

2. Oleg Penkovskiy, *The Penkovskiy Papers,* trans. Peter Deriabin (Garden City, New York: Doubleday and Company, 1965), p. 279.

3. See Khrushchev's use of the formula in 1958 in *Plenum Tsentral'nogo Komiteta Kommunisticheskoi partii Sovetskogo Soiuza, 15–19 dekabria 1958 g.: Stenograficheskii otchet* (Moscow, 1958), p. 69; and Matskevich's statement a year later in *Plenum Tsentral'nogo Komiteta Kommunisticheskoi partii Sovet-*

skogo Soiuza, 22–25 dekabria 1959 g.: Stenograficheskii otchet (Moscow, 1960), pp. 320–321.

4. Ploss, *Conflict and Decision-Making*, p. 176; also, G. Kotov, "O perspektive sblizheniia kolkhoznoi i sovkhoznoi form khoziaistva", *Voprosy ekonomiki*, no. 2 (February 1961), p. 27.

5.

Number of kolkhozes and sovkhozes in USSR, 1956–1965.
(end of year)

Type of farm	1956	1957	1958	1959	1960	1961	1962	1963	1964	1965
Sovkhozes	5,098	5,905	6,002	6,496	7,375	8,281	8,570	9,176	10,078	11,681
Change	100	116	118	127	145	162	168	180	198	229
Kolkhozes	83,000	76,500	67,700	53,400	44,000	40,500	39,700	38,800	37,600	36,300
Change	100	92	82	64	53	49	48	47	45	44

Sources: Narodnoe khoziaistvo SSSR v 1958 godu: Statisticheskii ezhegodnik (Moscow, 1959), p. 349; *Narodnoe khoziaistvo SSSR v 1962 godu: Statisticheskii ezhegodnik* (Moscow, 1963), p. 225; *Narodnoe khoziaistvo SSSR v 1965 g.: Statisticheskii ezhegodnik* (Moscow, 1966), p. 257.

6. D. S. Polianskii in *Plenum Tsentral'nogo Komiteta Kommunisticheskoi partii Sovetskogo Soiuza, 10–18 ianvaria 1961 g.: Stenograficheskii otchet* (Moscow, 1961), p. 32.

7. "Perepiska s chitaleliami," *Kommunist* no. 8 (May 1961), pp. 113–114.

8. See table in note 5 above.

9. There were, however, occasional brief references to the formula. For example, the shortened account of a letter to the agricultural department of *Pravda* by A. Emel'ianov, Candidate of Economic Sciences, in "Problemy sel'skoi ekonomiki," *Pravda*, April 24, 1966.

10. Ploss, *Conflict and Decision-Making*, chap. 4, esp. p. 133.

11. Citation of Khrushchev's Memorandum to the Presidium in N. S. Khrushchev, *Stroitel'stvo kommunizma v SSSR i razvitie sel'skogo khoziaistva* (Moscow, 1962–1963), IV, 90; Polianskii in *Plenum . . . , 22–25 dekabria 1959 g.*, pp. 32–33; Podgornii, *ibid.*, p. 61.

12. Matskevich, *ibid.*, p. 322.

13. Khrushchev, *ibid.*, p. 409.

14. K. Burilkov, "Zabota o kolkhoznykh stroikakh," *Sel'skaia zhizn'*, May 6, 1965; also N. Leshchenko and N. Khelemendik, " 'Mezhkolkhozstroi' zhdet priznaniia," *Sel'skaia zhizn'*, December 24, 1953.

15. S. Semin, "Mezhkolkhoznye i gosudarstvenno-kolkhoznye sviazi i problemy ikh razvitiia," *Voprosy ekonomiki*, no. 1 (January 1967), pp. 124–125.

16. For example, see A. Pakhomov, "Organizatsiia remonta sel'sko-khoziaistvennoi tekhniki kolkhozov," *Voprosy ekonomiki*, no. 12 (December 1959), pp. 40–41; and S. Davidiuk (letter to Khrushchev), "Chto volnuet predsedatelia kolkhoza," *Sel'skaia zhizn'*, December 13, 1960.

17. A. Moiseenko, "Kazhdomu kolkhozu — mekhanicheskuiu masterskuiu," *Izvestiia*, December 14, 1958.

18. For example, Davidiuk ("Chto volnuet") mentions pressure on his farm to use RTS services by threats of withholding of spare parts. This was a common complaint.

19. P. Buianov, "Uluchshat' proizvodstvenno-tekhnicheskoe obsluzhivanie kolkhozov," *Voprosy ekonomiki,* no. 1 (January 1959), p. 116.

20. *Ibid.,* p. 118.

21. *Plenum . . . 15–19 dekabria 1958 g.,* p. 60.

22. *Plenum . . . 10–18 ianvaria 1961 g.,* p. 543.

23. V. V. Matskevich, "Ekonomicheskie problemy dal'neishego razvitiia sel'-skogo khoziaistva," *Voprosy ekonomiki,* no. 6 (June 1965), p. 5. One of the kolkhozy visited by the author in 1963 had been severely hurt by such a transfer. It had been given the opportunity to purchase a large adjacent MTS repair plant, but had decided not to do so. The plant had subsequently been transferred to the Moscow Oblast Sovnarkhoz, which had converted it to the production of large construction cranes. Ever since, the kolkhoz had been suffering from a lack of adequate repair facilities for its growing tractor pool.

24. A. Ezhevskii, "Povyshat' kul'turu tekhnicheskogo obsluzhivaniia," *Sel'-skaia zhizn',* April 17, 1965.

25. Edict of the Presidium of the Supreme Soviet of the USSR of December 29, 1961, "Ob ugolovnoi otvetstvennosti za prestupno-nebrezhnoe ispol'zovanie ili khranenie sel'skokhoziaistvennoi tekhniki," *Pravda,* December 30, 1961.

26. "Pol'zuites' uslugami spetsializirovannykh remontnykh masterskikh 'Sel'-khoztekhniki'," *Sel'skaia zhizn',* October 9, 1965.

27. For example, M. Kurochkina, "Pochemu my otkazalis' ot 'dobryhk uslug'," *Izvestiia,* September 17, 1964; A. Dobriakov and N. Kozlov, "Interesy proizvodstva — na pervyi plan," *Sel'skaia zhizn',* October 29, 1964; K. Danilov, "Dogovor prishlos' rastorgnut' . . . ," *Sel'skaia zhizn',* September 13, 1964; G. Koshkarev and V. Bondarev, "Tekhnika ne dolzhna byt' besprizornoi," *Sel'skaia zhizn',* January 22, 1965.

28. "Kolkhoznyi traktor i 'Moldsel'khoztekhnika'," *Sovetskaia Moldaviia,* June 12, 1968.

29. See, for example, the complaint by the Chief of the Kurgan Inspectorate for State Technical Supervision, V. Lanskikh, "Kontroler lishennyi prav," *Pravda,* June 12, 1968.

30. See Khrushchev's Memorandum to the Presidium of the CC dated August 4, 1962 in Khrushchev, *Stroitel'stvo kommunizma,* VII, 126.

31. Decree of the CC, CPSU and the Council of Ministers, USSR of April 18, 1958, "O dal'neishem razvitii kolkhoznogo stroia i reorganizatsii mashinno-traktornykh stantsii," N. D. Kazantzev, ed., *Istoriia kolkhoznogo prava, sbornik zakonodatel'nykh materialov SSSR i RSFSR, 1917–1958 gg.* (Moscow, 1959), II, 479.

32. Howard Swearer, "Agricultural Administration Under Khrushchev," in Roy D. Laird, ed., *Soviet Agricultural and Peasant Affairs* (Lawrence, Kansas: Univerity of Kansas Press, 1963), pp. 25–26.

33. "Kak raikom nachinaet rabotat' posle perestroiki svoego apparata" (unsigned), *Part. zhizn',* no. 2 (January 1958), p. 40.

34. M. Polekhin and F. Iakovlev, "O nekotorykh voprosakh organizatsionno-partiinoi raboty," *Part. zhizn',* no. 13 (July 1960), p. 12.

35. Decree of the CC, CPSU of January 26, 1959, "O sozdanii partkomov v

krupnykh partorganizatsiiakh kolkhozov i sovkhozov," *Spravochnik partiinogo rabotnika* (Moscow, 1959), pt. 2, pp. 574–575.

36. Polekhin and Iakovlev, "O nekotorykh voprosakh."

37. Khrushchev in *Plenum . . . 22–25 dekabria 1959 g.*, pp. 381–383. The *Yearbook* of the *Large Soviet Encyclopedia* for 1960 carried a special passage with an impressive graph devoted to the achievements of Riazan Oblast in meat deliveries (*Ezhegodnik Bol'shoi Sovetskoi entsikopedii: 1960* [Moscow, 1961], p. 138).

38. See Khrushchev's Memorandum to the Presidium of the CC, dated October 29, 1960, in Khrushchev, *Stroitel'stvo kommunizma*, IV, 182; see also, his remarks in *Plenum . . . 10–18 ianvaria 1961 g.*, p. 592.

39. Merle Fainsod, *How Russia Is Ruled* (rev. ed., Cambridge: Harvard University Press, 1963), p. 226.

40. Decree of the CC, CPSU and the Council of Ministers, USSR of February 21, 1961, "O reorganizatsii Ministerstva sel'skogo khoziaistva SSSR," *Spravochnik partiinogo rabotnika,* (Moscow, 1961), pt. 3, pp. 342–352.

41. Decree of the CC, CPSU and the Council of Ministers, USSR of February 26, 1961, "O perestroike i uluchshenii organizatsii gosudarstvennykh zakupok sel'skokhoziaistvennyh produktov," *ibid.,* pp. 358–366, esp. p. 362.

42. L. Merdik, "Zagotoviteli ili organizatory proizvodstva?", *Sel'skaia zhizn'*, February 4, 1962.

43. Theodore Shabad, "Top Farm Agency Named by Soviet," *New York Times,* April 30, 1962.

44. See the chart on the structure of agricultural administration in the RSFSR in Fainsod, *How Russia Is Ruled*, p. 567.

45. The number of TPA's steadily increased until it was about double the original 960 by October 1964.

46. By 1964 there were already experiments with more specialized guidance by the staffs of the TPA's. For example, instead of a single all-purpose specialist, the TPA's in some areas began assigning teams of agronomists and zootechnicians to each group of kolkhozes (A. Vorobets, "Inspektor-organizator na konkretnom uchastke," *Sel'skaia zhizn'*, May 12, 1964).

47. "Novyi etap v razvitii sel'skogo khoziaistva," *Sovetskaia Rossiia,* March 20, 1962.

48. Khrushchev, *Stroitel'stvo kommunizma*, VII, 174.

49. Khrushchev speech in *Plenum Tsentral'nogo Komiteta Kommunisticheskoi partii Sovetskogo Soiuza, 5–9 marta 1962 goda: Stengraficheskii otchet* (Moscow, 1962), p. 75.

50. See, for example, I. Moroz, "Apparat partkoma za rabotoi," *Part. zhizn'*, no. 7 (April 1964), p. 37.

51. Khrushchev speech, "Vsemerno ukrepliat' proizvodstvennye kolkhozno-sovkhoznye upravleniia," *Pravda*, June 30, 1962.

52. For an interesting interpretation of the November 1962 Party reorganization with a slightly different emphasis see Jeremy R. Azrael, *Managerial Power and Soviet Politics* (Cambridge: Harvard University Press, 1966), esp. pp. 145–147. Azrael unfortunately neglects the administrative implications of the bifurcation of the Party apparatus, with the result that he exaggerates the extent of the gains by the managerial elite.

53. See, for example, "Konkretnost', delovitost'," *Pravda*, May 27, 1964; "Znanie dela — osnova rukovodstva," *Pravda*, August 25, 1964.

54. See, for example, N. Osadchenko, "Ne k litsu belotserkovtsam," *Pravda Ukrainy*, July 16, 1963; "Edinstvo slova i dela," *Part. zhizn'*, no. 17 (September 1963), pp. 4–5; "Apparat partiinogo komiteta," *Part. zhizn'*, no. 10 (May 1964), p. 5; I. Pronin, "Tsentral'naia figura apparata partkoma," *Part. zhizn'*, no. 12 (June 1964), p. 35.

55. F. Kuchumov, "Zhdali inspektora, a priekhal . . . upolnomochennyi," *Sovetskaia Rossiia*, April 29, 1962; B. Opalatenko, "Opiat' upolnomochennye?" *Part. zhizn'*, no. 6 (March 1963), pp. 20–21.

56. V. Khalmanov, "Proizvodstvennoe upravlenie ili raizo?" *Sel'skaia zhizn'*, November 27, 1963.

57. Theodore Shabad, "Soviet Premier Scores Secrecy," *New York Times*, August 10, 1964.

58. For a detailed explanation of the organizational changes introduced at the November (1964) Plenum see "Vernost' leninskim organizatsionnym printsipam" (lead editorial), *Pravda*, November 18, 1964.

59. Brezhnev in *Plenum Tsentral'nogo Komiteta Kommunisticheskoi partii Sovetskogo Soiuza, 24–26 marta 1965 goda: Stengraficheskii otchet* (Moscow, 1965), p. 5. Since that time there has been a steady increase in the number of rural raions. As of July 1, 1967 there were 2,746 rural raikoms and, presumably the same, or perhaps a slightly larger number of rural raions, since a small number of raions are administered by city Party and governmental organs (Otdel organizatsionno-partiinoi raboty TsK KPSS, "KPSS v tsifrakh," *Kommunist*, no. 15 [October 1967], p. 101).

60. V. V. Matskevich, "Na uroven' novykh zadach," *Sel'skaia zhizn'*, June 24, 1965.

61. Brezhnev in *Plenum . . . 24–26 marta 1965 goda*, pp. 10–12.

62. *Ibid.*, p. 21.

63. *Ibid.*, p. 27.

64. For example, see the remarks of L. Ia. Florent'ev, First Secretary of the Kostroma Obkom in *Plenum . . . 24–26 marta 1965 goda*, p. 177.

65. *Ibid.*, pp. 216–218.

66. *Ibid.;* see also, A. Karapetian, "Kogda traktoru tesno," *Izvestiia*, June 12, 1965; and A. Goldyrev and I. Koniushin, "Traktoru — polnuiu nagruzku," *Izvestiia*, December 26, 1964. Brezhnev actually signified his approval to these programs at the March (1965) Plenum (*Plenum . . . 24–26 marta 1965 goda*, p. 21).

67. See, for example, G. Makeev, "Dorogi vedut v MZhS," *Bakinskii rabochii*, August 19, 1965; and A. Sobolev, E. Vtorykh, and M. Rogachev, "Prokatnye stantsii — eto vygodno," *Sel'skaia zhizn'*, April 29, 1965.

68. D. Polianskii, "O roli soiuza rabochikh i krest'ian v pereustroistve sovremennoi derevni," *Kommunist*, no. 15 (October 1967), p. 24.

Index

Administrative structure, Soviet principles of: *edinonachalie* (one-man management), 105, 109, 132, 134, 136, 166, 270–271; *funktsionalka* (functional principle), 139–140, 143, 153, 162, 253; *kollegial'nost'* (collegiality), 105; production-branch principle, 139–140, 147, 154, 160, 163; production-territorial principle, 139, 159–160, 163

Agrarian theory, socialist: and agrarian question, 3–13, 19, 33, 209; and consistently socialist enterprise, 83–84, 313, 343; and farm machinery, theoretical aspects of, 3, 5–7, 10–11, 17, 68, 75, 77, 80. *See also* Lenin Cooperative Plan

Agricultural procurements. *See* Obligatory deliveries; Payments in kind

Agricultural production, planning of, 109–110, 169–175

Agro-Industrial Combines (AIK, IAK), 79–81

Andreev, A., 56, 120–121, 162, 163, 181, 266, 286

Angelina, P., 128, 151

Antipov, N., 154, 172

Arutiunian, Iu., 268, 271, 275

Ashanin, V., 268

Baryshev, N., 259–260

Belov, Fedor, 180n, 283

Benediktov, I., 116, 119–121, 123, 162, 266, 314

Berdyaev, Nicholas, 10

Berezin, A., 251

Borisov, Iu., 224

Brezhnev, L., 363–365

Brzezinski, Zbigniew, 64, 382 n.4

Bukharin, N., 21, 22, 158, 212

Chernov, M., 151, 153, 155–158, 173

Chubar', V., 154

Churaev, V., 300

Collectivization of agriculture, 30, 42–44, 46, 48, 196–197; and MTS, 38–39, 42, 44, 74–77, 82, 111–112, 197–198, 209–213

Communist Party:

Central Committee Plenary Sessions: January (1933) Joint Plenum of Central Committee and Central Control Commission, 220, 221, 228; November (1934),

245–246; February (1937), 252; June (1937), 155; February (1947), 56–57, 129, 162–163, 181, 276–277; September (1953), 122–125, 290–291; February–March (1954), 293, 297; February (1958), 326; January (1961), 348; November (1964), 362; March (1965), 363–364

Congresses and Conferences: Eighth Congress (March 1919), 17; Tenth Congress (March 1921), 19; Twelfth Congress (April 1923), 21, 24; Thirteenth Congress (May 1924), 25; Fifteenth Congress (December 1927), 30–33; Sixteenth Conference (April 1929), 40, 77–79; Sixteenth Congress (June–July 1930), 81; Seventeenth Congress (January–February 1934), 49, 51, 146–147, 240–243, 246–247; Eighteenth Congress (March 1939), 203, 253; Nineteenth Congress (October 1952), 58–59, 121; Twentieth Congress (February 1956), 169, 301; Twenty-third Congress (March–April 1966), 362

Cooperation (cooperative system), 5, 9, 25–28, 37–39, 42, 46, 71–72, 78–79, 140–141, 211, 345. *See also* Lenin Cooperative Plan

Membership, recruitment, and coverage, 22–25, 194–197, 203, 214–215, 228–230, 235–236, 253–254, 267–355

"Support points," 197, 216–218, 338. *See also Nomenklatura; Obkom; Politotdel;* Primary Party organizations; *Raikom*

Davies, R., 150n

Dembo, L., 81

Denisov, G., 309

Eikhe, R., 153, 161, 240

Engels, F., 4–5

Evdokimov, G., 263

Ezhevskii, A., 349, 350

Fainsod, M., 24, 203, 224, 235, 239, 299

Farm machinery policy, 10, 17–18, 22, 29–32, 39–43, 61–62, 68, 81, 90, 317–318, 324, 326–327, 346–352; and supplies, 29–30, 37, 39–40, 50, 54, 347, 349, 351

Fraer, S., 108, 282

421

RUSSIAN RESEARCH CENTER STUDIES

* Out of print.
† Publications of the Harvard Project on the Soviet Social System.
‡ Published jointly with the Center for International Affairs, Harvard University.